The Rise of a University Teaching Hospital

A Leadership Perspective

The University of Iowa Hospitals and Clinics

The Rise of a University Teaching Hospital

A Leadership Perspective

The University of Iowa Hospitals and Clinics

SAMUEL LEVEY

DEREK MAURER LEE ANDERSON MATTHEW SCHAEFER

With the assistance of JAMES HILL and JOSEPH DOEBELE

FOREWORD by ROBERT G. PETERSDORF, M.D.

Health Administration Press
Chicago, IL 1996

01   00   99   98   97   5   4   3   2   1

Library of Congress Cataloging-in-Publication Data

Levey, Samuel.
   The rise of a university teaching hospital, a leadership perspective : the University of Iowa Hospitals and Clinics, 1898–1995 / Samuel Levey, and Lee Anderson, Derek Maurer, and Matthew T. Schaefer, with contributors.
      p.   cm.
   Includes bibliographical references and index.
   ISBN 1-56793-048-4
   1. University of Iowa. Hospitals and Clinics—History.   2. University hospitals—Iowa—History.   I. Title.
   [DNLM: 1. University of Iowa. Hospitals and Clinics.   2. Hospitals, University—history—Iowa.   3. Hospitals, Teaching—history—Iowa. WX 28 A18 U58r 1997]
   RA982.I6U55   1997
   610'.71'1777—dc20
   DNLM/DLC
   for Library of Congress   96-36389
                                                                             CIP

The paper used in this publication meets the minimum requirements of American National Standard for Information Sciences—Permanence of Paper for Printed Library Materials, ANSI Z39.48–1984.   ∞ ™

Health Administration Press
A division of the Foundation of the
   American College of Healthcare Executives
One North Franklin Street, Suite 1700
Chicago, IL 60606
312/424-2800

Contents

6
The University Teaching Hospital's Changing Covenant,

Foreword

In 1998, the University of Iowa Hospitals and Clinics (UIHC) will celebrate their 100th anniversary. To commemorate the occasion, Samuel Levey and his associates have written a case study of the hospitals from their inception to the present. Given the truism that if you have seen one academic medical center, you have seen one academic medical center, is this a worthwhile exercise? And, if it is, why the University of Iowa?

In many ways, UIHC is typical of a state-owned institution that is a part of that state's major public university. It is unique in its rural small-town location. For many years its state funding was dependent on care rendered to indigent patients. Often the resources were inadequate, and UIHC did not achieve "major league" status, really, until after World War II. Indeed, had it not been for Abraham Flexner's recommendation to the Rockefeller Foundation to infuse UIHC with generous support, the hospital (and its medical school) might never have reached adulthood, much less thrived. But thrive they did, and for a variety of reasons, including the growth of research, the advent of specialization, the need for a cutting-edge tertiary care institution in the state, and the necessity for a venue to educate health professionals; the UIHC can now count itself as one of the colossi of academic medical centers. Although it played catch-up to its neighbors in Minnesota and Michigan, and in the Northeast, in many ways UIHC typifies the evolution of academic medicine in this country and provides a prime example of how academic medicine came to be what it is today.

The Teaching Hospital and the Medical School

From its beginning, UIHC has been associated with the UI College of Medicine (COM). The medical school is about thirty years older than the hospital, and the first university hospital was built because the university and the community hospital with which it was affiliated could not resolve their conflicts. Although the Flexner Report in 1909 did not treat the University of Iowa's clinical curriculum kindly (it deemed the facilities inadequate, the part-time faculty wanting, and the clinical material sparse), it served as a stimulus for the hospital to improve itself.

The governance of the hospital and its medical school has always been contentious. Early on the hospital was run by nurse-superintendents, who took their orders from the dean of the medical college. With one exception, they turned over frequently. They were replaced by physician-superintendents who, for the most part, also reported to the dean; but the relationships were often stormy, and the longevity of the physicians was no greater than that of the nurses. All of this changed in 1928 when Robert E. Neff was appointed hospital superintendent. Neff, who differed from his predecessor in not being a physician, gained considerable autonomy for the hospital, in part because the deanship was vacant from 1933 to 1935, and during that three years the medical school was run by a committee of faculty. An even more radical change took place in 1946 with the appointment of Gerhard Hartman as superintendent. Hartman refused to work under the dean. For most of his term, he reported either to the university president or the board of regents, or to a vice president for health sciences when there was one. This modus vivendi continued when John Colloton was appointed in 1971.

Colloton was arguably the most effective hospital chief executive of his era. A brilliant administrator, he said grace over a phased building project (none of it at state expense), which left UIHC with one of the best physical plants in the country. He was also a superb organizer, fundraiser, and politician, and an articulate spokesman for academic medicine. For most of his 22-year stint he worked in exquisite harmony with the COM's dean, Dr. John Eckstein. The dean supplied the intellectual muscle and the hospital director the organizational genius. For reasons that are not clear, Colloton and Eckstein ended their terms in a sea of acrimony. In the early nineties, when both men were at, or close to, the end of their terms, two reviews were carried out—one by the medical school faculty and the other by a university committee. Both implied that the hospital had become too powerful and had a unique advantage because the hospital director had direct access to the university president, while the dean had to report through the vice president for academic affairs. Ultimately, the recommendation that the hospital director report to a vice president for academic affairs or to the dean was rejected by the board of regents. After John Colloton resigned in 1993, a vice president for health sciences (not a physician), to whom both the dean and the hospital director were supposed to report, was appointed; but he is already gone. A vice president for health sciences has never been part of the culture at Iowa, and whether such a position is necessary will, I am sure, be carefully considered. It is also fair to say that the controversy between the dean and the hospital director, and sometimes the vice president, is common throughout the country, and is not restricted to the University of Iowa.

My view is that the abrasive interface that often exists between dean and hospital director is simply a question of whether the "chemistry is right" between these two individuals. If there is mutual respect, a sense of shared purpose, and occasionally even affection, then the academic medical center will run well. Absent such an environment, trouble will surely ensue. Equally important is the reality that power must be shared on an equal basis. If one unit is perceived to hold most of the resources—and in recent years that has usually been the hospital—it leaves a fertile field for conflict. I perceived such an imbalance when I visited the University of Iowa in the late 1980s. Most of the action was on the hospital side. The clinical chairs who operate in that kind of environment will always go where the money is—usually to the hospital director, diminishing the dean's power and prestige, and undercutting his ability to lead the faculty. I also hold the bias that these administrative marriages are not meant to last forever. Ten years is a good period and fifteen is the most one can ask for. At UIHC the terms of the director and the dean were 22 and 20 years respectively. Maybe it was time to turn over the leadership team.

The Teaching Hospital and the University

Throughout the century, since the cornerstone was laid in 1897, the UIHC has been owned by the university. This places the fiduciary responsibility for the hospital in a board of regents, which acts like a board of directors or a board of trustees. It also insinuates the university president squarely into hospital governance. This has been the case of the University of Iowa. Not only have the regents been responsible for programmatic initiatives, capital expenditures, and administration of state funds, but they, and certainly the university president, often have gotten into the middle of squabbles between the dean and the hospital director, as well as the faculty. Moreover, university regents and university presidents have a much more expansive agenda than the teaching hospital, and are subject to pressures by state legislatures. They also may not be altogether knowledgeable about the world in which the hospital lives. All of these conditions have pertained from time to time at UIHC and have been the basis for the hospitals' consistent aim for autonomy.

The story is told that a fate worse than death for a university president is not that he has one teaching hospital, but that he has two! It should also be said that in today's world the pressures on teaching hospitals and universities are very different. For most hospitals, managed care and free-market competition inject the aura of the business world. This includes mergers and acquisitions, hospital and practice networks, vertical integration, massive shifts of patients from inpatient to outpatient venues, and many deals that may mean gains or losses of millions of dollars. All of these events are a long way from the ivy-covered walls of the university, with its ponderous decision-making processes, its insistence on collegiality, and its clumsy attempts at faculty decision making. I have stated elsewhere that the faculty senate does not belong in the decision-making arena of the teaching hospital. Today's hospital (and its adjunctive health science schools) must be flexible, entrepreneurial, imaginative, and willing to take risks. UIHC has shown these traits over the years. That is why the regents showed considerable wisdom when they rejected a plan to have the hospital director report to the university's vice president for academic affairs, just like the dean of the school of medicine, and that is why I also believe that vice presidents for health affairs must be clinically knowledgeable and sophisticated.

I have come to the conclusion that public universities should divest themselves of their hospitals, or at the very least, find mechanisms to put them at arms' length from their parent universities. I surfaced this idea in my Gregg lecture to the American Association of Medical Colleges in 1982, and was soundly taken to task for it by the then-chair of the Association. But since that time many universities have experimented with different governance mechanisms, all of which have been aimed at separating the hospital from the university. By and large, these alternative mechanisms have worked. After all, in the private sector many teaching hospitals, such as Yale, Johns Hopkins, Massachusetts General (Harvard), and Northwestern have always been owned and governed separately from their parent universities, and these relationships have not been detrimental to medical education, graduate medical education, patient care, or research. The late Dr. Robert Ebert made the point that hospitals and universities are different species, and, like it or not, that is even more true today.

What Should Teaching Hospitals Aspire to Be?

The history of the UIHC has been punctuated by implosions that seemed to tear the hospitals or the medical school apart. On the surface, these could be characterized as personality conflicts, and egos often did clash.

There were also, however, programmatic and philosophical issues that left deep chasms between the faculty and the administration of the hospital, the medical school, and the university. An example is the hospital's original mission as the site of care for the indigents of the state. The faculty's belief that it had the right to private practice in the hospital soon intruded and was the cause of much conflict. The "private practice" wing of the faculty was supported by the hospital, which stood to gain much heftier revenues from private patients than from indigent ones. Those on the faculty who championed private practice also believed strongly in the part-time status of the faculty, while those who felt that private practice interfered with the hospital's educational mission advocated full-time status for the faculty. It is clear that two classes of faculty evolved: the "haves," mainly surgeons and surgical subspecialists, and the "have-nots," who were full-time and much more poorly paid, and who could be called, in today's vernacular, primary care physicians. These differences were also expressed between those who visualized the teaching hospital as a bastion of specialization and tertiary care, as opposed to those who felt that training general practitioners had to be high on the agenda of an academic health center like Iowa.

Perhaps the differing philosophies extant in the Iowa medical center came to the fore most clearly during the reviews of the hospitals and medical school that appeared in the beginning of the nineties. There were strong advocates for returning the hospitals to the womb of the university—to have it serve as the "clinical laboratory" of the faculty, a laboratory in which students could gain practical experience and learn. This rather narrow concept was vigorously opposed by people like John Colloton, who felt that UIHC (and teaching hospitals in general) were hospitals first, and teaching laboratories second. In the 1980s Colloton argued that teaching hospitals had a covenant with a greater society than the university—that they had to exist not as ivory towers of healthcare but as institutions that are part of a national and local system of healthcare, and that they must march to a social as well as an educational drummer. Colloton also advocated recognition of the higher costs that teaching hospitals incur to produce their social goods and decried the need for them to participate in the cauldron of market competition without such consideration. But participate they must, much as their colleagues elsewhere in the country, and if institutions like UIHC wish to compete—and, incidentally, stay alive—they need to enter the marketplace arena.

What of the Future?

In this brief foreword, I have concentrated on some of the more contentious issues that have characterized teaching hospitals in general, and UIHC in particular. Accentuating the problems more than the successes, however, should not be perceived as a negative commentary on UIHC. On the contrary, UIHC is a tremendous success story—one of the most dazzling in academic history. From what was fundamentally a one-room school house just 100 years ago has risen a magnificent academic medical center, replete with a superb physical plant, a bevy of productive and well-funded research programs, a sound educational agenda that now includes an increased and appropriate emphasis on primary care, excellent residency programs, a fine faculty, and a well-deserved reputation for cutting-edge, innovative programs in patient care. It has in place a new, enthusiastic management team whose members recognize that the medical school and hospital must work together if both are to prosper. It is resident in a state where it is clearly the dominant player, and in which legislatures have more often been supportive than negative. It is also in a state that to date, at least, has been spared most of the darker side of managed care. In short, the University of Iowa Hospitals and Clinics are as well positioned as anyone to face the future, turbulent though that future may be. Others in the public hospital sector should strive to emulate their success.

Robert G. Petersdorf, M.D.
President-Emeritus, Association of American Medical Colleges
Distinguished Professor of Medicine, University of Washington
Distinguished Physician, VA/Puget Sound Health Care System

Seattle, Washington
July 1996

Acknowledgments

Writing a commemorative history of a complex healthcare institution can be a daunting endeavor, especially when the subject is a major university teaching hospital. The research for this centennial project could not have been completed without the assistance, support, and contributions of many individuals, including present and emeritus faculty, administrators, and staff at the University of Iowa.

The project was launched in the spring of 1993, with the appointment of the UIHC History Advisory Committee. We are extremely grateful to them for helping us to get started and for pointing out potential problem areas. Committee members included Lee Anderson, Ph.D., Iowa City historian; Myrtle Aydelotte, Ph.D., R.N., former dean of the college of nursing, past director of nursing services of UIHC, and professor emerita of nursing; Frederick C. Blodi, M.D., professor emeritus of ophthalmology and former department head; Adrienne Drapkin, director of the UIHC Medical Museum; Johann L. Ehrenhaft, M.D., professor emeritus and former chairman of the division of cardiothoracic surgery; Lloyd J. Filer, Ph.D., M.D., professor emeritus of pediatrics; Lewis E. January, M.D., D.Sc., professor emeritus of internal medicine; James Kaufman, Ph.D., coauthor of a University of Iowa history; Gerhild Krapf Greenhoe, J.D., assistant to the director of UIHC; Edward E. Mason, Ph.D., M.D., professor emeritus of surgery; and the late Jack Moyers, M.D., professor emeritus of anesthesiology and former head of the department. We owe a special debt of gratitude to Gerhild Krapf Greenhoe, who spent many hours reading drafts of the manuscript, providing criticism and counsel, and serving as liaison to the office of the UIHC director. Her work on our behalf was invaluable and her enthusiasm contagious.

John W. Colloton, former director of the University of Iowa Hospitals and Clinics (UIHC) and assistant to the university president for Statewide Health Services, and current vice president for Statewide Health Services, immediately saw the merits of the proposal for developing a comprehensive managerial history of UIHC and provided continual encouragement and support. In addition, we owe him a debt of gratitude for providing us with access to his extensive personal records and for extending his patience through several rounds of interviews. Without his cooperation and prodigious memory this work would have terminated at the conclusion of chapter four. Three individuals in his office were helpful in retrieving documents and in providing general assistance: Stacey T. Cyphert, Ph.D., Nancy L. Kirkpatrick, and Mary Ann Hauth.

Former Iowa State Board of Regents president Marvin A. Pomerantz was immensely helpful in reflecting on relationships between the university and the medical center. Former university president Hunter H. Rawlings, III generously gave us access to more recent presidential papers and also shared his insights. Former provost and interim president Peter E. Nathan and vice president for research David J. Skorton both shared their impressions and analyses of recent history. Mark E. Schantz, university general counsel, advanced the process for gaining access to the presidential papers, and university archivist Earl M. Rogers provided considerable assistance once we were there. We owe him a large debt for his cooperation throughout.

Arthur E. Bonfield, John F. Murray Professor of Law and chair of the University Review Committee for the College of Medicine, shared his insights regarding the academic medical center and its relationship to the University.

University of Iowa Foundation president Darrell D. Wyrick generously shared his broad-ranging knowledge of the medical center's history. Michael J. New, Foundation vice president contributed additional recollections and perspectives. Publication of this book was made possible in part through gifts to the University of Iowa Foundation, for which we are very grateful.

Richard F. Hansen, cofounder of the architectural firm of Hansen Lind and Meyer deserves special recognition for sharing his knowledge and recollections of the UIHC capital development program as well as his managerial insights.

Gerhard Hartman, Ph.D., UIHC superintendent between 1946 and 1971 and first director of the graduate program in hospital and health administration at Iowa, suggested useful information sources, and through interviews assessed strategic dilemmas faced by university hospitals and academic health centers, and by UIHC in particular.

Former dean of the college of medicine, John W. Eckstein, M.D., was extremely helpful and devoted many hours to a series of interviews and general discussions regarding future prospects in academic medicine. Interim deans of medicine James A. Clifton, M.D., and Richard G. Lynch, M.D., provided important facts and analyses. Former executive associate dean Paul M. Seebohm, M.D., communicated valuable insights and shared vital historical documents from his personal collection. We valued the assistance of two individuals in the office of the dean of medicine: William L. Lillibridge, special assistant to the dean, who shared key documents and interpreted events, and Sally J. Knipfer, administrative assistant, who provided volumes of vital information.

A number of former and current UIHC administrative staff assisted in a variety of ways. Kenneth H. Yerington, associate director of UIHC and director of financial management and control, gave us access to volumes of financial and statistical data and helped in assessing their significance. Mark J. McDermott, manager of financial analysis gave generously of his time in reviewing our statistics and correcting our errors, and Jo Ellen Browning was also helpful in our compilation. John H. Staley, Ph.D., chief operating officer, Alan J. Burgener senior assistant director, H. J. Black, former pharmacy department director, Sally Mathis, R.N., former director of nursing service, Colleen J. Goode, R.N., Ph.D., former interim director of nursing service, Ken D. Davenport, director of facilities services, and William D. Stoddard, senior assistant director, contributed important perspectives; and Theodore J. Yank, assistant to the director, provided useful archival materials.

We owe a debt of gratitude as well to each of the following faculty members for sharing their knowledge and perceptions: Francois Abboud, M.B., Ch.B., professor and head, department of internal medicine; Reginald R. Cooper, professor and head, department of orthopaedics; Charles Driscoll, M.D., former professor and head, department of family practice; Edmund A. Franken, M.D., professor and former head, department of radiology; Brian F. McCabe, M.D., professor and former head, department of otolaryngology; Frank H. Morriss, M..D., professor and head, department of pediatrics; Jennifer R. Niebyl, M.D., professor and head, department of obstetrics and gynecology; Robert G. Robinson, M.D., professor and head, department of psychiatry; Robert T. Soper, M.D., professor and former interim head, department of surgery; John S. Strauss, M.D., professor and head, department of dermatology; John H. Tinker, M.D., professor and head, department of anesthesia; Thomas A. Weingeist, Ph.D., M.D., professor and head, department of ophthalmology; and Richard D. Williams, M.D., professor and head, department of urology. In addition, Robert L. Rodnitzky, M.D., chief of staff of UIHC and professor of neurology, was interviewed and provided assistance. Interviews were also conducted with the following faculty members: Douglas M. Behrendt, M.D., professor and chair of the division of cardiothoracic surgery, and Nicholas P. Rossi, M.D., professor in that unit; John C. Van Gilder, M.D., professor and chair of the division of neurosurgery; Janusz Bardach, M.D., professor emeritus and former chair of the division of plastic surgery; George Kalnitsky, Ph.D., professor emeritus of biochemistry; and Joseph A. Buckwalter, M.D., professor, I.V. Ponseti, M.D., professor, and the late Michael Bonfiglio, M.D., professor, of the department of orthopaedics. Each of them deserves special acknowledgment.

In addition, I had the benefit of many corridor conversations with clinicians, administrators, and others who were interested in the work we were doing and volunteered their recollections.

Kenneth Hendrickson, Ph.D. collaborated in researching nineteenth- and early twentieth-century medicine and politics in Iowa. Other contributors include Peter Hilsenrath, Ph.D., Steven J. Bucklin, Ph.D., and Judy Berck. Several past and present graduate students in hospital and health administration served as assistants to the authors: Robert Baxter, Dan Perryman, Wende Swanson, Greg Tarquinio, Lisa Tweedy, Sean Wolfe, and David Zahn; in addition, Dan Dominguez, Astrid Knott, Eric Stenner, and Jorg Westermann read the manuscript and provided comments.

We would like to extend our special thanks for the diligent and perspicacious efforts of the external reviewers for the Health Administration Press who critiqued the manuscript, provided advice, and made numerous creative suggestions: Richard M. Knapp, Ph.D., executive vice president of the Association of American Medical Colleges, Washington D.C., and Duncan Neuhauser, Ph.D., professor of epidemiology and biostatistics at Case Western Reserve University, Cleveland, Ohio, and editor of *Medical Care*. Thomas McCarthy, Ph.D., health care consultant, Potomac, Maryland, also served as an external reviewer and provided many suggestions.

Linda Levey, my wife; Mary Ann Colloton; and Kathy Penningroth read the entire manuscript and gave us the benefit of their constructive criticism.

Working with our publishers has been a most enjoyable and productive experience. We would like to thank Thomas P. Dolan, Ph.D., American College of Healthcare Executives president, for his encouragement, and the past and present directors of the Health Administration Press together with the Press staff team for their interest, assistance, and enthusiasm.

Samuel Levey
Iowa City, Iowa
September 1996

Introduction

The teaching hospital—the heart of modern academic medicine—is one of twentieth-century America's most striking institutional achievements. Admired the world over as the "gold standard" of medical science and practice, U.S. teaching hospitals stand both as monuments to Americans' abiding faith in the curative powers of science and as symbolic and functional flagships of the modern healthcare system. Their tripartite missions of teaching, research, and patient care crown the system of "hierarchical regionalism" that has dominated healthcare policy in this century, wherein new medical knowledge and practices are developed at advanced centers and then disseminated outward to community hospitals and physicians.[1] While some 350 Council of Teaching Hospitals members—including 118 academic medical centers—today constitute only a small fraction of the country's nearly 6,500 hospitals and a smaller part still of the trillion dollar–plus healthcare system, they provide a disproportionate share of many specialized services. For example, in 1992 they provided 75 percent of residency training in the United States, supplied almost 60 percent of regional trauma services, performed more than half of organ transplantation and a quarter of open heart surgery, and dispensed a third of uncompensated care.[2] This is a case study of the rise of one such institution, the University of Iowa Hospitals and Clinics.

The concept of the teaching hospital is an old one, particularly so in Britain and in Western Europe,[3] but the modern American teaching hospital is of relatively recent origin, a product of the far-reaching transformation of medical education and practice in the late nineteenth and early twentieth centuries. In many respects the Johns Hopkins Hospital, opened in the 1880s, served as a prototype of the teaching hospital. But Hopkins, like others of its kind, ultimately owed its success to the rise of the new scientific medicine grounded in close laboratory and clinical observation of disease pathology, an associated emphasis in medical education on rigorous scientific training in laboratory and clinical settings, and the emergence of an educated middle class positioned both economically and culturally to value the physician, the hospital, and the legitimizing power of medical science and technology.[4]

By the 1920s teaching hospitals had achieved a preeminent position in a healthcare marketplace oriented around professionalized health care services. More regulated than in the nineteenth century, twentieth-century medicine conferred unprecedented authority upon physicians as scientific professionals and as gatekeepers, controlling access to and directing the operation of an ever-widening array of medical services centered to an increasing degree in the hospital. The emergence of the teaching hospital was a critical element in the political and cultural rise of organized medicine. Just as important, the teaching hospital nurtured a new elite of academic physicians devoted, at least in principle, to the advancement and propagation of medical science and technical expertise, and who exercised considerable influence over the evolution of health care organizations in America.[5] As the recognized center of medical-scientific research and state-of-the-art patient care, the teaching hospital also became firmly established as the locus of an increasingly formalized system of undergraduate and graduate medical education.

In many respects, the experience of teaching hospitals during the Great Depression and World War II contrasted sharply with their brisk expansion in the preceding decades. Generally, the economic collapse of the 1930s affected medical schools and their teaching hospitals as it did the rest of society, forcing dramatic reductions in budgets for teaching, research, and patient care alike. The early 1940s, which saw the enlistment of medical education into the American war effort, continued the pattern of austerity and uncertainty. Nonetheless, teaching hospitals emerged from both depression and war with their image, if somewhat shaken, still largely intact. Perhaps ironically, the 1930s and 1940s brought significant advances in many areas, including medical scientific research, technological innovation, management practices, and patient care standards.

World War II marked a watershed in the history of America's teaching hospitals. The partnership forged between academic science and government during the war years, cemented by massive outlays of federal funds in the postwar decades, fueled a second and even more ambitious wave of expansion in the 1950s and 1960s. Makers of health policy, a broad coalition from both sides of the political spectrum, directed new streams of public resources to academic medical centers, reasoning that all Americans stood to benefit from medical knowledge discovered in laboratories and tested in teaching hospitals. Biomedical research and training grants, dispensed primarily by the National Institutes of Health (NIH), powered much of the expansion at the top of the medical hierarchy, while the Hospital Survey and Construction Act (Hill–Burton Act) of 1946, which formally introduced the principle of regional planning as well as federal participation in hospital construction, drove expansion at the community level. By 1965, total federal funding for research and training in biomedical areas reached $1.2 billion; it surpassed $1.6 billion in 1970. Meanwhile, between 1947 and 1971 some $3.7 billion in Hill–Burton funds aided the expansion of America's community and regional hospitals.

In the mid-1960s, President Lyndon Johnson's Great Society agenda explicitly identified the nation's health as a federal responsibility and proposed a new alliance between government and the health professions, universities, hospitals, and other healthcare providers. The Medicare and Medicaid programs enacted in 1965 to provide specifically for the healthcare needs of the elderly and indigent were central elements of the Great Society vision, and together these programs became the primary vehicle for the federal government's involvement in healthcare. The growing availability of private health insurance, usually a benefit of full-time employment, also bolstered the demand for healthcare goods and services and added to the increasing revenues of healthcare providers. Enriched by these money streams, teaching hospitals flourished. Overall, postwar healthcare policies significantly enhanced the place and prestige of academic medicine, vesting academic physicians with a new measure of esteem and accomplishing much the same for teaching hospitals.[6]

The advent of graduate education in hospital administration paralleled the rapid expansion of the hospital sector in the 1950s and 1960s. The first master's degree program began at the University of Chicago School of Business in 1934, while the University of Iowa established America's first doctoral program in hospital administration in 1950 under the leadership of Gerhard Hartman, himself Chicago's first Ph.D. in hospital administration and economics. Through the next two decades, master's programs offering terminal professional degrees in hospital administration grew rapidly in number and enrollments. A combination of demand for administrators with advanced degrees and substantial grant funding, initially from philanthropic organizations such as the W. K. Kellogg Foundation and subsequently from the federal government, propelled this growth in training programs.

Despite advances on many fronts in the 1950s and 1960s, that "golden age" of academic medicine, if such it truly was, did not endure long. Some commentators insist that academic medicine's political and scientific foundations began to erode as early as the late 1950s and that this trend accelerated through the 1960s and 1970s, eventually provoking a rhetoric of crisis in teaching hospitals and academic medical centers.[7] The real extent of that crisis is debatable; nonetheless, it was true that teaching hospitals faced two serious challenges. First, in an era of growing distrust of established institutions, academic medicine and teaching hospitals suffered from what Eric Cassell labeled the "demystification of physicians and medicine."[8] They were targeted for criticism by Congress and state legislatures, by women and minorities, and by other sectors of the public at large, as well as by special interests such as the health insurance industry and large employers, all of whom objected to spiraling healthcare costs, inequities in the distribution of services and benefits, and the overall lack of accountability in the healthcare system. In the 1970s and 1980s, partly as a result of such criticism and partly as a result of concern over mushrooming federal budget deficits, the rate of growth of federal support to academic medical centers and their teaching hospitals declined from the steep upward trend of the two previous decades. Second, by the 1970s teaching hospitals faced competition from increasingly aggressive community hospitals, now strengthened by federal funding for hospital construction under the Hill-Burton Act, by federal funding for care of the elderly and indigent under Medicare and Medicaid, and by teaching hospitals' own successes in producing the highly trained specialists needed to staff competing institutions.

Debate within the business, professional, and public sectors over market-driven restructuring of the healthcare system in the 1990s only intensified the unease at teaching hospitals.[9] Referring to growing competitive pressures on medical service providers, especially the "frenzied" embrace of managed care, an editorial in the November 1994 *New England Journal of Medicine* stated bluntly, "The future viability of academic medical centers is threatened."[10] It may indeed be true that teaching hospitals, because of their unique role, have more to fear from current trends than do most other providers. Teaching hospitals' distinctive patient populations, their technology-intensive and highly specialized services, their large staffs of highly trained professionals, and particularly their expenses associated with teaching and indigent care obligations usually translate into higher patient charges, making such institutions, as one worried observer noted, "noncompetitive in a price-sensitive environment."[11] Without special consideration for teaching hospitals, one medical school dean warned, market-driven reforms "could deliver a devastating blow to the quality of medical care in this country."[12]

Such concerns call to mind historian Roy Porter's *caveat* that in the vast panorama of western civilization health care "has always been, to a large degree, a buyers' market."[13] Yet despite the gloomy rhetoric, a survey by the Association of American Medical Colleges showed that the nation's leading teaching hospitals enjoyed continued profitability throughout the early 1990s. In addition, funding for NIH programs rose 55 percent from 1980 to 1992, and medical faculty practice plan revenues rose nearly 400 percent in the same period.[14] Moreover, teaching hospitals bring unique advantages to a competitive marketplace, including their reputations for high-quality care, their large networks of providers and insurers, their enormous stores of physical, human, and technological resources, and their significant, if diminished, reservoirs of political and cultural goodwill. How administrators deploy those assets in the face of major changes in the organization, financing, and delivery of healthcare services will be a key to the teaching hospital's future.

Despite the teaching hospital's importance in modern health care and the lessons embedded in its complex history, the new medical historiography has little to say about it. For example, two excellent recent works on the history of American hospitals, written by two of our most prominent medical historians, give the teaching hospital little more than passing mention.[15] Meanwhile, existing histories of teaching hospitals are, for the most part, the products of retired physicians or administrators who choose to celebrate a particular institution, the "great men" associated with it, and their contributions—however marginal—to the advancement of medical science and practice. Inevitably, some of these works are of far more value and interest than others, and inevitably too, the best of the genre deal with well-known eastern institutions.[16]

At the same time, both recent works and more traditional histories tend to focus narrowly on the modern hospital as a medical institution—that is, as a workshop for physicians and an instrument of physicians' professional dominance in healthcare.[17] In fact, the history of the teaching hospital opens a unique window on a broad panorama of twentieth-century American culture and politics. The public has long viewed the teaching hospital as a laboratory of medical science and technology as well as medical education, often both the first and last line of defense against the burdens of disease and debility. But many health professions, especially medicine, nursing, and hospital administration, have seen the teaching hospital as a principal venue for the often conflict-ridden process of defining professional jurisdiction and prerogative. Meanwhile, politicians and other policymakers have used the teaching hospital as a testing ground for public policy developed to guide the organization and delivery of healthcare services. In many important respects, then, the teaching hospital has been as much a creation of culture and politics—both legislative and interprofessional—as of science.

Far removed from historic centers of money and power in American society, located in a modest midwestern city in a state that remains predominantly rural and small town both demographically and culturally, the University of Iowa Hospitals and Clinics may seem a curious object of study. After all, its story is, in some degree, an intensely local one, tinged inevitably by the peculiarities of place and personalities. However, there is also much that is common to all teaching hospitals in the metamorphosis of an unprepossessing university hospital, originally intended as a clinical training base for medical students, into a nationally recognized institution for highly specialized care and home to an impressive roster of renowned research scientists.

The founding of the University of Iowa College of Medicine in 1870, and even more the opening of the first University Hospital in 1898, marked the advent, however halting, of a new era in medical science, medical practice, and medical education. The cardinal points of that era were the acceptance, at least among physician–elites and influential sectors of the public, of the basic precepts of scientific medicine; the integration of laboratory science and hospital-based clinical training into medical education; the promulgation and enforcement of standards of medical education and practice through physician licensing laws; and recognition of the state's legitimate interest in public health issues ranging from the suppression of contagious disease to the training of physicians.

Whatever its promise, however, the University of Iowa's turn-of-the-century teaching hospital, like most such institutions, represented a blend of old and new, and its weaknesses—notably facilities overcrowded by patients and students, teaching methods and record systems of dubious merit, and part-time, mostly non-resident clinical faculty—were characteristic of the time. Based on two 1909 visits to the University of Iowa as part of his study of American and Canadian medical education, Abraham Flexner submitted a damning report on the medical program, prompting a cooperative effort among university authorities, members of the state board of education, and ultimately state legislators to salvage the college of medicine and the hospital. One key to that reconstruction effort was passage of indigent care laws in 1915 and 1919 that brought thousands of indigent patients, children and adults, to the University of Iowa Hospitals. A second key—an ironic one— was Abraham Flexner's role in the early 1920s in winning major grants for the university from the Rockefeller Foundation and the General Education Board to underwrite construction of Iowa's new medical center.

While that early twentieth-century era of reform and expansion was one of substantial accomplishment, it also posed a new set of problems for the University of Iowa Hospitals.[18] First, the dramatic increase in patient numbers, chiefly a result of the indigent care laws, revealed serious defects in the hospitals' administrative apparatus, a problem intensified in the 1920s by the state legislature's imposition of a spending cap for indigent care. Conflict over the issue of hospital administration, pitting the dean of the college of medicine against a succession of hospital superintendents, proved one of the most intractable problems of this century. Second, the broad-ranging reform of both the college of medicine and University Hospitals sparked intense conflict with the Iowa State Medical Society on several important issues, including the recruitment of "outsiders" to the medical faculty, the restriction of hospital staff privileges to faculty members only, and the conduct of private practice within the hospitals by medical faculty.

Plummeting land values and crop prices that assailed Iowa's economy in the early 1930s forced drastic adjustments in state budgets, including university appropriations, and University Hospitals survived on sharply reduced funding only by adopting a quota system for indigent admissions and exercising severe economies in daily operations. In the early 1940s, the world war lifted Iowa's economy from depression, but University Hospitals saw little immediate benefit, struggling still under budget restrictions and severe wartime staffing problems. However, the hospitals did see innovations in several areas during the years of depression and war. During the 1930s, the clinical departments regularized their residency programs in accordance with standards set by national specialty boards. Likewise, helped by the first trickle of external research grants, medical research enjoyed noteworthy successes, especially in Elmer DeGowin's work with blood transfusion and storage—work of paramount importance in the war effort—and Emory Warner's pioneering work on vitamin K. Meanwhile, the profession of hospital administration reached a new level of competence at the University of Iowa in the 1930s and 1940s, as it did at many other teaching hospitals.

In the postwar years, University Hospitals underwent a dramatic trans-formation largely because of major policy and program initiatives that injected the federal government into the organization, delivery, and funding of Iowa healthcare and into the affairs of University Hospitals. After a slow and uncertain start, federal funding for medical research and training accomplished much the same result in the college of medicine and carried important implications for the University Hospitals as well. By the mid-1970s the federal government—acting through a variety of agencies—eclipsed the influence of the state and the private sector in policymaking and in funding at the university's medical center and the renamed University of Iowa Hospitals and Clinics.

By the 1990s, thanks to the extraordinary pace and breadth of change in the previous decades, a new generation of leadership at University of Iowa

Hospitals and Clinics had inherited an enterprise fundamentally different from the struggling indigent care facility of the 1930s and early 1940s, and different too from the emerging tertiary care facility of the 1970s and early 1980s. Still, virtually all of the problems and issues facing those new leaders had historical roots—some very deep, some less so. A partial list includes the potential for conflict between the director of the hospitals and the dean of the college of medicine, the greater competition from community hospitals and regional medical centers, the pressures of state and federal regulatory mandates, and the increasing emphasis on cost control from public and private agencies.

The degree to which current and future leaders can sustain and enlarge the University of Iowa Hospitals and Clinics' advantages—for example, its status as Iowa's only comprehensive tertiary care facility, its sizable reservoir of practitioner and patient loyalty, its long-standing relationship with the state government and with various agencies of the federal government, and its extensive connections to Iowa's healthcare infrastructure—remains to be seen. In the end this teaching hospital, like other teaching hospitals, must contend for market share in an increasingly competitive environment and must do so under the added burdens of politics and tradition and the costs of medical education and research. Much as was true at the opening of the first University of Iowa Hospital in 1898, the patients who enter the hospitals and clinics' imposing pavilions today place profound hopes and expectations in the array of technologies and expertise found there. In a very real sense, the University of Iowa Hospitals and Clinics' future, even more so than its past, lies in maintaining a workable balance between those hopes and expectations and the cost of services provided.

This history of the University of Iowa Hospitals and Clinics began with ambitions that far exceeded both the resources at hand and even the publisher's considerable patience. Such, in some sense, is the human condition. Moreover, the problem of balancing ends and means in this instance reflected the optimism that often accompanies the start of a new and exciting project, and it reflected, too, the interdisciplinary nature of the working group, a diverse cast with backgrounds in hospital and health administration, history, English, and journalism. After months of research and deliberation, the authors arrived at a more manageable scope for the project; what was originally and no doubt naively conceived as an encyclopedic history of a university teaching hospital, with balanced treatment of the many and varied clinical and operating departments, became a work focused primarily on the changing configuration of management concerns and problems in such a complex and dynamic institution.

To the extent that one university teaching hospital can represent its peers, we hope this work will illuminate the major themes common to all.

The question of governance comes to mind as perhaps the most fundamental of these issues. For just as Iowa officials have struggled for more than a century to define the relationship of the teaching hospital to the medical school, the university's central administration, and state government, so too have most universities with teaching hospitals experienced difficulties in managing their own institutional arrangements. In fact, their diverse circumstances have prompted the great majority of academic medical centers to adopt a governing structure in which both teaching hospital director and medical college dean report to the same central administration figure, usually a vice president for health sciences, a structure the University of Iowa adopted in 1993. Likewise, many if not most academic medical centers have responded to the imperatives of the healthcare environment with similar initiatives to bolster their primary care services, form their own health maintenance organizations, buy private physician practices, and even enter into for-profit ventures.

The authors hope that this study of the University of Iowa Hospitals and Clinics will contribute to a better theoretical understanding of the teaching hospital as an institution shaped by conflict and cooperation as well as by the dynamic forces of culture, politics, and economics. Indeed, that hope sustained this project for nearly four years.

Notes

1. The concept of "hierarchical regionalism" is taken from Daniel Fox, *Health Policies, Health Politics: The British and American Experience, 1911–1965* (Princeton, NJ: Princeton University Press, 1986), p. ix.

2. *AAMC Data Book* (Washington, DC: Association of American Medical Colleges, 1995), Tables G8, G11, and G12.

3. See, for example, Susan C. Lawrence, "Entrepreneurs and Private Enterprise: The Development of Medical Lecturing in London, 1775–1820," *Bulletin of the History of Medicine* 62 (Summer 1988): 171–192.

4. Kenneth M. Ludmerer, *Learning to Heal: The Development of American Medical Education* (New York: Basic Books, 1985): 219–233.

5. Ibid., pp. 207–218.

6. See John C. Burnham, "American Medicine's Golden Age: What Happened to It?" *Science* 215 (March 1982): 1474.

7. See, for example, David Rogers and Robert Blendon, "The Academic Medical Center: A Stressed American Institution," *The New England Journal of Medicine* 298 (April 27, 1978): 940–950.

8. Eric Cassell, "The Changing Concept of the Ideal Physician," *Daedalus* 115 (Spring 1986): 197.

9. See, for example, Janice Hopkins Tanne, "Washington to New York: Drop Dead," *New York* 27 (July 18, 1994): 26–28.

10. Jerome P. Kassirer, "Academic Medical Centers Under Siege," *The New England Journal of Medicine* 331 (November 17, 1994): 1370–1371.

11. Spencer Foreman, quoted in John K. Iglehart, "Rapid Changes for Academic Medical Centers," *The New England Journal of Medicine* 331 (November 17, 1994): 1391.

12. "Washington to New York: Drop Dead," pp. 26–33. For further views, see Arnold M. Epstein, "U.S. Teaching Hospitals in the Evolving Health Care System," *Journal of the American Medical Association* 273 (April 19, 1995): 1203–1207.

13. Roy Porter, *The History of Medicine: Past, Present, and Future* (Uppsala: Institutionen for ide-och lardomshistoria, Uppsala Universitet, 1983): 15.

14. Ibid.

15. Charles Rosenberg, *The Care of Strangers: The Rise of America's Hospital System* (New York: Basic Books, 1987); Rosemary Stevens, *In Sickness and In Wealth: The American Hospital in the Twentieth Century* (New York: Basic Books, 1989).

16. The most ambitious and best of the genre is surely A. McGehee Harvey, Gert H. Brieger, Susan L. Abrams, and Victor A. McKusick, *A Model of Its Kind: A Centennial History of Medicine at Johns Hopkins,* 2 vols. (Baltimore: Johns Hopkins University Press, 1989). See also Frederic A. Washburn, *The Massachusetts General Hospital: Its Development, 1900–1935* (Boston: Houghton Mifflin Co., 1939); Nathaniel W. Faxon, *The Massachusetts General Hospital: 1935–1955* (Cambridge, MA: Harvard University Press, 1959); and Benjamin Castle, David Crockett, and S. B. Sutton, eds., *The Massachusetts General Hospital* (Boston: Little Brown, 1983).

17. Paul Starr's landmark study of American medicine, for example, included insightful sections on the hospital, with particular attention to the role of the hospital in bolstering the status and authority of physicians. See Paul Starr, *The Social Transformation of American Medicine: The Rise of a Sovereign Profession and the Making of a Vast Industry* (New York: Basic Books, 1982), especially chapter 4, "The Reconstitution of the Hospital."

18. With the opening of the Children's Hospital in 1919, the University Hospital became the University Hospitals, a name retained until the 1972 adoption of the current University of Iowa Hospitals and Clinics.

1

Medicine, Medical Education, and Hospitals in Nineteenth-Century Iowa

Late on the morning of May 13, 1897, near the intersection of Linn Street and Iowa Avenue in the heart of Iowa City, Dr. William Middleton, dean of the University of Iowa medical faculty, tapped into place the cornerstone of the first teaching hospital on the university campus.[1] Addressing the small group of invited faculty in the formal manner of the time, Middleton predicted that future generations would marvel at the building that would rise on that spot. For Middleton's colleague, professor of materia medica Charles Chase, the hospital represented the "crystallization of hopes long deferred."[2]

In fact, the University of Iowa Hospital was of far more significance than Middleton and Chase could have known. While, as Middleton predicted, the hospital proved to be a landmark in the history of the University of Iowa, its construction also coincided with and in some respects symbolized important transitions in chemistry and the biological sciences, establishment of standards of medical practice and education—especially standards of clinical training—and the organization and function of American hospitals. The new University Hospital also symbolized an important shift in the state of Iowa's commitment to medical education and in the structure and function of American universities.[3]

1

Through much of the nineteenth century, healthcare in Iowa and elsewhere in the United States centered on home, family, and community. In a largely underdeveloped society, the burden of disease was heavy, and women—in their multifaceted roles as wives, mothers, and dutiful daughters, and as organizers of a variety of community services—were the chief primary care providers, employing knowledge and remedies drawn from regular and sectarian medicine, family recipes, and native American traditions.[4] Several factors, including low population densities, the cost of the physician's services, cultural biases against elitist professional monopolies, poor transportation, and the shortcomings inherent in the medical science of the day, limited the role of the physician in the nineteenth-century healthcare marketplace.

In the early nineteenth century and to a diminishing extent as the century progressed, "regular" physicians embraced a system of medical science whose origins stretched to the ancient world. While alien to the twentieth-century mind, that system—based, as is often said, on "bleeding, purging, and puking" to restore a balance of bodily "humors"—was widely accepted not only by regular physicians but by substantial segments of the public and many alternative medical practitioners as well. Within that consensus, as Charles Rosenberg argues, the therapies of the day were effective. Whether or not they achieved a "cure" in the modern understanding of the word—by and large, of course, they did not—they nonetheless produced the results expected by both physician and patient.[5] Within that system, medical technology found little place; physicians grounded their diagnoses chiefly in "signs" elicited from the patient.[6] At the same time, the nineteenth century was a golden age of sectarian medicine, as homeopaths, hydropaths, Thomsonians, eclectics, and others jostled for position with regular physicians in a radically democratic and entrepreneurial healthcare marketplace in which there were few constraints, apart from civil suits for malpractice, on the practice of medicine.[7]

Nineteenth-century medical education, for regular physicians and sectarians alike, was uneven at best. Preceptorship was the common mode of training, as the would-be physician "read medicine" with an established practitioner, picking up the rudiments of the prevailing medical science and some experience with the more common disease states. Most medical schools of the time were proprietary in nature, and all were, like the practice of medicine, unregulated. A medical diploma was, in some circumstances, a useful ornament to the physician, but it was not a prerequisite to medical practice nor was it a guarantee of a thorough medical education.

The founding of the University of Iowa in 1847 had little immediate impact on either the quality of medical education or the conduct of medical practice in Iowa. In part, that reflected the limited resources available for investment in higher education. In part, too, it reflected philosophical uncertainty over the state's administrative and financial responsibilities to its public university in general and to professional education in particular. Residents in many parts of the state exhibited a deep-seated suspicion of the university as an elitist institution and a fount of uncertain moral values. The fact that Johnson County, the home of the university, was a Democratic party stronghold and notoriously "wet" in the face of a rising prohibition movement only reinforced such sentiments within the Republican party, which controlled state government through most of the century and which, by the 1870s, also became the party of temperance.

The university's—and the state's—first connection with medical education came through the nomination of the Keokuk College of Physicians and Surgeons as the university's medical department in 1850, but the Keokuk school was purely a proprietary operation and received no state support beyond the university's imprimatur on its graduation certificates. In 1868, however, the University of Iowa Board of Trustees sanctioned the transfer of medical education to the Iowa City campus, and the state legislature concurred, albeit without a major financial commitment to the new school. From the opening of the University of Iowa Medical Department in the fall of 1870, the state's involvement in medical education grew incrementally, if erratically, first, through state appropriations for operating expenses and capital improvements and, second, through greater administrative oversight of the medical department by both the board of trustees and the legislature.

The early years of medical education at the University of Iowa coincided with the opening of a new order in medical education and practice in Iowa and across the nation. In Paul Starr's now famous "transformation," the keys to the future lay in a newly emergent scientific medicine, hospital-based clinical training, the standardization of medical education, the licensing of physicians, and an increasingly active role for the state in public health issues. Funded by a millage tax approved by the state legislature in 1896 and completed in 1898, the first University Hospital—the "grand, good hospital" in one admirer's words[8]—symbolized medicine's new order in Iowa, marking the intellectual and institutional triumph of scientific medicine and cementing the vital partnership between the state and medical education at the University of Iowa.

Medicine and Health in Frontier Iowa

In the 1830s and 1840s, a series of forced agreements with native American peoples ceded to the federal government nearly all of the 56,000 square miles of land that constitute the present state of Iowa. White settlers moved rapidly westward from the Mississippi River into eastern Iowa and eastward from the Missouri River into southwestern Iowa, and the state became the twenty-ninth member of the union in 1846. The U.S. census of 1850 listed Iowa's population at just over 192,000, and by 1860 the total reached nearly 675,000.

The burden of disease was high among those who settled the rolling hills between the Mississippi and Missouri Rivers in the mid-nineteenth century, a stiff disease gradient produced by the rapid influx of population and associated environmental change. By the 1850s and 1860s, debilitating and sometimes fatal diseases were endemic. The most important diseases— but, ironically, perhaps the least noted at the time—were those of childhood, especially scarlet fever, diphtheria, whooping cough, and measles. Adults were at risk from a variety of maladies, ranging from the common complaints still widespread today to more serious afflictions such as tuberculosis, typhoid, and erysipelas. Women were particularly susceptible to infections during childbearing, with puerperal fever a frequent and often fatal event. Smallpox and cholera epidemics appeared intermittently.[9]

Known by various names and borne on the waves of migrating white settlers, malaria became a normal part of life in Iowa and the midwest, especially so in the river bottoms and poorly drained areas.[10] One early Iowa settler commented extensively on his experience with "the ague" in the late 1830s and early 1840s.[11] The observations of one mid-century traveler through the Mississippi Valley were typical. "I can hear of no spot high or low, wet or dry, wood or prairie, village, town or city so-called that is not invaded," he wrote. Indeed, "to find a single family some member of which has not had a chill or two would be a curiosity."[12] To some extent at least, early white settlers came to accept "the shakes" of malaria as a normal part of the "seasoning" process.

Healthcare in mid-century Iowa was largely a domestic matter, carried out in the patient's home, most likely under the direction of women. The family was apt to call upon the services of a physician, even if one was available, only to attend to critical events that exceeded the scope of domestic medicine.[13] Although a few towns had so-called poorhouses and welfare lodgings for transients and indigents, institutions intended specifically to administer healthcare were rudimentary and generally organized only on an ad hoc basis, and few patients or physicians had access to a hospital. In any event, hospital care was of dubious value at best; even in the urban centers of the eastern United States, an inordinate risk of infection attended hospital care through much of the century, a phenomenon known by the name "hospitalism." In most cases, the home provided a far more healthful environment for the convalescent patient.

The frontier physician depended for the most part on the art rather than the science of medicine in treating his patients; a reassuring bedside manner was likely the physician's greatest gift. The physician was also unlikely to make use of the few available diagnostic tools, such as the stethoscope and thermometer, relying instead principally on a dialogue with the patient—a patient history, in more modern terms—in making a diagnosis. The physical examination of the patient was cursory at best, usually consisting of visual inspection, commonly with the patient clothed. In addition, the physician might take a wrist pulse and place his ear against the chest to judge the vigor of a patient's heart and lungs, and, depending on the patient's complaint, might also inspect the stool and urine.[14]

Physicians and patients alike faced disease with no more than a few sovereign remedies at their command; a simple anodyne and recommendation of bedrest were perhaps the most effective regimens available. Ironically, prior to the late nineteenth century, the handful of truly effective measures, such as vaccination to prevent smallpox and the use of quinine to treat malaria, were anomalies within the prevailing theories of health and disease, theories that did not recognize specific disease entities nor specific remedies. Orthodox medicine depended on bleeding, blistering, cupping, sweating, and the administration of emetics and cathartics to restore a proper humoural balance. Well into the late nineteenth century, purgatives remained one of the few therapeutic options available to physicians.[15] Among the less heroic remedies were various salves, plasters, and poultices, as well as turpentine and alcohol. Given the state of medical science and practice, the best medical care was conservative rather than heroic, relying on the self-limiting nature of most afflictions and the remarkable recuperative powers of the human body.

The physician making his way through rural Iowa on horseback also carried a rudimentary set of surgical instruments, including saw, forceps, and pliers. Surgery of any kind entailed considerable risk prior to the era of antisepsis. Nonetheless, the physician would be called upon to perform simple surgical procedures, including setting bones, stitching wounds, lancing boils, and pulling teeth. The most common major surgery was amputation, a procedure often conducted on a kitchen table and one carrying considerable risk for the patient. Frontier physicians, like their urban counterparts, seldom ventured into the abdomen or chest cavities because of the risk of complication and infection.[16] Nonetheless, in one remarkable case, a Wapello, Iowa, physician surgically extracted a bar of lead from the stomach of a patient. "On Christmas day, 1854," Dr. John Bell, Jr., related, "I was summoned to see L. W. Bates, age 32, who, it was said, while performing the feat of running a bar of lead down his throat had accidentally let it slip, so that it descended into his stomach." After chloroforming his patient, Bell cut through the abdominal wall, made an incision in the man's stomach, and with a long pair of tongs, extracted a ten-and-three-quarter-inch lead bar. Surprisingly, Mr. Bates recovered.[17]

Medical Education and Hospitals

Medical education, like medical care, was a hit-and-miss proposition in frontier Iowa, thanks to the lack of enforceable professional standards. However, within months of the establishment of the University of Iowa in February 1847,[18] physicians from around the state met in Iowa City—then the state capital—to lobby for establishment of a medical department at the university. The practical needs of a new state, they argued, included doctors as much as lawyers and teachers. The university board of trustees designated a lot for a medical building on condition that the school be operational within three years and cost not less than $1,000 to construct, but that project failed and interest then shifted to the establishment of a branch medical department in another city.

In the spring of 1850, the board of trustees approved Davenport's College of Physicians and Surgeons of the Upper Mississippi as the state-sanctioned medical school. That was a short-lived distinction, however, since the school relocated to Keokuk over the summer. John Sanford, a state senator and soon-to-be dean of the new Keokuk school, convinced the legislature to approve the proposed Keokuk College of Physicians and Surgeons as the medical department of the state university and secured a $5,000 grant from the sale of state lands to bolster the school. When Governor Ansel Briggs vetoed the grant, a consortium of Keokuk merchants and town officials made an offer of money, land, and buildings to the Davenport faculty if they would relocate.[19] From the outset, then, the school relied on donations from the community as well as on student fees for operating revenues, while the chief benefit of university affiliation was the University of Iowa name affixed to its diplomas. In return, the school afforded service and a measure of prestige to the community, even as it enhanced the stature and, presumably, the fees of its faculty-practitioners.

In the fall of 1850 the Keokuk College of Physicians and Surgeons was the only medical school in Iowa, and, in keeping with the low levels of public education of the time and the need to maximize enrollments, admissions standards were low. Instruction was largely didactic in nature, and students endured several hours of lectures daily. The letters of one student in the late 1850s suggest that the lecture schedule was irregular, as was the school calendar, and that a good many students were less than enthusiastic in their attendance and overall performance.[20] Nonetheless, the normal curriculum of the day might afford the medical student a grounding, however uncertain, in both the necessary basic sciences—chemistry, physiology, and anatomy—and the major clinical areas—surgery, theory and practice of medicine, and obstetrics and gynecology—along with some acquaintance with the materia medica. The academic calendar at Keokuk, as was the norm, ran no more than 16 weeks, from October to March, and students repeated the same sequence of lectures over the course of two years to earn a degree, although many began practice after a single winter's lectures.

Unlike many proprietary medical schools of the era, the Keokuk College of Physicians and Surgeons afforded some rudimentary clinical training in the hospital setting, most of which seems to have consisted of surgical demonstrations. The first "University Hospital" opened in Keokuk in 1851 as a teaching facility for the college and served in that capacity into the 1860s. However, like nearly all American hospitals of the time, the Keokuk hospital was little more than an almshouse for the indigent sick, and likely not a very healthful one at that, a sharp contrast to the later institutions that stood at the center of a much different system of medical practice and medical education.

With two wards and several private rooms, the Keokuk hospital was often strained beyond its 80-bed capacity, particularly during epidemics. Like other dynamic river towns, Keokuk had a significant itinerant population who, having no established family network to care for them, were a potential community problem in the event of illness; also like other river towns, Keokuk carried a reputation—not altogether undeserved—as a locus of "miasmatic" disease routinely associated with low-lying areas, stagnant water, and decaying vegetation. For the community, the hospital was a great boon, a "welcome refuge in affliction" as well as a venue for "valuable clinical illustration," according to an 1851 report in the *Western Medico-Chirurgical Journal.*[21]

During the cholera epidemic of 1850, local authorities quarantined victims and suspect newcomers in the Keokuk hospital. Contemporary reports attributed the relatively low death toll at Keokuk to its stricter quarantine laws and its success in isolating victims; other river towns had not fared so well. In the wake of that 1850 epidemic, town leaders persuaded the college's medical faculty to found a board of health in order to continue their work in public sanitation.[22] The new board inspected private premises, ordered the removal of waste and health nuisances at the property owner's expense, ordered standing water drained and cellars, stables, and warehouses dug out and cleaned, and applied the few disinfectants of the day—salt, lime, and lime chloride—to organic wastes. Whether because of such public health efforts or not, the incidence of cholera in Keokuk dropped off in the 1850s, although it swept other Mississippi River towns from time to time, reportedly spread from an epicenter in St. Louis. Such community service helped to build a strong base of support for the College of Physicians and Surgeons in the Keokuk community, reinforcing the influence of its graduates, who spread rapidly to communities throughout the state.

From 1860 to 1880, Iowa's population swelled from 675,000 to 1,625,000, and the consequent urbanization and economic development, spurred by technological advancements such as the railroad and telegraph, transformed Iowa's rural, frontier economy and society almost overnight. From 1860 to 1880, the number of farms in Iowa tripled, and the total value of farmland increased fivefold. As the economy expanded, and as towns and cities multiplied, the formal practice of medicine expanded rapidly, keeping pace with a growing market demand for professional healthcare services and, to some extent, creating that demand. An 1876 Iowa State Medical Society census of medical practitioners in 23 counties—about a quarter of the state—listed 598 physicians, including 17 women and 367 medical school graduates. Those 598 physicians served a population of nearly 450,000, a physician-to-population ratio of 1:750. All told, the census counted 428 regular physicians, 72 eclectics, 60 homeopaths, 3 Thomsonians, 2 spiritualists, 2 oculists, 1 electrician, and 34 nondescript.[23] Similarly, medical directories of the 1880s listed some 2,000 regular physicians in all of Iowa, more than 300 homeopathic physicians, and as many as 150 eclectics.[24]

The demand for physicians in Iowa fueled an unprecedented, if short-lived, expansion in medical education, mirroring a national trend that pushed the number of U.S. medical schools from 57 in 1880 to 160 in 1900.[25] In 1895, according to the federal Bureau of Education, 113 regular medical schools enrolled 18,500 students and graduated 4,200 new MDs.[26] Entrepreneurial ambition and prestige were central to the founding of most such schools, and—apart from the medical department that opened on the University of Iowa campus in 1870—the 13 medical schools that opened around the state of Iowa in the last decades of the nineteenth century were proprietary enterprises.[27] In the absence of uniform educational standards, little was required to launch a medical school beyond a teaching faculty of perhaps a half-dozen general practitioners, rooms for lectures, and students who could afford the fees. Regular physicians opened medical schools in the far corners of Iowa, from Sioux City and Council Bluffs on the Missouri River to Keokuk on the Mississippi. Meanwhile, despite the regulars' dominance in Iowa medicine, competing sects, each with its own understanding of disease processes and corresponding therapeutic regimens, attracted significant followings in the chaotic free market in healthcare, and some also opened their own medical schools. The University of Iowa Homeopathic Medical Department, for example, opened its doors in 1877 pursuant to a mandate from the state legislature; the Iowa Eclectic Medical College opened in 1881 as the medical department of Drake University in Des Moines; King Eclectic Medical College, also in Des Moines, opened in 1883; and the Still College of Osteopathy opened in the capital in 1898.

The growing demand for professional medical services—and, hence, for medical education—led to the first attempt in Iowa to regulate the practice of medicine and, indirectly, to set standards of medical education. In 1886, proponents of physician licensure—including elites among both the regulars and the more respectable sectarian groups—achieved passage of "An Act to Regulate the Practice of Medicine and Surgery in the State of Iowa." Taking effect in January 1887, the law required medical practitioners to register with the state and established a board of medical examiners made up of regular, homeopathic, and eclectic physician members. The law required candidates for physician licensure either to undergo examination by the board or to present a "genuine" diploma from a medical school "legally organized and in good standing" as determined by the board.[28]

By 1890, 41 states and territories had enacted similar medical licensing acts, 34 of them requiring only the diploma for licensure. Such practice acts constituted only a modest step at best toward the reform of medical education and practice, and unlicensed medical practitioners continued to flourish. In retrospect, the Iowa Board of Medical Examiners' ability to enforce standards of medical education was doubtful. Indeed, one historian has expressed doubt about "just who such [licensing] laws were intended to exclude" and suggests that the chief targets may have been the outright quacks and charlatans, including itinerant vendors of nostrums.[29] In any event, one unfortunate effect of early medical practice acts was to foster the proliferation of medical schools of dubious character, schools dubbed diploma mills by their critics; in most respects, the expansion of medical education in late nineteenth-century Iowa was an unhappy reflection of that larger national trend.

Much the same impulse that led to passage of Iowa's first medical practice act in 1886 also led officials in some of Iowa's larger communities to establish hospitals as isolation wards for quarantined patients and as facilities for limited medical and surgical care. Thus, the constellation of demographic, economic, and cultural factors that transformed so much of Iowa society also began the slow transformation of the hospital from an undifferentiated welfare institution meant to house society's "delinquents, defectives, and dependents," in William Graham Sumner's memorable formulation, into an institution oriented to the provision of healthcare for all classes. Despite the absence of uniform standards and the admittedly uncertain value of their services, those hospitals were generally welcome additions to Iowa communities.

Florence Nightingale's ideas regarding hospital design and management were pervasive in post-Civil War Iowa and throughout America. While there may have been little that was original in Nightingale's teachings, she was extraordinarily successful in interpreting and applying the central moral concerns of respectable Victorian society to the hospital setting. In Nightingale's view, the hospital was a microcosm of society at large, its mission hinging on the implementation of strict rules of conduct, order, and cleanliness, all of which were, whatever their origins, vast improvements on existing hospital practices. For Nightingale, the age-old problem of hospital infection was evidence of disorder and could be overcome only by moral and physical exertion. In line with that, her vision of the ideal hospital relegated medicine to "a minor role," while emphasizing the importance of "nursing, cleanliness, and diet."[30] In some important respects, then, the hospital of the late nineteenth century was both forward looking and tradition-bent, blending modern notions of professional care and medical science with a heavy dose of moralism.

The word hospital, from the Latin *hospes,* is of medieval origin, denoting hospitality shown to travelers. In the nineteenth century, charity and community service, impulses often organized and managed by women, were powerful motives for hospital development. The decades immediately after the Civil War saw the establishment of several voluntary hospitals in Iowa, all of them more or less faithful to Nightingale's teachings. The Catholic hospitals were first to appear. In 1867, the Sisters of Mercy, a Catholic service order originating in Ireland in the 1820s, opened a hospital in Davenport for "care of the poor and insane of Scott county," followed by several efforts in Iowa City, Des Moines, Dubuque, Council Bluffs, Sioux City, Anamosa, Burlington, and Clinton. Another Catholic order, the Sisters of the Third Order of St. Francis, opened St. Joseph's Hospital in Keokuk in 1886.[31] Those institutions were among the more than 150 Catholic hospitals nationwide in the mid-1880s, most of them managed and staffed by orders of women religious.[32] Nondenominational, voluntary hospitals appeared in Iowa at a later date, including the Jennie Edmundson Memorial Hospital in Council Bluffs in 1887, the Ottumwa Hospital in 1892, and the Cottage Hospital in Creston in 1894.[33]

In contrast to the fairly rapid expansion of voluntary hospitals, state sponsorship of hospitals developed slowly, and its focus was solely on facilities for society's most helpless and—to some nineteenth-century elites—least appealing members, the retarded and mentally ill. Driven by the conviction that the advance of "civilization" in Iowa meant an inevitable rise in the rate of insanity, the Iowa General Assembly in 1855 approved a bill that led in 1861 to the establishment of Iowa's first mental hospital in Mount Pleasant. Twelve years later, a second state hospital for the insane opened in Independence, and a third in Clarinda in 1888.

Notwithstanding the good intentions of their sponsors, the typical Iowa hospital of the late nineteenth century might offer the patient room, board, and a few days' rest, but could do little to cure or ameliorate most serious conditions. Moreover, the harsh realities of hospital experience belied Florence Nightingale's optimistic vision of the hospital as a well-ordered microcosm. To much of the public, and for good reason, the hospital remained a place to avoid at all costs. Nonetheless, a few late nineteenth-century hospitals did present physicians and medical students with an opportunity, however limited, for clinical study, providing laboratories stocked with indigent patients in various extremes of illness who could be counted on to submit without protest to the inspections and manipulations of strangers.

The University of Iowa Medical Department

In 1855, the Iowa legislature designated Des Moines, located in the central part of the state, as the state capital. The new constitution, enacted in 1857, reiterated that designation but specified that the state university remain in Iowa City as compensation for the loss of the seat of state government. Moreover, according to article nine, section eleven of the constitution, "the State University shall be permanently established at one place, without branches at any other place, and the University fund shall be applied to that institution and no other," a provision that expressly forbade operations like the medical department then functioning in Keokuk. Still, the Keokuk College of Physicians and Surgeons, by virtue of tradition as much as anything else, maintained its status as the university's medical department for several more years, by which time the Keokuk school was deeply rooted in the Iowa community of medical practitioners.

By the 1860s, some of the state's leading medical and political figures, citing the constitution's "branchless" clause, lobbied for the transfer of medical education to the university campus. However, not until 1868 did the university board of trustees agree to establish a new medical department in Iowa City, and then only over vocal opposition from the Keokuk school and its supporters. One of the most potent weapons of Keokuk's faculty, friends, and supporters was the Iowa State Medical Society, many of whose members were Keokuk alumni. In addition, a past society president, John Hughes, was dean of the college. Through its large body of alumni and its political connections in Des Moines, the Keokuk school resisted relocation efforts, arguing that Iowa City had a limited patient base and no clinical facilities.[34] Meanwhile, the communities of alternative medical practitioners—homeopaths and eclectics among others—objected on the ground that they had as much right to a department in the state-supported university as did the regulars.

Chief among the new medical department's champions was U.S. circuit judge and University of Iowa law professor John H. Dillon. Well respected in Iowa legal circles and among members of the university board of trustees, Dillon had, two years earlier, cited the unity clause in the constitution in working to bring the law school from Des Moines to Iowa City. In his medical department campaign, Dillon enlisted the help of Dr. Washington Freeman Peck, a young, energetic surgeon from Davenport. Having trained as a surgeon at Bellevue Medical College in New York and served as Bellevue house surgeon in 1863, Peck served in a military hospital during the Civil War before settling in Davenport, where he quickly earned a reputation as a skillful surgeon and confident diagnostician. In 1876, Peck won election as president of the Iowa State Medical Society; he later served as vice president of the American Medical Association and was a charter member of the American Surgical Association. Dillon and Peck found an effective ally in John P. Irish of Iowa City, a long-time Democratic politician as well as a journalist and a member of the board of trustees. Others enlisted in the Iowa City cause were James Black, president of the University of Iowa from 1868 to 1871 and an ex-officio member of the board of trustees, Iowa governor Samuel Merrill, board of trustees president L. W. Ross of Council Bluffs, and C. W. Slagle of Fairfield.[35]

In September 1868, Peck presented his plan for a medical department in Iowa City to the board of trustees, who then appointed a three-member committee, including Black and Ross, to investigate the proposal. Not surprisingly, the committee submitted a resolution recommending that a department be established at the Iowa City campus with chairs in surgery, anatomy, materia medica, obstetrics, theory and practice of medicine, and chemistry.[36] As approved by a majority of the board of trustees, the resolution included the stipulation, perhaps meant to set the school apart from proprietary medical colleges, that it was "not to be conducted on a money-making basis." At the same time, however, the board ruled that "all tuitions and fees from the department shall accrue to the benefit of the department," maintaining that such charges "are nominal, to be used entirely for defraying the necessary expenses of the institution"—a reflection of the fact that the state legislature was unlikely to appropriate funds for the purpose. "The several professors in said department," the board continued, "shall serve without compensation."[37] The administration of the department was to rest with the medical faculty, who were to "provide all needful rules and regulations and report same to the Board of Trustees at the close of each year." The board also scheduled the opening of classes no later than the fall of 1870 and set fees of five dollars for matriculation, eighty dollars for lectures, and thirty dollars for graduation. At its June 1869 annual meeting, the board appropriated $1,900 to renovate South Hall on the grounds of the university to house the medical department and provided an additional

$725 for specimens and equipment, expenditures that marked the first step in an evolving and sometimes troubled partnership between the state and its medical college.[38]

Approval of the new school by the board of trustees shifted attention to the 1870 session of the Iowa General Assembly, where opponents hoped to overturn the board's decision. As the new medical department canvassed for students in the spring of 1870, members of the Iowa State Medical Society, in defense of the Keokuk College of Physicians and Surgeons, passed a resolution condemning "the unnecessary multiplication of medical colleges in localities remote from hospitals and facilities for clinical teaching" and warning against promoting yet another source of "incompetent practitioners, who bring reproach and opprobrium upon the noble and humane profession."[39] The school's detractors noted that Iowa City, connected to the outside world only by a rail line, lacked both a vigorous economy and a large patient base, while Keokuk was a prosperous river town that provided a ready source of clinical subjects for the medical school.[40] Similar resolutions brought before the legislature by Keokuk partisans led to the introduction of a bill, Senate File 179, to abolish the Iowa City school—a bill that passed the senate but failed in the house.

Even then the new medical department's fate was not settled, since the same session of the legislature abolished the university's board of trustees and created in its stead a new nine-member board of regents,[41] a reorganization seen by some as a slap at the medical department and one that, in any event, afforded a last opportunity for opponents to seek the department's dissolution. At its first meeting, the board of regents entertained a resolution to discontinue the medical department, but it was defeated by a narrow five-to-four margin, the majority led by the state governor and the university president. In defeat, the minority read into the minutes of the board's second meeting their "protest against actions of the board for refusing to suspend operations of the Medical Department."[42]

The new medical school barely survived a grave-robbing scandal in its first year, an incident that seemed to confirm popular suspicions that respectable medical educators by day were ghoulish grave robbers by night in desperate search of material for the dissecting room. The incident began with the discovery that the newly interred body of an elderly lady had been secretly removed from the local cemetery. Suspicion fell immediately on students and faculty of the medical department, and when a notebook belonging to the medical building janitor was found near the opened grave, the case against the department appeared indisputable. With the local citizens in a fury, John Irish, the local newspaper editor and supporter of the medical department, intervened and had the medical students surreptitiously return the body. Still, word of the grave robbing spread far and wide, and the wrath of indignant Iowans subsided only slowly after the resignation of the professor of anatomy, James Boucher.[43]

The medical department's mostly nonresident faculty traveled to Iowa City each week for one or two days to deliver lectures to the medical students and did so without salary from the state for the first two years. In addition to dean Washington Peck, who held the chair in surgery, the original faculty included Gustavus Hinrichs of Iowa City in chemistry, William B. Robertson of Muscatine in theory and practice of medicine, William D. Middleton of Davenport in physiology, Philo J. Farnsworth of Iowa City in materia medica, James H. Boucher of Iowa City in anatomy, John C. Schrader of Iowa City in obstetrics and gynecology, and John H. Dillon of Davenport in a special chair in medical jurisprudence.

In fact, all of the physician-faculty were generalists. Formal specialization in training and practice was an invention of the twentieth century and was frowned on by the American Medical Association in the nineteenth century, in part because of the long-standing link between specialization and quackery and in part because of "leveling" sentiment within the AMA that resisted the elitist connotations of specialization.[44] Furthermore, the specialism of the late nineteenth century accommodated considerable movement within and between basic science and clinical areas. In the course of his career in the medical department, for example, William Middleton moved first from physiology to theory and practice of medicine and then to surgery, a pattern reflecting the prestige accruing to clinical over basic science areas and to surgery over all others.

The faculty had more in common than just their Iowa roots. One such characteristic was their relative youth. At the opening of the school in the fall of 1870, William Robertson was the oldest of the group at age 39; John Schrader was barely in his 30s; and William Middleton and Washington Peck were just 26 and 28, respectively. With the exception of Philo Farnsworth, all had served in the Civil War, Peck, Robertson, and Schrader as army surgeons—an experience that very likely helped to knit the group together in the difficult early years. Also, Middleton had studied under Peck and, like Peck, had received a degree from Bellevue Medical College in New York, and Robertson, who had taken a degree from Jefferson Medical College in Philadelphia in 1856, attended Bellevue in the winter of 1868–1869. Farnsworth, meanwhile, was a graduate of the College of Physicians and Surgeons of New York.[45]

Early on, gifts and student fees played a major part in financing the medical department. The state's penurious general assembly assiduously watched the department's and the board of regents' accounts, routinely billing the department for relatively small amounts. Quite unlike twentieth-century experience, patient care provided no revenues; free medical care was necessary to provide an adequate supply of training cases. In short, the medical department was a shoestring operation until late in the century. Nonetheless, in 1873, the medical faculty claimed that the school was "now in a prosperous condition," with enrollments climbing and sufficient clinical cases at hand—some of those imported from Davenport.[46] Moreover, by the mid-1870s, state appropriations did cover some two-thirds of operating costs, including, from 1872, $900 annual salaries for the medical department's part-time professors.[47] The provision of salaries still left the medical faculty on a far more tenuous footing with the university than their faculty colleagues in other departments. One member later remarked that "we were left to do our work independently and . . . were but nominally affiliated with the university."[48]

Medical students of the time were expected to be of good moral character, but their educational qualifications were minimal. A high school education was not among the medical department's early prerequisites for admission, and the first year of medical education at the University of Iowa included a preliminary two-week course to ensure modest competence in the basic skills. The curriculum was the conventional two-year ungraded course running from October to March and organized in fall and winter terms around a Christmas break. First- and second-year students attended the same series of five daily lectures and four weekly clinical demonstrations. Degree requirements included three years' study of medicine, normally consisting of one year's practical training under a preceptor and two courses of lectures at the university, plus a written thesis and a comprehensive examination. However, attrition from the first to the second year was severe, as just 13 of the 37 students in the first class of 1870–1871, for example, appeared in the roster of 71 students the following year.

The medical department instituted an optional three-year graded curriculum in 1876. Reorganized in 1879 in conjunction with an extension of the academic year from sixteen to twenty weeks, that three-year curriculum was recognizably modern in outline, if not in content. The first-year curriculum chiefly addressed what would later be known as the basic sciences: anatomy, physiology, chemistry, materia medica, and practical anatomy. It also included mandatory, if limited, clinical sessions and an introduction to dentistry, as the university's dental school would not be established until 1882. Second-year students began work in clinical areas: surgery, theory and practice of medicine, obstetrics, pediatrics, and ophthalmology and otology. Third-year students in the optional curriculum took more advanced work in the clinical areas and assisted in clinical demonstrations.

Although the medical department promoted the three-year curriculum over the older two-year course, most students—surely to no one's surprise—preferred the latter option. After all, medical students then and since have been notorious in their insistence on a "practical" education. In 1880, the three-year curriculum attracted a total of 36 students—10 first-year, 16 second-year, and 10 third-year. The two-year course, in contrast, enrolled a total of 114 students, 69 first-year and 45 second-year. In line with recommendations of the Association of American Medical Colleges, the medical department began a phase-out of the two-year course in 1888, with the last class graduating in 1890.

The 1870s and 1880s brought other improvements in curriculum and facilities, this despite the fact that medical department reports of the era were replete with requests for equipment and supplies—requests that, by and large, fell on deaf ears. In 1879, a high school diploma was among the admissions requirements. In 1882, William Robertson, who was president of the Iowa State Board of Health as well as professor of theory and practice of medicine, instituted a course of lectures on sanitary science and public hygiene, while he and his colleagues and their successors slowly incorporated rudimentary technological aids, such as the thermometer and microscope, in their instructional routines. Also in 1882, after a concerted lobbying campaign, the medical faculty occupied new quarters constructed with a $30,000 appropriation from the normally tight-fisted state legislature. Medical department boosters claimed that the new medical building—located next to the old South Hall—was "the most complete medical college building in the West."[49] Finally, in 1889–1890, the medical department lengthened the academic year to six months, extending from September to March.

Improvements came always with an eye toward fiscal considerations and the possible impact on student enrollments. Most important, at the University of Iowa as at other medical schools, a too rapid increase in fees or in educational standards risked the loss of students to weaker proprietary schools. In 1883, fearing a disastrous drop in enrollments, the regents' committee on the medical department quashed a suggested doubling of student fees intended to make the department "self-sustaining financially."[50] By the late 1880s and early 1890s, however, students' expectations regarding the quality of medical education had risen significantly; indeed, medical faculty claimed in 1891 that twenty students had left the school in the previous year because the "department is not furnishing a first class medical education."[51]

Partly as a result of changing student attitudes, some—at least within the medical department and also within the university administration—entertained more ambitious aims for medical education, aims limited always by scarce resources. For example, in a letter to President Schaeffer in 1888, Dean Washington Peck noted, "I like the plan of the Michigan

Medical Department." However, Peck conceded, "Of course we cannot make our plan the same, but we can work in that direction until we become better equipped."[52] To some extent, the vision of men like Washington Peck was itself limited. Despite his credentials, Peck never wholeheartedly embraced the aseptic and antiseptic handling of wounds and instruments and reportedly took delight in taunting students who did not share his appreciation for the stench of rotting flesh. It appears that Peck's nod to standards of cleanliness never extended beyond a tin hand basin, soap, and a towel in the amphitheater clinic. Meanwhile, his surgeon's gown hung stiffly from a hook throughout the school year, gathering layer upon layer of stain and filth as he carried out his clinical demonstrations.[53]

To be sure, Peck's rejection of Joseph Lister's work on wound infection was not unusual in the 1870s and 1880s. It was only in the later years of the century that bacteriology provided a convincing explanation of Lister's strictly empirical work and buttressed the emergent germ theory of disease. Physicians of Peck's generation by and large accepted infection of wounds as a normal part of the recovery process and distinguished between "good" and "bad" pus in evaluating wound suppuration. Moreover, the germ theory, whatever its virtues, introduced an unwelcome element of chance into the hitherto certain connection—promulgated by Florence Nightingale and other authorities—between morality and sickness and health.

From the 1870s through the 1890s, student enrollments in the medical department rose rapidly, with the exception of a brief slump in the early and mid-1880s reflecting competition from Iowa's several new proprietary schools. At the same time, however, the percentage of female students fell precipitously (Table 1.1). In 1870, the formal admissions policy declared the school open "upon equal terms to students of both sexes," making the medical department the first coeducational medical school west of the Mississippi River. Eight of the 37 students in the first class were women, six of whom returned in 1871–1872, and Philo Farnsworth assured the board of regents in 1871 that "we have in our instruction and exercises entirely ignored the question of sex." "Work went on," he said, "to the mutual

Table 1.1   Medical Department Enrollments, 1870–1895

	1870	*1875*	*1880*	*1885*	*1890*	*1895*
Male	29	92	141	96	133	198
Female	8	9	9	3	11	4
Total	**37**	**101**	**150**	**99**	**144**	**202**

Source: Board of Regents Biennial Reports.

benefit of all, with the utmost propriety and decorum."[54] Farnsworth's assurances notwithstanding, medical faculty at the University of Iowa, like their colleagues elsewhere, thought their female students generally ill-suited for the work and appear to have accepted them largely out of desperation. In subsequent decades, as total enrollments increased sharply, the proportion of female students dropped from 22 percent in 1870 to 6 percent in 1880 and to just 2 percent in 1895.

Hospital Facilities and Clinical Training

A lack of clinical training was one of the greatest shortcomings of the University of Iowa Medical Department in the late nineteenth century, echoing both the lack of facilities and the absence of a clear imperative to provide such instruction. By and large, the Iowa medical faculty, like their peers in other schools, tended to see the bedside lesson as a useful but nonessential aspect of medical education if adequate lectures and demonstrations were provided. In any event, they had little choice in the matter; few medical educators did. An 1873 national survey—surely incomplete—counted only 178 U.S. hospitals of all types, including insane asylums.[55] From the last half of the eighteenth century, of course, a few American hospitals had been providing resources for clinical instruction. The Pennsylvania Hospital, the nation's oldest (founded in 1751), was one example, and schools such as Harvard and Michigan incorporated ward rounds into the curriculum as early as the middle of the nineteenth century. Yet medical education throughout the nineteenth century consisted chiefly of a mix of preceptorship, lectures, and demonstrations, while clinical teaching was haphazard even in the best of circumstances.

Charles Rosenberg asserts that the "tight integration of hospital routine and medical school curriculum" in the teaching hospital "did not become a regular feature of medical education until after the First World War."[56] On the whole, the University of Iowa experience bears out that assertion. Still, the piecemeal integration of hospital and classroom teaching began in the last two decades of the nineteenth century, with Johns Hopkins University setting the standard. The Johns Hopkins Hospital, opened in 1889, was designed specifically to serve the needs of medical education,[57] and in the 1890s, Hopkins instituted the now familiar system of junior and senior clerkships as well as the formalized "grand rounds" adapted from German practice and popularized by William Osler.[58] By the early twentieth century, the Hopkins example, albeit imperfectly imitated, had won wide acceptance. When Abraham Flexner's report on medical education appeared in 1910, the hospital experience, most often in the form of "section teaching" with small groups of students supervised by a clinical instructor, had become an important component of medical education, its value limited at most schools chiefly by unacceptably high student-to-patient ratios.[59]

No sooner had the University of Iowa Medical Department begun its first course of lectures in the fall of 1870 than interest in a hospital connection arose. Yet, with limited resources available to them, the board of regents put the best face on scant facilities, dismissing the "superficial knowledge of disease" likely to be gained by a student in a large hospital "where so many cases are seen without the opportunity for thoroughly studying them."[60] The present medical department, in the view of the regents, afforded "a most thorough combination of didactic, clinical, and practical teaching."[61] The medical department itself claimed that clinical instruction did not suffer "for want of subjects" representing "nearly every form of disease" as well as "most major surgical operations."[62]

The first of the clinical teaching facilities for the medical department was in South Hall, next to Old Capitol. Originally a dormitory and later a classroom building, South Hall was remodeled to include an amphitheater, referred to by students as the "bullpen," with room for more than 200 students to view lectures and clinical demonstrations. Faculty members brought their own patients to the bullpen for use as teaching subjects, sufficient, according to the department, to provide fifty hours of clinical instruction per year. From the outset, however, Dean Washington Peck sought to complement clinical demonstrations with hospital clinical experience. While working as a public health officer in Scott County in 1868, Peck had observed the "sick house" established by the Sisters of Mercy in Davenport, and, aware that the Sisters worked without recompense, he calculated that if they could be persuaded to send a contingent to a clinical facility in Iowa City, the medical department would gain a low-cost teaching venue and would benefit from their charitable work.

The first attempt, in 1871, to establish a hospital in Iowa City under the Sisters of Mercy failed for want of adequate funding.[63] However, Peck arranged for the mother superior of the Davenport house to send a mission to Iowa City in September. In the meantime, the medical department acquired a second site for clinical training in the Mechanics Academy, a classroom building donated by the university for the department's use. Built in 1842 by the Iowa City Mechanics Mutual Aid Association, the Academy had gone on to become not only the first public school in Iowa City but also the first building to house the new state university, its profile mimicking that of the original state capitol building three blocks to the west. To cover the costs of renovation, which totaled $5,000, Dean Peck and his associates raised nearly $4,000 from the city of Iowa City and from private citizens, and the board of regents provided almost $1,500. Refitted as a 20-bed hospital with an added surgery theater, the Mechanics Academy functioned as a teaching hospital and as a charity hospital and dispensary, providing free care to the indigent of Johnson County. The hospital board was composed of medical faculty members, both attending and consulting. In response to Peck's invitation, the Sisters of Mercy assumed nursing duties; thus, the building became known, informally at least, as "Mercy Hospital" and "Sisters Hospital."

By late in 1873, a visitor to the two-story building would find a scrubbed, whitewashed, and neatly ordered hospital with two wards—men's and women's—and four private rooms, living quarters for the Sisters, and a small chapel.[64] According to the hospital rules, as presented to the Johnson County Board of Supervisors on June 25, 1873, "the Mechanics Academy has been set apart for hospital purposes, to be managed by the members of the medical department of the University and by such members of the regular profession in Iowa City as may be necessary to insure the successful operation of the same." Nursing service, the report continued, "is to be conducted by ladies, especially educated for the care of the sick and known as the Sisters of Mercy." The rules also noted that "the successful operation of the hospital" required "that the county agree to pay for six patients per week at the rate of four dollars per week, each patient, throughout the year."[65]

The medical department shamelessly promoted the hospital as a "facilit[y] for clinical instruction unsurpassed in the Western states," and in their annual reports to the regents, they pointed out the service to the state rendered by the hospital. In 1873, for example, the medical department claimed that "clinics have been very largely attended by patients from various parts of the state." In 1875, the department noted, "The value of services thus gratuitously rendered to the patients coming from different counties of the state will aggregate, at a very low estimate, between six and seven thousand dollars."[66] Despite the promotional cant, the building proved to be inadequate for its purpose. Later testimony portrayed the Mechanics Academy as small and poorly ventilated, its roof on the point of collapse, and threatened by fire from faulty chimney flues. In addition, the hospital was too cramped, even with the dining facilities moved to the basement, to accommodate both patients and the attending Sisters, the latter often forced to sleep on the floor.[67] Contrary, then, to the promotional excesses quoted above, the 1880 medical faculty report to the board of regents conceded, with regard to the Mechanics Academy, that " 'hospital' [was] almost a misnomer."[68]

Conflict developed early on between the Sisters of Mercy and university authorities over several issues. For example, the Sisters and much of the local community as well commonly referred to the Mechanics Academy as Mercy Hospital, although the hospital was, as one report made plain, "not under the control of the Catholic Church . . . but under the control of the

Board of Regents of the State University, superintended by the Order of the Sisters of Mercy."[69] Conflict arose also over issues of maintenance and house-keeping, responsibility for which was not clearly drawn, and over financial issues. The Sisters charged those patients who had the means to pay; others received care gratis. By the early 1880s, the hospital's annual income averaged $2,500, but average expenses exceeded income.[70] Hospital operations were occasionally subsidized by community donations and fundraising events, and the Sisters themselves relied on charity from the local community for their personal needs. Meanwhile, the state's investment was only grudging. More important, the Sisters of Mercy and the university differed over the hospital's mission. For the Sisters, the purpose of the hospital enterprise was to care for the poor and the sick; nursing, then, was their sole objective, much as in Florence Nightingale's ideal hospital. Moreover, the hospital was also a convent. In contrast, the medical department adopted a much different and more secular view, one in which the hospital served as an educational institution, its purpose revolving around medical procedures rather than nursing.

By 1881, the Iowa City convent had become an independent house, and the Mother Superior, Sister Isidore, proved to be a strong-willed and competent administrator. In 1885, perhaps in part as a result of urging from the medical faculty, the Sisters of Mercy established an independent hospital, renovating a vacant mansion two blocks from the Mechanics Academy and converting the nearby carriage house to a surgical amphitheater. This new facility, known as the new Mercy Hospital, opened in 1886 and represented a considerable advance over the Mechanics Academy. The Sisters relied on the medical department faculty for clinical diagnosis and treatment of hospital patients, allowing them also to use hospital patients for bedside lessons and to perform operations in the adjoining amphitheater. In addition, each year a senior class member served a six-month period in residence as assistant in medicine and surgery. As a result, the department shifted its main base of clinical teaching and reduced the Mechanics Academy hospital to an obstetrics clinic.

Because the convent owned the new Mercy Hospital, the Sisters might have expected the medical faculty to take a less proprietary tone and to treat them as partners rather than subordinates. In 1885, aiming to formalize relations between the Sisters of Mercy and the university regarding hospital operation, the medical faculty recommended "that a suitable instrument be prepared which shall serve as a satisfactory guide for future reference."[71] However, it was a regents investigation in 1887 that finally led to the adoption of formal rules. A special committee of the regents reported that it had "found much of misunderstanding caused by the fact that there was no definite understanding as to the relations of the University and the

Medical Faculty with the Hospital and the further fact that the Hospital Board, consisting of Medical Faculty of the University, held no meetings and practically had no control or management for the same so far as relates to the clinical patients therein." To address the problems, the regents committee prepared "rules for the government of the hospital" that would, among other things, "define the duties of the Medical Faculty in matters connected to the hospital."[72] The outcome, a list of nine points defining the responsibilities of the regents, the medical faculty, and the Sisters of Mercy, was agreed to by all sides. "The Medical faculty and such medical men as they may designate" would serve as the board of the hospital and enjoy broad authority in daily operations. Meanwhile, the Sisters would "attend to the care of the rooms and the wards, supply food as directed by the proper medical authority, administer prescribed medicines, supply clean clothing for beds, nurse the sick, and watch at night when necessary." The board of regents, meanwhile, was to be the final arbiter of all disputes.[73]

Those guidelines failed to resolve significant areas of conflict, including problems arising from the overlap of responsibility and conflicting spheres of authority. Issues relating to administration, patient care, and even hygiene continued to vex the medical faculty and the Sisters of Mercy. In 1887, the regents committee on the medical department proposed a university-owned hospital, arguing that "the sooner the institution is independent in this respect the better for all," and in 1889 the committee noted again that the "time for demanding better accommodations" had arrived. Only construction of a university-owned hospital, the committee argued, would put an end to the problems surrounding the clinical training program.[74]

The Campaign for a New Hospital

Dismayed by their experience with the Mercy Hospital affiliation and increasingly concerned to provide clinical experience for a rapidly expanding medical student body, University of Iowa officials, led by President Charles Schaeffer, concluded that the only solution was construction of a university hospital. Most American medical schools at the close of the nineteenth century faced an essentially similar dilemma. In the major metropolitan areas of the east and midwest, medical schools often adapted existing community and voluntary hospital facilities to the needs of medical education, much as the University of Iowa had tried to do, and often encountered similar problems as well. But most schools did not have that option. Nor did most command the resources to build adequate facilities of their own, a bind that contributed to the turn-of-the-century wave of medical school closures and mergers.

For the University of Iowa Medical Department, the need for a new hospital highlighted the advantages and also the disadvantages of the integration of the medical school into the state university. On the one hand, the university-owned hospital proposed by the board of regents and university officials would give the medical school control over facilities and staff, and such a hospital could be designed specifically around the mission of medical education and could be built close to classrooms and laboratories. On the other hand, the necessary appropriation from the state legislature could be won only through the rough-and-tumble of legislative politics, certainly unfamiliar territory for most academic physicians of that era or any other. In addition, an investment of the order needed to fund a new hospital would bring with it increased state scrutiny of the medical department and hospital operations.

Quite unexpectedly, the need for a hospital came to the attention of the state legislature through an investigation of charges leveled against the medical department by the irascible professor of chemistry, Gustavus Hinrichs. Although a promising scientist, educator, innovator, and "academic entrepreneur extraordinaire,"[75] Hinrichs had since his arrival at the University of Iowa in the 1860s earned a reputation as an arrogant and overbearing man given to intemperate verbal attacks on those around him. In the early 1880s, the board of regents relieved him of his collegiate department professorship for his indiscriminate public excoriation of his colleagues and superiors, particularly then university president Josiah Pickard. Reduced to the status of chemistry lecturer, Hinrichs unleashed a storm of charges against everyone from the regents to the university administration to Dean Washington Peck, whom he charged with incompetence, corruption, and bullying of medical department faculty. The regents soon dismissed Hinrichs; however, his charges against Peck lingered.[76] In 1888, a legislative joint committee investigated Hinrichs' allegations of misconduct under Peck's regime. Not surprisingly, the medical faculty and their supporters closed ranks around their dean and repudiated Hinrichs' claims, and the investigating committee subsequently cleared Peck of all charges. However, the committee was severely critical of the hospital and underlined the need for a new facility, an idea approved by the board of regents and applauded by a surprised and delighted medical faculty.[77]

The need to recruit faculty was one of the chief arguments for a new hospital. By 1890, only four of the eight founding members were still with the medical department, but salaries of clinical faculty, at $950 annually, were substantially unchanged since the mid-1870s, although the faculty in the basic sciences had seen significant increases. In addition, a makeshift hospital and a limited patient base made it difficult to recruit capable replacements. In 1869, for example, Iowa City's population was about 6,500, a figure that increased only to 7,500 in 1898. At a June 1891 meeting, the board of regents noted the importance of having a resident faculty in Iowa City but concluded that it was not a realistic goal, "considering the small salaries at our disposal and other difficulties in a city the size of Iowa City," not least the department's marginal clinical facilities.[78] To underscore the point, a Chicago physician of some note, Ludwig Hektoen, was a candidate in 1891 for the chair left vacant by the retirement of Washington Peck, but Hektoen found prospects at the university disappointing and returned to Chicago where he eventually became professor of pathology at Rush Medical College.

The quest for an appropriation to construct a new hospital proved a long and tedious one. It was only the tireless effort of Charles Ashmead Schaeffer, university president from 1887 to 1898, that brought the campaign to a successful conclusion. Overall during President Schaeffer's tenure, the university flourished as it had not before. As enrollments swelled from the 500–600 range of the 1870s and 1880s to 1,300 by the late 1890s, state appropriations increased, the university recruited promising faculty in many departments, and the campus added six new buildings, including Schaeffer Hall.[79] The remarkable growth of the University of Iowa in the 1890s—a pattern that carried through the first three decades of the twentieth century as well—paralleled the growth of the Iowa economy as well as the broader post-Civil War expansion of the American university system and not only the centralization of higher education but also the production of specialized knowledge in the universities, functions previously spread across a spectrum of public and private institutions.[80]

The marriage of the medical school and the university was one of the striking features of that new regime in American higher education, and boosters carried high expectations for that marriage. For medical schools like the University of Iowa Medical Department, university affiliation ensured some degree of financial stability, while the medical schools in return enhanced the prestige of the universities and swelled the ranks of politically influential alumni. In addition, over the long term, university-affiliated medical schools became centers of medical scientific research and created an expanding community of academic physician-scientists who subsequently exerted a major influence on the professional development of American medicine.[81] At the University of Iowa, university president Charles Schaeffer, like his predecessor James Black (1868–1870) who had been important in founding the medical department, had trained in the sciences. Because of his background he was more disposed to promote practical learning and specifically the infrastructure for education in the health sciences than was the case with previous university presidents, most of them trained for the ministry. For a time Schaeffer also occupied the chair in chemistry left vacant by Gustavus Hinrichs' forced departure from the university. Schaeffer was thereby a member of the medical faculty and an ex officio member of the Mercy Hospital board and was intimately aware of that hospital's shortcomings.

Schaeffer hoped to command the attention of state legislators, who approved, amended, or denied appropriations recommended by the regents, and in his 1889 report to the board of regents Schaeffer established a theme that he would press in letters and speeches for the next several years. The "question of Hospital facilities," he wrote, "has for some years been a matter of serious concern to the faculty . . . the University Hospital [i.e., the Mechanics Academy hospital] not being constructed for any such purpose . . . and rapidly falling into decay." "Were it not for an arrangement made some years earlier with the Sisters of Mercy," he noted, "whereby the larger number of patients have been accommodated in another building, the department could not have been satisfactorily run as long as it has." In short, Schaeffer concluded, "the state needs a body of trained physicians and a thoroughly equipped Hospital is a necessary adjunct to a school of medicine."[82]

In his efforts to sway legislators, Schaeffer used the university's legislative contacts, lobbyists, and a public relations campaign. Schaeffer was ably assisted—indeed, sometimes led—by his most important political allies, among them, Johnson County representative John Springer, state superintendent of public instruction Henry Sabin, board of regents member Al Matthews, and western Iowa lawyer Shirley Gilliland, the last serving as Schaeffer's adviser on activities in the state senate. Medical students also took up the fight, as did the student newspaper. "The need of the hour is a hospital," ran the front-page editorial in *The Vidette-Reporter*, on November 14, 1895, "and we ought to enter into the matter with all the power we can muster to obtain the necessary appropriation."[83] Meanwhile, the complexion of the community of Iowa medical practitioners had changed considerably since the medical department's early days. Most importantly, the influence of the Keokuk College of Physicians and Surgeons had diminished markedly, thanks both to an extraordinary influx of out-of-state medical graduates in the decades after the Civil War and to the rapidly increasing numbers of the University of Iowa Medical Department's own graduates. As a result, the university's medical school enjoyed an unprecedented degree of support among Iowa physicians by the 1890s.

Because of the work of Schaeffer and his stalwarts, hospital appropriation bills survived committee consideration in 1892 and 1894, although on each occasion they failed to pass both houses of the legislature. Some legislators viewed the proposed 1/5 mill tax as too extravagant in view of Iowa's still largely agricultural economy. Moreover, the state had provided the university with an annual appropriation for operating expenses since 1878, and most legislators thought the state's financial support of its university a settled matter. However, Schaeffer had hit upon the millage idea as early as 1889, prompted in part by a federal Bureau of Education report on state support for universities, and he had then won support from Henry Sabin, the state superintendent of public instruction, before approaching Governor Larrabee with the idea.[84] In 1893, Schaeffer reiterated Bureau of Education findings regarding university support for the edification of legislators and other policymakers, noting that Michigan had a tax of $\frac{1}{6}$ mill to raise $400,000 yearly; Wisconsin used $\frac{9}{40}$ mill, also to raise $400,000; Nebraska had a $\frac{3}{8}$ mill tax; and Ohio dedicated $\frac{1}{20}$ mill to its public university.[85] Overall, Schaeffer argued, Michigan had spent $966,000 on state university capital improvements from 1860 to 1893, Wisconsin $790,000, and Minnesota $609,000, compared to the paltry $240,000 in Iowa.[86] Capital investment in the university's medical program would not only bolster the education of Iowa physicians, Schaeffer and other hospital supporters pointed out; it would also enhance the medical department's service role. "In the state there are hundreds of indigent people suffering from lack of medical and surgical treatment," the board of regents argued, "but who are unable to buy it." "To such the duty of the state is as plain, as urgent, as it is in the care of the deaf, the dumb, the blind, or idiotic," the regents claimed. Medical care for the indigent was "not an expense to the state, but an economy." The proposed millage tax was, in truth, "not a tax" but "a Christian benefaction, a tender, hopeful, helping hand."[87]

By the 1880s, as already noted, Iowa was no longer the rural, frontier state of only two decades earlier; indeed, Iowa's farm population began its long decline in the decade of the 1880s. One result of the growth of an educated, urban middle class was to make the Republican party a party of reform. Admittedly, that reform impulse was halting and uncertain and at times poorly focused and directed; nonetheless, it was typical of an emergent activism on the part of state governments in many parts of America, an activism driven by the premise that the powers of government could and should be used to police the excesses traceable to explosive economic and demographic growth in the Gilded Age.[88] In Iowa, the creation of a state board of health in 1880 and passage of legislation to regulate pharmacy, dentistry, and medicine in the 1880s were symptomatic of the new political consciousness, represented also in the movement to effect a system of statewide prohibition and to impose regulation in areas as diverse as mine safety, local building codes, railroads, and milk distribution.[89]

Whatever its shortcomings, the late nineteenth-century reform effort in Iowa readily embraced the proposed university hospital, particularly since the middle-class champions of reform were, by and large, also the chief constituency of the university and the new scientific medicine. Nonetheless, a wave of anti-incumbent sentiment—reinforced by a split within the Republican party over prohibition—complicated the political picture in the late 1880s by giving the Democratic party—a party more attuned to classical laissez-faire liberalism—control over state government. The Democratic party won the Iowa governorship in 1889 and a majority position in the state legislature in the early 1890s, and it was not until 1894 that Republicans recaptured the governorship and both houses of the legislature.[90]

The Republican party that returned to power in Iowa in the mid-1890s enjoyed a broader, more populist base and an enlarged progressive wing more determined than ever to use state government as an instrument of reform.[91] That determination, combined with the easing of the financial panic that had begun in 1893 and a lowering of the university's proposed property tax levy from 1/5 to 1/10 mill, brightened prospects for passage of a funding bill. In February 1894, Charles Schaeffer's senate contact, Shirley Gilliland, apprised the president that the current bill was "cut down to my liking."[92] In addition, Gilliland praised the decision to include the hospital in a more general plan for university construction, a device that broadened the appeal of the funding measure. Although Gilliland's optimism was premature in 1894, the next legislative session, convened in early 1896, did pass the funding legislation, leading at last to the construction of the long awaited University Hospital.

The University Hospital and the New Medical Science

January 10, 1898, was visitors' day at the new University Hospital, the second hospital facility used for clinical training at the university but the first constructed expressly as a hospital. Of the hundreds who toured the premises on opening day, most viewed its wards, offices, and clinical amphitheater with "admiration and words of wonder," according to a report in the local press. "Magnificent," proclaimed the *Weekly Republican,* as it described the celebration of "a red-letter day in the history of Iowa's greatest educational institution." Hospital superintendent Jennie Cottle noted that she had "been in and through Johns Hopkins hospital, and though the authorities of that institution showered far more gold upon their building, they cannot surpass Iowa's new hospital today."[93]

Work on the building had begun only a year before. In January 1897, the building committee of the board of regents took construction bids for the hospital and accepted the $43,915 figure of general contractor James Howie of Dubuque. Using plans developed by the Cedar Rapids architectural firm of Josselyn and Taylor, in consultation with the medical faculty as well as the building committee of the board of regents, Howie began construction in the spring of 1897. Within the space of seven months the old Mechanics Academy hospital was pulled down and the new 65-bed teaching hospital rose in its place—although not without resistance from concerned citizens who protested the closing of Linn Street between Iowa Avenue and Jefferson Street because it would limit access to St. Mary's Church.[94]

Standing on a quarter-acre of land and boasting a staff of fifteen, including a superintendent, a medical director, a half-dozen members of the medical faculty, a resident, a wardmaster, and five nurses, the University Hospital was an imposing structure for its time and place—a building in two parts, one four stories and the other three. The board of regents, who had worked hard to secure building funds, and who the year before had promised to deliver the "best hospital in this state," now called it "one of the most complete hospitals in every particular west of Chicago."[95] Like Johns Hopkins Hospital, the University of Iowa Hospital was built for clinical teaching and stood within two blocks of the Medical Building, site of the department's administrative offices, laboratories, and classrooms. Unlike the Hopkins' detached pavilions, however, the pavilions of the University of Iowa Hospital—both the original structure and the additions that followed in later years—were joined to an administrative center as wings in the form of a letter "H." The floor plan reflected the influence of bacteriology and the recent introduction of antisepsis and aseptic procedures on hospital design, diminishing concern over separation and segregation of patients as a precautionary measure in the control of hospital infection and making the detached pavilion a thing of the past. Meanwhile, the many tall windows and high ceilings ensured that the wards would have good natural lighting and ventilation. As with most new construction of that time and since, there were problems as well, including a leaky roof and substandard walls.[96]

The hospital featured two large wards named for W. F. Peck and W. S. Robertson, respectively, honoring founding members of the medical faculty. Smaller wards accommodated eye patients, nose and throat cases, and childbirth. Visitors interested in up-to-date features admired the steam heat and gas and electric lights. They might also have noted private rooms, administrative offices, two operating rooms, a dispensary, a 200-seat amphitheater, a kitchen, and a dining room. In its early years, the hospital staff offered clinical services in the four major specialties of the era: surgery, medicine, diseases of women, and head specialties.

According to "Rules and Regulations for the Government for the University Hospital," a document prepared by the medical faculty and approved by the regents in 1897, the hospital administration extended from the board of regents down through the medical dean and hospital director to the student nurse (Figure 1.1).[97] In an effort to avoid the overlap in spheres of authority that had troubled the medical department in the past, the board of

Figure 1.1   University Hospital Organization, 1898

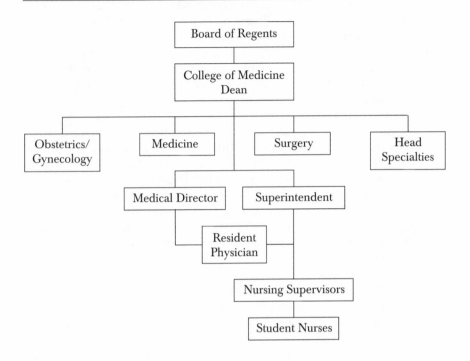

regents made the rules more detailed in scope than the 1887 rules for Mercy Hospital had been. The regents reserved to themselves the final authority on all matters relating to administration, discipline, and appointments to the hospital staff, while the medical faculty was expected to run the hospital. A staff consisting of clinical faculty, one resident assistant, and nursing students attended to both inpatients and outpatients, most of them indigent. Hospital director Elbert W. Rockwood, the University Hospital's first chief executive officer, had nominal authority over the hospital staff, including the resident physician and the superintendent, although Rockwood was professor of chemistry rather than a clinician.

Like most hospital superintendents of her time, Jennie Cottle—reported as a graduate of the nurses' training course at Massachusetts General Hospital but in fact a graduate of a Detroit training school—lived in the hospital and was expected to visit each patient daily. With the hospital matron, she maintained an inventory of hospital supplies and issued them to medical faculty and residents as needed, and Cottle had charge of the housekeeping personnel, including kitchen staff and janitors. As superintendent of the nursing school, one of some 400 in America at the time, Cottle admitted nursing students, supervised the care of patients, and dismissed nurses when necessary. The students themselves—five in the first class of 1898—comprised an unpaid hospital nursing staff, performing a wide range of duties that included cleaning, changing linen, and serving meals. Their two-year training school course involved "practical work in wards, theoretical work in class and lecture rooms and a complete course in invalid cookery," and promised preparation for private as well as hospital duty.[98] Although the nurse training course lengthened to three years in 1902, the emphasis in nursing education was clearly more on practical than on theoretical work, reflecting the fact that the nursing school, unlike the medical school, was an integral part of the hospital and thus under the control of the hospital administration. The apprenticeship system of nursing education stood in sharp contrast to the trend away from apprenticeship in other professional areas, notably medicine; it was a convenient choice for the hospital, however, one that led to long hours of ward service and the consignment of limited classroom work—mostly lectures by medical faculty—to the late afternoon and evening hours.

The transitional nature of the late nineteenth-century hospital, exacerbated by the lack of a clear definition of spheres of jurisdiction, soon led to friction within the hospital administration and to complaints from the board of regents regarding lax hospital management procedures.[99] One result was Cottle's abrupt resignation in January 1900, an event that symbolized women's increasingly precarious position in healthcare. By the late nineteenth century, the professionalization of healthcare services and the movement of healthcare from the home to the market—an evolution aptly symbolized by the rise of the modern hospital—had set in motion a major shift in the general organization and management of healthcare, presaging the "professional dominance" enjoyed by physicians over other healthcare professions throughout much of the twentieth century. At the same time, the advent of scientific medicine also focused attention on medical procedures in the hospital setting and, in turn, enhanced the authority of physicians in hospital management and patient admissions.[100] Surgical advances were central to that transition. Appendectomies, for example, became routine procedures, as did dramatic orthopædic procedures performed on children. As a result, fee structures in turn-of-the-century hospitals were increasingly correlated with specific medical procedures, while the costs and benefits of nursing services receded to the background. The authority of female hospital superintendents like Jennie Cottle was one casualty of that complex transition, helping to make the superintendent's position at the University of Iowa Hospital a revolving door for much of the next two decades.

In the hospital wards, medical faculty treated patients with the assistance of the hospital resident and gave clinical lessons to medical students. The resident, successor to the earlier house physician, was so named because he lived in the hospital and was expected to attend to the immediate care of patients. Medical students carried out clinical examinations at bedside and observed treatments administered by attending physicians, who included community physicians as well as medical faculty. Judging from regulations governing student conduct in the hospital, the medical students of the era were not models of decorum. "If any student be guilty of any improper conduct, such as smoking, whistling, singing, or spitting upon the floors in the amphitheater, halls or wards . . . it shall be the duty of the superintendent to at once forbid him such improper conduct."[101] Likewise, anecdotal evidence from contemporaries suggests a remarkable level of boisterousness outside the hospital and classrooms as well. In addition to department of medicine faculty and students, staff privileges extended to "all reputable practitioners in the state who may wish to make use of it for their patients," a concession granted to ward off complaints from local physicians who resented the construction of such a facility for the exclusive use of the medical faculty— still part-time educator-practitioners who used the hospital for the treatment of their private patients.

Hospital regulations treated patients sternly. They were not permitted to talk among themselves about their diseases, and slovenly behavior was forbidden as was the possession of books or pictures of an "immoral or indecent character."[102] From the patient rights perspective of the late twentieth century, the attitude that ruled the conduct of patients in 1898 conveys the air of a harsh Victorian parent toward misbehaving children. And the moral mission of the nineteenth-century hospital extended to the selection of patients. Those with "diseases of an offensive nature"—venereal diseases, for example—were not admitted, although later hospital records show the admission of many syphilis cases, the result of more effective treatment, improved standards of hygiene, and, as Morris Vogel notes, the growing dominance of medical over so-called moral decisions in hospital patient admissions.

Patient admissions at the University of Iowa Hospital were predominantly indigent teaching cases subsidized by local governments; however, increasing numbers of private patients augmented admissions figures, many attracted by the potential of new surgical procedures to relieve a variety of deforming and previously fatal afflictions. In 1898, the cost for indigent patients was $7 per week, $5 of which was paid by their home county, while private room rates were $10 to $20 per week. At the outset, and contrary to expectations of most state legislators, the University Hospital was not self-supporting, even with economies realized by a part-time medical faculty and a resident and staff nurses who were officially students rather than employees; it was not until the turn of the century that the hospital's accounts reached a break-even point.[103]

In some important ways, standards of care available to patients in the new University Hospital reflected the precepts of the emerging scientific medicine. For example, anesthesia and antisepsis, watchwords of modern medicine in 1898, were listed among the hospital's assets in local newspaper accounts. Indeed, by 1898, the germ principle of disease etiology was a fixed point in the Iowa medical faculty's understanding of the nature of illness, its origin, and its progress through the body. In 1892, the medical department established a chair of pathology and bacteriology, and the laboratory became an important arena of investigation.[104] Traces of the unhygienic Washington Peck, gore-smeared and reveling in the rankness of suppurating wounds, had disappeared even from the ward that bore his name, as the teaching hospital haltingly emerged to become the center of advanced medical science, medical practice, and medical training.

Late nineteenth- and early twentieth-century advances in clinical procedures and technologies and their centralization in the hospital eventually created institutions that attracted rather than repelled patients, especially middle-class, paying patients.[105] Nationally, the numbers of hospitals increased dramatically in the late nineteenth and early twentieth centuries, and even in Iowa, a newly built "modern" hospital at the turn of the century featured brightly lit and well-ventilated wards in which orderly housekeeping was practiced and hygienic standards observed. In the 50 years between 1870 and 1920, in response to a variety of cultural and demographic as well as scientific and technological factors, the hospital in America developed from a warehouse for society's castoffs, a place where the poor went to die, to an efficiently run hygienic workshop for the practice of scientific medicine.[106] In line with the emergence of the modern hospital, hospital managers in 1899 formed the Association of Hospital Superintendents, renamed the American Hospital Association in 1908, to bring greater order and status to their work.

Medical historians agree, however, that the introduction of clinical technologies into the hospital setting was slow and to some extent grudging.[107] Even prominent clinicians like William Osler viewed much of the new technology with some skepticism, seeing it as no more than an adjunct to traditional clinical practice centered on careful observation and skillful deduction. Also, to some at least, the laboratory threatened to devalue the clinician's time-honored skills, and, in any event, much of the new science was of limited usefulness to the clinician in alleviating the suffering of real patients. At the same time, hospital managers, operating on principles born in the nineteenth-century charity hospital, challenged the introduction of the new technologies on economic grounds. Important advances in pathology and chemistry—for example, the chemistry of blood and urine—nonetheless forced the establishment of laboratory facilities in many hospitals by the turn of the century, and hospitals also began billing for laboratory tests apart from the normal daily charge for room, board, and care, converting laboratory facilities into sources of hospital revenues. While the diagnostic powers of the new technologies ran well ahead of therapy, selected advances—for example, x-rays, diphtheria antitoxin, and serological tests for syphilis—had a major impact on public opinion and boosted the hospital's image as a center of technical efficacy.[108]

The Medical Department and the New Medical Science

In an 1891 letter to university president Charles Schaeffer, Philo Farnsworth, professor of materia medica from 1870 to 1892 and a persistent—if not always reliable—critic of the department and of Washington Peck's leadership, charged that his colleagues were incapable of taking the steps needed to modernize the teaching of medicine at the university. "They are not harmonious enough," he said, and they "are afraid of losing their places, or have not views broad enough." Moreover, in Farnsworth's view, the dean was more interested in his own reputation than in bettering the medical department. "The days of cheap men and makeshift ways," Farnsworth warned the president, "have passed."[109] Three months after Peck's death in 1892, John Schrader, professor of obstetrics and gynecology, also complained of deficiencies, defending a request for additional medical department funding with the comment that "this department has never been properly equipped."[110]

To be sure, the University of Iowa Medical Department, like nearly all medical schools of the time, expanded its facilities and faculty only slowly and erratically in the late nineteenth century. Indeed, the faculty of the early 1890s had scarcely changed in nature and number from that of the early 1870s. Moreover, as already noted, the medical department adapted only slowly to the new scientific medicine—in part, as Schrader argued, because of limited funding and in part, as Farnsworth charged, because of limited vision. As the century drew to a close, one medical department supporter decried the fact that "the medical department of our beloved State University is so meagerly endowed," and he prodded president Schaeffer "to bring our department's facilities up to the standards . . . of the times."[111]

Perhaps in part because of such criticisms, the 1890s did bring significant change to the medical department, not just in the clinical teaching opportunities afforded by the University Hospital but also in personnel and curriculum. One important initiative was the recruitment of new faculty members who had pursued postgraduate medical education in the scientific centers of Europe, home to the most sophisticated laboratory medicine of the time.[112] Lawrence W. Littig, who held the chair of theory and practice of medicine from 1891 until 1903, was one example, having studied in Leipzig, Paris, and Vienna after taking his medical degree from the University of Iowa in 1883. A second major initiative, mentioned earlier, was approval of a chair in pathology and bacteriology in 1892. Lawrence Littig was a staunch advocate of that innovation, and his protégé Walter Lawrence Bierring, an 1892 Iowa graduate, was Littig's hand-picked candidate for the new chair. In 1894, Bierring returned to the university from his own postgraduate travels in Europe and, applying knowledge gained at the Pasteur Institute in Paris, prepared an anti-diphtheria serum with the help of his colleague John Schrader, "who kindly provided the horse for the experiment." Working with what he boasted was the first successful serum produced west of New York City, Bierring tried his product "in very large doses" on himself and claimed success in its use in "over 300 cases of diphtheria." In 1903, Bierring succeeded his mentor Littig as head of theory and practice, Littig having resigned in a huff when denied the chair of surgery.[113]

In 1896, the medical department also extended the curriculum to four academic years of six months, in accordance with the precedent set by Johns Hopkins in 1893. The new curriculum established the basic pattern of medical education that has continued to the present. Students in their first two years studied the basic sciences—anatomy, physiology, general chemistry, pharmacology, pathology, histology, and bacteriology—as well as an introduction to materia medica, therapeutics, and physical diagnosis. The third and fourth years took students into the clinical areas, ranging from theory and practice of medicine (internal medicine) and surgery to obstetrics and gynecology. In addition, fourth-year students took increasing responsibility for patient care and for clinical demonstrations before their junior colleagues.

The sporadic and uneven development of American medical education at the University of Iowa and elsewhere reflected the local nature of late nineteenth-century reform efforts, the limited resources available to medical schools, and the limited mechanisms to enforce meaningful standards. In an 1891 letter to President Schaeffer, for example, Philo Farnsworth dismissed requirements set by the Iowa Board of Medical Examiners as "make believe" meant to "frighten other institutions in the state" but "of little force anyway."[114] Revised state medical practice acts in the 1890s and early 1900s—1899 in Iowa—augmented the authority of state medical boards by requiring an examination of all applicants for licensure, and the formation of the National Confederation of State Medical Examining and Licensing Boards in 1891 provided a national forum for the exchange of ideas. Yet the reluctance of state boards to surrender their autonomy in setting educational standards and designing licensing examinations sharply limited the potential for national reform.

Similarly, the Association of American Medical Colleges, founded in 1877 and reorganized in 1890, was hamstrung by the lack of both the means and the will to impose higher standards on its own, often woefully substandard, member schools. The association set more ambitious goals for admissions and curriculum, but its recommendations, adopted at the University of Iowa and similar institutions, were not enforceable and were largely ignored by the proprietary diploma mills most in need of reform. Meanwhile, the American Medical Association was barely visible in the nascent late nineteenth-century movement for reform of medical education. The AMA's influence over medical education, and its broader claim to recognition as the voice of American medicine, came to the fore only after the association's reorganization in 1901, a reorganization that simultaneously broadened the association's membership base, centralized its administrative structure, and led to the creation of the Council on Medical Education.

The late nineteenth century was also a transitional era in which medical scientific research was in its infancy and the nature and scope of academic medicine was not yet fixed. Burdened with lectures, demonstrations, clinical duties, and private practice, Lawrence Littig, Walter Bierring, and their colleagues, while adequately trained, had little time for independent research. Moreover, medical schools and teaching hospitals of the late nineteenth century afforded little in the way of research facilities and even less incentive to faculty inclined toward research. Contemporaries extolled the scientific accomplishments of a few "great men," and medical historians have generally followed suit, but much of what passed for medical scientific discourse at the time was little more than rank speculation disguised in the new language of science. Moreover, dedicated physicians were legitimately divided over the meaning and implications of scientific medicine,[115] and most practicing physicians, thanks to the generally lackluster state of medical education, could not appreciate the significance of the most advanced science of the day. Because of that, late nineteenth-century American medical science consisted largely of library research and simple clinical description rather than laboratory work, and the U.S. Department of Agriculture and the U.S. Army's Office of the Surgeon General were the most important sites of ongoing medical scientific research.

Conclusion

The half-century between the founding of the University of Iowa in 1847 and the laying of the hospital cornerstone in 1897 brought fundamental changes to medicine and to medical education in Iowa and across the

United States. Because of that, the prospects of the average patient under the care of an Iowa physician improved considerably in the last decades of the nineteenth century. For the first time, physicians skilled in the latest techniques, particularly those physicians with advanced training in Europe, performed medical and surgical interventions that were, on the whole, more likely to be helpful to the patient than injurious. In addition, the more progressive physicians had a fair understanding of the etiologies of contagious diseases such as cholera, tuberculosis, and diphtheria, while the application of quarantine and hygienic measures did much to stem the spread of such common afflictions.

With the diffusion and acceptance of the germ theory of disease, responsible medical practitioners also adopted more antiseptic methods, and they likewise added technologies that included the thermometer, the stethoscope, and the sphygmomanometer, as well as a range of diagnostic tests to their expanding armamentarium.[116] At the same time, hospitals became the physician's workshop, the site of the best medical knowledge, diagnosis, and therapy. As such, hospitals became increasingly valuable both as houses of healing and as sites for clinical teaching, and their numbers multiplied accordingly, while hospital administration emerged as a profession, with a growing body of specialized knowledge and its own professional organization.

As the University of Iowa Medical Department flourished in the 1890s, the stature of its proprietary competitors within the state diminished. With a number of medical schools competing for a limited pool of students, enrollments became uncertain and financial difficulties increasingly common. Perhaps most important, higher expectations both in clinical education and in the basic sciences placed insupportable demands on the shaky financial bases of such institutions: by 1899, all but five of Iowa's proprietary schools had closed, victims of rising costs, shrinking student bodies and revenues, and rising standards of medical education enforced, however imperfectly, by state and national standards-setting bodies and by student expectations.

Thus, the history of health care practices and institutions in nineteenth-century Iowa is a case study that, in many important respects, parallels national trends. At midcentury, untrammeled free enterprise in medical education and practice flourished, and competition was the rule among medical schools and among medical practitioners. In that competitive environment, the University of Iowa Medical Department established in 1870 survived the challenges of its rivals, most especially the Keokuk College of Physicians and Surgeons, because of its connection to the state university and because of the financial support of the state legislature, albeit grudging and meager in the early years. Construction of the University Hospital in the late 1890s marked a new phase in the state government's partnership in medical education in Iowa, a partnership long resisted by many legislators and their constituents but one that grew even more important in the twentieth century. Of course, greater oversight was the price of greater state support, and each small increment of financial commitment from the state brought increased accountability to the board of regents and, on occasion, to the state legislature itself.

The University of Iowa Hospital was also symbolic of the emerging new order in American medicine that was fast supplanting an older regime based on free market principles both in medical practice and in medical education. Admittedly, the hospital, despite its "modern" furnishings and the glowing testimonials of its supporters, could not match the material, technological, and scientific sophistication of major east coast institutions such as Johns Hopkins and Massachusetts General, or even midwestern hospitals such as the University of Michigan Hospital. On a larger scale, too, of course, it paled in comparison to the European centers of scientific and medical thought and practice. The University of Iowa Hospital in 1898 was, in some sense, a provincial institution, the product of a developing economy and society and, like the university of which it was a part, captive to its cultural and geographical isolation. Nonetheless, the hospital stood as testament to Iowans' expanding faith in the new medical science, and the hospital's principal shortcomings, most modern observers could agree, were those of turn-of-the-century medical science itself.

Notes

1. For the sake of convenience, the name University of Iowa, is used throughout, even though the school was correctly known as State University of Iowa prior to the mid-1960s and was often known informally as Iowa State University in the late nineteenth and early twentieth centuries.

2. "Cornerstone Laying," *The Vidette-Reporter*, May 15, 1897.

3. Historians have extensively documented that transition. See, as examples, Paul Starr, *The Social Transformation of American Medicine: The Rise of a Sovereign Profession and the Making of a Vast Industry* (New York: Basic Books, 1982); Charles E. Rosenberg, *The Care of Strangers: The Rise of America's Hospital System* (New York: Basic Books, 1987); Kenneth E. Ludmerer, *Learning to Heal: The Development of American Medical Education* (New York: Basic Books, 1985); Alexandra Oleson and John Voss, eds., *The Organization of Knowledge in Modern America, 1860–1920* (Baltimore, MD: The Johns Hopkins University Press, 1979).

4. See Ronald L. Numbers and Judith Walzer Leavitt, eds., *Medicine Without Doctors: Home Health Care in American History* (New York: Science History Publications/USA, 1977).

5. Charles Rosenberg, "The Therapeutic Revolution: Medicine, Meaning, and Social Change in Nineteenth-Century America," in Charles Rosenberg and Morris J. Vogel, eds., *The Therapeutic Revolution: Essays in the Social History of American Medicine* (Philadelphia: University of Pennsylvania Press, 1979), pp. 3–25. For a more detailed discussion, see John S. Haller, Jr., *American Medicine in Transition, 1840–1910* (Urbana: University of Illinois Press, 1981), especially chapter 1, "Every Man in His Humor," and chapter 2, "When Lancet Was King."

6. See Lester S. King, *Medical Thinking: A Historical Preface* (Princeton, NJ: Princeton University Press, 1982), especially chapter 3, "Signs and Symptoms."

7. See Norman Gevitz, ed., *Other Healers: Unorthodox Medicine in America* (Baltimore: Johns Hopkins University Press, 1988).

8. John C. Schrader, quoted in "Cornerstone Laying," *The Vidette Reporter*, May 15, 1897.

9. See Richard Shryock, *Medicine in America: Historical Essays* (Baltimore: Johns Hopkins University Press, 1966), pp. 1–45; R. Carlyle Buley, "Pioneer Health and Medical Practices in the Old Northwest Prior to 1840," *Mississippi Valley Historical Review* 20 (1933–34): 497–520; Erwin H. Ackerknecht, "Diseases in the Middle West," in *Essays in the History of Medicine in Honor of David J. Davis, M.D., Ph.D.* (Chicago: University of Illinois Press, 1965), pp. 168–181.

10. The most systematic study of malaria is Erwin H. Ackerknecht, *Malaria in the Upper Mississippi Valley, 1760–1900,* Supplements to the *Bulletin of the History of Medicine*, no. 4 (Baltimore: Johns Hopkins University Press, 1945). For a local perspective, see J. J. M. Angear, "Defective Drainage in Green Bay Township, Iowa," *Transactions of the American Medical Association* 25 (1874): 395.

11. Cyrus Sanders, "Journal of Cyrus Sanders," *Iowa Journal of History and Politics* 37 (1939): 52–88.

12. John Duffy, "Medicine in the West: An Historical Overview," in James O. Breeden, ed., *Medicine in the West* (Manhattan, KS: Sunflower University Press, 1982), p. 8.

13. Information about the first medical practitioners in Iowa is scant and unreliable. In the view of Walter Bierring, the history of the practice of medicine in Iowa had its beginning with the arrival of Dr. Frederick Andros in Dubuque in 1833 and his subsequent establishment of a medical practice. Like so many of his professional brethren of that frontier time, Andros was a colorful figure. According to a fellow physician, he went about his work with a tall silk hat "in which he carried his letters, red bandanna, cigars, stethoscope, and either a clean or dirty collar." See Walter Bierring, "Iowa Medicine Prior to 1850," in *One Hundred Years of Iowa Medicine* (Iowa City: The Athens Press, 1950), pp. 9–20.

14. Charles Rosenberg, "The Practice of Medicine in New York a Century Ago," in Ronald L. Numbers and Judith Walzer Leavitt, eds., *Sickness and Health* (Madison: University of Wisconsin Press, 1978), p. 63.

15. Charles Rosenberg, *The Care of Strangers*, pp. 28, 29, 159.

16. See William Rothstein, *American Medical Schools and the Practice of Medicine* (New York: Oxford University Press, 1987), pp. 73–76; see also Paul Starr, *The Social Transformation of American Medicine*, pp. 156–158.

17. *Boston Medical and Surgical Journal* 61 (January 19, 1860): 488–493.

18. For the history of the University of Iowa, see Stow Persons, *The University of Iowa in the Twentieth Century: An Institutional History* (Iowa City: University of Iowa Press, 1990); and John C. Gerber, Carolyn B. Brown, James Kaufmann, and James B. Lindberg, Jr., *A Pictorial History of the University of Iowa* (Iowa City: University of Iowa Press, 1988).

19. See John T. McClintock, "Medical Education in Iowa," in *One Hundred Years of Iowa Medicine*, pp. 240–242; Faye Harris, "A Frontier Community: The Economic, Social, and Political Development of Keokuk, Iowa from 1820 to 1866," Ph.D. Dissertation, University of Iowa, 1965, p. 212. See also, Ferdinand J. Smith, "The Transition from Franklin Medical School to the Keokuk College of Medicine of the State University of Iowa," *Journal of the Iowa State Medical Society* 26 (October 1936): 595–597; (November 1936): 656–662; (December 1936): 707–709; William Hanchett, "A Medical Student in Keokuk: Letters of Joshua Nichols Speed, 1858–1860," *Annals of Iowa* 37 (Fall 1964): 416–435.

20. William Hanchett, "A Medical Student in Keokuk."

21. "University Hospital," in *Western Medico-Chirurgical Journal* (August 1851), quoted in Clyde Boice, "Hospitals in Iowa," in *One Hundred Years of Iowa Medicine*, pp. 371–375.

22. The importance of epidemic disease, especially cholera and yellow fever, in the advance of public health institutions is a theme developed by John Duffy; see, for example, "Social Impact of Disease in the Late Nineteenth Century," *Bulletin of the New York Academy of Medicine* 47 (July 1971): 797–811.

23. David S. Fairchild, "Medicine in Iowa From Its Early Settlement to 1876," collected reprints from the *Journal of the Iowa State Medical Society,* D.S. Fairchild, ed., 1912, p. 75. In fact, the total here is

602, suggesting the possibility that a handful of physicians classified themselves in more than one category.

24. *Annual Directory of Homeopathic Physicians of Iowa, Minnesota, and Wisconsin* (Iowa City, IA: Iowa City Publishing Company, 1880), pp. 1–7; *Medical and Surgical Directory of the State of Iowa, 1883–1884* (Clinton, IA: Allen Steam Printing and Binding, 1883).

25. See *Vital Statistics, Health and Nutrition* (Series C 1-155), National Office of Vital Statistics, United States Public Health Service.

26. Bureau of Education, Department of the Interior, *Report of Commissioner of Education, 1895.*

27. John T. McClintock, "Medical Education in Iowa," in *One Hundred Years of Iowa Medicine*, pp. 224–309.

28. *Laws of Iowa, 1886*, chapter 104.

29. Samuel L. Baker, "Physician Licensure Laws in the United States, 1865–1915," *Journal of the History of Medicine and Allied Sciences* 39 (April 1984): 173–197; see also, Paul Starr, *The Social Transformation of American Medicine*, pp. 103–112.

30. Charles Rosenberg, *The Care of Strangers*, pp. 131–141.

31. See Clyde Boice, "Hospitals in Iowa," pp. 371–419. See also Sister Mary Brigid Condon, R.S.M., *From Obscurity to Distinction: The Story of Mercy Hospital, Iowa City, 1873–1993* (Iowa City, IA: Mercy Hospital, 1993), pp. 1–10.

32. Charles Rosenberg, *The Care of Strangers*, p. 111.

33. Boice, "Hospitals in Iowa," pp. 371–387.

34. See the unpublished Charles Chase manuscript on the history of the University of Iowa College of Medicine, 1920, State Historical Society of Iowa, Iowa City.

35. See William Middleton's "Medical Department, Iowa State University," in *Medicine in Iowa: From Its Early Settlement to 1876*, pp. 50–65. See also, Clarence Ray Aurner, *History of Education in Iowa, Vol. IV* (Iowa City, IA: The State Historical Society of Iowa, 1916), pp. 131–145.

36. Board of Trustees Minutes, September 18, 1868, University of Iowa Archives.

37. Ibid.

38. Series I (William Haddock), Box 7, "Medicine Reports," June 20, 1870, University of Iowa Archives.

39. McClintock, "Medical Education in Iowa," p. 271.

40. See Faye E. Harris, "A Frontier Community: The Economic, Social, and Political Development of Keokuk, Iowa from 1820 to 1866," chapter 4, "Economic and Social Development, 1850–1857," Ph.D. Dissertation, University of Iowa, 1965. For a parallel case at the University of Michigan, see Horace W. Davenport, *Fifty Years of Medicine at the University of Michigan* (Ann Arbor: The University of Michigan Medical School, 1986).

41. *Laws of Iowa, 1870*, p. 166.

42. Board of Regents Minutes, June 28 and June 30, 1870, University of Iowa Archives.

43. See John P. Irish, "Some Episodes in the History of the Founding of the Medical College of the State University of Iowa," *Iowa Journal of History and Politics* 18 (January 1920): 125–129. See also Chase manuscript, chapter 5/6, p. 13.

44. Rosemary Stevens, *American Medicine and the Public Interest* (New Haven, CT: Yale University Press, 1971), pp. 43–49.

45. See McClintock, "Medical Education in Iowa," pp. 268–275; Carl Cone, *History of the State University of Iowa: The College of Medicine* (Unpublished manuscript, 1941), pp. 47–49, 65–75, University of Iowa Archives. In 1872, two additional lecturers were brought into the teaching curriculum: Dr. E. H. Hazen of Davenport gave lessons on ophthalmology and otology, and Dr. Mark Ranney of the State Asylum for the Insane in Mount Pleasant spoke on the subject of insanity.

46. Medical Faculty Report to the Board of Regents, March 5, 1873, Series I, Box 7, "Medical Reports," University of Iowa Archives.

47. Board of Regents Minutes, June 20, 1872, University of Iowa Archives.

48. P. A. Farnsworth to G. E. MacLean, May 10, 1901, Series I (William Haddock), Box 6, "Medical History," University of Iowa Archives.

49. See Walter Bierring, " Reveries of a Doctor: The Old Medical Building," *The Iowa Alumnus* (February 1919).

50. Board of Regents Minutes, June 21, 1882, and March 7, 1883, University of Iowa Archives.

51. C. W. Littig to C. A. Schaeffer, January 20, 1891, Series I (William Haddock), Box 6, "Medicine Lab/Equipment," University of Iowa Archives.

52. W. F. Peck to C. A. Schaeffer, December 15, 1888, Box 1, CA Schaeffer Papers, University of Iowa Archives.

53. See Chase manuscript, chapters 8, 9, "Developmental Days."

54. Annual Report of the University of Iowa Medical Department, February 28, 1871, Series I (William Haddock), Box 7, Folder 1, University of Iowa Archives.

55. J. M. Toner, "Statistics of Regular Medical Associations and Hospitals of the United States," *Transactions of the American Medical Association* 24 (1873): 314–333. More than one-third of the institutions in Toner's count were asylums. Overall, Toner's count of hospitals is suspect; more than half of the institutions he included were located in New York, Massachusetts, and Pennsylvania.

56. Charles Rosenberg, *Care of Strangers*, p. 192. See also Kenneth Ludmerer, "The Rise of the Teaching Hospital in America," *Journal of the History of Medicine and Allied Sciences* 38 (October 1983): 389, 402.

57. See A. McGehee Harvey, Gert Breiger, Susan Abrams, and Victor McKusick, "A Model of Its Kind: A Century of Medicine at Johns Hopkins," *Journal of the American Medical Association* 261 (June 2, 1989): 3136–3142. See also Richard Shryock, *The Unique Influence of the Johns Hopkins University on American Medicine*, Copenhagen: Ejnar Munksgaard, 1953, pp. 14, 24. A few American medical schools did sponsor their own hospitals before the Hopkins opened in 1889; see William Rothstein, *American Medical Schools and the Practice of Medicine*, pp. 39–63.

58. Kenneth Ludmerer, *Learning to Heal*, pp. 60–61.

59. See Thomas S. Huddle and Jack Ende, "Osler's Clerkship: Origins and Interpretations," *Journal of the History of Medicine and Allied Sciences* 49 (October 1994): 496–497.

60. Biennial Report of the Iowa State Board of Regents, 1871, p. 56, University of Iowa Archives.

61. Medical Department Announcement, 1870, University of Iowa Archives.

62. Functional Annual Report of the Medical Department, February 28, 1871, Series I (William Haddock), Box 7, "Medical Reports," University of Iowa Archives.

63. Ibid.

64. "Our Hospital," *The Vidette-Reporter*, November 15, 1873.

65. See excerpt from the *History of Johnson County, Iowa* 1883, pp. 395–397, in J. T. McClintock, Folder 1, University of Iowa Archives.

66. University of Iowa Medical Department Reports to the Board of Regents, March 5, 1873, and June 29, 1875, Series I (William Haddock), "Medicine Reports," University of Iowa Archives.

67. See Sister Mary Brigid Condon, *From Obscurity to Distinction*, pp. 177–187.

68. Medical Faculty Report to the Board of Regents, February 28, 1880, Series I, Box 7, "Medical Reports," University of Iowa Archives.

69. *History of Johnson County*, 1883, p. 397, in J. T. McClintock, Folder 1, University of Iowa Archives.

70. See Sister Mary Brigid Condon, *From Obscurity to Distinction*, pp. 7–33.

71. Series I (William Haddock), Box 7, "Medical Reports," June 12, 1885, University of Iowa Archives.

72. Board of Regents Minutes, September 20, 1887, University of Iowa Archives.

73. Ibid.

74. Board of Regents Minutes, June 21, 1887, and June 18, 1889, University of Iowa Archives.

75. James O. Freedman, *Idealism and Liberal Education* (Ann Arbor: The University of Michigan Press, 1996), p. 73.

76. For Hinrichs' testimony on the occasion of the investigation of 1888, see "Report of the Joint Committee Appointed by the 22nd General Assembly to Investigate the State University of Iowa," May 15, 1888, State Historical Society of Iowa, Des Moines, Iowa. After his dismissal, Hinrichs found employment as a chemistry instructor at St. Louis University, where he continued to publish attacks against his former employer and colleagues; see John Springer telegram to C. A. Schaeffer, March 9, 1892, Box 3, Folder 12-3, C. A. Schaeffer Papers, University of Iowa Archives.

77. Biennial Report of the Board of Regents, 1889, p. 5, University of Iowa Archives.

78. Board of Regents Minutes, June 16, 1891, University of Iowa Archives.

79. Series II (William Haddock), Box 4, "Budget and State Appropriations," University of Iowa Archives.

80. See Oleson and Voss, *The Organization of Knowledge in Modern America, 1860–1920*, especially Edward Shils, "The Order of Learning in the United States: The Ascendancy of the University," pp. 19–47.

81. Ludmerer, *Learning to Heal*, pp. 123–138.

82. Charles Schaeffer, Report to the Board of Regents, 1889, p. 23, University of Iowa Archives.

83. "Medical Department," *The Vidette-Reporter*, November 14, 1895.

84. H. Sabin to C. A. Schaeffer, December 1, 1889, Box 2, Folder 6-3, C. A. Schaeffer Papers, University of Iowa Archives.

85. U.S. Department of the Interior, Bureau of Education, *Report of the Commissioner of Education, 1887–1888* (Washington, DC: U.S. Government Printing Office, 1889), pp. 623–626.

86. Biennial Report of the Board of Regents 1895, p. 10, University of Iowa Archives.

87. Ibid., p. 5.

88. For general discussion, see William R. Brock, *Investigation and Responsibility: Public Responsibility in the United States, 1865–1900* (New York: Cambridge University Press, 1984).

89. Established to collect vital statistics and to control the spread of infectious diseases, the Board of Health brought the force of law to bear on a variety of public health problems. In addition, the board served as a "pulpit for dissemination of the gospel of scientific medicine" in the 1880s and 1890s. See Lee Anderson, "'Headlights Upon Sanitary Medicine': Public Health and Medical Reform in Late Nineteenth-Century Iowa," *Journal of the History of Medicine and Allied Sciences* 46 (April 1991): 178–200. For a detailed view of prohibition in late nineteenth-century Iowa, see Dan Elbert Clark, "The History of Liquor Legislation in Iowa," *Iowa Journal of History and Politics* 6 (1908): 339–374, 501–608. For the story of Governor William Larrabee and railroad regulation, see Leland Sage, *A History of Iowa* (Ames: Iowa State University Press, 1974), pp. 204–208. For an exhaustive list of regulatory initiatives of the era, see John E. Briggs, *History of Social Legislation in Iowa* (Iowa City: The State Historical Society of Iowa, 1915), pp. 91–143.

90. Leland Sage, *History of Iowa*, pp. 209–214. See also Frank J. Stork, and Cynthia A. Clingan, *The Iowa General Assembly: Our Legislative Heritage, 1846–1980* (Des Moines, IA: Iowa State Senate, 1980), p. 6.

91. Leland Sage, *History of Iowa*, pp. 214, 216–233.

92. S. Gilliland to C. A. Schaeffer, February 13, 1894, Box 4, Folder 16, C. A. Schaeffer Papers, University of Iowa Archives.

93. "The New Hospital Opens," *Iowa City Weekly Republican*, January 19, 1898.

94. See "The New Hospital," *The Vidette-Reporter*, January 28, 1897. Although *The Vidette-Reporter*, in its January 11, 1898 edition, set the hospital's bed count at 65 later reports differed. The first annual report of the University Hospital, dated 1912, put the number at 50, and Carl Cone claimed 100 beds in his *History of the State University of Iowa: The College of Medicine*, p. 136. It is not clear whether the differing totals are simply in error, whether they reflected the disparity between beds actually in place and total bed capacity, or whether they included both private beds and ward beds.

95. Biennial Report of the Board of Regents, 1897, p. 6, and Biennial Report, 1899, p. 12, University of Iowa Archives.

96. See, for example, Board of Regents Minutes, September 20, 1898, University of Iowa Archives.

97. "Rules and Regulations for the Government of the University Hospital," June 10, 1897, Record Group 27, "University Hospital," Box 6, Miscellaneous 1900–1977, "Hospital Rules, 1897–1978," University of Iowa Archives.

98. See Elizabeth K. Means, "History of the College of Nursing: The State University of Iowa," in *Nurses Alumni Association Directory*, University of Iowa Nurses Alumni Association, 1951.

99. Board of Regents Minutes, June 8, 1898, University of Iowa Archives.

100. Morris J. Vogel, *The Invention of the Modern Hospital*, pp. 69–72.

101. "Rules and Regulations for the Government of the University Hospital."

102. Ibid.

103. Board of Regents Finance Committee Minutes, Report of the Secretary—University Hospital Accounts, 1901, University of Iowa Archives.

104. See Walter L. Bierring, "The Story of Bacteriology at the University of Iowa," *Journal of the Iowa State Medical Society* 27 (October 1937): 555–557; (December 1937): 656–659.

105. See Joel D. Howell, *Technology in the Hospital: Transforming Patient Care in the Early Twentieth Century* (Baltimore, MD: Johns Hopkins University Press, 1995).

106. Charles Rosenberg, *The Care of Strangers*, pp. 5–9, 111–118.

107. Ibid., pp. 161–165.

108. Ibid., pp. 154–161.

109. P. J. Farnsworth to C. A. Schaeffer, July 1891, Series I, Box 6, "Medical Needs," C. A. Schaeffer Papers, University of Iowa Archives.

110. Report to the Board of Regents, March 9, 1882, University of Iowa Archives.

111. Fred Becker to C. A. Schaeffer, August 2, 1898, Box 5, File 26, C. A. Schaeffer Papers, University of Iowa Archives.

112. For discussion of the "continental tour" and the development of American academic medicine, see Thomas Neville Bonner, "The German Model of Training Physicians in the United States, 1870–1914: How Closely Was It Followed?" *Bulletin of the History of Medicine* 64 (Spring 1990): 18–34.

113. See Bierring, *A History of the Department of Internal Medicine*, p. 33; Bierring, "The Modern Treatment of Diphtheria with Demonstration of Method of Preparation of Antitoxin," reprinted in *Journal of the Iowa State Medical Society* 25 (April 1925): 7.

114. P. J. Farnsworth to C. A. Schaeffer, March 19, 1891, Box 3, File 10-6, C. A. Schaeffer Papers, University of Iowa Archives.

115. See, for example, Russell C. Maulitz, "Physician Versus Bacteriologist," in Maulitz and Diana E. Long, eds., *Grand Rounds: One Hundred Years of Internal Medicine* (Philadelphia: University of Pennsylvania Press, 1988), pp. 91–107; Gerald L. Geison, "Divided We Stand: Physiologists and Clinicians in the American Context," in *The Therapeutic Revolution*, pp. 67–90; L. S. Jacyna, "The Laboratory and the Clinic: The Impact of Pathology on Surgical Diagnosis in the Glasgow Western Infirmary, 1875–1910," *Bulletin of the History of Medicine* 62 (Fall 1988): 384–406.

116. See, for example, William Middleton, "The Thermometer in Disease," *Iowa State Medical Society Transactions* 2 (1872–76): 124–130.

2

The Emergence of the Modern University Teaching Hospital, 1898–1928

The opening of the University Hospital in 1898 represented a new beginning for the University of Iowa Medical Department, renamed the college of medicine in the university's 1901 reorganization. Not only did the new hospital mark a major improvement in physical facilities; it also presaged a fundamental change in the locus of medical practice and medical education, both of which became centered in the hospital in the next two decades. Just as important, the hospital's early history coincided with a fundamental shift in the locus of decision making with regard to medical education and hospital policy, as outside actors and forces increasingly challenged the college of medicine's autonomy over hospital operations. Overall, the operation of a modern teaching hospital proved to be far more difficult than it had seemed from the viewpoint of the 1890s. It also taxed the means of a small university in a small midwestern town.

In the early years, the state government, the board of regents, and even the university administration had largely left the medical department to fend for itself, paying faculty salaries with the money from student fees and asking the university only for relatively small amounts to cover its most pressing needs. Dean Washington Peck's strategy in the 1870s and 1880s of affiliating with Mercy Hospital in order to provide clinical instruction was one example of the department's forced reliance on makeshift educational arrangements.

43

However, the other side of that equation was the nearly complete autonomy the department enjoyed in hiring faculty and assistants, setting admission standards and determining the curriculum, and deciding which students would be graduated to almost certain state licensing.

This balance had already shifted noticeably by the time the University Hospital opened in 1898. While the $55,000 needed to build the hospital was, at least by present standards, a small investment for state legislators and their taxpaying constituents, that investment represented a greater stake than the state had previously held in its medical school, a commitment that carried with it a greater interest in and control over medical education and one that cemented a developing partnership between the University of Iowa College of Medicine, the University Hospital, and the state. At the same time, a powerful national reform movement, represented in Abraham Flexner's 1909 visit to the university, further complicated the issue of control over operation of the hospital and the college. Funded in his study of medical education by the Carnegie Foundation for the Advancement of Teaching, the opinionated and forceful Flexner took as his mission the reordering of medical education in the United States and Canada according to the scientific model established in Europe and reproduced at Baltimore's Johns Hopkins University.

In just ten months, Flexner reviewed 155 medical schools, finding grievous fault with nearly all of them. More than half eventually closed. In his brief visit to the University of Iowa College of Medicine—it lasted less than a day—Abraham Flexner found much to criticize. First, he objected to the college of medicine's non-resident, part-time clinical faculty and the quality of instruction they provided. Second, he charged that the hospital's physical plant was insufficient for the needs of the college. Third, and most important, Flexner decried the lack of "clinical material" for teaching purposes in a community the size of Iowa City. Contrary to Flexner's expectations, however, his report only solidified the state's commitment to the university's medical facilities and set off a chain of events that resulted in the building of an entirely new medical campus and that boosted the college of medicine, however briefly, to the top rank of American medical schools.

One of the chief mechanisms of that remarkable transformation was Iowa's indigent care laws of 1915 and 1919, laws that funneled both indigent patients and increasing amounts of state revenues to the University Hospital. However, state monies alone could not and did not support the emergence of a first-rank medical school and teaching hospital at the University of Iowa. The second, and decisive, factor was a massive infusion of funds from two Rockefeller philanthropies, the Rockefeller Foundation and the General Education Board. The inflow of Rockefeller funding was engineered, iron-ically, by Abraham Flexner himself, and it built a new general hospital and medical laboratories building that joined the Children's and Psychopathic Hospitals on the new campus west of the Iowa River.

That the University of Iowa College of Medicine was one of the schools to survive the Flexner review was, at least to the school's supporters, a blessing. But survival also had its costs, material and otherwise. The rehabilitation of the college of medicine required the state of Iowa to make an open-ended commitment to indigent patient care, to underwrite the salaries of more and better faculty physicians and other staff, and to fund construction of new facilities for the college and its hospital. And to secure and maintain a place in the emerging national system of medical education, the college also acceded to standards of national origin, to demands from the New York–based Rockefeller Foundation, and even to the meddling of Abraham Flexner himself in its internal matters. All of these events flowed, in due course, from the original impulse to provide Iowa with a medical college and, in turn, to provide the medical college with its own hospital.

University Hospital, 1898–1909

The manifold complexities that must come together in running a modern hospital became apparent to university officials early on, as responsibility for the thousand-and-one details—ranging from bed linen and meals to surgical supplies and nursing services, all previously overseen by the Sisters of Mercy—now fell upon the college of medicine. Likewise, the full weight of financial responsibility fell on the college. In all, the fact that the college of medicine—and by extension the university and the state of Iowa—held responsibility for the mundane details of hospital provisioning and administration provoked a minor crisis, a circumstance that brought the state, through the board of regents and through direct legislative appropriations, into a more fully realized partnership with the university in operating the hospital.

One sign of trouble was the turnover in hospital superintendents. Jennie Cottle, the superintendent who had lavished such praise on the new hospital when it opened in 1898, stayed less than two years in the job. In part, the problem in the superintendency lay in the wide scope of the job. According to the hospital rules of 1897, the superintendent was to "have the general control of all the departments of the Hospital, of all subordinate officers, attendants, and domestics, and the charge of the grounds, buildings, and appurtenances." In addition, she was to admit all patients, including emergency cases, keep all patient records (such as they were at the time), "collect and receive all moneys from patients," oversee the hospital's dietary service, "hire and dismiss all servants employed in and about the Hospital," and keep an inventory of all furniture and other property. Finally, she was to "have charge of the Training School for Nurses as well as of the nurses connected with the Hospital."[1]

As suggested in the previous chapter, the worrisome turnover in the superintendent's position also owed much to gender conflict within the rapidly evolving hospital. While the hospital, then and later, maintained an overwhelmingly female workforce, mostly nursing personnel, it was an institution increasingly and overwhelmingly under the dominance of males. Meanwhile, the superintendent's job description reflected nineteenth-century norms of hospital organization, norms established for largely undifferentiated charitable institutions in which women played central roles as administrators and as laborers. The opening of the new University Hospital, however, marked the advent of a new era, one in which hospitals, particularly teaching hospitals, fast became identified as healthcare institutions controlled by male physicians. The result was a widening gulf between Jennie Cottle's job description and the realities of the superintendent's position.

A succession of superintendents followed Cottle, three of them in three years, before the situation stabilized with the appointment of Mary Nesbitt, who took the job in 1904 and stayed until 1913. During Nesbitt's tenure, the dimensions of the hospital superintendent's role, both formal and informal, changed significantly. By 1904, a hospital matron had assumed many of the more routine housekeeping duties, and the gradual increase in supervisory nursing staff over the years eased the superintendent's workload. At the same time, the medical faculty and especially the dean of the college of medicine seized more authority over hospital administration, leaving the superintendent with more circumscribed, if still ill-defined, administrative duties and with the responsibility for nursing services and the nursing school.[2]

To some extent, the medical director's role in hospital administration suffered a similar fate. A position held by Elbert W. Rockwood from 1898 to 1904, by William R. Whiteis from 1904 to 1906, and by Lee Wallace Dean from 1906 to 1909, the medical director's position involved relatively minor duties in terms of the hospital's daily operation. The medical faculty elected one of its members to the position on a year-to-year basis, and while the director had nominal responsibility for the entire hospital, the real importance of his position lay in his responsibility for the general supervision of medical care and teaching, areas in which his authority overlapped that of the superintendent, although only the director could intervene in the medical care given patients. In 1921, the medical director's post was a casualty of Lee Wallace Dean's concerted effort to centralize authority over the college of medicine and the University Hospital in the dean's office; thus, throughout much of the period from 1898–1928 and increasingly so in the last half of that period, it was the dean who, through various devices, wielded effective executive power over the hospital.

Initially, the hospital suffered financial as well as administrative problems, as earnings fell well short of expenditures. As early as June 1898, a board of regents hospital committee report labeled the hospital's business practices "inadequate" and recommended changes that placed the hospital under stricter oversight by the regents' executive committee.[3] Under the new regime, the executive committee approved the purchase of all supplies and materials thirty days in advance in order to force better planning of purchases. The new rules also required that the hospital administration submit monthly reports to the regents. Over the next several years, the regents became even more involved in the hospital's routine business affairs. In 1900 they ordered their secretary, William Haddock, who resided in Iowa City and whose office was in Old Capitol, to keep records of the hospital's accounts and of its storeroom supplies.[4] Not surprisingly, Haddock soon found that responsibility—which today would be called "micromanagement"—untenable, and less than a year later the regents reversed the order. Close oversight continued, however, as the regents mandated that "officers, matrons, or nurses" keep the daily accounts and submit meticulous records to Haddock on a weekly basis.[5] Eventually, the regents cut back the weekly reporting requirement, too, and scheduled reports on a monthly basis. The benefits of closer oversight are uncertain. The hospital appears to have balanced its books by counting the regents appropriation as earnings and by excluding heating, building repairs, and clinic costs from expense accounts.[6] Even with the aid of such accounting devices, hospital accounts ran often in the red.[7]

Notwithstanding such problems, a catastrophe demonstrated how far the relationship between the state and its college of medicine had come in just a few years. In March 1901, fire consumed the college of medicine building, along with the nearby South Hall. The medical building that burned had cost $30,000 in 1882. To replace it with facilities meeting the standards prevailing in the first decade of the twentieth century entailed the construction of two new buildings, formally named the Medical Laboratories and the Anatomy Building. Located just a block from the hospital and, unlike the hospital, constructed of fireproof materials, the new buildings cost $165,000, an impressive sum for the time but one in line with the state's growing economy and one that the 30th General Assembly accepted with little complaint.

Even before the disastrous fire of 1901, attitudes of state legislators toward the university and its college of medicine had shifted significantly. Prior to the 1890s, the pattern of state appropriations for the university as a whole was erratic. However, the 1/10th millage tax that Charles Schaeffer had finally won in 1896 after years of struggle was renewed even before its five-year term expired. Moreover, in 1902, the 29th General Assembly voted to double the millage, to ⅕th mill. With little serious debate, the legislature extended the millage another five years in 1907,[8] a pattern that ensured a reliable stream of funding for the university. Income also increased from year to year because of higher property valuation. As a result, total state support for the university more than doubled from 1903 to 1909, rising from $225,000 to some $500,000; it continued to climb, reaching $1 million in 1917, $2 million in 1922, and $3 million in 1924. Overall, state appropriations for the university rose from some 4 percent to 12 percent of total state spending in the period from the mid-1890s to the early 1920s.

State funds financed a new hospital wing that opened in 1908—at a cost of $62,900—and brought the total number of beds to 125. While existing records are incomplete, the hospital admitted some 1,100 patients in fiscal year 1904, an increase of more than 300 from the previous year; by 1911, admissions were up to 1,775 each year and rising. Although apparently justified on the basis of patient demand, the hospital addition of 1908 nonetheless pulled the hospital balance sheet from a $2,600 surplus to a $1,400 deficit despite a jump in revenues from $36,300 to $40,700.[9] Such outcomes suggest that the University of Iowa Hospital's administrative and operational procedures were still far from perfect—this at a time when the profession of hospital management was rapidly developing elsewhere, with its own professional association, professional journals, and textbooks. Patient care at Iowa also lagged behind the better teaching hospitals owing, in part at least, to the hospital's lack of laboratory space and equipment and the college of medicine's relatively low expectations regarding faculty research; and the number of patients available for teaching purposes still did not match that at Johns Hopkins and a handful of other prestigious schools.

Flexner's 1909 Visits

Abraham Flexner arrived in Iowa City by train at 4 o'clock on a Friday afternoon in late April 1909. Writing from St. Louis, Flexner had advised University of Iowa President George E. MacLean that he would arrive from Des Moines at 4:00 p.m. and leave for Omaha just after midnight. In the space of those few hours, he would tour the university's medical facilities and examine student records and other documents. "I am sorry to be in such haste, but I have a long journey ahead of me, and I must make very close connexions," Flexner explained.[10]

President MacLean accompanied Flexner on his inspection tour of the University of Iowa medical facilities.[11] MacLean knew enough about Flexner's mission to be concerned about its result, but to some extent at least, his concern was misdirected. Flexner represented the Carnegie Foundation for the Advancement of Education, which, in addition to Flexner's study of medical education, also sponsored a pension fund for university professors, and it was the latter that most concerned MacLean and the university administration. MacLean and Flexner, then, were operating on two quite different tracks on that spring day in 1909, MacLean thinking of financial benefits that might accrue to the university from the Carnegie Foundation and Flexner focusing narrowly on the quality of medical education. President MacLean perhaps did not appreciate that the future of the medical school and the University Hospital hung in the balance on that April evening.

Abraham Flexner's extensive review of American medical education still occasions considerable historiographical debate.[12] Flexner was, after all, a high school teacher by profession; his expertise in higher education, quite apart from medical education, was self-proclaimed. Although he had recently published a well-regarded book on higher education, his engagement by the Carnegie Foundation owed as much to family and personal connections as to his own professional qualifications. Likewise, little was original in Flexner's assessment of the current state of medical education or in his vision for its future. In general, standards of medical education and, just as important, expectations of the country's medical students had risen rapidly in the closing years of the nineteenth and the early years of the twentieth centuries. As a result, many marginal schools, as was the case in Iowa, had already closed. It may be, then, that Flexner's greatest accomplishment lay not in his specific findings nor in his ideas for the future of medical education but in his ability to focus and articulate widely held concerns and to pose a coherent plan of action to correct the worst deficiencies. In any event, at the University of Iowa, Flexner's criticisms served as a catalyst in accelerating the pace of reform and provided much needed leverage for those, like Presidents George MacLean and Walter Jessup, who spearheaded the local reform effort.

Abraham Flexner's vision of medical education was an ambitious one, centered on higher admissions requirements, expanded instruction in the laboratory sciences, and clinical instruction based on access both to a large number and wide variety of hospital and dispensary patients and to clinical laboratories for diagnosis and analysis. Flexner's plan also included a full-time medical faculty, standardized hospital record keeping, and control of a modern hospital wherever possible. As mentioned earlier, the model for this vision was the medical school of Flexner's alma mater, Johns Hopkins University, an institution incorporating, in Flexner's mind, the best elements of both European and American medical education.[13]

Flexner was impressed with the classrooms and laboratories at the University of Iowa College of Medicine and with its records pertaining to basic science instruction. But his visit to University Hospital must have hinted at disaster, especially when Flexner could find no one to explain how bedside teaching was carried out; when he could find no hospital records "worthy of the name"; and when he discovered that no hospital report had been compiled.[14] Flexner was by all indications a courteous man, but he was also candid. Surely, during the course of that painful inspection, President MacLean knew that the clinical component of the medical school, including the hospital, would fare poorly in Flexner's final report.

Abraham Flexner left on the midnight train to Omaha to inspect Creighton University's medical school and from there proceeded to Lincoln to visit the University of Nebraska's medical facilities and the Lincoln Medical College.[15] From Lincoln, Flexner wrote President MacLean asking for further information.[16] One month later he wrote again, this time from his office in New York, reminding MacLean that "some of the medical men" at Iowa had promised to provide him with "a detailed report of the dispensary and of the hospital . . . and the medical budget of the university showing the total cost of your medical instruction." Flexner asked MacLean to see to the forwarding of those materials at the earliest possible date.[17]

Abraham Flexner's full report compiled from on-site impressions and later documentation arrived at President MacLean's office in mid-June 1909. Flexner praised both the physical facilities and the quality of instruction given in the basic sciences, which he called "generally good and at some points excellent." Anatomy, under Henry J. Prentiss, was particularly strong in Flexner's estimation. "A better equipped department, more enthusiastically conducted, is hardly to be found anywhere in the country," he wrote. "There is unmistakable evidence of excellent teaching and intelligent scientific activity." Flexner was less impressed with the physiology department, under John T. McClintock, and pathology and bacteriology, under Henry Albert, but he noted that "the men in charge of them are . . . zealous and energetic; their ideals are high, and the equipment in the shape of apparatus and books, modern and sufficient."[18]

However, Flexner charged, "The clinical situation is of a different order, altogether." First, both dean James R. Guthrie and surgery chair William Jepson lived far from Iowa City—Guthrie in Dubuque and Jepson in Sioux City—and only came to the university to conduct their teaching and attend to patients two days each week. "Under these conditions," Flexner observed, "the clinical side cannot develop as a unit, nor can there grow up between the scientific men and the partly non-resident clinicians the close interrelations characteristic of a medical department that functions as a whole." One result, as Flexner saw it, was an "unorganized and more or less antiquated" approach to teaching. In turn, disorganization led to haphazard record keeping in the hospital and to inadequate and ill-defined clinical instruction. Although Flexner did not mention the University Hospital's meager laboratory facilities in his report, it is clear from other correspondence that he considered the hospital to be lagging in this essential area of clinical education as well.[19] In any event, "it is impossible," he wrote in his official report, "to say what ground the clinical teaching has actually covered, just as it is impossible succinctly to describe what takes place in the way of clinical discipline," and "the hospital is, in its teaching aspects, headless."

Flexner found the problem of "clinical material" equally troubling. The hospital, "in which less than 90 beds are available for teaching purposes," simply did not provide enough cases for the 100 third- and fourth-year students. Moreover, half of all cases clustered in the head specialties, leaving students with insufficient exposure to internal medicine, surgery, and especially obstetrics, the last providing fewer than one-fifth the number of deliveries Flexner considered adequate for a senior class of fifty. He also noted a complete lack of specific instruction in infectious diseases and the "far too limited" opportunity for postmortem work. "It is thus indisputable that more clinical material, and of greater variety, must be obtained," he asserted.

Based on those observations, Flexner's recommendations were painfully direct. The clinical faculty's approach to teaching, he argued, could be remedied relatively easily with a change in personnel, in particular through "a resident dean, a resident clinical faculty, and a hospital superintendent familiar with the technique of modern medical teaching." At the same time, he maintained, "it is necessary at once to adopt a more adequate form of taking case histories and keeping case records; the students must be trained to be parts of the hospital in its primary function of curing disease, and the records of every case should at every stage indicate what the student has seen and done and how it has been checked up or controlled by interne [sic], staff officer, and professor, so that the complete record may regularly form the basis of conference and discussion." These, Flexner said, were the measures needed simply to take full advantage of currently available facilities and patients.

However, such steps would not "of themselves cure the more fundamental difficulty" of ensuring an adequate number of patients for teaching purposes. "That calls for an enlarged hospital, an increased and expensive faculty," Flexner warned. He admitted that the increase in admissions standards from one to two years of undergraduate work scheduled for the fall of 1910 would reduce the number of medical students and thereby improve the patient-to-student ratio, and he noted also that a better-quality faculty would attract more patients. However, in Flexner's view, those changes would not suffice to rectify the problems in clinical instruction, and he doubted, in fact, that the university's prospects would be favorable even with a far greater investment of resources. "A proper provision for medical education in centres of population like Chicago and Minneapolis is proving a heavy load to carry," he noted, and "far heavier, of course, will be a satisfactory provision in a small inland residential community" such as Iowa City. In essence, Flexner recognized that the University of Iowa could, with a greater investment of state resources and better management, bring its hospital and clinical teaching program up to the standards he urged, but he questioned the wisdom of doing so.

> Is it wise educational statesmanship to endeavor, against the grave obstacles inhering in the situation, to develop a department which will at every stage consume an ever increasing proportion of the resources of the university? . . .
> [I]n view of the fact that a decided reduction in the number of medical schools is called for, it is worth considering whether the general interest, educational and social, will not best be served by a differentiation which will in future limit medical teaching to institutions in large centres. . . .
> These considerations ought to be carefully weighed by institutions that, now comparatively undeveloped on the clinical side, must contemplate in the near future a large expenditure on that score, if they persist.

The universities of Missouri and Wisconsin had faced similar prospects, Flexner pointed out, and had cut their programs back to two years of basic science instruction. The reality was that bigger, better endowed medical schools would "crowd schools of inadequate clinical resources very hard . . . [T]o hold its own in such a competition will prove an increasingly disproportionate burden on the income of any institution laboring, on account of location, under grave disadvantages."

At the least, Flexner recommended closing the University Hospital and paring the college of medicine back to a two-year basic science program. Upgrading medical education at the University of Iowa would require an open-ended financial commitment by the state for the hiring of resident, full-time clinical faculty, for a larger and better-equipped hospital, and for the care of more patients at state expense. Flexner thought such a financial commitment unwise not only because the attempt might fail under pressure of competition for students from medical schools in Chicago and other regional centers, but also because a school such as the University of Iowa did not fit his plan for a rational nationwide system of medical education. The country needed fewer and better-trained doctors, Flexner held, and saving what he perceived to be marginal medical schools would not serve that end. Indeed, at a time when the state's doctor to population ratio stood at 1:605, he believed that Iowa already had "between two and three times as many doctors as are really needed" and that there was "from the standpoint of the public interest no reason why a great number of physicians should be produced."[20]

Yet in suggesting the measures by which Iowa could bring its program up to his demanding standards, Flexner, whether he meant to or not, encouraged the school's supporters to undertake a salvage operation. Moreover, Flexner appeared open to persuasion on the fundamental point of maintaining a medical college at Iowa City, and, thus encouraged, the school's advocates embarked on a spirited effort to address the criticisms of "the implacable little schoolmaster from Louisville."[21] Moreover, not everyone took Flexner's scathing report seriously. William Jepson, the surgery chair whom the report directly rebuked, crudely dismissed Flexner's motives in the parlance of the times as " 'drumming up trade,' (as the Jew would say) for Minneapolis and Chicago."[22] Others surmised that as Flexner was not a physician, he was no expert on how to run a medical school.[23] Walter Bierring, chair of internal medicine, was the only clinician to refute Flexner's report with facts and reasoned arguments. Bierring acknowledged certain shortcomings that Flexner had pointed out, such as the lack of a system for keeping case records and overall administrative weaknesses, but he disputed Flexner's contention that there was too little material to provide students with adequate clinical experience, noting that students were presented with "an average of 8 to 10 new cases each week." The newly inaugurated hospital dispensary service, of which Bierring was justifiably proud, also bolstered the number of patients available for teaching. Finally, Bierring observed that while the hospital had no isolation ward for infectious diseases, such cases were numerous enough among the general mix of patients to suit the college's needs.[24]

In the end, however, there was no rebutting Flexner, in part because the standards he espoused had been generally accepted well before his famous report and had already begun by 1910 to reshape medical education in Iowa and across America. One telling symptom was the financial distress that spread among weaker medical schools at the turn of the century, resulting in a wave of medical school closures and mergers. In Iowa, the Keokuk College of Physicians and Surgeons and the Drake University Medical Department—apart from the University of Iowa, the only medical schools remaining in the state—had been limping toward collapse for some years. In addition, organizations such as the American Medical Association and its Council on Medical Education, the American College of Surgeons, the Association of American Medical Colleges, and the American Hospital Association, were exerting increasing pressure for reform, even as states adopted more rigorous physician licensing requirements. Moreover, behind that broadening emphasis on reform lay the Progressive era's faith in scientific management and in the application of rational principles alike to business and industry, government, education, and hospitals.

The demise of the University of Iowa Board of Regents in 1909 and the creation of a new Iowa State Board of Education with responsibility also for the agricultural and technical college at Ames, the state teachers' college in Cedar Falls, and schools for the deaf and blind brought a particularly dedicated and energetic advocate to the fight to save the college of medicine just as Flexner's report circulated among the medical faculty. Although the passing years have no doubt exaggerated the role of Cedar Rapids newspaper publisher William R. Boyd in saving the hospital and college of medicine, Boyd did play an important part, as chair of the board of education finance committee, not only in convincing Flexner of the state's commitment to upgrading its medical school but also in procuring the funding and support needed to do so. Boyd first intervened with the board of education to forestall any decision to kill the medical college until its supporters could make their case directly to the legislature in January 1910. In the meantime, Boyd shifted funds from other university accounts to the college of medicine and persuaded the university faculty at large to delay asking for increases for their own departments in order to divert funds to the medical school.[25]

Boyd also used his professional acquaintance with Henry S. Pritchett, president of the Carnegie Foundation, to arrange another visit by Flexner to the University of Iowa campus in late October 1909. This time Flexner stayed several days and brought with him as consultant Robert H. Whitehead, dean of the University of Virginia College of Medicine in Charlottesville. University of Iowa officials hoped that Whitehead would offer a more sympathetic review of their college, since his own was similarly located in a small community some distance from population centers. In general, however, Whitehead confirmed Flexner's earlier evaluation, citing the same flaws and attributing them to the same antiquated teaching methods that "prevailed in our medical schools of the past, but which do not respond to the modern demand for efficient training."[26]

But Whitehead sounded a far more hopeful note regarding prospects for the University of Iowa College of Medicine. Both he and Flexner, convinced by Boyd that the state intended to make a real effort to reform the program, centered their recommendations on Iowa's need to recruit a top-notch clinician—preferably an internist, in Whitehead's view—to lead the college, and to pay this clinician whatever sum was required. "If you will but procure the right leader and stand behind him, you can achieve a result for which the people of Iowa will be grateful to you; and you will set an example that will be potent for good throughout the country," Flexner wrote to James H. Trewin, president of the board of education.[27]

Remaking the College of Medicine

University officials and the board of education responded in piecemeal fashion to Abraham Flexner's admonition to "get a great clinician and build your school around him" and his recommendation to hire a resident dean. The first casualty was internal medicine chief Walter Bierring, who admittedly embodied some of the faults Flexner identified.[28] Bierring maintained a large private practice in addition to his teaching duties, and as head of internal medicine, vice dean of the college, and recently medical director of the University Hospital, he surely bore his share of responsibility for weaknesses in clinical teaching. Yet Bierring was likely better qualified to address existing weaknesses in the college than were the clinical faculty who remained. He had published papers in respected medical journals, and he went on to enjoy a long and distinguished career after his forced resignation from the college of medicine, serving as president of the American Medical Association in 1934–1935 and head of the American Board of Internal Medicine from 1936 to 1939.

The search for a new internal medicine head began as early as March 1910, even before Bierring's resignation, when James Guthrie, attending a conference in Baltimore, visited Johns Hopkins to ask for the names of likely candidates. In April, board of education president James Trewin wrote Abraham Flexner seeking his advice, and later Guthrie visited both Harvard University and the Carnegie offices in New York.[29] Campbell Palmer Howard of McGill University in Montreal, although not the first candidate for Bierring's position, had the confidence of all of those whom President MacLean, Dean Guthrie, and William R. Boyd consulted; he came to the University of Iowa with excellent credentials, not least his close family connection with William Osler. Campbell Howard negotiated a salary of $4,000, far above the prevailing part-time salaries, on the understanding that he would devote his full time to teaching, research, and care of University Hospital patients.[30] At the same time, John T. McClintock, professor of physiology, became vice dean of the college of medicine, and Lee Wallace Dean, chair of the head specialties, became director of the hospital.

The next to feel pressure was William Jepson, who reneged on his promise to take up residence in Iowa City. While apparently a competent surgeon with some inclination to carry on research activities, Jepson's residence in Sioux City left the surgery department bereft of leadership and organization. Despite that, he held his position until forced to resign in 1913. William R. Whiteis, an obstetrician on the hospital staff, was installed as temporary head of surgery while the search for a permanent chair took place. John Bowman, George MacLean's successor as university president, who was a close associate of Abraham Flexner and previously secretary to the Carnegie Foundation, began that search independently, consulting with prominent Iowa physicians as well as with contacts in Ann Arbor, New York, Boston, Baltimore, and Chicago. However, when Bowman settled on Charles J. Rowan of Chicago's Rush Medical College in late September 1913 and recommended him to the board of education, board president Trewin took offense that Bowman had upset traditional protocol by ignoring Dean Guthrie in the selection process. Bowman answered that he considered the situation an emergency, noting his grave misgivings about William Whiteis' poor reputation as a teacher and administrator and noting rumors within the state's medical community that Whiteis would gain the permanent appointment. Trewin nonetheless insisted that both Guthrie and Whiteis participate in recommending Jepson's successor.[31]

The issue soon took on a rancorous edge. While President Bowman had no confidence in either Guthrie or Whiteis, the board's Trewin questioned Bowman's judgment in choosing an "assistant to the assistant in the Chair of Surgery in a College of no higher rank than our own," although Rowan was, in fact, an assistant professor and Flexner had been more favorably disposed to Rush than to Iowa.[32] The two executives exchanged terse and contentious letters in which they wrangled over protocol, procedures, and lines of authority. "You say we have an exceptional opportunity to build up the Department of Surgery," Trewin wrote. "In my judgment, this cannot be done by the exercise of arbitrary power by the President of the University or the board of education and certainly not b[y] ignoring the Dean of the Medical College." In the end, the board of education directed Bowman, by unanimous vote, to operate through the channels Trewin had suggested, allowing Guthrie to recommend a permanent head of surgery, a recommendation that Bowman would then forward to the board for action. In December 1913, the process culminated in Bowman's original choice, Charles Rowan, being offered the post. That affair was only one instance of the troubled relationship between Bowman and the board of education that led to Bowman's early resignation in 1914.

In the last of the changes to follow immediately upon the Flexner report, James Guthrie, who had steadfastly refused to move from Dubuque to Iowa City, gracefully exited the deanship in July 1914 in return for the title dean emeritus, although he remained as head of the department of obstetrics and gynecology for another year before yielding that position to William Whiteis. In the meantime, Lee Wallace Dean, an 1896 graduate of the college of medicine and a faculty member since 1898, succeeded Guthrie in the deanship. An ambitious man, Dean was not only chair of head specialties; he was also, as previously noted, hospital medical director, and maintained a large private practice at Mercy Hospital.

Lee Wallace Dean brought to the deanship an authoritarian management style and a penchant for the centralization of authority. Inheriting a loose collegial structure born in an era of part-time and mostly nonresident faculty, Dean shortly effected a fundamental administrative restructuring of the college of medicine, while also strengthening his hold over the University Hospital. In November 1914, after only a few months in his new office, Dean complained of a "lack of system" in the administration of the college. In a letter to new university president Thomas H. Macbride, Dean noted that too many important decisions were made without reference to the dean's office, and to redress that problem he offered new regulations to bolster his own position, which Macbride later incorporated in "Rules governing the conduct of business in the College of Medicine."[33] Wielding the new rules, Dean set in place an administrative structure in which clear lines of authority led directly to the dean's office, an administrative revolution that, whatever its virtues, fueled significant resentment within the college and inhibited the growth of an effective hospital administration.

Lee Wallace Dean also presided over a major expansion of the college of medicine through the late teens and early twenties. The college budget multiplied several times over in the two decades after Abraham Flexner's visits, rising from $25,000 in 1908–1909 to $63,000 in 1914–1915, Dean's first year at the helm, to $125,000 in 1920–1921 and to $270,000 in 1926–1927, Dean's last year in office. Since faculty salaries accounted for nearly all of the college budget at the time, the rapid increase in budget figures represented chiefly the growth of faculty numbers and a significant increase in average faculty salaries. The faculty count—including professors, associate professors, assistant professors, lecturers, assistants, instructors, and demonstrators—rose from 18 in 1908–1909 to 41 in 1914–1915 and to 67 in 1924–1925. Meanwhile, faculty salaries, which had ranged roughly from $1,100 to $2,000 in the pre-Flexner era, rose to the range of $4,000 to $6,000 for department heads and $2,000 to $3,000 for junior faculty by the end of Dean's tenure in 1926–1927. By 1925, internal medicine and surgery were the largest of the college's nineteen departments in terms of staff numbers, with nine each, followed by Lee Wallace Dean's own head specialties with seven, and obstetrics and gynecology and two basic science departments—physiology and anatomy—with five each.[34]

Just as important, as the college of medicine faculty grew in size, it also changed significantly in complexion, a change perhaps best exemplified in the hiring of Campbell Palmer Howard and Charles Rowan. Howard and Rowan were the most prominent examples of the academic and intellectual cross-breeding that Abraham Flexner had argued was necessary to revive the inbred college of medicine and to integrate it into the larger scientific community. Because of that, however, they also served as lightning rods for many critics of the college and the hospital, especially those disgruntled by the inroads of such outsiders. Whether or not either Howard or Rowan fulfilled Flexner's definition of "a great clinician" able to put Iowa on the medical map and draw patients to its relatively remote location is another question. "There is no magnet like reputation," Flexner had written; "nothing travels faster than the fame of a great healer; distance is an obstacle readily overcome by those who seek health." "The poor as well as the rich," he noted, "find their way to shrines and healing springs."[35] By most accounts, Charles Rowan, although greatly admired by his students, was neither a magnet nor a scientific investigator. Campbell Howard, however, represented a different and more complicated case.

Howard's experience at the University of Iowa suggests that Flexner's "great clinician" argument conflated two distinct elements: on the one hand, greatness as measured by one's peers, by networks of relationships, publications, and elections to national societies and, on the other hand, greatness as measured by patient admissions. Campbell Howard clearly excelled at the first of these. During his years at Iowa, Howard produced a stream of papers for publication both individually and in collaboration with his University of Iowa colleagues. He also became an associate member of the Association of American Physicians in 1911 and a full member in 1914, and Howard—along with George Canby Robinson, George Dock, James B. Herrick, and Frank Billings—organized the Central Interurban Club, an elite association modeled on the east coast Interurban Clinical Club founded by William Osler in 1905. Moreover, one of Howard's subordinates offered the observation that Howard was "one of the foremost bedside teachers on the continent."[36]

For all the attention accorded Howard and Rowan—and the fact that controversy did occasionally surround them—the faculty member who perhaps filled the "great clinician" role better than any other was the orthopædic surgeon Arthur Steindler. Steindler did not come to the university through extensive recruiting efforts at prestigious schools or even through consultation with influential figures at east coast medical centers; instead, Steindler's recruitment was largely a matter of chance. Austrian by birth and by education, Arthur Steindler began teaching at Drake University's medical school in 1910 on the advice of his American mentor, orthopædist John Ridlon of Chicago's Home for Crippled Children. While in Chicago, Steindler also made the professional acquaintance of Charles Rowan, and it was through Rowan that Steindler began conducting clinics in orthopædic surgery twice a week at the University of Iowa Hospital. When Drake's medical school closed in 1913, Rowan secured for Steindler a faculty position in his own department of surgery.[37] The state indigent care laws passed in 1915 and 1919—and described in more detail in a later section— soon provided thousands of patients to Steindler's burgeoning orthopædic service. In time, Steindler's reputation soared, and he became the University Hospitals' "magnet."

The piecemeal closure of Iowa's proprietary medical schools and, finally, of the Drake University School of Medicine in 1913 dropped statewide medical school enrollments from 660 in 1903–1904 to a low of 99—all at the University of Iowa—in 1913–1914.[38] The latter figure marked a sharp decline from the 202 students enrolled at the college of medicine in 1895 and even more so from the 267 of 1908–1909. In the same period, the number of medical graduates, reflecting the overall drop in enrollments and the normally high attrition rate from freshman to senior classes, fell even more precipitously to just thirteen. However, a vigorous expansion in medical school enrollments and improvement in the quality of medical education succeeded that dramatic decline, an expansion that paralleled in many ways the increase in numbers and in quality of college of medicine faculty.

As shown in Table 2.1, student enrollments recovered rapidly from the low in 1913–1914, reaching 143 in 1915, 230 in 1920, and 417 in 1925. Aside from the remarkable climb in student numbers, especially in the 1920s, two features of that demographic profile are particularly noteworthy. The first is the continuing low proportion of female enrollments; indeed, the number of female medical students—never more than a dozen—was quite independent of total enrollments, suggesting the imposition of informal admissions restrictions on women. A second noteworthy feature, hidden in the aggregate figures in the table, was an astonishing rate of attrition. The 1900 medical student body, for example, included 101 first-year, 74 second-year, 39 third-year, and 19 fourth-year students, while the fall of 1922 brought 137 first-year, 81 second-year, 55 third-year, and 38 fourth-year students to campus. Rising performance standards were the chief factor behind the continued high attrition rates of the 1920s, and the sparse available evidence suggests that both faculty and administration in the college of medicine, sensitive to the political risk of formal limits on enrollments, relied upon attrition to hold clinical classes in the junior and senior years to manageable levels.

The first three decades of this century brought significant strengthening of the college of medicine's admissions requirements and curriculum, the latter including the lengthening of the academic year from 26 to 36 weeks in 1902. In 1900, two letters of reference from established physicians and a

Table 2.1   College of Medicine Enrollments, 1900–1925

	1900	*1905*	*1910*	*1915*	*1920*	*1925*
Male	221	232	178	142	224	407
Female	12	10	10	1	6	10
Total	**233**	**242**	**188**	**143**	**230**	**417**

Source: Board of Education Biennial Reports.

high school diploma, with evidence of proficiency in Latin and college preparatory credits in the sciences and mathematics, were sufficient for admission to the college. Those students lacking the necessary academic credentials had the option of admission by examination in science, history, mathematics, English, and Latin. In 1910, requirements rose to include two years of college, with one year each of physics, chemistry, biology, and a foreign language. By 1925, admission standards had become more specific and more rigorous, requiring sixty semester hours of college credit in specified subject areas and a grade point average equal to that required for graduation by the University of Iowa College of Liberal Arts. One sign of the times was the replacement of the Latin requirement by either French or German. Finally, the admissions policy by the mid-1920s gave formal preference to Iowa residents.

As Kenneth Ludmerer has noted in detail, "learning by doing," a concept borrowed from progressive education circles, had become the keynote of medical education by the early twentieth century, heightening the emphasis on laboratory and clinical work. In 1925, according to the university catalogue, the University of Iowa College of Medicine curriculum for first-year students included 560 hours of instruction in anatomy, with 374 of those hours devoted to the laboratory. The first-year curriculum included lesser concentrations in histology (186 hours total, 111 in the laboratory), physiology (119 total, 51 laboratory), physical chemistry (102 total, 51 laboratory), embryology (96 total, 45 laboratory), and neuroanatomy (74 total, 40 laboratory). In the second year, the focus shifted to pathology (289 total, 204 laboratory), physiological chemistry (204 total, 102 laboratory), physiology (187 total, 102 laboratory), pharmacology (153 total, 51 laboratory), bacteriology (170 total, 102 laboratory), materia medica (60 total, 60 laboratory), hygiene (51 total, 34 laboratory), and neuropathology (68 total, 51 laboratory). Second-year students also received their first glimpse of clinical work via a brief course in physical diagnosis.

The third-year curriculum brought a shift to major clinical areas, with a mix of lectures and clinical experience. Surgery (264 hours total, 162 clinical) was the largest component of the third-year curriculum, supplemented by courses in genitourinary surgery and surgical anatomy. In second place came internal medicine (204 total, 136 clinical), followed by clinical microscopy (136 total, 136 laboratory). Obstetrics and gynecology accounted for a total of 136 hours, all of it lecture time. The curriculum also provided 116 hours of physical diagnosis, including 82 clinical hours. Pediatrics, psychiatry, preventive medicine, therapeutics, and toxicology were areas of minor concentration, claiming between 17 and 51 hours each of curriculum time. Fourth-year students continued along much the same lines. Once again, surgery and internal medicine claimed the greatest share of the curriculum (574 of 1,166 total hours). All told, four clinical areas—surgery, internal medicine, obstetrics and gynecology, and eye, ear, nose, and throat—accounted for more than 81 percent of total hours (950 of 1,166) in the fourth year, with over 71 percent (678 of 950 hours) devoted to clinical work.

By the 1920s, standards of student performance had also increased, as evidenced by the high attrition rate over the four years of the medical school curriculum. The recruitment of aggressive and highly regarded new faculty members was one key to rising educational standards. For example, one former student remembered Campbell Howard as "a big man, physically and mentally," a man whose classroom demeanor was "pretty tough," and a man who did not treat his students with kid gloves. William Osler's *The Practice of Medicine* was Howard's "bible" in both classroom and clinical settings, and he could, students testified, recite from the volume from memory. To his students, then, Campbell Howard was apparently an intimidating—and perhaps remote—presence; nonetheless, "everybody respected him."[39] Buttressing the authority of figures like Howard, the college of medicine promulgated increasingly formal standards for grading and for defining satisfactory progress through the program.

The internship, which expanded formal medical education beyond the four-year curriculum, also became standardized in the teens and twenties, augmenting the increasingly cramped undergraduate clinical curriculum. After much debate, the Iowa State Board of Medical Examiners in 1917 instituted a one-year internship requirement as a prerequisite to licensure for students enrolling in medical schools on or after January 1, 1918, and that requirement entered the state statute books by act of the legislature in 1927.[40] However, with nearly eighty fourth-year students enrolled at the University of Iowa College of Medicine in 1924–1925, there were just 46 internships available in the seven AMA-approved programs in the state, 28 of those positions at University Hospitals.[41] Clearly, many graduates would have to serve their internships either in unapproved or out-of-state hospitals or begin practice in states that did not require an internship for licensure, evidence that the college, even at that early date, produced more graduates than the Iowa health care market demanded or could absorb.

Early internship programs at the University of Iowa were of the "straight" variety, with interns serving a single specialty for the duration of their one-year appointments. Over the years, interns became an increasingly important element in patient care and in undergraduate clinical instruction, providing both the college of medicine and the hospitals a relatively inexpensive source of labor. In 1919–1920, the University Hospitals offered thirteen internship positions, five in the head specialties, three in surgery, two in internal medicine, and one each in obstetrics-gynecology, orthopædics, and pediatrics. The hospitals provided room, board, and laundry to interns as well as a $125 stipend in return for services rendered. By the end of the 1920s the hospitals had instituted a "rotating" internship program in which interns—labeled "junior interns"—gained experience in several specialties. Thirty "senior interns" continued for one or more additional years in the "straight" internship programs. The system of junior and senior interns was a precursor of the internship-residency structure that emerged in the 1930s.

The Indigent Care Laws

Newspaper publisher William R. Boyd from Cedar Rapids was fond of telling how he had once visited his schoolteacher sister, whose duties included caring for a young pupil crippled by polio. Pursuing the boy's case, Boyd secured treatment for him at University Hospital under the care of William Jepson, but Boyd also saw the hardship the one dollar per day clinical cost imposed on the boy's family. In Boyd's telling, he and board of education president James Trewin conceived and drafted a law whereby the state of Iowa would pay for the medical treatment of children whose families could not afford such care. That law was real enough, and the incident Boyd reported may indeed have happened; but Iowa's indigent care laws had deeper roots than Boyd's anecdote implied, and the true story of the laws' origins was, if less heartwarming, far more interesting from a historical perspective.[42]

For decades, the state's counties had paid to have poor residents receive medical and surgical treatment at local hospitals or from local doctors, and Johnson County's "paupers" had served the clinical teaching needs of university medical faculty since the 1870s. In the years just prior to passage of the first indigent care law in 1915, clinical pay patients made up 85–95 percent of the hospital's total patient volume. Some of those were paying patients who were billed at ward rates roughly half the private rate and charged no physician fees; the remainder were indigent cases, cared for at county expense. Also, the state itself had for just as long borne the cost of caring for the indigent at its institutions for the deaf, blind, feeble-minded, and insane. This perhaps set the precedent for a 1905 law creating a state tuberculosis sanitorium at Oakdale, a law providing that patients "without means to pay for transportation and treatment at this institution" would receive care at state expense up to a maximum of $20 per month.[43] Moreover, immediately after Abraham Flexner's report on the college of medicine, the board of education had urged "a comprehensive system of taking care of the poor of the state" as part of its program of reform for the medical school.[44] Thus, the idea of providing medical services to the poor at public expense, particularly at University Hospitals, was well established before passage of the first indigent care law in 1915.

The state of Michigan enacted an indigent care law in 1913, providing state-funded care for children at the University of Michigan Hospital in Ann Arbor. That law was the direct inspiration and model for Iowa's law; various Iowa officials, including William R. Boyd and Lee Wallace Dean, had visited the Ann Arbor school and hospital in October 1914. There Dean not only had gathered ideas for revamping Iowa's record-keeping and admitting procedures, but also had been impressed with the mechanism Michigan's law provided to ensure an adequate clinical volume for its university teaching hospital. After returning to Iowa City, Dean had presented a draft of nearly identical legislation to the medical faculty, providing medical and surgical treatment at University Hospital for indigent children under the age of sixteen.[45] After revision, including some changes suggested by James Trewin, the legislation went before the Iowa General Assembly in January 1915 under the sponsorship of Senator Eli Perkins.[46]

Known as the Perkins Bill, that legislation made a fairly uneventful passage through the legislature, eased no doubt by the lobbying of Boyd, Trewin, and, among others, Arthur Steindler. However, a small cell of opposition led by Senator James M. Wilson of Centerville tried to insert language stipulating that state patients should receive care at county hospitals whenever possible and be sent to the University Hospital only if the needed care were not available locally. That effort at instituting decentralized indigent care—and the benefit of state funding that went with it—failed, but it would resurface again and again in later years. In the end, Wilson and other detractors joined their senate colleagues in unanimously approving the final version of the bill as reported back from the House of Representatives. Governor George W. Clarke signed the Perkins Act into law on March 9, 1915, to take effect on July 4 of that same year.[47]

The basic outline of the Perkins Act was simple. Any child under age sixteen "afflicted with some deformity or suffering from some malady that can probably be remedied" and whose family or legal guardian did not have the means to pay for treatment could receive medical or surgical care at University Hospital at state expense. The law assigned to the state's district courts the responsibility to certify both medical and financial need on the part of the child and the family, and it was by order of the court that the child was committed for treatment at the hospital. By its own authority or upon "complaint filed by any probation officer, school teacher or officer, superintendent of the poor, or physician authorized to practice his profession in the state of Iowa," the district court appointed a physician to examine the child and report his findings, followed by a formal hearing with the county attorney and the child's parents or legal guardian in attendance. If the judge found that the child indeed suffered from a treatable condition and that the parents or guardian could not afford such treatment, and if the parents or guardian consented, then the judge entered "an order directing that the said child shall be taken or sent to the hospital of the medical college of the state university of Iowa for free medical and surgical treatment and hospital care."

Bowing to the sensitivities of local physicians, admission of the child to the University Hospital was contingent upon an assessment by the physician in charge "that there is a reasonable probability that the child will be benefited by the proposed medical or surgical treatment." If admitted, the child received all necessary care, and physicians, surgeons, and nurses were allowed no compensation beyond the regular salaries they received from the university. Meanwhile, the hospital's expenses for "medicine, treatment, nursing and maintenance furnished to said patient" were reimbursed "from the general funds of the state not otherwise appropriated." In addition to medical care, the Perkins Act allowed University Hospital to charge to the state the cost of returning the child home. It also provided for care of university students and allowed other state institutions to send any of their residents or inmates, regardless of age, to University Hospital for treatment, provisions not found in the Michigan law. In such instances, the hospital's expenses were reimbursed by the state's general fund as in other Perkins cases, while all transportation costs were covered by the institution sending the patient.[48]

It was some months before local officials responded to the opportunity the Perkins Act afforded for the medical treatment of poor children within their jurisdictions, and longer still before the law achieved its full effect. But when it did, it brought revolutionary change to the University Hospital (Table 2.2). In the law's first fiscal year, the hospital admitted 400 children under the Perkins Act, a number that more than doubled the following year. At the same time, state reimbursements under the Perkins Act doubled the hospital's receipts in the law's first year. In succeeding years, total admissions to the hospital rose dramatically, surpassing 5,600 in 1919, with patients covered under the Perkins Act accounting for 19.5 percent of total admissions. Note, too, that the number of clinical pay patients dropped substantially after 1919, with the inclusion of indigent adults in the category of state patients.

With some minor changes in language and in the court procedures certifying medical and financial need, the Haskell-Klaus Act of 1919 extended the benefits of the Perkins Act to the state's indigent adult population. Sponsored by Senator Haskell of Cedar Rapids and Representative Klaus of Earlville, the bill received final approval with no dissenting votes in either the House or Senate on March 13, 1919, and Governor William L. Harding signed the extended version of indigent care into law on March 20.[49] For

Table 2.2   Hospital Admissions by Patient Classification

Fiscal Year	1914	1915	1916	1917	1918	1919	1920	1921	1922
State	—	—	400	870	1,386	1,104	2,987	3,344	4,917
Clinical	2,235*	1,991*	2,846†	3,322†	3,208†	3,406†	2,853	2,110	1,986
Private	111	371	573	880	998	1,164	1,428	1,166	1,167
Total	2,346	2,362	3,819	5,072	5,592	5,674	7,268	6,620	8,070
Patient-Days	na	54,878	81,704	113,304	120,557	124,306	163,418	170,671	175,129
Average Length of Stay (Days)	na	23.2	21.4	22.3	21.6	21.9	22.5	25.8	21.7

*Includes both indigent and clinical pay.
†Includes both indigent adults and clinical pay.
Source: University Hospital Annual Reports; Hospital Superintendent's Report, File 18, 1922–23, W. A. Jessup Papers,University of Iowa Archives.

the University Hospital, the Haskell-Klaus law intensified the revolution begun by the Perkins law. By the early 1920s, indigent patients—Perkins and Haskell-Klaus—made up more than half of total admissions. As initially under the Perkins Act, the hospitals' operating budget doubled in the first year after Haskell-Klaus, then doubled again over the next four years, surpassing $1 million annually.[50] Importantly, private patient admissions rose dramatically also in the late teens and early twenties. From 1911 through 1915, private patients accounted for roughly 11 percent of total patient admissions, whereas from 1916 through 1921 private patients represented 18 percent of admissions. Those numbers marked a significant shift in the hospital's image among paying patients, a shift perhaps boosted by the indigent care laws' implicit sanction of the University of Iowa Hospital.

The growth in patient admissions, both private and indigent, did not affect all clinical departments equally (Table 2.3). Throughout much of the period, the head specialties (eye, ear, nose, and throat) and surgery counted the largest number of admissions. The head specialties accounted for 27.5 percent of total admissions in 1911, 25.4 percent in 1916, and 26.3 percent in 1921, with tonsillectomies and adenoidectomies together comprising roughly a quarter of the department's caseload. Surgery accounted for 26.6 percent of total admissions in 1911, 26.0 percent in 1916, and 18.4 percent in 1921, with abcesses, fractures, cancers, hernias, and appendicitis dominating case lists. In fact, from 1911 to 1915, hernia and appendicitis cases made up 40 percent of the total of surgical cases, testimony to the new eagerness with which surgeons approached abdominal surgery. Internal medicine—18.4 percent of total admissions in 1911, 14.6 percent in 1916, and 18.2 percent in 1921—was the third-largest of the clinical departments. Its caseload—including arthritis, cancers, gastrointestinal disorders, and heart disease—served to reflect the historical shift away from acute, especially infectious, diseases to chronic and degenerative afflictions. Together, obstetrics and gynecology saw their share of patient admissions decline slightly, from 13.1 percent in 1911, to 10.0 percent in 1916, and to 11.2 percent in 1921, no doubt in part a reflection of the influx of indigent children in the patient mix. However, the number of hospital births rose from 60 in 1911 to nearly 200 annually in the immediate post–World War I years, a measure of the importance of obstetric care among the population of indigent adult patients. Pediatrics, a department established in 1915, immediately carved out a service niche under the Perkins regime, averaging 325 admissions per year from 1916 to 1919, some 6 percent of total hospital admissions in that period—6.3 percent in 1921. From 1917, the separate reporting of orthopædics admissions cut into the total for surgery, while orthopædics, under Arthur Steindler's direction, quickly established itself as a major department, with 18.7 percent of total admissions in 1921.

The onset of the Perkins law prompted Superintendent Josephine Creelman and the university secretary William Bates, in August 1915, to calculate the actual cost of patient care in order to set charges for state patients, apparently the first attempt to determine the hospital's per diem patient care cost.[51] The calculations of Creelman and Bates fixed the rate at $1.71 per day, or almost $12 per week, which was double the rate the hospital had previously charged for county patients.[52] Experience soon revealed that even the higher rate was insufficient to cover costs, and the problem of establishing a realistic rate to charge the state for indigent patients grew larger in the years ahead as the number of state patients spiraled rapidly upward.

The rapid growth in patient volume during the teens and twenties accompanied major changes in the hospital's physical facilities. Even before passage of the indigent care laws, the hospital added an east wing (1908),

Table 2.3   Hospital Admissions by Department

	1911	1912	1913	1914	1915	1916	1917	1918	1919	1920	1921
Surgery	472	538	561	615	565	991	1,467	1,003	1,005	1,290	1,220
Medicine	326	335	385	549	448	559	591	1,080	1,682	1,489	1,202
Obstetrics	134	144	190	204	207	200	242	222	289	411	405
Gynecology	98	137	143	157	145	183	174	311	289	364	335
Head Specialties	489	564	629	701	606	970	1,337	1,536	1,343	1,938	1,743
Dermatology	—	—	—	9	25	66	99	74	31	66	60
Orthopædics	—	—	—	—	—	—	—	977	834	1,274	1,240
Pediatrics	—	—	—	—	—	286	342	389	281	436	415
Total	1,775	1,903	2,089	2,346	2,362	3,819	5,072	5,592	5,674	7,268	6,620

Source: University Hospital Annual Reports.

a six-story northeast wing (1912), and a larger seven-story northwest wing (1914). While the 300-plus beds available when the Perkins law first took effect were more than adequate to handle the average daily census of 136, the post-Perkins census jumped to 251 patients per day in fiscal year 1916 and to 310 the following year.[53] An Isolation Hospital, opened in 1918 and situated on Market Street behind the main hospital, answered Abraham Flexner's criticism that not enough contagious disease cases were available to medical students and also addressed the critical need for an isolation unit for Perkins children with communicable diseases. With those additions, expansion reached its practical limit on the old medical campus.

A project discussed even before the Flexner review,[54] the Children's Hospital—which opened in early 1919 after serving as a barracks during the final months of World War I—represented a new departure for what was now properly the University Hospitals. Occupying an oak-studded site on the west side of the Iowa River on a 28-acre tract the university had recently purchased with an eye to establishing a new medical campus, the one-story, pavilion style building housed ninety to 100 beds in its orthopædic wing and forty to fifty beds in the pediatric wing.[55] In addition to the wards, operating rooms, x-ray room, therapy and play rooms, brace shop, and laboratories, Children's Hospital also provided space for schooling the children whose treatment kept them there for extended stays. More significant, its westside location marked the beginning of the end for the eastside medical campus.

Controversies over Hospital Rules

The rapid pace of growth compounded and complicated the process of administrative reform in the University Hospital, a process that had begun soon after Flexner's review and resulted in a sometimes confusing series of changes in policy, lines of authority, and personnel. Some of those changes were deliberate and strategic, but most were ad hoc responses to specific problems or crises; still others represented the spoils of turf warfare within the university hierarchy. At bottom, however, the critical issues for the University Hospital divided into three major categories: the relationship of the hospital to its own medical staff as well as to the outside medical community, the hospital's identity as distinct from that of the college of medicine, and the implications—financial and political—of the hospital's expanding role as the state of Iowa's indigent care institution.

The years immediately following Flexner's report brought important, if sometimes controversial, changes in the rules governing medical practice within the hospital, changes formalized by the board of education in late December 1913—and subsequently revised in some particulars.[56] The least controversial of the new rules, not always strictly applied, restricted clinical faculty to practice in their respective specialties, a major milestone reflecting the growing maturity of academic medicine and the emergence of well-defined specialties in the academic setting. A second and much more controversial rule condemned the common practice of fee-splitting, by which university physicians divided fees from private patients with referring physicians. A third and equally controversial rule limited staff privileges at the University Hospital to the medical faculty.

Retiring university president George MacLean acknowledged the problem of fee-splitting in 1911 and exhorted the board of education to "get rid of the taint of commercialism" at the hospital.[57] Although commonplace throughout the United States, fee-splitting was universally scorned by reformers and by the American Medical Association. President MacLean's statement generated a squall of bad publicity for the University Hospital and its physicians, especially as the newspaper article reporting it also carried a lengthy defense of the practice by an unnamed "prominent surgeon and physician of Iowa City and the university."[58] The *Journal of the Iowa State Medical Society* railed against the college of medicine for tolerating the division of fees, and its editor, David S. Fairchild, warned new University of Iowa president John Bowman not to deny the existence of fee-splitting at University Hospitals, since, as Fairchild wrote, "There is an abundance of evidence to show that some of the most prominent members of the clinical faculty have been engaged in the business of dividing fees with the profession."[59] The new rule against fee-splitting took the form of an oath, reading "I hereby promise, upon my honor as a gentleman, that I will not, so long as I am a member of the staff of the college of medicine of the State University of Iowa, practice division of fees in any form." In 1914, Arthur Dean Bevan, chairman of the American Medical Association Council on Medical Education, added his weight with a warning to President Macbride that the practice of fee-splitting put the school's accreditation at risk.[60] In 1915, the Iowa legislature made the practice illegal.

The decision to close the University Hospital to outside physicians provoked similar controversy, albeit on different grounds. In 1912, President Bowman surveyed medical schools at Indiana University, Johns Hopkins University, the University of Michigan, and the University of Minnesota and found that all had closed staffs, restricting clinical faculty to practicing only in their own specialties.[61] Moreover, University of Iowa Hospital rules had, from the first, designated the medical faculty as the hospital's medical staff, while nominally extending staff privileges to the larger community of Iowa physicians. In fact, outside physicians had admitted only 34 patients to the University Hospital in 1912. Nonetheless, the formal limitation of staff privileges was of symbolic importance, and because of that it sparked bitter resentment within the local medical community. The rule also drew opposition from at least one board of education member. Believing that as a public institution the hospital should open its private wards to all of the state's doctors, the critic dismissed both of the university's main arguments in favor of the rule—namely, that it was needed to ensure the competence of doctors practicing within the hospital and, moreover, that the income from private patients helped sustain service to the clinical wards. To the one argument, he countered, "I do not understand why a private patient is not as well or better qualified to determine the competency of the doctor who shall treat him than the body of laymen who constitute the Board of Education." To the other, he contended that closing the hospital to outside physicians was nothing more than an attempt "to extend [the hospital's] exclusive use for commercial gain to a few medical men arbitrarily chosen by the Board."[62]

Nor was the medical faculty itself of one mind with regard to a closed staff. In fact, when surveyed in late 1914 about the hospital rules, only three members—Campbell Howard, Charles Rowan, and John McClintock—spoke clearly in favor of the closed-staff restriction. The rest either favored an open–staff policy because it was a valuable source of referrals for their clinics, as expressed by surgeon William Whiteis and dermatologist John B. Kessler, or opposed private practice altogether, as in the case of anatomy's Henry J. Prentiss and physiology's Henry Chase. But those favoring the policy carried more weight than the others. McClintock, the vice dean, was active in the American Medical Association and so was vested in reform from an ethical and professional standpoint; Rowan had made a closed-staff policy a condition of his employment; and Howard threatened to resign if the hospital's private wards were opened to outside physicians.[63] A year after adoption of the rules, Dean Lee Wallace Dean noted a decline in the number of patients and of patient referrals to University Hospital, a decline that Dean attributed to the closed-staff rule but one that might also have reflected the elimination of fee-splitting.[64] In any case, the closed policy survived and was included in a revision of the hospital rules approved by the board of education in June 1915.[65]

Whatever the controversy that surrounded them, the new hospital practice rules placed University Hospital alongside the country's leading teaching hospitals.[66] In this instance, the high ground of reform also made good business sense, at least for the long term. The income from private patients enhanced the hospital's revenues, accounting for some $15,000 annually in President Bowman's 1914 estimate,[67] and private practice fees were an indispensable source of earnings to members of the clinical faculty. As long as the University of Iowa could not afford to replace the private earnings of its clinical faculty with full-time salaries, a goal beyond the means of any American medical school at the time, private practice in closed wards [i.e., "geographic full-time"] would be essential to hiring and retaining top-flight faculty. A decade later the private practice issue rent the college of medicine in two, but for the moment the policy achieved a practical and useful compromise.

Problems in Hospital Administration

Abraham Flexner had very little to say about hospital management from a strictly administrative point of view; Flexner made his recommendations with an eye to improving medical education rather than creating efficiencies for their own sake within teaching hospitals. When Flexner spoke, for example, of the need for improved record keeping and for "a hospital superintendent familiar with the technique of modern medical teaching," he was addressing the needs of the college of medicine, not the needs of the hospital. Similarly, when Dean Whitehead of Virginia urged the college to seek "an active capable leader to reorganize the work of the hospital," he meant a dean of medicine, not a hospital superintendent. University Hospital was at this time (in 1909) understood to be an adjunct of the college of medicine and only that; its separate identity was scarcely, if at all, discernible.

In the teens and twenties, a significant expansion and differentiation of hospital staff accompanied the growth in patient volume and physical plant, and those factors, in turn, placed far greater demands on the University Hospital's administration. Between 1914 and 1919, the number of doctors on staff doubled to more than 40; the number of interns doubled, as well, to 14; and the number of nurses nearly tripled to 150, with a consequent increase in supervisory nurses from 11 to 22. Also, by 1910, a hospital pharmacy—supplying preparations manufactured in the college of pharmacy—and a hospital dietitian expanded the roster of hospital services and, as described further on, a full-fledged nutrition department began operation in the early 1920s. Likewise, in 1924, various patient social service functions were combined in a single social service department with a staff of four, a department reorganized in 1927.

The 1924–1925 university catalog listed a hospital administrative staff of eight, including the superintendent, Bert W. Caldwell, his assistant superintendent, Clarence E. Hewitt, the business manager, Ralph A. Bates, an accountant, Bernice Larkin, and a head of social service, Alice Fiske. Under the category "professional staff," the catalog listed staff physicians and researchers, a hospital pharmacist (female), a dental surgeon, and seven dietitians—all told, 52 names. Twenty-three interns assigned to the various clinical departments filled out the medical staff. Lois Blanche Corder, as acting director of nurses and principal of the school of nursing, headed a supervisory nursing staff of forty that included two assistant superintendents of nursing, a night supervisor, seven department supervisors, and 27 head nurses and assistants. The great majority of hospital workers were, of course, excluded from that published list, including the student nurses—209 first-, second-, and third-year students in 1924–1925—who provided the bulk of nursing services; the women and men who staffed the kitchens; and support personnel in areas such as housekeeping, maintenance, and grounds.

Hospital expenses kept pace with the growth in personnel, service, and physical plant, some of that increase resulting from new technologies and new procedures such as the growing use of x-rays, but most of it attributable to the sheer size of the hospital in all of its aspects. In the years from 1908–1909 to 1914–1915, hospital expenses nearly doubled from $34,000 to $63,000. From 1914–1915 to 1918–1919, with the Perkins law in operation, expenses rose more than fivefold to $326,000. In the latter period, expenses charged to administration rose from $3,000 to $14,000; the cost of provisions rose from $37,000 to $117,000; the bill for medicines and supplies rose from $8,500 to $56,000; and household charges rose from $28,000 to $77,000. From 1919, the Haskell-Klaus law helped to push expenses even higher, with the total exceeding $1 million in 1927–1928.

In the face of growing administrative burdens, the post-Flexner years brought a major effort to redefine the hospital superintendency. In December 1914, the medical faculty recommended adoption of a committee report on the duties of a hospital superintendent, a report compiled with input from John A. Hornsby, an editor of *The Modern Hospital,* and Winford H. Smith, superintendent of the Johns Hopkins Hospital, and one that included a list of duties and responsibilities for a full-time superintendent.[68] The board of education had foreseen some change in the hospital's administrative structure as early as 1912, when it stated in its biennial report that "enlargement of the hospital . . . will, in the end, call for the reorganization of the administration."[69] But the immediate cause of the faculty's proposal was not an organized attempt to plan for the future; rather, Superintendent Josephine Creelman was demanding to be relieved of duties not related to her work as principal of the nursing school.[70] The addition of a matron and an enlarged staff of supervisory nurses had eased the superintendent's responsibilities, but with more physical space, more employees, and more patients than ever before, the situation demanded a full-time administrator with appropriate training, experience, and pay.

By that time, hospital superintendency was an established profession.[71] The existence of a professional association, the American Hospital Association, and professional journals such as *The Modern Hospital* paralleled the emergence of a managerial philosophy specifically derived from and applied to hospital administration and of doctors and others specifically trained for careers in hospital management. One of the striking features of the new profession was its domination by men, a fact recognized in the University of Iowa medical faculty report of 1914. Whereas women had dominated the field of hospital administration throughout the nineteenth century, the new managerial class was overwhelmingly male and enjoyed considerably higher status and salary expectations.

Both John A. Hornsby and Winford H. Smith, the experts consulted by the medical faculty committee, insisted that the male hospital superintendent's authority must match the position's responsibilities.[72] "The superintendent of the hospital should, of course, be held accountable for everything that goes on and is done in the institution," Hornsby wrote, and "responsibility must carry with it authority." He detailed the personal control the superintendent should have over the purchase of all supplies, over the kitchen and dietary service, over the "housekeeper, the matron and the head janitor." "If the house is not clean and orderly," Hornsby counseled, "he, as the recognized head, will be criticized and no one else." In Hornsby's view, the superintendent also held sway over the engineering and maintenance staff and over all of the clinical departments' pathology laboratories, "because his patients are being drawn upon for material, he has to purchase the supplies for the department, the salaries are paid out of his funds and the medical staff will hold him responsible for the work that is done."

Smith emphasized that the superintendent should be a doctor. Although "a man is not qualified for a superintendent simply because he has a medical degree," Smith wrote, "a medical man can settle the various questions arising in the hospital, can conduct the business of the hospital with greater ease and with much less friction between departments, and can control the house staff much better, because of his medical training, than a layman." He went on to suggest that of the twenty or so physicians he knew to be training in hospital administration at Johns Hopkins, Massachusetts General Hospital, Boston's Peter Bent Brigham Hospital, and "half a dozen other institutions," "it is possible that one of these assistants might be attracted to your hospital." Hornsby, too, offered that "there are men who have been through all this, who know the game thoroughly and you can get one of them," and he suggested that the new superintendent's salary should be about $4,000 a year, which at Iowa would put him on a par with top clinical faculty. "This $4000 salary should not cost the hospital a cent," Hornsby added. "The superintendent should be able to save several times that amount if he is the right sort of man, by practicing various economies that he will know how to practice."

Dean Lee Wallace Dean was reluctant to follow through on the hiring of a full-time superintendent as Hornsby and Smith had advised. Dean went along when the faculty recommended in October 1914 that the change be made as soon as possible, and he even cited Hornsby and Smith as models of the kind of superintendent he would like to see.[73] But when Dean finally forwarded the recommendation to President Macbride in December, he asked that it be "temporarily placed on file and adopted only after we are certain as to just how we want the rules fixed"—revision of the hospital rules of December 1913 was pending and would not be completed until mid-1915. Shortly thereafter, in a letter to board of education member George Baker, Dean expressed a different reservation. "It is not clear in my mind," he wrote, "that with the falling off in the number of patients [following implementation of the rules closing the staff and ending fee-splitting] that it is necessary for us to have a male superintendent."[74]

Despite Dean's reluctance, the board of education referred the faculty's recommendation to its finance committee, where it languished for almost a year, until September 1915. At that time the committee proposed "to hire a male superintendent of the University Hospital, if the right man could be secured at a reasonable rate."[75] The salary offered, $2,750, was well above the $1,800 paid Josephine Creelman but well below the figure Hornsby recommended, and for such a sum the "right man" was William T. Graham, the physician head of Methodist Hospital in Des Moines, who assumed the superintendency at University Hospitals on January 1, 1916.

Delay, equivocation, and a certain flintiness in the matter of hiring a full-time superintendent—owing in no small part to Dean Lee Wallace Dean's desire to retain authority over the hospital—led to a decade of confusion and conflict in hospital management and to continuing ambiguity in the superintendent's authority and responsibilities. For example, the superintendent's job description provided by the medical faculty included supervision of functions already overseen by other officials. The university secretary, William Bates, already kept the hospital's financial records; university building superintendent, James Fisk, already managed any repairs, alterations, or construction within the hospital, as well as many large equipment purchases; and the clinical department heads already supervised the hospital interns under their charge. Yet the faculty committee report assigned all of these functions to the superintendent without any guidance concerning his formal relationship with other officials. In light of Dean's ambivalence toward the hospital superintendent and the uncertain administrative climate of Thomas Macbride's caretaker presidency,[76] William T. Graham entered an unsettled situation in which many players, not always the most obvious, had a hand in running the hospital.

Most important, Graham ran headlong into Lee Wallace Dean's concerted effort to expand and consolidate his power as dean of the college of medicine, which meant placing the University Hospital firmly within his administrative domain as well. Thus, while backing the faculty's recommendation to hire a full-time hospital superintendent, Dean simultaneously tried to delay its implementation and to limit the superintendent's authority. In Dean's view, "The superintendent of the University Hospital shall be recognized as the head of the hospital department, and shall be guided by the same rules as the head of any other department [i.e., within the college of medicine]."[77] Under the circumstances, and quite apart from questions of his character and ability, William Graham's chances of success as hospital superintendent were slim and his three-and-a-half-year tenure was an unhappy one for all concerned. To make matter worse, the problems that arose in those troubled years apparently did not suggest to Lee Wallace Dean, to President Macbride's successor Walter A. Jessup, or to the finance committee chairman William R. Boyd that the system was faulty. In short order, much as had been the case early in the twentieth century, a succession of unsatisfactory executives, each with uncertain authority, moved through the superintendency without improving upon it in any discernible way.

One notable feature of William Graham's tenure was the financial loss the hospital sustained in the wake of the Perkins law. As detailed earlier in this chapter, the Perkins law more than doubled the number of patients coming into the hospital, and state payments came to account for half of hospital revenues by the early 1920s. While the 1915 review that set the per diem cost of indigent care at $1.71 was an admirable attempt to establish a baseline cost of patient care at University Hospitals, that financial review nevertheless failed to account for the cost of heat, lighting, and maintenance—a flawed accounting custom dating to the hospital's first decade. As Perkins patients became an ever greater share of the overall patient load, the per-patient loss stemming from this accounting error lay at the heart of a serious fiscal crunch, one that led the medical faculty in 1919 to the despairing realization that the "hospital cannot in any sense be a self-supporting institution."[78]

A second notable feature of Graham's tenure as hospital superintendent was the influenza epidemic in the autumn of 1918,[79] a crisis that further taxed the already overburdened hospitals and further tarnished Graham's reputation. In September 1918, the University of Iowa, like many college campuses, had the look of a military camp, as the Student Army Training Corps absorbed most of the male student body. Housed at government expense in temporary barracks and campus buildings, the student cadets— some 2,000 of them from across the United States—provided a breeding ground for the influenza that spread like wildfire through the cadet ranks and, to a lesser extent, through the rest of the university and Iowa City communities in late September. By October 1918, the influx of influenza patients had overrun the University Hospital's isolation wards, and Mary Haarer, the superintendent of nursing, orchestrated a community effort to care for patients in now empty fraternity houses, the law building, the women's gymnasium, the Masonic Temple, and the Elks Lodge. Support for the operation came from several sources, including private contributors, the United States Army, Red Cross volunteers, nursing students, junior and senior medical students, the college of dentistry, and the home economics department, with Haarer, Lee Wallace Dean, Charles Rowan, and Campbell Howard making daily rounds of each of the ad hoc isolation facilities.

The height of the epidemic came in the first week of October and sparked extraordinary containment measures. Armed soldiers patrolled the university campus to enforce quarantine regulations; student cadets were barred from attending university classes; the Iowa City board of health ordered the closing of all public places, including churches, theaters, and public and private schools; and President Walter Jessup instituted stringent new university regulations, including faculty surveillance of students and reporting of suspected influenza cases to the hospitals.[80] By October 5, local newspaper stories claimed as many as 250 influenza cases among the student cadets, and several Iowa City physicians each reported seeing as many as 25 victims among their patients. Although President Jessup declared that officials had the epidemic under control, he also counted 480 cases in quarantine in the various isolation facilities, some thirty of whom were female students quarantined in Currier Hall.

By October 17, the worst had passed in Iowa City; however, with the epidemic still raging across the state, the secretary of the state board of health ordered the closing of all public places statewide, a preventive measure encouraged by federal authorities. Because of its exemplary control efforts, the University of Iowa was exempt from that closure notice, and student cadets resumed classes on October 21. Female students, meanwhile, although barred from the campus after 6 p.m., had been in class since October 1. By October 22, newspaper accounts placed the number of influenza cases in the university at 100, down from a high of 1,000 just two weeks earlier, and deaths among student cadets, most of those from bacterial pneumonia, had fallen from seven per day to none. By the end of the crisis in late October, 76 of Mary Haarer's nurses had been stricken with influenza, and one supervisor and five students had died.[81]

William Graham, of course, had no control over the influenza epidemic. Likewise, he had neither originated the faulty accounting system nor had he set the inadequate rate the University Hospitals charged the state for the care of indigent patients. Yet the multiple crises inevitably drew attention to his weaknesses as an executive. In October 1918, surgery head Charles Rowan called privately for his removal, telling Lee Wallace Dean, "I still do not regard Dr. Graham as a satisfactory hospital superintendent, chiefly because of his procrastination," perhaps referring to Graham's part in handling the influenza epidemic.[82] By December, Dean and President Jessup were in agreement with Rowan and quietly began searching for Graham's replacement. Moreover, Dean advised Jessup that the next superintendent "must be given to understand that he must not make any trouble for any members of the [medical] staff."[83] At the same time, Dean shied from telling Graham that he was no longer wanted, instead hoping to persuade Rowan to do so.[84]

The entire issue came to a head in the spring of 1919, as an external audit by Arthur Young & Co. of New York confirmed that hospital accounts had sunk $74,000 into the red. The finance committee of the board of education met in early April to address the problems raised by the operating deficit and to take steps to halt the flow of red ink. The committee instructed the university secretary not to authorize any further hospital purchases except by order of the committee, relieving William Graham of his last vestige of authority. The committee also put higher per diem rates into immediate effect and empaneled a committee to determine and report on the actual cost of running the hospital.[85] Conspicuous by his absence from that crucial finance committee meeting was Graham, who two weeks later was asked to resign effective July 1, 1919.[86]

The Young & Co. audit uncovered problems in the hospitals' accounting system, among which was the keeping of two sets of books, one by Graham and one by William Bates, the university secretary. A more general survey of hospital procedures, carried out at about the same time by John F. Bresnahan of Chicago, noted considerable disorganization and "a great waste of food and supplies." Bresnahan also laid out a reorganization plan that essentially affirmed the principles Hornsby and Smith had articulated before Graham's hiring, specifically that the superintendent should have broad responsibility for everything in the hospital except medical care and should wield the authority needed to meet that responsibility. Bresnahan went even further, stipulating that the superintendent should "be responsible to the President of the University and to him alone." He proposed an organizational structure for the hospital featuring an executive committee made up of the medical dean and selected department heads and faculty, "this council to be the common meeting ground of staff and administrator."[87]

Bresnahan was not the only one who recognized that the superintendent had not been vested with sufficient authority to be an effective administrator. In his complaint about Graham the previous October, Charles Rowan had written, "I don't think his work could be satisfactory under the present system of giving him so little authority and requiring him to depend so much on Mr. Bates [university secretary] and Mr. Fisk [building superintendent]." Dean, to whom Rowan's comments had been addressed, later acknowledged that Graham had been working under constraints not of his own devising and that the next superintendent should be paid a higher salary and given full charge of the hospital's business affairs.[88]

The search for the next superintendent, however, was not made easier by past experience. One prospect, Walter E. List of Johns Hopkins, agreed to come to Iowa, but only at a salary of $10,000, a figure equal to that of President Jessup. List received his $10,000 from the University of Chicago instead.[89] Consultant John Bresnahan had placed his own hat in the ring by stating his salary and other requirements at the close of his report, and although a promising negotiation between Bresnahan and Dean took place over several weeks that summer, in the end Bresnahan's wife could not be convinced to move from Chicago to Iowa City.[90] Nor is it clear that Dean was genuinely prepared to cede executive control of the hospital to the superintendent—one of Bresnahan's stipulations—for he was at that very time preparing a new revision of the hospital rules that kept the superintendent's subordination to the dean of medicine intact.[91]

With Graham gone and Haskell-Klaus patients beginning to arrive, the hospitals urgently needed a superintendent. In desperation, Dean doubled back on his search and reconsidered a candidate previously rejected on the advice of none other than former president John Bowman, now administrative director of the American College of Surgeons.[92] That candidate, Herbert O. Collins, was in 1919 the superintendent of Winnipeg General Hospital in Winnipeg, Manitoba, and had previously superintended the Minneapolis City Hospital. The basis upon which Bowman had advised against considering Collins is unknown, but Collins' personal bearing and professional experience must have persuaded Dean and Jessup that he could do the job, for they recommended him to the board of education, which hired him effective September 1, 1919, at a salary of $6,600 a year.[93]

Herbert Collins lasted just ten unhappy months as superintendent. President Jessup ultimately charged that he was "utterly incapable of coordinating certain large units" of the hospital and called him "the champion 'buck-passer' of the organization." Because of Collins' incompetence, Jessup argued, he, Dean, Bates, and members of the finance committee "were forced to devote vastly more time than in any previous year, to the hospital, in order to keep the service going at all."[94] Jessup might have added that within weeks of coming to Iowa City, Collins had put his general competence in question by submitting a monthly budget report that did not take overhead costs into account—the same overhead costs to which the Arthur Young & Co. report had devoted so much attention.[95] Meanwhile, the residual inflationary pressures of World War I combined with the influx of Haskell-Klaus patients to again jeopardize hospital fiscal projections. A new report on hospital costs completed in April 1920 found that the state had paid for 59,453 patient days at the rate of $2.75 per day during the previous three fiscal quarters, but that the actual daily cost was $3.39, a loss totaling more than $38,000. Rates for all patients—state, clinical, and private—were then adjusted upward.[96] Such problems landed at Herbert Collins' door, just as had happened to William Graham before him.

Collins, of course, was not without his corresponding version of the truth. Despite the adoption of some of John Bresnahan's proposals concentrating more formal authority over business affairs in the office of the superintendent, Lee Wallace Dean held tenaciously to final executive control over the hospital. Moreover, Collins complained, "shortly after my arrival, Dr. Dean wrote me a letter, informing me that I was to have authority and responsibility over the entire Hospital 'except the Nursing Service,' " whose superintendent, Mary Haarer, reported directly to Dean. And as the dietary and steward's departments reported to the nursing superintendent, Collins wrote, "the ruling that the Superintendent was to have no jurisdiction over the Nursing Service . . . exempted from my control at least two-thirds— and the most important two-thirds—of the Hospital service." "The fact that the Supt. of Nurses now at the University Hospital was, a few years ago, an unsuccessful applicant for a similar position at the Minneapolis City Hospital, and that another appointment was made there on my recommendation, has not helped the situation," he continued.[97]

Collins painted a picture in which his authority was so circumscribed that it rendered him unable to carry out the duties assigned to him. Besides the intrusions of Dean and the nursing superintendent, "the Superintendent of Grounds and Buildings of the University was in charge of the mechanics . . . including control of repairs and any building operations, and had charge of a few of the janitors. He also had charge of the laundry." At the same time, "the Dean of the College of Pharmacy had charge of the Drug Room, selecting the Pharmacist, buying and controlling the dispensing of all drugs and medicines," and "the Secretary of the University purchased all supplies except the drugs." The superintendent "exercised some control over the balance, consisting chiefly of the office force and the housekeeping."[98] All outside experts, of course, had previously insisted that the superintendent have direct executive power over all of the above functions.

Nor was Collins' depiction of the finance committee very flattering. He cited several examples of problems he had referred to the governing body for decision, only to have the committee refer the problems in turn to other committees that never met, never reported, and never reached decisions. However, Jessup cited Collins' complaints as a perfect example of his "buck-passing." "Excuses were offered on every hand," Jessup charged. "Somebody else was to blame for every shortcoming whether it involved the Superintendent of Grounds and Buildings, the Superintendent of Nurses, the purchasing department, the Finance Committee, the pharmacists, or what not."[99]

But even if Collins was fully as incompetent as Jessup and Dean claimed—indeed, it seems likely he was not fit for the job—still the hospitals' organizational structure was not fitted to the demands of the modern era, with too many centers of independent control over vital hospital functions, too much power in the hands of Dean Lee Wallace Dean, and too little oversight of the dean by the president or the board of education finance committee.

Nonetheless, the disastrous experience with Herbert Collins seems to have convinced Lee Wallace Dean, Walter Jessup, and the finance committee to weaken the superintendent's position even more. Appointing William T. Graham acting superintendent, the board of education then acceded to a proposal by Dean and Jessup to reorganize the hospital administration under a medical superintendent and a business manager, with the business manager directly responsible to the medical superintendent and with Dean assigning himself the part of medical superintendent. In response to this wholesale raid on the powers of the acting superintendent, the university secretary transferred his bookkeeper to the hospital to keep closer tabs on its monthly reports.[100] There followed another search and the hiring of another superintendent amid promises of full authority within the hospital, but that man, Arthur J. Lomas, resigned after just eighteen months to become superintendent of the Maryland State Hospital.

As suggested by the accompanying organization chart (Figure 2.1), more than bad luck plagued the university in its attempts to find a competent hospital superintendent. At different times, three outside consultants outlined an organizational structure for the hospital resting on the foundation of a strong superintendent vested with full authority over all hospital functions and answerable directly to the university president; yet such powers were never delegated in anything more than name, leaving the luckless superintendent in a hopelessly ambiguous position. When, for example, the best available experts on hospital administration advised university officials in 1914 to invest in a thoroughly trained, modern superintendent, they opted instead to save $1,250 and hire William Graham, a kindly old doctor from Des Moines who had begun his career before the turn of the century. Later, Lee Wallace Dean and Walter Jessup were advised not even to consider Herbert Collins, but they recommended him anyway, to the detriment of the hospital administration. Through it all, Dean continued to meddle in the administration of the hospital, while refusing to accept responsibility for the failures in hospital operations.

Women in the Hospital: Nursing and Nutrition

From its modest beginning with a handful of students under Superintendent Jenny Cottle's tutelage in 1898, the University Hospital Training School for

Figure 2.1   University Hospitals Organization Chart, c. 1926

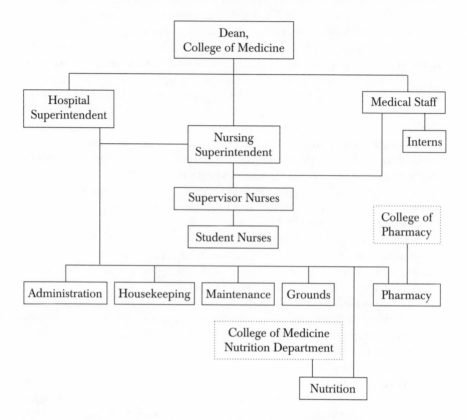

Nurses expanded in the early years of the twentieth century, more or less in keeping with the expansion of the hospital itself.[101] The school enrolled 14 students in 1900, 18 in 1905, 46 in 1910, and 86 in 1915. Like much else about the hospitals, the influx of indigent patients in the late teens and twenties accelerated growth in the training school; enrollments swelled to 137 in 1920 and to 203 in 1925, by which time the name had been changed to University of Iowa School of Nursing.[102] By the 1920s, the demand for nurses, coupled with diminished interest in nursing careers and competition from more than 50 other training programs in the state, elicited an active recruitment effort aimed at high school age women.[103] At the same time, the school began to accept "affiliated" students—that is, students from other nurse training schools—in 1920, affording them access to the broader range of practical experience in the University Hospitals. In 1925, 44 affiliated students enrolled alongside the 203 regular students.

From the first, nursing students were chiefly a source of underpaid labor, an increasingly critical one as the hospital underwent its rapid expansion, and nursing education was never more than a secondary consideration for the hospital administration. Initially, the formal nursing curriculum embraced 65 lectures—given by medical faculty—in anatomy; physiology; materia medica; hygiene; dietetics; bacteriology; obstetrics; gynecology; infectious diseases; diseases of the eye, ear, nose, and throat; and diseases of children. Students also received cursory instruction in medical, surgical, obstetrical, and special nursing, as well as in invalid cookery, massage, and hospital and ward management. While the training course spanned three years, it was for several years an ungraded course in which first-, second-, and third-year students attended the same lectures, much as had been the case in medical education through most of the nineteenth century. Moreover, lectures and recitations constituted only a small part of the training regimen, most of which came on the hospital wards where student nurses were the primary caregivers.

By 1915, the curriculum was a graded one, reorganized into freshman, junior, and senior years. The new organization also reflected, in some degree, practice now accepted in medical education, with the basic sciences preceding clinical instruction. First-year students studied anatomy, physiology, bacteriology, pathology, and gynecology; second-year students picked up the rudiments of general medicine, materia medica, toxicology, hygiene, and anesthetics; and third-year students studied general surgery, eye, ear, nose, and throat, obstetrics, bandaging, pediatrics, and urinalysis. By 1925, the curriculum included a four-month preparatory term embracing the bulk of the basic science instruction as well as lectures in hospital economy, history of nursing, ethics of nursing, and physical education. At the end of that probationary period, nursing students underwent the "capping" ritual and embarked upon the wards and also upon an expanded classroom curriculum incorporating 122 hours of lectures for freshman students, 213 hours for juniors, and 105 hours for seniors.[104] Students continued their extensive ward and special service work, for example, devoting three months to the medical service; one month each to neurology, communicable diseases, gynecology, urology, and eye, ear, nose, and throat; two months to orthopædics; and two months each to obstetrics and surgery.[105]

Over the years, admissions requirements, like the curriculum, became more stringent. As late as 1915, minimum standards specified little more than an age range of 20 to 30 and a grammar school education, although with the understanding that high school graduates would receive preference in admissions. By 1920, the age specification had broadened to 19 to 32, perhaps reflecting the shortage of candidates. Meanwhile, admissions standards mandated a high school education, or its equivalent, and specified that candidates be "physically fit" as well. A standard application form of the mid-1920s asked for detailed information about the candidate and her background, including employment history, financial resources, race, church membership, and marital status. The last was an especially sensitive point, since, as one form letter from the mid-1920s explained to would-be applicants, the school had experienced "some trouble" with married, divorced, and separated women, and the superintendent did not want "to be troubled by any indiscretions."[106] Admissions procedures also required submission of a physician's certificate attesting to the applicant's general state of health, an assessment followed by an examination by the training school physician prior to acceptance.

Like other major nursing schools in America, the University of Iowa Training School for Nurses was much influenced by the British tradition of nursing education and its emphasis on "rigid discipline, hierarchical authority, efficient organization, and autonomy of nursing service," although institutional constraints largely precluded the last of those goals. Moral character, too, was a major concern, at the University of Iowa as at other schools, owing in part to the shady image of nursing during much of the nineteenth century and in part to the fact that the nursing superintendent had charge of dozens of young, single women.[107] The school housed nursing students in dormitory fashion, first in residential neighborhoods surrounding the hospital, then, after 1914, in a permanent nurses' dormitory built at a cost of $50,000, and, from the 1920s, in Westlawn on the new westside medical campus. By 1928, Westlawn housed 414 nurses—students and supervisory nurses—in 245 rooms with a library and recreation rooms. Regulations governing student life off the wards were strict, specifying hours of rising, study, meals, and retiring, and setting standards for dress and decorum.

While the work of the student nurse may have been, as the university proclaimed, "a high privilege and a sacred duty,"[108] the student's life on the wards was demanding. In the early days of the training school, prior to the development of the hospital service infrastructure, student nurses assumed responsibility for nearly all of the work associated with patient care, from scrubbing and waxing the floors to preparing and serving meals. In addition, then and later, the more senior of the students went, from time to time, on private duty assignments, with their fees paid to the hospital.[109] By the 1920s, student nurses still worked eight-hour daily hospital shifts, with one afternoon off per week and a half-day off on Sunday.

On the wards, the relationship between doctors and nurses, especially student nurses, was normally "distant and authoritative."[110] In illustration of that distance, Lee Wallace Dean once demanded that all nurses—students and graduates—submit to throat cultures, only to find that nearly all were carriers of communicable disease. According to one unwilling subject, Dean filled the isolation wards with nurses and, "had there been isolation quarters enough," would have left no one but "a foreign girl dishwasher" and a handful of nurses "to run the hospital."[111] Much the same distance often characterized the relationship between student nurses and their supervisors as well. Sometimes the result of personal temperament, student-supervisor conflict was also a reflection of differences in social class and of the two-track system of nursing education that saw some students—generally those of middle-class background and education—groomed for hospital supervisory positions and the remainder consigned to an uncertain future in private duty nursing.[112]

Under the circumstances, tension and conflict were inevitable and led to occasional student rebellions at some nursing schools.[113] Official acknowledgment of such occurrences at the University of Iowa was rare. Still, as early as 1901, a group of eight student nurses at the University of Iowa Hospital objected to the lengthy and strenuous training program, charging that, while "excellent," the program was not "sufficient to warrant three years' time."[114] A further hint of dissent among the ranks of student nurses came from the 1919 organization of a student council whose representatives "might present any subject or problem concerning the nurses . . . as a composite whole and not as a collection of individual factions." Meeting in the medical amphitheater in October 1919, the students' first official act was to dispatch their newly elected officers to meet with school principal Mary Haarer, notifying Haarer of their decision to organize and also to discuss a student disciplinary case.

In January 1920, organization members approved a motion recommending adoption of the university's more flexible "late leave permission" system in place of the rigid 10 p.m. curfew then in place for nursing students. An October 1920 amendment to the organization's constitution denied the benefits of membership to those who declined to pledge one dollar in dues, leaving the nonjuring students "directly under the military discipline of the Training school." In November 1920, members approved motions to demand "open house" (i.e., do away with the curfew) on Friday nights, to allow parlor visitations after ten o'clock on Saturday evenings, and to have an orchestra one Friday night each month. Overall, Haarer's efforts to guide her students' enthusiasm for self-expression and self-government into safer, perhaps more "ladylike," channels—for example, bringing in the university's dean of women to advise the group—appear to have accomplished little, although, in January 1921, the group did discuss her concerns over smoking and card-playing and agreed to do away with card-playing on Sunday nights.[115]

Underlying the early history of nursing education at University Hospitals, and in many respects interlaced with that history, was the effort, particularly by nursing elites, to achieve professional status for nurses and nursing. The boom in hospital construction in the first three decades of the twentieth century and increasing levels of professional staffing in hospitals—trends readily apparent at the University of Iowa Hospitals and, to a lesser degree, in hospitals across the state—enhanced the visibility of nursing as a profession. Burgeoning numbers of nurse training schools were obvious manifestations of an emerging nursing profession, as were state licensing laws, the first enacted in North Carolina in 1903. The birth of the Iowa State Association of Graduate Nurses in 1904 was part of a political strategy to obtain a state licensing law, a goal achieved in 1907. By 1910, 27 states had nurse licensing acts, and, by 1923, all states, plus Hawaii and the District of Columbia, had such statutes in force.

Although desirable objectives, state licensing laws did not, in the words of early nurse advocate Lavinia L. Dock, constitute an "automatically working machine" that would define and protect nurses' professional jurisdiction. Licensing laws or no, Dock argued in 1901, the most important long-term aim for her profession was "a recognized standard of professional education."[116] However, nursing elites faced formidable obstacles in their efforts to effect a reform of nursing education. First, nursing became almost exclusively a feminine occupation in the early twentieth century, a product of economic, ideological, and disciplinary calculations.[117] Second, there was no Abraham Flexner, backed by tens of millions of dollars in philanthropic monies, behind the effort to upgrade the nursing profession through educational reform. Third, the hospitals that sponsored nursing education depended on the unpaid labor of student nurses and also provided an increasing share of graduate nursing opportunities; hence, they had little incentive to raise educational standards. Fourth, physicians likewise resisted nursing reform, guarding their professional turf jealously; as the University of Iowa catalog explained it, nursing education was "under the general direction" of the college of medicine.[118] Finally, as is often the case in feminized occupations, nurses were a highly fragmented and poorly organized occupational group, and nursing elites faced considerable opposition among the rank and file to any measures of professional uplift.

The reform program, emphasizing formal education rather than practical training and the concurrent development of graduate education, threatened traditional power relationships in the rapidly evolving healthcare field, and especially in the early twentieth-century hospital. At the University of Iowa, the superintendents of nursing were able to expand the nursing curriculum substantially; however, superintendents nominally controlled only the theoretical or classroom portion of the curriculum, while, through the 1920s, student nurses still worked 48-hour weeks in the hospital, with just three weeks' vacation each year. In a real sense, then, nursing students were caught between the rising educational expectations of professional elites on the one hand and the unremitting work expectations of hospital management on the other.

In 1919, the school of nursing and the university inaugurated a combined five-year course leading to the bachelor of science degree with nursing certificate, one of sixteen such programs in the United States in 1923. However, like the medical school's nineteenth-century experiment with simultaneous two- and three-year programs, the more demanding combined course in nursing attracted few students at the University of Iowa or elsewhere. The nurse training school also began to offer graduate courses in the early 1920s, designed to augment graduate nurses' skills in administration and nursing education and, through its extension division, offered a short-lived course in public health nursing open to graduates of approved nurse training schools. Likewise, the first formal proposal for a full-fledged college of nursing at Iowa surfaced in the early 1920s, with the argument that higher educational standards would enable nurses to make a greater contribution to public health. Most important, the proposal would grant to the college authority over nursing administration and personnel assignments—both graduate staff and students—in the University Hospitals. Meanwhile, the plan would eliminate the complete maintenance provided student nurses, instead paying an hourly wage for their services. An attached budget estimated $49,000 in additional costs beyond the current $176,000 annual allotment for hospital nursing services.[119] However, an autonomous college of nursing, precisely because it addressed some of nursing's chief professional weaknesses, stood little chance of approval in the 1920s.

The observations of Effie J. Taylor, who turned down the superintendent's job in 1922 and later became dean of the Yale University School of Nursing, neatly summarized the problems facing nursing and nursing education at the University of Iowa. In a December 1921 letter to Superintendent Arthur J. Lomas, Taylor raised her concern over whether or not the nursing superintendent enjoyed faculty status in the university, questioning Lomas's contention that the training school was "a recognized department of the University." After a campus visit in January 1922, Taylor's concerns, heightened by first-hand observations and by conversations with nursing personnel and medical faculty, were both broader and deeper. In a January 1922 letter to Lee Wallace Dean, Taylor noted that the University of Iowa training school was, simultaneously, "under the administration of the Superintendent of the Hospital" and was "maintained by the hospital," while also under the "general direction" of the college of medicine. Taylor expressed her complete bewilderment over the exact meaning of that arrangement, but she was clear in her conviction that it was unacceptable. Meanwhile, in Taylor's view, the demands of hospital work overshadowed the "too meager theoretical instruction given."[120] It is little wonder, then, that Taylor declined the position of superintendent.

Much the same picture characterized the position of the supervisory nursing staff in the first decades of this century. While the numbers of graduate nurses employed in the University Hospitals multiplied rapidly, and while their educational and caregiving responsibilities grew in proportion, their position in the hospital hierarchy, although somewhat ambiguous, remained a subordinate one, the object of competition between hospital superintendents and medical staff. At the same time, however, from the point of view of patients, the graduate nurse emerged as a strong figure on the hospital wards in the early decades of the twentieth century, an intermediary in the physician–patient relationship but more accessible than the physician and more immediately identified with the increasingly disciplined hospital regimen. Over the long term, nurses' relative accessibility and highly visible role in hospital patient care bolstered their professional ambitions, as nurses emerged as a counterbalance to the increasingly and perhaps inevitably depersonalized nature of hospital healthcare.

In many respects, the experience of the female nutrition staff in the college of medicine and in the University Hospitals paralleled that of the nursing staff.[121] The increasing differentiation of the hospital's service functions in the early decades of this century and the concerted effort of Campbell Howard of internal medicine and Ruth Wardall of home economics led to creation of the nutrition department in 1920.[122] Incorporating educational, research, and hospital service functions, the nutrition department was, in effect, a clinical department within the college of medicine and the University Hospitals. Ruth Wheeler, who graduated from Vassar College in 1899 and earned her Ph.D. under Lafayette Mendel at Yale University in 1913, came to Iowa City to assume leadership of the new department.[123]

As a female department head, Ruth Wheeler confronted the politics of gender in her efforts to carve a niche for herself and for her department in a keenly competitive institutional environment ruled by males. Not surprisingly, Wheeler's quest for money, space, and authority—the sine qua non of institutional life—triggered sometimes fierce squabbles between Wheeler and other department heads, between Wheeler and the hospital superintendent, between Wheeler and the dean of the college of medicine, and also between the superintendent and the dean. On several occasions, the squabbles forced President Walter Jessup into the largely unwanted role of final arbiter.

Ruth Wheeler's male colleagues conceded, albeit often grudgingly, the need for a well-ordered nutrition service in the University Hospitals— what Wheeler dismissed as the "feeding machine." However, Wheeler's colleagues were, for the most part, openly hostile to her contention that the nutrition department, like other college of medicine departments, had legitimate educational and research functions. Wheeler established the first master's degree program in hospital nutrition in the United States, requiring, in accordance with graduate college regulations, that students complete thirty semester hours of graduate coursework. Twenty hours of study in nutrition constituted the core of the program, embracing nutrition seminars and courses in physiology, hygiene, and diet therapy. Students also completed ten hours of work in a minor area—either chemistry or economics—and produced a thesis defended before a panel consisting of Wheeler, two physicians, and a faculty member from the student's chosen minor. In addition to their strictly academic burdens, nutrition students gained practical experience working 48-hour weeks in the several hospital service areas in return for a $100 annual stipend.

In all, it was a rigorous schedule indeed, and Wheeler argued in the spring of 1923 that her nutrition interns warranted the "complete maintenance"—that is, room, board, and laundry—awarded medical interns.[124] The hospital superintendent, Arthur Lomas, whose budget would bear the cost, objected bluntly that nutrition interns came to the hospitals "to get experience in their line . . . rendering the hospital nothing in return." Lomas' position, especially his gratuitous dismissal of hospital nutrition as a "line" of work rather than a profession, was suggestive of general attitudes toward Wheeler and her department within the college and the hospitals, an attitude shared by Lee Wallace Dean.[125] In this instance, however, President Jessup sided with Wheeler, and her interns moved into a frame house near the hospital in the fall of 1923.

Ruth Wheeler was similarly adamant in her demands for research opportunities in nutrition, without which, she noted, her department could never be "a real Department of Nutrition and not merely a hospital dietary department." As part of that research plan, Wheeler proposed that each of her interns devote three months of the twelve-month master's degree program to research, freed from daily duties in the hospital dietary service.[126] In the spring of 1923, Wheeler presented the plan to Dean Lee Wallace Dean, who rejected it out of hand. Turning Arthur Lomas' argument regarding the value of the nutrition interns' service on its head, Dean asserted, "Hospital internes [medical and nutrition] are primarily appointed for service in the hospital and not for research work,"[127] and there the matter ended. At the same time, however, Wheeler raised the issue of a full-time research assistant for her department to conduct independent research and to supervise graduate students' laboratory work. The graduate college authorized a meager salary of $1,800 for the position, a sum insufficient to attract a desirable candidate, and Wheeler once again sought the support of President Jessup. She reported that the "feeding machine" was "pretty well organized" and that it was time to attend to "the research side of our work . . . in order to build up a center for graduate work in nutrition."[128] Perhaps under Jessup's prodding, the graduate college responded with an authorized salary line of $2,250, with which Wheeler secured the services of a young graduate of her own program, one with previous staff experience in the nutrition department.

In 1923, the staff of the hospital dietary service included an administrative dietitian who served as Wheeler's chief assistant; two assistant dietitians who ordered supplies and planned and supervised preparation of food for patients, staff, and employees—all told, some 3,600 meals daily; a therapeutic dietitian who took charge of special diets and supervised the diet kitchen; and dietitians assigned individually to pediatrics, orthopædics, and the diabetic home (this last an operation funded in part by a grant from the Rockefeller Foundation through the work of Campbell Howard). In addition to their service duties, Wheeler's staff shared teaching duties, instructing nutrition interns, nurses, home economics students, and junior medical students in the practical and technical aspects of scientific nutrition.

Staff salaries ranged from $1,800 for the pediatric dietitian to $3,000 for Wheeler's chief administrative dietitian. At the time, there were precious few occupations affording women such incomes; average incomes for schoolteachers and female factory workers, for example, were perhaps $600.[129] More to the point, staff salaries in nutrition compared favorably to the $2,000 to $3,000 paid junior faculty in the clinical and basic science departments of the college of medicine. Wheeler herself earned $5,000, putting her on a par with most clinical department heads, although most of the latter, of course, supplemented their income through private practice. In addition, staff benefits in the nutrition department included room and board, and staff also shared a hospital dining room with physicians and the upper levels of hospital administration, apart from nurses and other hospital employees. Ruth Wheeler, then, proved to be a very capable competitor in the rough-and-tumble atmosphere of the college of medicine and the University Hospitals.

Ruth Wheeler was elected president of the American Dietetic Association (ADA) in 1924 and again in 1925, a period in which association membership rose nearly 50 percent to just over 1,000. She was also chiefly responsible for establishment of the *Journal of the American Dietetic Association* in 1925, a quarterly journal addressing both administrative and therapeutic aspects of nutrition. As ADA president, Wheeler campaigned for higher standards for association membership and for nutrition training programs, arguing that scientific credentials were the key to women's status in nutrition and in the broader health science community.

By and large, the early history of the nutrition department at the University of Iowa echoed experience elsewhere in the United States as nutrition departments, organized and staffed by women, struggled for recognition in the rapidly expanding medical scientific world. Overall, as at Iowa, the research role of women in nutrition was perhaps most problematic, and, from the outset, the field of nutrition research was partitioned along gender lines, with women maintaining a base chiefly in home economics and hospital nutrition and men holding fast to older laboratory sciences such as physiology and chemistry that tended to exclude women from participation. Separate female and male professional institutions reflected that gender division. Women invested their professional energies in the American Home Economics Association, organized in 1908, and the ADA, founded in 1917. In contrast, the initial membership of the prestigious American Institute of Nutrition, founded in 1928, was almost wholly male.

In the fall of 1925, Ruth Wheeler submitted her resignation, effective in August 1926, in favor of a position at her alma mater, Vassar College. By that time, both the nutrition department's original supporters, Campbell Howard and Ruth Wardall, had departed, Howard bound for McGill University in Montreal and Wardall for the University of Illinois. That combination of events opened the door to the dismemberment of the nutrition department, largely the work, it appears, of Lee Wallace Dean. Under a reorganization plan instituted in the fall of 1926, nutrition lost its status as a college of medicine department, replaced by a new nutrition department—one without formal academic status in the graduate college—organized in the University Hospitals. The second part of the plan placed responsibility for the graduate program in hospital nutrition with an assistant professor of nutrition in the internal medicine department. Writing from the University of Illinois, Ruth Wardall expressed her dismay over the reorganization directly to Lee Wallace Dean, but to no avail.[130]

Before her departure, Ruth Wheeler recommended Kate Daum as her successor. Born in Great Bend, Kansas in 1892, Daum had earned bachelor's and master's degrees in home economics from the University of Kansas in 1913 and 1916. After several years of teaching home economics at various state universities, Daum had enrolled in Katherine Blunt's graduate program at the University of Chicago and received her Ph.D. in chemistry and nutrition in 1925. Daum joined Ruth Wheeler's staff in 1925 as a research assistant; prior to that, she had been instrumental in organizing the nutrition department at Columbia-Presbyterian Hospital in New York.[131] In the 1926 reorganization, Daum became Wheeler's academic successor, as assistant professor of nutrition in internal medicine, a position she held for the next thirty years.

Kate Daum continued Ruth Wheeler's demanding graduate program, a program that shared many features with the nurse training program. Meanwhile, Florence Ross, who came to the University of Iowa from Simmons

College in Boston, became head of the hospitals' nutrition department, succeeding Wheeler as head of the dietary service. Ross's tenure, however, was short and troubled, in no small part because of ambiguities inherent in the relationship between the academic and practical components of the ongoing graduate program in hospital nutrition. As a result, Kate Daum emerged in the fall of 1927 as both assistant professor of nutrition and head of the hospitals' nutrition department, a solution with fiscal as well as administrative virtues since it eliminated Ross's $3,300 salary from the hospitals' budget.

Like nursing students, nutrition interns were young, single women, and their life at the university had a monastic character. Over the years, in fact, several nuns enrolled in the nutrition program. Daum discouraged young mothers from entering the program, warning one that hospital nutrition might not be "a wise choice for her" because of the long hours of work demanded in the profession and the low pay.[132] Also, like nursing students, nutrition interns lived in Westlawn where they were relatively isolated from much of campus life. Consistent with practice in the school of nursing, Daum imposed strict rules of dress and deportment, evaluating students' integrity, disposition, and "culture"—the last defined as "refinement, polish, manners, [and] broad interests."[133] Upon graduation, most nutrition students moved from one community of women to another, reflecting the cultural connection between hospital nutrition and "women's work" and the very real problems in combining marriage and children with such a demanding career.

Like Ruth Wheeler, Kate Daum maintained a high professional profile. Already in 1927, Daum was head of the American Dietetic Association's Diet Therapy Section, and throughout her career she continued her interest in therapeutic and educational issues. Daum was also a principal figure in the organization of the Iowa Dietetic Association, inviting nutritionists from around the state to an inaugural meeting in Waterloo in February 1930.[134] Daum began her research career early on, focusing in particular on diabetic metabolism, nutrition in arteriosclerosis and cardiac failure, and also on child nutrition, although she seems to have had only limited dealings with the Iowa Child Welfare Research Station, an interdisciplinary research institution founded in 1917 and the first of its kind in North America.[135]

Kate Daum's dual role as head of the dietary service and assistant professor of nutrition in internal medicine denied her the authority and status enjoyed by Ruth Wheeler, who had headed a full-fledged academic department in the college of medicine. Daum was well aware of what had been lost in the restructuring of 1926–1927. Nutrition was, she lamented, "the neglected and forgotten child of medicine," largely because "food is the chief commodity and the kitchen the important workshop" of the hospital dietitian. In Daum's estimation, the status of nutrition personnel stood only "a little above that of the ward maid in the hospital caste system." In light of the importance of nutrition in the prevention and treatment of disease, both in the hospital and in society at large, Daum argued that the head of the nutrition department and her principal staff should be accorded the same standing and respect as others of like training and responsibility, a reference to the heads of the clinical departments in the college of medicine.[136] Yet, as matters stood, Daum's administrative staff, notwithstanding their extensive teaching responsibilities in the graduate program, lacked academic status in the university and could not participate in formal student examinations under graduate college rules.

Flexner Returns

Abraham Flexner's return to the University of Iowa in December 1920 received little attention, at the time or since. Yet, for Flexner and for the university, that 1920 visit was critically important, signaling Flexner's approval of Iowa's decade-long reform effort and triggering extensive negotiations between the university and the country's major philanthropies that resulted in a stunning private grant of $2.25 million for a new hospital and medical laboratories building. Despite continuing problems with organization and administration of the medical complex, especially University Hospitals, Flexner's sanction was a measure of the real progress the university had made vis-à-vis the evolving national standards in medical education; at the same time it stood as evidence of Flexner's own realization that such standards must be adaptable to differing regional, social, and economic circumstances.

Flexner had left the Carnegie Foundation in 1912 and soon became assistant secretary, later secretary, of the General Education Board, a Rockefeller philanthropy. He continued to focus his efforts on reforming medical education, but whereas in his earlier review he had taken as his standards the most prestigious private schools of the east—primarily Johns Hopkins and Harvard—by 1920 he recognized the shortcomings inherent in attempting to impose such standards across the board on all medical schools. He had seen, for example, that the African American medical schools of the South could never hope to command sufficient resources to emulate elite programs, yet that those schools played an important role in educating black doctors. As a result, Flexner urged the AMA Council on Medical Education and Hospitals and the General Education Board to apply relative, rather than absolute, standards in their evaluations of medical schools and to promote improvement, rather than uniformity, in medical education.[137] By that more practical measure, the half-century history of the University of Iowa College of Medicine came off well indeed.

Further, Johns Hopkins and other premier private schools proved not to be the ideal institutions that a younger Flexner had supposed. For example, Johns Hopkins' trials with a full-time faculty plan, implemented in 1913 with $1.5 million in General Education Board funding, revealed the same divisions among clinical faculty as were apparent at the University of Iowa when the issue of private practice was discussed. That is, those with the best prospects of obtaining substantial income from private fees opposed the plan eliminating private practice and placing all medical faculty on full-time salaries, while those disposed to favor research accepted the plan's limitation on their income in exchange for the support it gave their research activities. By 1920, though, even some of the latter had grown resentful of the plan's inflexibility, and they resented Flexner and the General Education Board for insisting on the full-time plan as a condition of funding.[138]

Finally, Flexner was concerned not just with the overall supply of physicians and the quality of their education but also with their distribution. In the early 1920s, Flexner directed a General Education Board study of physician distribution by Lewis Mayers and Leonard V. Harrison. Published as *The Distribution of Physicians in the United States*, that study detailed the increasing concentration of physicians in urban areas and the corresponding decline of medical services in rural America.[139] Although this aspect of Flexner's thinking never developed the clarity or compelling force of his earlier pronouncements, it was a central factor in his renewed interest in the University of Iowa College of Medicine. Combined with an evolving realization that some of Flexner's stated goals had been unrealistic and that educational standards must be adaptable to the needs of different communities and institutions, the question of physician distribution seems to have pointed more or less directly to the utility of providing support to public as well as elite private institutions.

Among public institutions, the University of Iowa enjoyed Flexner's particular favor. He genuinely admired William R. Boyd, Walter Jessup, and other Iowa figures with whom he came in contact. Flexner lauded Boyd as "the highest type of American citizen: absolutely correct, candid, and straightforward; absolutely without personal ambition; absolutely devoted to the welfare of his State and particularly to the upbuilding of the State University," and he described Jessup as "a perfectly corking fellow, solid, hard headed." Flexner's personal regard for Iowa leaders cemented the professional relations needed to build a partnership between the Rockefeller organizations and the state of Iowa.[140]

Flexner's two-day visit to the University of Iowa in December 1920 convinced him that its leaders were sincere and capable in their efforts to complete the reforms begun ten years earlier. In his official report he noted with approval the reorganization of the university's governing board and the increase in state financial support for the institution. He was especially pleased to report that "in ten years every head of an important clinical department has been dropped and in no instance has the place been filled either by a wrong man or by a graduate of the University of Iowa." Instead, he happily reported, "the best men available have been sought and imported." The core clinical departments all had established laboratories staffed by full-time technicians. In addition, the college had added departments of pharmacology and psychiatry, each headed by eastern-educated men of good reputation.

To its credit, the school also had anticipated the eventual replacement of its entire physical plant by acquiring land on the west side of the Iowa River and building there the Psychopathic and Children's hospitals and the Westlawn nurses' dormitory—the last not yet completed at the time of Flexner's 1920 visit. University officials planned to add to that campus a new general hospital and medical school building; however, Flexner was critical of the plan to complete the new facilities "piece by piece over a period of eight to ten years. "In my judgment," Flexner wrote, "this would be a very unfortunate policy to be compelled to pursue for the personnel." Moving the hospital across the river department by department over a period of years would, he thought, "destroy team work and impair the momentum which the reform movement now has gained." Flexner noted that the estimated $5 million cost of the new medical plant had kept the board of education from asking the legislature for funding of the entire project at once because "the legislature is made up largely of farmers and agriculture is now in a depressed condition." But, he said, Boyd had agreed, when asked, that an "outside contribution" to the project might well spur the legislature to approve requests over and above the normal appropriation. "If co-operation between the General Education Board and the state can be arranged, the medical school could be completed at once and the entire school . . . transferred to a new site," he suggested. And, he concluded:

> There is a great advantage in dealing with these tax-supported institutions in medicine. There is no question about maintenance or development and they are in a strategic position in reference to public health. The greatest service we can do and perhaps the only service is to help them over the brow of the hill in the matter of completing their facilities at once instead of dragging it out over a period of years.[141]

Ironically, then, Abraham Flexner emerged in the early 1920s as a tireless and influential advocate for the University of Iowa's plan to replace the hospital and medical laboratories. For most of the next two years he shepherded the proposal to seek foundation grants for a new medical complex through the philanthropic bureaucracies while Boyd, Jessup, Dean, and others formulated and reformulated building plans and lined up in-state support. Flexner and Iowa officials coordinated their efforts through frequent written communications and occasional meetings in New York.[142] Flexner took a direct and almost paternalistic role in guiding the process, going so far as to edit and revise university officials' correspondence with the foundations and in one case even composing a lengthy memorandum that President Jessup and the board of education submitted to the philanthropies as their own.[143] "I must stand by my child," Flexner noted early on.[144]

Flexner's plan was to obtain grants for Iowa from the Rockefeller Foundation, the General Education Board, and the Carnegie Foundation, each of which would contribute one-sixth of the project's $4.5 million cost while the state of Iowa would contribute matching funds. Governor Nathan Kendall formally endorsed the proposal in October 1922, when it appeared that the foundations were ready to act, and Kendall promised to deliver legislative approval of the state's share.[145] In the end, Carnegie balked at participation, citing both the Foundation's policy of not giving to tax-supported institutions and its already heavy financial commitments elsewhere. While Carnegie's withdrawal left the plan $750,000 short of the $2,250,000 goal, Abraham Flexner persuaded the Rockefeller Foundation and his own General Education Board to make up the difference, each contributing a total of $1,125,000. The General Education Board gave its final approval to the revised plan on November 24, 1922, and the Rockefeller Foundation did the same on December 6.[146]

With that, Flexner had engineered the first major private grant to a public university, overcoming the bitter opposition of fellow General Educa-tion Board trustee Frederick T. Gates.[147] With legislative approval of the state matching funds, which came on April 4, 1923, planning for the new medical campus could begin in earnest. More to the point, however, the college of medicine and University Hospitals were poised to embrace fully the new model of scientific medical education and practice, especially with respect to the new hospital. With physical facilities designed to accommodate better laboratories and modern record-keeping systems, as well as more patients and a greater emphasis on postgraduate education, the hospital could at last become the teaching facility needed to sustain Flexner's vision of what the medical college ought to be.

New Hospital Standards

The plan for the new medical campus included a more important role for the University Hospitals as adjuncts to the college of medicine. At the same time, however, the hospitals were increasingly subject to national standards promulgated by organizations such as the American College of Surgeons and the American Medical Association's Council on Medical Education and Hospitals. Moreover, those hospital standards, while still voluntary, existed quite apart from the needs and demands of medical education, providing an independent source of validation to the University of Iowa Hospitals and other such teaching institutions.

The American College of Surgeons (ACS) had taken a leading role in developing hospital standards practically as soon as it was organized in 1912, establishing a committee on standardization under physician-turned-efficiency-expert and reformer E. A. Codman. Issued in 1913, the committee's report formulated the organization's first set of goals, including permanent, standard patient records; a hospital staff organization divided hierarchically and along professional lines, one capable of ensuring review of all patient procedures; improved diagnostic and research facilities; professional hospital management and administration; and an emphasis on patient care as the hospital's top priority.[148] In 1916, the ACS campaign for hospital reform gained the support of the American Hospital Association as well as the Catholic, Protestant, and Methodist Episcopal hospital associations. In 1918, the ACS carried out its first wave of annual inspections with financial support from the Carnegie Foundation, visiting 692 hospitals with 100 beds or more, of which only 89 met its minimum standards. The inspection program gradually expanded in scope—until 1921 under the leadership of John Bowman, the former University of Iowa president and Carnegie executive—to include smaller hospitals, and in 1925 the ACS set up a permanent field staff to carry out inspections.

Meanwhile, beginning in 1914, the American Medical Association, which had earlier instigated much the same sort of campaign for the inspection and reform of medical schools, began to approach the question of oversight from the standpoint of evaluating hospitals as internship sites.[149] In 1918, AMA president Arthur Bevan announced the organization's intent to involve itself more deeply in the hospital standardization movement, and in 1920 the AMA's Council on Medical Education became the Council on Medical Education and Hospitals. The council began annual publication of detailed surveys of hospital services in each state in the *Journal of the American Medical Association*.[150] However, the ACS, already better established in the area, played a dominant role in shaping the nature and content of hospital oversight until the 1950s, when the ACS, the AMA, and the American Hospital Association negotiated to form the Joint Commission on Accreditation of Hospitals.[151]

Concern with the adequacy of patient records manifested itself at University Hospital at least as early as November 1914, well before the first ACS inspection but well after Abraham Flexner's 1909 criticisms. At that time, Campbell Howard of internal medicine noted that the hospital still lacked a consistent record-keeping system, whereupon the medical faculty appointed him to instruct the hospital matron in how to make and file accurate accounts of each patient's history and treatment.[152] A year later the faculty filed an internal report on progress in compiling records, pinpointing wide disparities among the different departments. For example, the department of surgery, under Charles Rowan, produced case histories and patient cards for all of its patients, while the department of head specialties, under Lee Wallace Dean, made cards for all of its patients and cross-referenced them with outpatient identification numbers. In contrast, the department of obstetrics and gynecology, under James Guthrie and then William Whiteis, lagged well behind in regard to patient records.[153] Campbell, Rowan, and others continued to push for better record keeping, and in 1920 the board of education finance committee approved formation of a hospital "Bureau of Information" to coordinate and regularize patient record keeping.[154]

With respect to staff organization, another of the American College of Surgeons priorities, there is no evidence that the faculty instituted any kind of general procedure review boards during this period, preferring to act as a faculty and not as a hospital staff. This perhaps reflected a crucial difference between university-owned teaching institutions and other classes of hospitals. Department heads retained a great deal of autonomy in medical as well as academic matters, and departments developed mechanisms, as Arthur Steindler did in orthopædics, to review diagnoses, procedures, and treatments, especially as interns and then residents took on a greater role in patient care. Finally, University Hospitals made steady progress in equipping and staffing laboratories for diagnostic and pathological follow-up in each department.

University Hospitals received ACS approval every year, starting as early as 1919 or 1920. To be sure, ACS standards were initially quite modest and only grew more rigorous as more hospitals met or exceeded them. This allowed the ACS in 1929 to demonstrate an impressive increase in the number and percentage of hospitals gaining a place on its approved list, from just 89, or 12.9 percent, of the 692 hospitals of 100 beds or more surveyed in 1918 to 1,245, or 93.3 percent, of the 1,334 surveyed in 1929.[155] Although its basic requirements remained little changed for more than a decade, the ACS did formulate new minimum standards to cover more and more aspects of hospital operation such as nursing, use of x-rays, outpatient departments, and traumatic surgery.

By the late 1920s, then, hospital standardization was a recognized movement under the leadership of the American College of Surgeons. An ever increasing proportion of hospitals, and certainly all of the most influential teaching institutions, submitted to ACS oversight in recognition of the status its seal of approval could confer. Moreover, once they subscribed to the ACS's standardization principles, hospitals could not afford to renege but were committed to following the dictates of increasingly more comprehensive national standards or risking professional ostracism. University Hospitals, by joining the cadre of approved hospitals early on, placed itself firmly in the mainstream of this national movement. In so doing, it also answered to national standards that lay outside the authority of either the University of Iowa or its college of medicine.

As hospitals joined in the standardization movement, they also became the focus of graduate medical education programs, a tacit recognition of the insufficiency of medical school clinical training. At first this trend simply formalized the hospital internship that had existed since the turn of the century or before and that attracted increasing numbers of medical graduates. The content of these internships, however, was often mediocre. Interns, who lived in the hospital and received board, laundry, and sometimes a small stipend, most often did not receive any organized course of education. Many hospitals viewed interns as cheap labor, and the chores they performed were more routine than instructive.[156] Nevertheless, by 1928, 95 percent of medical school graduates obtained some form of internship, although fewer than 10 percent of hospitals accepted female applicants for their internship programs in the 1920s.[157] In 1914, when the AMA Council on Medical Education first produced a list of hospitals approved for internships, the 508 approved hospitals reported a total of 2,667 interns; by early 1925, 524 approved hospitals reported a total of 3,825 interns, a 47 percent increase.[158]

The teens and twenties of this century also saw the emergence of several new clinical departments within the University Hospitals and the University of Iowa College of Medicine. Orthopædics was one of the largest and most important of those. More than half of the children admitted under terms of the Perkins Act presented diseases of the muscles, bones, and joints, and became patients of the orthopædic surgeon Arthur Steindler, who founded his fiefdom within the college of medicine on the care of the hundreds of indigent children that his orthopædic service drew to the University Hospitals. Although orthopædics remained under the department of surgery until 1927, in practical terms Steindler's operation functioned nearly as autonomously as any other department; certainly that was the case by the time Children's Hospital opened in 1919.

Meanwhile, an act of the Iowa General Assembly established the Iowa State Psychopathic Hospital at the University of Iowa in 1919. By reason of statute, the Psychopathic Hospital functioned as an independent unit within the college of medicine, with its own staff and its own nursing, dietary, and custodial services. Moreover, although it fell under the administrative aegis of the board of education, the law directed Psychopathic Hospital's director to coordinate certain services directly with the state's mental hospitals, which were under the Board of Control of State Institutions. But the director of Psychopathic Hospital was also by law to be a professor of psychiatry within the college of medicine, and as such reported to the dean of medicine and served as head of the new department of psychiatry.[159] The director's dual role and the unique place of Psychopathic Hospital in the pantheon of state institutions fostered some confusion about its relationship to the college of medicine and to University Hospitals. Even as late as 1949, long after Psychopathic Hospital had been integrated into University Hospitals, some organization charts still placed it in the same relation to the university president as the deans of medicine, dentistry, and pharmacy and, significantly, the superintendent of University Hospitals.[160]

Iowa's Psychopathic Hospital was among the first full-fledged psychiatric hospitals in the country following a new model being developed at leading centers for the study and treatment of mental diseases. Its establishment was planned at least as early as 1916, when Dean Lee Wallace Dean visited A. M. Barrett at Michigan's psychopathic hospital in Ann Arbor and received advice from other important figures at an institution that then stood at the cutting edge of psychiatry.[161] The Iowa State Board of Education appointed Samuel T. Orton, scientific director of the Institute of the Pennsylvania Hospital, as first director of Psychopathic Hospital. Orton, like the directors of the three psychopathic hospitals already in existence (Michigan, Boston Psychopathic Hospital, and the Phipps Clinic of Johns Hopkins), had trained at Danvers and Worcester state hospitals in Massachusetts, both of which ran psychopathology laboratories.

Also appearing in the teens and twenties were the department of pediatrics and the department of neurology. Both pediatrics and neurology were spinoffs from the department of theory and practice of medicine, or internal medicine, which in the early twentieth century was an ill-defined area embracing virtually everything not falling under the purview of surgery or obstetrics and gynecology. At a national level, the appearance of pediatrics as a distinct specialty owed much to an emerging emphasis on the care and nurturing of children, while at a local level it followed logically from the Perkins mandate of state-funded care for indigent children. In 1915, with internal medicine head Campbell Howard's concurrence, the board of education approved organization of the department of pediatrics with Dr. Albert H. Byfield as head.[162] In much the same way, neurology separated from theory and practice in 1919, the new department headed by Clarence E. Van Epps, who had been an assistant in theory and practice under both Walter Bierring and Campbell Howard.[163]

The department of theory and practice faced a major transition of its own in 1924 with the resignation of Campbell Howard. Howard, who had come to Iowa from McGill University in the wake of Flexner's 1909 reviews of the college, had turned down a number of offers from other institutions over the years, including the University of Michigan, and had, by all accounts, grown attached to the University of Iowa and the Iowa City community. He had strong family ties to McGill, however, and when the chair in medicine earlier occupied by his father came open he returned to Montreal. Fred M. Smith, like Charles Rowan a graduate and faculty member of Rush Medical College, succeeded Howard with the enthusiastic backing of both Rowan and Lee Wallace Dean.

The creation of new departments and turnover among faculty and department heads presented the college the opportunity to gradually replace part-time clinical faculty with full-time members. Nonclinical departments such as anatomy and physiology had, of course, been on a full-time basis since the turn of the century or before, while the process of building a full-time clinical faculty was supposed to have begun with Campbell Howard, who was appointed in 1910 on the understanding that he would give his full time to teaching and treating clinical patients in University Hospital. However, like many other clinical heads, Howard also did considerable consulting work around the state. The first truly full-time department head was psychiatry's Samuel Orton, who came to Iowa in 1919 at a salary of $8,000 per year. Orton received permission from the board of education finance committee to treat "a few" private cases in 1920; the fees from those cases, however, went not to Orton but to Psychopathic Hospital's accounts, to be put toward laboratory research.[164] Some attempt to limit private practice was also made in 1921 when Frederick H. Falls replaced the retired William Whiteis as head of obstetrics and gynecology at a salary of $4,500. Falls was to give three-quarters of his time to his teaching and clinical duties and to have just two hours per day for private cases.[165]

Albert Byfield's resignation as head of pediatrics in 1924 provided the opportunity to put that department on a full-time basis. Philip C. Jeans replaced Byfield at $8,000 on the understanding that he was to be full-time, and, to cement the arrangement, the General Education Board gave $49,000 over five years to the pediatrics department to fund full-time salaries. As in the case of psychiatry, all fees from private cases were handled through the university's financial office and credited to the department's budget for research and other overhead costs.[166] In the late 1920s and through the 1930s, Jeans established a significant reputation for his own and his assistants' research.

In 1926, Rockefeller money also tipped the balance toward a full-time plan in the department of obstetrics and gynecology. Frederick H.

Falls, the three-quarter-time department head, left in February of that year and was succeeded by Everett D. Plass, who accepted a $9,000 salary and consented to serve full time. The General Education Board then agreed to give $58,000 over five years to ensure that all faculty in that department served on a full-time basis. Again, fees from private cases were to go to the university's financial office, but with the first $10,000 in such income each year to be retained by the university's general fund to pay the department faculty's malpractice insurance premiums.[167]

The full-time movement left department heads in the most remunerative clinical practice areas untouched, notably in internal medicine and the various surgical specialties. In those areas, the university simply could not, even with support from the Rockefeller philanthropies, pay the salaries required to make up for the loss of private practice income, which in some cases ran to $15,000 to $20,000 annually by 1920. Moreover, university officials recognized that to try to institute a full-time regime in those departments would likely provoke a full-scale faculty revolt and, under the best of circumstances, wholesale resignations. In 1922, a medical faculty committee argued in favor of continuing the part-time system, citing, for example, the usefulness of private patients in supplementing clinical instruction. Campbell Howard, who was a member of that committee, was an outspoken opponent of the full-time plan, echoing his mentor William Osler. "Wherever it has been tried," Howard charged, "it has been a distinct failure." Conceding the virtues of full time but aware also of Campbell Howard's intense feelings on the matter, Lee Wallace Dean recommended to President Jessup that "Dr. Howard be always exempt" from any efforts to broaden the scope of the full-time plan.[168] The same admonition applied to Howard's successor, Fred Smith, although Smith came to the university at a salary of $7,000 and with the initial expectation—at least on the part of some on the board of education and in the university administration—that he would be full-time. The 13 faculty members listed as part-time in 1927 still represented fully a quarter of the 52-member clinical faculty, and almost 15 percent of the college's total of 89 faculty. Only obstetrics and gynecology, pediatrics, and psychiatry were completely staffed by full-time faculty, while dermatology and orthopædics, both small in faculty numbers, had no full-time members.

Changes in the departmental structure of the college of medicine, the relationship of the hospital to the college, and the role of faculty as teachers and physicians—in short, the changing social and demographic structure of academic medicine—did not occur in a vacuum. Nor did academic medicine develop independently of scientific and technological developments in the medical sciences. On the one hand, the rise of the teaching hospital—surely the most potent institutional symbol of the new scientific medicine—was a mark of the eagerness with which the public greeted each medical scientific advance; indeed, the increasing commitment of public funds to the University of Iowa College of Medicine and to the University Hospitals was telling evidence of the public's growing faith in medical science. On the other hand, institutions like the University of Iowa Hospitals were constantly made and remade by the internal dynamic of medical science and technology that created an ever expanding frontier of knowledge regarding the human body's mechanical and biochemical functions.

The modern hospital featured an increasingly sophisticated and expensive array of technologies. The roentgenoscope, or x-ray machine, had been in common use at larger hospitals for two decades or more, greatly enhancing physicians' diagnostic abilities. By the 1920s, improvements in x-ray technology meant that technicians could better control the radiation dosage, to the betterment of themselves as well as patients, and the therapeutic uses of x-rays became the subject of experimentation. The electrocardiogram, or EKG, while still relatively cumbersome, also represented a great advance in diagnostic technique, allowing the recording of a heart's electrical potential and its analysis for irregularities. Hospital pathology labs became filled with other devices that improved diagnostic capabilities, including centrifuges for processing blood and urine samples, microtomes for slicing tissue samples, and improved microscopes.

Dazzling new machines and implements tended to obscure the more mundane improvements taken for granted in many hospitals. Electrification, for example, did more than put power saws and drills into the hands of surgeons and better lighting into operating rooms; it also made possible incubators for premature babies and machines for better cleaning and laundering. Likewise, electrification made possible around-the-clock operation of hospital services. Further, the standard adjustable hospital bed dates from this period; ambulances came into greater use; and telephones and internal communication systems were built into new hospitals. At the same time, improved dietetics required bigger, more specialized kitchens and food delivery systems.[169]

The institution that emerged from all of this change was bigger and obviously much more complex than earlier hospitals, with more highly specialized constituent parts. There were, of course, more and better-defined medical specialties: however, beyond that lay important changes in other healthcare professions and the emergence of new areas of technical expertise. Nursing, for example, became more specialized and more sophisticated in its methods and in its knowledge base, while technicians of various sorts filled the labs and shops of the modern hospital, and interns and residents shouldered an increasing share of responsibility for patient care. Finally, the management of such institutions became increasingly complex, calling upon a wide base of knowledge and of administrative and financial expertise that few physicians cared to master.

Planning the New Medical Complex

The nature of the new teaching hospital was evident in planning for the new hospital and medical laboratories buildings at the University of Iowa. The nationwide boom in hospital construction in the teens and twenties nurtured a substantial market for planners and builders of hospitals. The number of U.S. hospitals swelled from 4,000 at the turn of the century to nearly 8,000 by the mid-1920s, and the total value of hospital physical plant grew from $127 million in 1900 to $3 billion in 1922.[170] No sooner had the Iowa legislature approved its share of funding for the project in April 1923 than proposals from prominent architectural firms began arriving on President Jessup's desk. Architects in Chicago, Denver, Minneapolis, and New York—all specializing in hospital design—offered their services.[171]

However, the same firm that had handled all of the university's architectural plans since 1912—Proudfoot, Rawson, and Bird of Des Moines—already had the contract. The firm's previous contracts with the university had included two hospital additions, two nurses' dormitories, and the Isolation, Children's, and Psychopathic hospitals. Less than three months before the legislature approved funding for the hospitals project, the board of education had announced a five-year extension of the firm's agreement with the University of Iowa and had also approved an increase in the firm's fee from 2.5 percent to 3 percent of each project's cost.[172] Clark Souers, who had designed and supervised construction of several previous university projects, was assigned to coordinate this latest and grandest project and to draw up the plans, with Proudfoot's assurance that it would be responsive to input from university officials.

That input came from several sources. First, President Walter Jessup played an important role as liaison and broker among the various interested parties, and the board of education's building committee exercised broad oversight of the entire project. Meanwhile, Dean Lee Wallace Dean and the medical faculty designated a building committee of their own to address their specific needs and desires regarding allocation of space and resources in the new facilities. Bert Caldwell, superintendent of the hospital from 1923 to 1925, oversaw many details of the planning process, as did James Fisk, the university's buildings and grounds superintendent, and William Bates, the university secretary and chief financial officer. Together their voices produced as much cacophony as concert, and led, in the way of all such human enterprise, to significant conflict.

Almost immediately, various university officials began to survey other teaching hospitals and to seek advice from national experts on hospital construction and management. The board of education quickly approved a large delegation "to visit and inspect [the] best medical plants in the country so that the Board will have the latest and most reliable information" to inform its decisions.[173] President Jessup obtained from S. S. Goldwater, a renowned figure in hospital management, a pamphlet titled "Preliminary Survey for Hospital Design" outlining the factors to be considered in determining crucial features of a final plan. Jessup also made informal contacts with other experts such as C. C. Burlingame of New York's Presbyterian Hospital, Winford Smith of Johns Hopkins, and University of Michigan President M. L. Burton. Meanwhile, Superintendent Caldwell traveled extensively seeking ideas and models suited to the University of Iowa's needs.

Goldwater's pamphlet advised builders of hospitals to estimate the size of their facilities based on the amount of money they had to spend, on local health and disease patterns, and on the existence of other facilities nearby. It assigned second priority to the distribution of beds "socially and clinically" within the hospital, meaning by payment category—ward beds for indigent and clinical pay patients, and semiprivate and private rooms for private patients—and by clinical service. A third factor to consider, according to Goldwater, was whether or not the hospital maintained a link with a convalescent care facility, since "it matters a great deal whether the average stay of hospital patients is twelve days or twenty." Fourth, Goldwater advised that administrative offices should be close to medical records rooms and other services to ensure efficient operation. Finally, the hospital's teaching function should be incorporated into the entire design, especially with regard to operating rooms, labs, and amphitheaters.[174]

The medical faculty's building committee addressed some of these questions in a report issued in July 1923, a report incorporating much of the advice and information the committee had so far received, especially the model provided by the University of Michigan's new hospital. The presence of the 155-bed Children's Hospital that housed both the pediatric and orthopædic services and the 60-bed Psychopathic Hospital for psychiatric patients also answered some important questions in the planning phase. The faculty recommended building a 740-bed hospital, allotting about 15 percent of beds to private patients and more than half of all beds to the surgery and head specialty services, with the bulk of the remainder going to internal medicine and obstetrics and gynecology. The faculty's report also advised the architect on the allotment of space for departmental offices and laboratories, operating rooms, outpatient services, x-ray services, and nutrition.[175]

The first confrontation over hospital design and layout came in the summer of 1923 when Dean Lee Wallace Dean met with architect Clark Souers, who presented Dean with a "complete" set of plans for review. Dean was upset that he had not been consulted earlier and was particularly incensed that James Fisk, the superintendent of buildings and grounds, had told Souers to consult with hospital superintendent Bert Caldwell over specific questions. Given Dean's longstanding struggle to subordinate the hospital superintendent, his response was predictable. "I will not remain Dean and have the business of the college of medicine conducted as it is now being done," Dean wrote to Jessup in yet another of his many letters of resignation.[176] The storm of Dean's indignation passed, as it always did, but not before he had asserted once again his primacy as dean over the hospitals and, more particularly, over the superintendent.

Dean's outburst, by exposing tensions among the principal actors, may in fact have helped to trigger two positive developments. First, the board of education's hospital building subcommittee, realizing that it lacked the expertise to make final decisions regarding the highly specialized field of hospital construction, determined to hire an outside expert to review plans for the project.[177] Second, all of the local players—the special committees of the faculty and the board of education, Jessup, Dean, Fisk, and Caldwell—met to forge at least a rough consensus on the building plans. Those planning meetings, in early December 1923, led to a new design that reduced the general hospital to 650 beds (530 clinical ward beds and 120 private) and that envisioned a separate 120-bed convalescent home, a 100-bed isolation hospital, and, in the future, a 100-bed venereal disease hospital. Combined with the Children's and Psychopathic hospitals, the former of which would soon expand from 155 to 225 beds, the hospital complex would have a total capacity of 1,200 beds. The General Hospital would comprise four stories arranged in long pavilions, with a smaller fifth floor containing the operating suites; the whole would be built in Gothic style "surmounted by a dome, as a counterpoise to [the] dome in Old Capitol located directly east of it across the Iowa River."[178] Despite that accord, questions again arose in early 1924. In this instance the controversy surrounded Arthur Steindler's advice to Souers on design changes, insistent advice that bypassed not only the faculty's building committee but the rest of the medical faculty and the dean as well. The faculty resolved that problem by voting to notify Steindler that only the building committee and the hospital superintendent could alter the plans.[179]

As problems mounted with the design revisions, Jessup and Dean approached experts C. C. Burlingame, S. S. Goldwater, and Winford Smith about the possibility of their consulting on the project. Goldwater and Smith politely declined,[180] but Burlingame, though unable to consider the consultancy because of other commitments, offered to look the plans over.

Jessup and Dean traveled to New York to meet with him, and there all three men agreed that the project required a full-time, on-site consultant, at least in the short term.[181] Their search turned up Christopher G. Parnall, who was leaving as superintendent of the University of Michigan Hospital to take an equivalent post at Rochester General Hospital in Rochester, New York, a facility then under construction.[182] Between the two assignments Parnall would have two months in which to oversee the Iowa project, from April 15 to June 15, 1924. For this service he negotiated the astounding fee of $8,000—more than Superintendent Caldwell's $7,900 total annual compensation. Although not among the first rank of figures in hospital administration, Parnall had guided Michigan's new hospital to completion on time and under budget. As the Michigan hospital was very much like the one projected at Iowa, in size, cost, and purpose, his experience would prove invaluable to the latter institution.[183] Moreover, Parnall went on to a very respectable career as director of Rochester General and as a leader in the American Hospital Association.

Parnall learned of the difficulties thus far encountered, including the architects' uncertainties in designing a "state-of-the-art" medical center, via a long letter from Caldwell.[184] Before beginning his consultancy, Parnall met with the faculty's building committee and with Jessup, Dean, Fisk, Caldwell, and Souers to hammer out a clear understanding of the scope of his responsibilities. He agreed to serve in no capacity other than consultant and demanded a secretary and draftsman, access to all necessary information, and the full cooperation of local officials.[185] These arrangements did not prevent misunderstandings and disagreements over final details of the plans, but they did establish Parnall's authority to decide some of the larger design questions.

Parnall quickly recognized that existing plans would outstrip the available money, and he moved quickly to scale them back. "It was quite early apparent that reductions would have to be made in the demands of various heads of departments for space in both buildings," Parnall wrote in his final report. He termed as "slight" the alterations he proposed for the medical laboratories building, even though they amounted to a 23 percent reduction in space. His problems with the hospital plans were even more substantial. The revised design presented to him "was not one which embodied the best practices in construction of teaching hospitals today," Parnall wrote. The 22-bed wards were too big and 40 percent of the ward beds were in a north-facing wing, which presented problems for heating and ventilation. In addition, hospital corridors were too long in Parnall's view, and administrative and service functions were not suitably arranged. Parnall proposed redesigning the hospital almost from scratch. Instead of a four-story structure spread out in long pavilions, he urged a more compact six-story building arranged around two courtyards with the isolation hospital incorporated into the first floor. He also made generous provision of space for outpatient service, emergency surgery, and intern and resident accommodations. Parnall's plan, though it eliminated some of the more elaborate features of previous versions, still provided 700 total beds.[186]

Parnall's alteration of the medical laboratories building plans may have rankled members of the faculty, but there was no arguing with the ultimate limiting factor of cost.[187] Still, his changes to the hospital design sparked a nearly unanimous effort by the faculty to overrule the highly paid consultant. Superintendent Bert Caldwell wrote Charles Rowan outlining his objections to Parnall's plans, calling the isolation ward too big, the food and dietary service unworkable, and the space assigned to outpatient service and to resident and intern accommodations too large. Parnall had allowed for sixty residents and interns—nine of them women—which Caldwell said was far in excess of the customary ratio of one intern to twenty patients. Caldwell also doubted—rightly, as it turned out—whether the hospital "[would] ever have more than six female interns living in hospital at any one time."[188] With the faculty's backing, Caldwell proposed cutting to 55 the number of isolation beds and to fifty the accommodations for interns and residents. He also sought to reduce the space for emergency surgery and outpatient services.[189]

Oscar H. Plant, head of the department of public health and hygiene and also head of the faculty's hospital building committee, did not concur with the complaints about Parnall's redesign. Plant agreed with Parnall generally about the importance of keeping the hospital's teaching function "foremost in mind" when deciding how to allocate space within the new building and, more specifically, with Parnall's particular revisions to the plans. Plant wrote to Parnall, now in Rochester, to tell him of the faculty's action, thus inviting Parnall to reply directly to his critics. Parnall objected that outpatient service, for example, was "perhaps the most valuable part of the hospital for teaching," that superintendent Caldwell was "just wrong" about the food service, and that the number of hospital interns was increasing yearly.[190] The matter rested there for the time being, as construction of the medical laboratories building was under way and it was not necessary to settle the disagreements over the hospital immediately. In the end, perhaps what was most remarkable was not that there were disagreements over details of the plan but that the design process granted a hearing to so many interested voices.

Problems in Hospital Management Revisited

The revolving-door hospital superintendency became vacant again just as the Iowa legislature prepared to act on funding to match the Rockefeller grants for the new hospital. Arthur J. Lomas left in March 1923, after just 18 months as superintendent, to take a similar position at the Maryland State Hospital, and the opening at Iowa, given the likelihood of its acquiring a whole new medical plant, attracted many applicants. Among them were Robert Neff, administrator at Indiana University Hospitals; Christopher G. Parnall, who, as we have seen, later took the consultancy at Iowa on his way to the top post at Rochester General; and Bert Caldwell, a physician with substantial administrative experience—with Rockefeller medical campaigns in the Balkans and Mexico, as hospital administrator of the U.S. Canal Zone from 1905 to 1915, with the U.S. Surgeon General's office in Washington, D.C. during World War I, and with the U.S. Public Health Service.

Of the three, Neff was the most eager. Possessed of a peculiar attraction to Iowa, Neff had applied for the position when Lomas was hired, and told Jessup this time, "I continue to be interested in any opening you might have in your administrative departments."[191] Nonetheless, it was Caldwell who won the position.[192] According to William R. Boyd, the board's finance committee chairman, it did not take Caldwell long to antagonize hospital staff, especially the superintendent of nurses. He also offended the families of indigent patients, whom he equated with city slum-dwellers, and he so alienated the university secretary that William Bates practically refused to deal with him. In short, Boyd wrote, Caldwell was making enemies "faster than a regiment could patch things up."[193]

His personal bearing aside, Caldwell faced a situation in which his specific duties were fluid and subject to change according to the exigencies of the moment. Moreover, Dean Lee Wallace Dean continued to assert his executive authority over the hospital superintendent, delegating responsibilities as any executive would. For example, after a state prohibition agent mistakenly reported that the hospital pharmacy had dispensed five gallons of alcohol without recording its destination, Dean insisted that Caldwell take personal charge of alcohol and narcotics distribution in the hospital. Caldwell just as strongly refused, arguing that he could not possibly oversee such details and still carry out his responsibilities as superintendent. Caldwell managed to avoid alcohol duty, but that small victory did not increase the scope of his authority nor did it endear him to Dean.[194]

More galling to Caldwell was Dean's expectation that he take major responsibility for coordinating work on the new hospital while administering the old one. This Caldwell did throughout the early stages of planning, visiting other hospitals to gather information and participating in the meetings and activities of the faculty and executive building committees. By the spring of 1925, just as construction began on the medical laboratories building, Caldwell had apparently had enough of the give-and-take over space and beds and designs and contracts, and he loosed a tirade at President Jessup demanding certain information on equipment and personnel for the new hospital and giving the president a deadline of less than a day to respond. Caldwell followed with a request for a $1,500 raise, to $9,400, which the board of education promptly denied. Then, on June 1, Caldwell issued Dean an ultimatum to grant the raise and provide him with additional staff to help with his extra duties or to retain his current salary and allow him to stick to his original agreement, which was to superintend only the existing hospital's operations. With the ultimatum came a letter of resignation in the event that Dean refused to choose one or the other alternative.

While Dean seems not to have responded, the board of education accepted Caldwell's resignation on August 1, effective September 1, 1925.[195] Bert Caldwell, then, lasted for over two years at University Hospitals, the longest tenure of any superintendent since William R. Graham first held the job. Like those before him, Caldwell left under forced and unhappy circumstances. Caldwell, though, went on to success in his later career, serving as superintendent of the Tampa, Florida Municipal Hospital and executive secretary of the American Hospital Association beginning in December 1927.

In addition to the strains of planning and building the new medical campus, the rising tide of indigent patients and the costs associated with their care had become major complications in managing the University Hospitals in the 1920s. Owing perhaps to a persistent economic slump in the state's farm sector, Haskell-Klaus patients alone—that is, indigent adults—numbered almost 4,000 in fiscal year 1925 and accounted for more than 88,000 patient-days.[196] The expense of transporting indigent patients to Iowa City from every corner of the state was, by itself, a vexing problem, as transportation costs for Perkins and Haskell-Klaus cases totaled $204,000 in fiscal 1924, up from $156,000 the year before. Arthur Steindler's orthopædic service accounted for the largest single share of this expense, sometimes charging as much as $7,600 in a single month.[197]

As written, the indigent care laws committed the state to reimburse the university for all costs from its own general fund; thus, in theory, it was necessary for university officials only to fix an accurate per diem rate to charge to the state treasury. The same applied to transportation costs. As per diem charges rose, the state's total reimbursement for indigent care, including transportation, grew from $509,000 in 1920 to $957,994 in fiscal 1925. Concerned about state revenues in the midst of the agricultural depression and alarmed at the rising annual bill for indigent care, the 41st General Assembly in 1925 enacted a fixed rather than open-ended appropriation for treatment of Perkins and Haskell-Klaus patients, allotting $1.8 million, or $900,000 per year, for the biennium beginning July 1, 1925.

To be sure, indigent care costs had worried state and university officials alike since the Perkins Act was first enacted.[198] Disputes over indigent care costs sometimes reached an intense pitch, as when Bert Caldwell moved in late 1924 to confront the medical faculty for accepting patients as indigents and authorizing transportation for them even when they did not qualify for such aid. First, Caldwell approached Arthur Steindler, who had for some time been suspected of transporting his private patients at public expense, but Steindler replied that he was simply complying with the law mandating care for anyone certified by the state's county judges.[199] Notwithstanding Steindler's denial, Caldwell reported to the full medical faculty that many patients not eligible for free transportation were receiving it.[200]

The legislative appropriations cap set in place in 1925 gave the indigent care issue an urgency it had not had before. The $1.8 million appropriation for two years was less than the $2 million the board of education had sought when it became clear a limit would be enacted. In addition, although the legislature imposed a cap on spending, it did not restrict the number of patients who might be sent to University Hospitals under the law. Further complicating the issue, state senator Brede Wamstad of Osage, on behalf of physicians in Des Moines and rural Iowa, had proposed legislation to decentralize indigent care, raising the possibility that a large proportion of state patients would no longer enter University Hospitals at all.

Two million dollars, as it turned out, was about what indigent care cost the hospital for the two years from July 1, 1925, to June 30, 1927. When university officials recognized in November and December 1926 that indigent care costs would exceed the state appropriation, the board of education sought to have the state's budget director authorize additional spending up to $2 million, but the budget director released only an additional $50,000. As those funds were exhausted in April 1927 and the expected deficit surpassed first $50,000 and then $200,000, President Jessup and the board of education finance committee asked the state attorney general to review the hospital's legal situation regarding the funding cap. The attorney general ruled that the law did not provide for funding above the appropriation. The alternative, charging the final $238,000 deficit to funds for the next biennium, as Jessup noted, left only $1.6 million for indigent care for the next two years.[201]

In response to that fiscal crisis, the medical faculty, top university officials, and the board of education concurred in limiting service to state patients for the first time since enactment of the indigent care laws, taking 138 beds out of service by the end of 1928 and reducing the average daily census of state patients from 540 to 388. University Hospitals then began compiling a waiting list of indigent patients, which grew quickly from 109 in December 1927, to 253 by January 1928, and to 788 by April 1929.[202] Officials also implemented other cost-cutting measures, including layoffs of hospital employees and increased scrutiny of state and clinical patients' financial circumstances to ensure that only the truly indigent would receive treatment.[203] Those steps succeeded in keeping indigent care expenses close to the state appropriation, but at the cost of taking beds out of service and building up a backlog of patients waiting for treatment.

The Lee Wallace Dean Affair

In the spring of 1927, in the midst of construction of the new hospital and the indigent care crisis, a storm of quite a different sort broke over the college of medicine and the University Hospitals. The first signs of trouble were the May 4 resignations of Charles J. Rowan, head of surgery, Frank J. Rohner, acting head of internal medicine, and Jesse L. McElroy, who had succeeded Bert Caldwell as hospital superintendent in 1925. Initial press reports attributed the resignations of Rowan and Rohner to "disagreement with the administration policy of Dean L. W. Dean," although Rowan's ill health was also said to be a factor in his decision.[204] No sooner had rumors of the resignations been confirmed than the Johnson County Medical Society—with many medical faculty among its members—resolved "to notify President Jessup and the board of education, that the [society] stands for the ideals of Doctors Rowan and Rohner and does not endorse the present administrative policy of the college of medicine," although with no hint of what the society found objectionable about college policy.[205]

As the drama unfolded over the next several weeks, attracting statewide attention by the press and prompting an investigation by the board of education, factional lines that had developed within the college of medicine over a period of years became visible. At bottom, the episode demonstrated that Dean Lee Wallace Dean, though not without his supporters, had lost the confidence of most of the senior medical faculty, local physicians, and even the school's students. In the end, six faculty, including Dean, left the college as a direct result of the dispute, and several more chose to tender their resignations ostensibly for other reasons, leaving the college without a dean, a nursing superintendent, or a hospital superintendent. Surgery, otolaryngology, and psychiatry lost their department heads; internal medicine lost two respected faculty members; and the entire staff of anesthetists walked out early on contracts that were about to expire.

Charles Rowan led the anti–Dean faction, declaring in his resignation letter, "The way in which affairs of the college of medicine are now being administered has led me to the conclusion that the school will deteriorate to [a] considerable extent in the near future and under these circumstances, I do not feel that my continued presence will accomplish any good." Rohner, who had joined the internal medicine department in 1915, was far more blunt. "I have resigned," he wrote, "because I have no confidence in, or respect for the present head of the medical school."[206] It took a bit longer to articulate the specific issues that gave rise to the general dissatisfaction reflected in those early statements, but, by the end of May, the medical faculty had hammered out a list of actions requested of President Walter Jessup.

Several points bore directly on administrative policies of the college. First, the faculty asked Jessup not to appoint a new dean "who does not have the full confidence of the medical faculty and who has not been approved for the position by the medical faculty" and that Jessup "make no more appointments to faculty positions without the approval of the faculty." Second, the faculty requested that in matters of the college budget, educational standards, and administrative policies, "you will place at the disposal of the faculty all pertinent information available to you in order that its deliberations and recommendations be not misguided as in the past by partial or misleading information." Further, on those occasions when their recommendations were overruled, the faculty requested that they "be notified in writing of the executive authority responsible for such refusal and the reason therefor." Third, the faculty requested "that in the future no pressure shall be brought to bear on the faculty to relax its rules or standards of scholarship in favor of any individual because of political affiliations or personal favoritism" and that "the faculty shall not . . . be under duress to obscure or divert attention from practices within the university which it considers as abuses." Finally, the faculty asked Jessup to facilitate more equal relations between the college of medicine, "including its hospitals," and other administrative units of the university, "notably the department of grounds and buildings and the purchasing department."[207]

The issues raised by the medical faculty demonstrated a general feeling of alienation from decision- and policy-making authority in the college, following a decade and more of Lee Wallace Dean's authoritarian rule. Faculty members argued that they had not been properly consulted in the making of appointments and that the administration's consultation on other matters had been insincere and self-serving. In addition, individual faculty members used terms such as "high-handed" to describe Dean's "one-man" rule over the medical college when they appeared before the board of education's four-member investigating committee.[208] Regarding the issue of favoritism, one case involved Joe Mayo, son of the famous Charles Mayo, who in 1925 had complained of unfair treatment after his grades and school performance at Iowa had slipped. Dean's inquiries into the matter, directed to his colleagues, did not appear disinterested, as he and the young Mayo had socialized and gone on fishing trips together.[209] As to the elevated position of the buildings and grounds superintendent, James Fisk, and the university secretary, William Bates, Rowan had remarked on this at least as early as 1918 in connection with William Graham's unfortunate experience as hospital superintendent. Moreover, John F. Bresnahan, the consultant hired in 1919 to review policies and organization of the hospital, had explicitly urged that authority over certain areas be vested in the hospital superintendent, areas that instead remained in the hands of Fisk and Bates.

Two days after the initial resignations, the board of education, at Jessup's urging, accepted Dean's resignation as dean. As he had submitted at least half a dozen resignation letters over the years, the board had only to cite the most recent one, dating from the previous winter. Dean publicly expressed satisfaction at being relieved of his administrative burdens, stating he was "convinced that it is for the good of the college of medicine that a change be made in the administration."[210] For the moment, Dean stayed on as chief of head specialties, but the pressure did not ease. The Johnson County Medical Society took its resolution to the board of education and moved to organize the school's alumni throughout the state. Returning to Iowa City from vacation, Wesley E. Gatewood of internal medicine, who had been an early test of Dean's determination to deny private practice privileges to junior faculty, resigned with a fierce letter condemning Dean. Also, 400 medical students, in an impressive display of support for Rowan, marched in ranks of four to his home to ask him to reconsider his resignation. Most damaging, however, was the board of education investigation that began on May 11 behind closed doors in Old Capitol, during the course of which various department heads predicted even more resignations in the event that Dean remained affiliated with the college of medicine in any capacity.[211]

The combination of pressures finally forced Dean's resignation from the faculty. In a letter addressed to President Jessup but distributed to the local press as well, Dean touched off another round of angry countercharges with the implication that the entire dispute centered on the question of private practice in University Hospitals. Declaring private practice to be the cause of most complaints about the hospital from around the state, Dean implied that other doctors were turning away state patients in order to hold beds for private patients. Unlikely though it may have seemed, he portrayed himself as opposed to any private practice whatsoever at University Hospitals and called not only for an end to outside remuneration for faculty doctors but also for a change in state policy to allow for local hospitalization of indigent patients, who, he said, overburdened the university facilities and hampered both teaching and research.[212]

The medical faculty responded to Dean's fulminations with charges of hypocrisy, pointing out that Dean carried out a busy private practice throughout his career at the university, that his own department had averaged 19 empty beds per day during the period when the indigent waiting list had first reached alarming proportions, and that Dean had asked for and received an increased allotment of private beds in the new hospital. The faculty claimed that Dean's letter brought out "in unmistakable terms the insincerity and duplicity which was the cause of lack of respect for and confidence in Dr. Dean and which resulted in the present crisis in the affairs of the Medical School." The faculty also noted that Dean had originally condemned the idea of decentralized care for the indigent on the ground that it would ruin the college of medicine. In closing, the faculty unanimously declared, "None of the points discussed in Dr. Dean's letter are issues in the current crisis." "This [crisis] has arisen," they asserted, "through distrust of the integrity of the Dean and of the methods of administration of the college of medicine and we feel that his letter is an effort on the part of a discredited man to embar[r]ass further and to disrupt the Medical School."[213]

While the faculty, too, was guilty of a degree of disingenuousness in some of its arguments, still the broad base of opposition to Dean—and to any future role for him in the college—was damning in itself. And if, as Dean implied, private practice was a factor in the faculty's uprising, still the faculty was able to press a strong case against him based on years of autocratic administration and favoritism without having to resort to arguments about the apportionment of private beds or cases. By the end of May, Dean had lost all credibility as dean and department head. The board of education, in concluding its investigation and seeking to put an end to the dispute, approved Dean's resignation from the faculty along with the resignations of all of the others concerned.[214] On the subject of the deanship, the board of education concurred with its investigating committee that a new dean should serve primarily in an administrative capacity and not be allowed the distraction of private clinical practice. Also, the board argued that the dean should have charge of the University Hospitals.[215]

For President Jessup, the whole affair was troubling not only because of the turmoil it caused in his university and because of its implications for his leadership, but also because of his close personal friendship with Dean. Only the barest hints of Jessup's responsibility for policies in the college of medicine had surfaced during the attacks on Dean, but the faculty's demand to be consulted regarding appointment of a new dean and on other matters was a direct challenge to the president's prerogatives. Clearly, for officials in the university administration and for members of the board of education, the implications of the faculty revolt overshadowed the more practical problem of filling the several now vacant offices in the college of medicine and the hospitals.

In the wake of the explosion, William R. Boyd, long time board official and frequent spokesman, went to New York to get advice from the Rockefeller people on how best to control the damage. With its $2.25 million investment at stake and the new hospital already under construction,

Rockefeller officials were eager to help Iowa secure a top-flight executive for its vacant deanship. Judging from Boyd's telegrams to Jessup, they were also keen on putting an end to any move by the faculty to gain a greater say in administrative policy. On June 9, after several days of consultation with Abraham Flexner and others, Boyd wired, "Interview most satisfactory on all points—Says to grant demands would spell ruin—Your principles endorsed and says stand pat." The following day's message read, "Confidential— Am receiving most sympathetic and helpful suggestions—Am told this is only a renewal of old fight to block real modern medical education— Faculty control impossible—They would refuse to have hands tied on anything—Suggest what would seem to be ideal dean and superintendent of hospital."[216]

Boyd's messages raise a number of troubling questions regarding the relationship between the Rockefeller philanthropies and the University of Iowa. First, they appeared to contradict repeated assertions—heard most often in the 1923 campaign to win legislative approval of matching funds for the new hospitals complex—that the Rockefeller Foundation and General Education Board attached no strings to their financial support and sought no influence over local decisions. Indeed, when the University of Wisconsin refused a Rockefeller gift similar to that given Iowa, Boyd himself wrote Wisconsin's governing board a long and emphatic denial of any improper Rockefeller influence at his university.[217]

Second, the hard line that Abraham Flexner urged upon Jessup against the medical faculty and the simplistic equation of anti-Dean with anti-reform sentiment, displayed a disturbing distrust of open decision-making processes. Perhaps that attitude owed something to the fact that most of the institutions supported by the Rockefeller philanthropies were private ones, not public; perhaps, too, it was a measure of the times, when standards of accountability for executives were far different than they are today. Nonetheless, the advice Boyd forwarded to Jessup from New York suggested a not very subtle hostility toward the movement for intrainstitutional consensus, given that the faculty had demanded only a say in the important decisions affecting the college of medicine and given also that the issues in dispute in the spring of 1927 surfaced repeatedly in the next several decades. In any event, Boyd's June 10 telegram left no doubt that the need of an "ideal" executive as dean had as much to do with short-circuiting faculty participation in the college's administrative affairs as with giving the school a capable and worthy leader. The capable and worthy leader who three months later was appointed to the deanship carried, perhaps unknowingly, the burden of this baser motivation, a burden that extended to his successors as well, who proved far less adept in managing affairs.

President Jessup had already formulated his response to the faculty by the time Boyd's telegrams began arriving; therefore, the advice from

Rockefeller officials, chiefly Abraham Flexner, may not have had any impact on Jessup's position. At the least, Jessup's inclinations paralleled the advice from New York, conceding nothing but the promise to consult with the faculty before recommending a new dean and other faculty members. That much the board of education had already directed Jessup to do anyway. Jessup's hard-line stance led to the last spasm of the crisis, the resignation of Psychopathic Hospital director Samuel T. Orton who had been an active participant in the anti-Dean faction.[218] "The Orton matter they are willing to leave to you," Boyd telegrammed from New York, "but wish him to have laboratory facilities to complete his work" on a Rockefeller-funded research project.[219]

The events of May and June 1927, while the product of tensions accumulated over the years in a single institution, had apparent parallels elsewhere. Iowa State Board of Education president George T. Baker, in correspondence with an unnamed physician, remarked that such "blowups" were not unknown in other medical schools. "Notable examples are to be found in Pennsylvania, Michigan, Illinois and elsewhere," Baker wrote. "It is rumored that others are now pending."[220] Undoubtedly, some of the issues the Dean imbroglio brought to light carried wider significance, for example, the thorny question of private practice by clinical faculty, the problem of the proper relationship between the teaching hospital and the medical college, the strained relationship between the medical school and the state's physicians, and the emergence of a more hierarchical authority structure in the college of medicine.

For the University Hospitals, Dean Lee Wallace Dean was in some ways the embodiment of forces restraining its tendencies toward independence. In the face of explicit and expert advice regarding the proper scope of the hospital superintendent's authority, Dean acted at crucial moments to weaken the superintendent's position. Dean, it appears, viewed the University Hospitals largely as sources of clinical cases for teaching and, possibly, as venues for research. Despite his contrary protests in 1927, Dean also viewed private practice conducted in the hospitals as a right of senior faculty. The result was an institution uncertain of its identity and unable to define itself. Did the hospitals exist mainly to provide "clinical material" for undergraduate medical education and to augment faculty salaries, or to provide medical services to the state's poor? What place should private practice have in the hospital, and what part should the hospital play in the incipient medical research mission? Where did the hospital stand in relation to the college of medicine and the University of Iowa?

In the summer of 1927, with the college of medicine operating under the executive authority of junior dean John T. McClintock and the hospital under a faculty committee chaired by obstetrics and gynecology head Everett D. Plass, the most urgent priority, at least for the university administration, lay in finding a new dean. The search quickly centered on Henry S. Houghton, director of the Peking Union Medical College in Beijing, China. Peking Union was founded and fostered by the Rockefeller organization, and Houghton had served as its acting director for two years before assuming the permanent directorship in 1920. Flexner, who thought Houghton the right man for Iowa, worked both ends of the deal to bring them together, urging Iowa officials to offer the deanship to him and urging Houghton to accept the position sight unseen.[221] The college of medicine department heads approved of Houghton, with the exception of urology head Nathaniel G. Alcock and the new head of surgery, Howard L. Beye, who feared "possible criticism of Rockefeller domination" of the school.[222]

Houghton was favorably disposed toward the University of Iowa but was reluctant to leave Peking Union, and at one point he regretfully declined the university's offer. Eventually, however, Houghton changed his mind after continued entreaties from university officials and from Abraham Flexner, and with the understanding that he could delay his starting date to February 1928 in order to wrap up his affairs in China. Henry Houghton was appointed to serve as executive of both the college of medicine and University Hospitals, his $12,000 salary to be divided between them in the proportion of three-to-one.[223] Just as important, the new dean, unlike his predecessors, would have no clinical duties.

Before even beginning his appointment, Houghton submitted recommendations to the board of education regarding the near emergency in indigent care finances. One of those recommendations was the "prompt appointment of an expert hospital administrator [which] will almost certainly result in the gradual lowering of internal costs." That person was Robert E. Neff, the Indiana University Hospitals administrator twice passed over for the Iowa superintendency. Neff began work in late March 1928 at a salary of $7,500 per year.[224]

Meanwhile, construction of the new General Hospital, begun in early 1927, moved into its final phases a bit behind schedule and in some danger of going over budget. The general contractor, J. & W. A. Elliott Company of Minneapolis, petitioned the board of education in November 1927 for a one-month extension of its contract to July 1, 1928. Of more concern, however, was President Jessup's report that changes ordered by the faculty but not approved by the board of education would push the project $23,000 over budget. The board ordered the faculty to rein in its wants and assigned buildings and grounds superintendent Fisk to evaluate all of the changes to the original contract with an eye to eliminating extras and cutting the final building cost. Fisk later gained the board's authorization to "undertake and complete the work omitted from the contracts with the idea that substantial savings can be made."[225]

By early June 1928, finishing work was finally underway including the installation of laboratory and kitchen equipment and heating, plumbing, and electrical services. The architectural firm of Proudfoot, Rawson & Souers—with Clark Souers now a partner—certified completion of the general contractor's work on August 15, 1928, just ten weeks after the original due date. Equipping and furnishing the new building would take many more weeks, but it would be essentially ready for occupancy by the time of the official dedication in mid-November.[226]

The dedication was a three-day gala of formal dinners and receptions, a ball at the Iowa Memorial Union, and attendence at the Iowa-Wisconsin football game. It was also a ceremonial occasion of solemn orations, a convocation of visiting officials and dignitaries, and numerous addresses and presentations by prominent clinicians. In addition to President Jessup, Iowa Governor John Hammill, and members of the board of education, delegates from around the country included James B. Herrick of the University of Chicago, Hugh Cabot of the University of Michigan, G. Canby Robinson of Cornell University, and George H. Whipple of the University of Rochester. Also in attendance were such luminaries as William J. Mayo and Rockefeller Foundation President George E. Vincent. The event served as a homecoming for various former Iowa faculty as well. Campbell P. Howard, for example, came back to conduct a medical clinic, as did Charles J. Rowan, and Walter Bierring returned representing the National Board of Medical Examiners. Noteworthy by their absence were Lee Wallace Dean and the man perhaps most responsible for the new medical complex, Abraham Flexner.

While the celebration centered on the new Medical Laboratories Building and General Hospital, the project had also included a substantial addition and other improvements to Children's Hospital, a large addition to the Westlawn nurses' residence, and almost $900,000 for a new university heating and power plant, about $500,000 of which came from Rockefeller funding and state matching money.[227] But the medical facilities were the crowning glory. The 770-bed hospital conformed generally to the plan laid out by consultant Christopher Parnall five years before, taller and more compact than originally proposed, its separate wings arranged around a main courtyard, and its tallest section rising seven stories with a lofty view of Old Capitol and the central university campus three quarters of a mile to the east across the Iowa River.

Built of red brick with Bedford limestone trim in what has been called the English renaissance architectural style, the General Hospital and Medical Laboratories Building thus complemented the Children's and Psychopathic Hospitals and gave a remarkable unity to the new medical campus. But it was the hospital's Gothic tower, rising from the main courtyard, that commanded the most attention and immediately became the symbol of the institution. Designed by Amos B. Emery, who had studied architecture at the Sorbonne in Paris and had traveled Europe sketching its cathedrals before returning to Des Moines following his service in World War I, the tower featured graceful, ornamented spires atop its seven-story structure. The complex's one major extravagance, the tower was also the emblem of its pride.

Conclusion

The University of Iowa Hospital that opened in the winter of 1898 was, by standards current even two decades later, a grossly inadequate if not shabby facility. Nonetheless, in its time and place, the original University Hospital served an important need for the college of medicine and for the surrounding community. Moreover, it was surely the best hospital facility to be found between Chicago and Des Moines, and, perhaps most important of all, its renovation and eventual reconstruction ensured the survival of the nascent academic medical center in the troubled wake of Abraham Flexner's critical report. By 1910, a medical school could not hope to survive without access to a hospital for clinical teaching, and the diligence of Charles A. Schaeffer in pursuit of his dream of a modern university-owned hospital was, at the very least, a fortunate turn of events.

That the hospital encountered difficulties is perhaps no surprise; after all, medical education, medical practice, and hospital management itself were in a state of flux in the early twentieth century. Nonetheless, despite intermittent financial losses, poor staffing, and shaky organization, the hospital saw a steady increase in patient service in its first decade, and this, in turn, made possible significant growth in the college of medicine. As part of the post-Flexner reforms, the University Hospital's next phase included the building of new wings, the formulation of new rules regarding medical practice within its walls, and, most strikingly, the assumption of a major new responsibility for statewide indigent care. At the same time, innovations in faculty recruitment, medical education, and patient care—made possible in part by the growth of the hospital—carried the college of medicine to a new level of respectability. Abraham Flexner's tireless efforts to win Rockefeller monies in support of a new medical complex in the 1920s certainly attest to its developing reputation.

As is often the case, however, remarkable growth engendered problems and conflict that, in some degree, obscured the considerable accomplishments of the second and third decades of the century. For example, the substantial increase in patient admissions—for all of its benefit to the college of medicine, the hospital, and the state of Iowa—forced a rapid and unmanageable growth in physical facilities and staff, taxed the hospital's financial resources, and prompted a difficult re-examination of the conduct of indigent care. Meanwhile, in an era that saw the emergence of the ideal of a strong hospital superintendent, the divided control over the University Hospital hindered the kind of coordinated response that events seemed to demand. Ultimately, related and overlapping stresses in both the hospital and the college of medicine merged in a serious administrative crisis in 1927.

Oddly enough, that crisis broke just as the new General Hospital and Medical Laboratories, with outlying Children's and Psychopathic Hospitals and Westlawn nurses' dormitory, were rising on the west side of the Iowa River, symbols of a new pride and confidence in the University of Iowa academic medical center. Moreover, the underlying issues in that crisis— notably private practice in the University Hospital, the relationship of the hospital to the college of medicine, and the distribution of authority in the college—were only temporarily submerged in the university administration's desperate scramble to restore stability. As the following chapters illustrate, those issues reappeared in the decades ahead, growing more and more insistent with the passage of time.

Notes

1. "Rules and Regulations for the Governance of the University Hospital," adopted by the Board of Regents, June 10, 1897, Record Group 27, File 1, "Hospital Rules," University of Iowa Archives.

2. "University Hospital Rules, 1907," Record Group 27, File 1, "Hospital Rules," University of Iowa Archives.

3. Board of Regents Minutes, June 8, 1898, University of Iowa Archives.

4. Board of Regents Minutes, July 18, 1900, University of Iowa Archives.

5. Board of Regents Minutes, June 10, 1901, University of Iowa Archives.

6. Treasurer's Report to Board of Regents and Legislature, 1900, University of Iowa Archives.

7. Secretary's reports to board of regents, "University Hospital Accounts," 1899, 1901, 1903, 1905, University of Iowa Archives.

8. Board of Education Biennial Report, 1910, pp. 85–88, presents the story on the millage, leaving the impression that any heated discussion of the matter had long since cooled.

9. For figures on admissions and finance in 1903 and 1904, see Board of Regents Finance Committee, Reports of the Secretary–University Hospital Accounts, 1904, University of Iowa Archives. For admissions figures and finance in 1909 and 1910, see Board of Education Biennial Report, 1910, University of Iowa Archives.

10. A. Flexner to G. E. MacLean, April 22, 1909, File 19-5, G. E. MacLean Papers, University of Iowa Archives.

11. Stow Persons, "The Flexner Investigation of the University of Iowa Medical School," *Annals of Iowa* 48 (Summer/Fall 1986): 276.

12. For examples of the literature, see Robert P. Hudson, "Abraham Flexner in Perspective: American Medical Education 1865–1910," in *Sickness & Health in America*, Judith W. Leavitt and Ronald L. Numbers, eds. (Madison: University of Wisconsin Press, 1978), p. 109. Also, Howard S. Berliner,

"New Light on the Flexner Report: Notes on the AMA–Carnegie Foundation Background," *Bulletin of the History of Medicine* 51 (1977): 603–609.

13. See chapter 2 of Flexner's *Medical Education in the United States and Canada*, "The Proper Basis of Medical Education," pp. 20–27.

14. Abraham Flexner, "State University of Iowa Medical Department," File 19-6, G. E. MacLean Papers, University of Iowa Archives. See also Stow Persons, *The University of Iowa in the Twentieth Century*, pp. 277–278.

15. Flexner's reports on these medical schools can be found in *Medical Education in the United States and Canada*, pp. 259–261.

16. A. Flexner to G. E. MacLean, April 25, 1909, File 19-5, G. E. MacLean Papers, University of Iowa Archives.

17. A. Flexner to G. E. MacLean, May 24, 1909, File 19-5, G. E. MacLean Papers, University of Iowa Archives.

18. This and the following Flexner comments are from A. Flexner, "State University of Iowa Medical Department."

19. See, for example, A. Flexner to J. H. Trewin, November 9, 1909, File 19-6, G. E. MacLean Papers, University of Iowa Archives.

20. Abraham Flexner, *Medical Education in the United States and Canada*, pp. 224–5. For physician-population ratio, see Biennial Report of the Iowa State Board of Health, 1915, p. 77.

21. Flexner was so characterized by Hudson, "Abraham Flexner in Perspective: American Medical Education 1865–1910," p. 108.

22. W. Jepson to G. E. MacLean, July 19, 1909, File 19-6, G. E. MacLean Papers, University of Iowa Archives.

23. See, for example, E. W. Rockwood to G. E. MacLean, July 8, 1909, File 19-6, G. E. MacLean Papers, University of Iowa Archives.

24. W. L. Bierring to G. E. MacLean, July 9, 1909, File 19-6, G. E. MacLean Papers, University of Iowa Archives.

25. From W. R. Boyd's own "A Brief History of the College of Medicine of Iowa State University [sic]," appearing as an appendix in the Carl Cone history of the college.

26. R. H. Whitehead to H. S. Pritchett, November 7, 1909, File 19-6, G. E. MacLean Papers, University of Iowa Archives.

27. A. Flexner to J. H. Trewin, November 8, 1909, File 19-6, G. E. MacLean Papers, University of Iowa Archives.

28. See Lee Anderson and Lewis January, "Walter Bierring and the Flexner Revolution at the University of Iowa College of Medicine," *The Pharos* (Winter 1992): 9–12.

29. Ibid., 11.

30. Persons, *The University of Iowa in the Twentieth Century*, p. 286.

31. This controversy played out in a series of correspondence: C. J. Rowan to J. W. Bowman, September 30, 1913; Bowman to W. W. Pearson, October 1, 1913; Pearson to Bowman, October 4, 1913; L. W. Littig to Bowman, October 8, 1913; Bowman to J. H. Trewin, October 6, 1913; Trewin to Bowman, October 8, 1913; Bowman to Trewin, October 9, 1913; Trewin to Bowman, October 10, 1913; Bowman to Trewin, October 11, 1913; Trewin to Bowman, October 17, 1913; Bowman to Trewin, October 20, 1913; Trewin to Bowman, October 25, 1913; Trewin to Bowman, November 22, 1913, Series 1, File 7, "Medical Miscellaneous," University of Iowa Archives.

32. Flexner, *Medical Education in the United States and Canada*, pp. 207–208.

33. L. W. Dean to T. H. Macbride, November 23, 1914, File 6, 1914, T. H. Macbride Papers, University of Iowa Archives.

34. For figures on college of medicine budgets, see relevant Board of Education Biennial Reports; for staff numbers, see university catalogs.

35. Flexner, *Medical Education in the United States and Canada*, p. 144.

36. C. W. McClure to T. H. Macbride, May 20, 1915, File 13, 1915, T. H. Macbride Papers, University of Iowa Archives.

37. Joseph A. Buckwalter, "Arthur Steindler: Founder of Iowa Orthopædics," *Iowa Orthopædic Journal* 1 (1979): 5–12.

38. "Report on Medical Education in Iowa," *Journal of the Iowa State Medical Society* 4 (July 15, 1914): 79.

39. First-hand testimony comes from James Young, Oral Interview with Richard Caplan, September 25, 1985, University of Iowa Department of Internal Medicine Archives.

40. See *Acts of the 42nd General Assembly* (1927), chapter 51, and the revised Code of Iowa, 1927, Section 2540.

41. *Journal of the American Medical Association* 84 (March 28, 1925): 972.

42. Boyd's "Brief History of the Development of the College of Medicine" contains the trite account, pp. 6–8. Writing in the early 1930s at a time when the indigent care laws were under attack in the Iowa legislature, Boyd may have intended his story to emphasize the statutes' service mission to the state as opposed to their utilitarian function of supplying patients for teaching at University Hospitals.

43. See *Acts of the 31st General Assembly* (1905), chapter 120, section 10; also, the Biennial Report of the Iowa State Board of Health (1904–1906), p. 227.

44. The statement is taken from a 1921 review of the progress made toward these original goals, written into the Iowa State Board of Education Minutes, May 26–27, 1921, and compiled by the Rockefeller Foundation. Rockefeller Foundation Archives, Record Group 1.1, "Projects," Series 218A, "Iowa," Box 1, Folder 4.

45. See Medical Faculty Meeting Minutes, October 26, 1914, Record Group 15, University of Iowa Archives; see also W. R. Boyd to T. H. Macbride, "Memo relative to Hospital of the Medical College of The University of Michigan," c. October 1914, File 2, Folder 14, 1914, T. H. Macbride Papers, University of Iowa Archives.

46. See J. H. Trewin to L. W. Dean, December 15, 1914, File 6, 1914, T. H. Macbride Papers; also, Macbride to Gov. George Clarke, December 15, 1914; Macbride to Sen. Eli Perkins, December 15, 1914; and Perkins to Macbride, December 23, 1914, File 6, 1914, Folder 189, "State Relations," University of Iowa Archives.

47. See the Iowa Senate and House Journals for 1915; the Iowa Code of 1913, 1915, and 1919, pp. 720–27, and the supplement to the Iowa Code of 1915, pp. 23–28. Sticklers for precision will note that the bill was originally enacted as an addition to the code chapter pertaining to juvenile courts. When the code was subsequently reorganized, the Perkins Act, along with the Haskell-Klaus Act extending Perkins benefits to indigent adults, was placed in the code section relating to education. By this time (1919) the state attorney general had also clarified the matter of legal custody of children receiving treatment under the law, ruling that they were wards of University Hospital rather than of their respective district courts.

48. Quotations from *Code of Iowa, 1915*, pp. 23–28.

49. See the Iowa Senate and House Journals for the legislative session of 1919. The bill appeared in the House as HF 232 and in the Senate as SF 208.

50. "A Journey Through the State University of Iowa Hospitals," February 1935, Records Group 27, University of Iowa Archives.

51. Board of Education Minutes, August 23, 1915, University of Iowa Archives.

52. Board of Education Minutes, December 22, 1915, University of Iowa Archives. Ward rate obtained from University Hospital Annual Report, fiscal year 1914, University of Iowa Archives.

53. Census figures from college of medicine and hospital budgets, Annual File 1917–18, Folder 1, W. A. Jessup Papers, University of Iowa Archives.

54. See, for example, Board of Regents Minutes, February 17, 1909, University of Iowa Archives.

55. A detailed description of the Children's Hospital then being constructed is contained in the hospital's combined Annual Reports for fiscal years 1916–1917, published in May 1918, University of Iowa Archives. That report is, however, somewhat vague about the actual number of beds planned for each wing.

56. Board of Education Minutes, December 30, 1913, University of Iowa Archives.

57. *Iowa City Daily Press*, August 2, 1911.

58. Ibid.

59. The Bowman-Fairchild correspondence appeared in *Journal of the Iowa State Medical Society* 1 (September 15, 1911): 276–278.

60. A. D. Bevan to T. H. Macbride, April 6, 1914, File 6, 1914, T. H. Macbride Papers, University of Iowa Archives.

61. File 6, Folder "Annual Reports 1913," J. G. Bowman Papers, University of Iowa Archives.

62. J. G. Bowman to H. M. Eicher, March 7, 1914, File 7, Folder 25; Eicher to Bowman, March 9, 1914, File 5, Folder 1, J. G. Bowman Papers, University of Iowa Archives.

63. See L. W. Dean to G. T. Baker, January 6, 1915; Dean to Baker, January 11, 1915, File 8, Folder 6A, 1915, T. H. Macbride Papers, University of Iowa Archives.

64. L. W. Dean to G. T. Baker, December 31, 1914, and January 6, 1915, File 8, Folder 6A, 1915, T. H. Macbride Papers, University of Iowa Archives. In the earlier correspondence, Dean told Baker he "can't explain" the drop in patient numbers or outside referrals, perhaps indicating that he did not want to speculate as to the role of the fee-splitting rule in causing the decline.

65. Board of Education Minutes, June 15, 1915, University of Iowa Archives.

66. In late 1914, Dean undertook a survey similar to that of Bowman two years earlier, but sent it to a larger sample including all A-plus and A medical schools. Most of the leading institutions had closed staffs, except for those affiliated with public hospitals not under their direct control. Most, with the notable exception of the University of Michigan, also allowed private patients in their hospitals. See File 5, Folder 115, T. H. Macbride Papers, University of Iowa Archives.

67. See J. G. Bowman to H. M. Eicher, March 7, 1914, File 7, Folder 25, J. G. Bowman Papers, University of Iowa Archives.

68. L. W. Dean to T. H. Macbride, December 19, 1914, File 1, Folder 6, 1914, T. H. Macbride Papers, University of Iowa Archives.

69. Iowa State Board of Education Biennial Report, 1912, p. 165.

70. Creelman's demand is referred to in a letter from L. W. Dean to T. H. Macbride, November 21, 1914, File 1, Folder 6, 1914, T. H. Macbride papers, University of Iowa Archives.

71. See, for example, John A. Hornsby, *The Modern Hospital: Its Inspiration, Its Architecture, Its Equipment, and Its Operation* (Philadelphia: W. B. Saunders, 1913); Albert S. Ochner and Meyer Sturm, *Organization, Construction, and Management of Hospitals* (Chicago: American Hospital Association, 1910); Dorothy Aikens, *Hospital Management* (Philadelphia: W. B. Saunders, 1911). For a historical overview, see Robert Vogel, "Managing Medicine: Creating a Profession of Hospital Administration in the United States, 1895–1915," in Lindsay Granshaw and Roy Porter, eds., *The Hospital in History* (New York: Routledge, 1989), pp. 243–260.

72. J. A. Hornsby to J. Creelman, November 23, 1914, and W. H. Smith to C. P. Howard, December 10, 1914; both included in L. W. Dean to T. H. Macbride, December 19, 1914, File 1, Folder 6, 1914, T. H. Macbride Papers, University of Iowa Archives.

73. Board of Education Minutes, November 5, 1914, University of Iowa Archives.

74. L. W. Dean to J. T. Baker, December 31, 1914, File 8, Folder 6A, 1915, T. H. Macbride Papers, University of Iowa Archives.

75. Board of Education Finance Committee Minutes, September 20, 1915, University of Iowa Archives.

76. Macbride was already near retirement by the time he took the presidency on an interim basis following Bowman's unexpectedly short tenure. Given that he cited his weariness in his letter of resignation to the board of education dated July 29, 1916, it is easy to believe that Macbride might not have cared to interpose himself in the college of medicine's turf battles. See Board of Education Minutes, August 9, 1916, University of Iowa Archives.

77. Memo from Dean stored by the college of medicine in a box erroneously labeled "Affirmative Action, 1980–1981"; the box actually contains materials from the dean of the college of medicine from 1914 to 1952.

78. Medical Faculty Minutes, October 19, 1919, University of Iowa Archives.

79. For a broader view, see Alfred W. Crosby, *America's Forgotten Pandemic: The Influenza of 1918* (New York: Cambridge University Press, 1989).

80. The Coe College–University of Iowa football game was played as scheduled on Saturday, October 12, but the teams performed behind closed gates, with students and the public barred from attending.

81. For newspaper accounts, see, for example, *Iowa City Daily Press*, September 6 and October 24, 1918; see also, MS File, Series I, M–N, School of Nursing Influenza Epidemic Folder, University of Iowa Archives.

82. C. J. Rowan to L. W. Dean, October 25, 1918, File 1A, 1918–19, W. A. Jessup Papers, University of Iowa Archives.

83. L. W. Dean to W. A. Jessup, December 7, 1918, File 1B, 1918–19, W. A. Jessup Papers, University of Iowa Archives.

84. L. W. Dean to W. A. Jessup, December 18, 1918, File 1B, 1918–19, W. A. Jessup Papers, University of Iowa Archives.

85. Board of Education Minutes, April 7, 1919, University of Iowa Archives.

86. Board of Education Minutes, April 21, 1919, University of Iowa Archives.

87. J. F. Bresnahan, "Brief survey of the University Hospital," July 13, 1919, File 18, 1918–19, W. A. Jessup Papers, University of Iowa Archives.

88. C. J. Rowan to L. W. Dean, October 25, 1918; Dean to W. A. Jessup, December 7, 1918, File 18, 1918–19, W. A. Jessup Papers, University of Iowa Archives. It should, however, be noted that constrained or not, Graham probably was not suited to the position of superintendent. W. R. Boyd admitted as much in a letter to a *Des Moines Register* editor, writing, "The President of the University, the faculty of the College of medicine, and the governing board have felt for some time that the institution has grown beyond the capacity of the present superintendent. I do not wish to him any harm or injustice. He is a kindly man and has had large experience. . . . He is, however, growing old and has always been somewhat easygoing." See W. R. Boyd to S. McNamera, August 15, 1919, File 18, 1919–20, W. A. Jessup Papers, 1919–20, University of Iowa Archives.

89. W. A. Jessup to H. L. Harding, August 11, 1920, File 18, 1920–21, W. A. Jessup Papers, University of Iowa Archives.

90. L. W. Dean to J. F. Bresnahan, correspondence dated from July 2, 1919, to August 10, 1919, File 1E, 1918–19, W. A. Jessup Papers, University of Iowa Archives. Bresnahan, a surgeon, was no stranger to Iowa City, where he occasionally visited friends on the University Hospital staff.

91. Record Group 27, 1919, File 1, Folder "Hospital Rules," University of Iowa Archives.

92. Dean reported Bowman's advice in correspondence to Jessup, May 14, 1919, Folder 1C, 1918–19, W. A. Jessup Papers, University of Iowa Archives. He simply stated, "I have a note from Dr. John Bowman saying that the superintendent of the Hospital at Winnipeg Canada would not be the proper man for us to consider."

93. Board of Education Minutes, October 8, 1919, University of Iowa Archives.

94. W. A. Jessup to W. L. Harding, August 11, 1920, File 18, 1920–21, W. A. Jessup Papers, University of Iowa Archives. Jessup's letter to Harding answered charges that Collins had made in a letter to the governor. Jessup goes on for seven pages about Collins' failings and implies that he could say more. He offers to send the governor a "Bill of Particulars" detailing Collins' failures. Jessup's claim that he, Dean, and others spent "vastly more time" supervising the superintendent is corroborated by Board of Education Minutes from the period, which show again and again the close oversight they exercised over Collins; in practice, the hospital was run by committee. See Board of Education Minutes, January 10, January 17, March 6, April 20, May 19, and June 19, 1920, University of Iowa Archives.

95. L. W. Dean to W. A. Jessup, October 31, 1919, and Jessup to Dean, November 6, 1919, File 1C, 1919–20, W. A. Jessup Papers, 1919–20, University of Iowa Archives.

96. See Board of Education Minutes, April 21 and May 19, 1920, University of Iowa Archives.

97. H. O. Collins to Governor H. L. Harding, August 1, 1920, File 18, 1920–21, W. A. Jessup Papers, University of Iowa. Collins wrote the governor to complain that he had been "unjustly and discourteously treated; that an attempt has been made to place upon my shoulders responsibility for conditions not under my control; that promises made me when I was appointed . . . have not been kept; and that as a natural result my reputation as a Hospital Superintendent has been unnecessarily injured."

98. Ibid.

99. W. A. Jessup to H. L. Harding, August 11, 1920, File 18, 1920–21, W. A. Jessup Papers, University of Iowa Archives.

100. See Medical Faculty Minutes, August 2, 1920, and Board of Education Minutes for August 11 and October 10, 1920, University of Iowa Archives.

101. This abbreviated history of nursing and nursing education is adapted from Lee Anderson, "*Complete in All Its Parts": Nursing Education at the University of Iowa, 1898–1998* (Iowa City: University of Iowa College of Nursing, forthcoming 1997).

102. Enrollment figures from *State University of Iowa Catalog,* 1900, 1905, 1910, 1915, 1920, 1925.

103. See letters in MS File, Series I, M–N, School of Nursing–Miscellaneous, University of Iowa Archives.

104. Curriculum information is from *State University of Iowa Catalogs.*

105. Ward assignments are listed in MS File, Series I, M–N, School of Nursing–Miscellaneous, University of Iowa Archives.

106. MS File, Series I, M–N, School of Nursing–Miscellaneous, University of Iowa Archives.

107. Nancy Tomes, " 'Little World of Our Own': The Pennsylvania Hospital Training School for Nurses, 1895–1907," *Journal of the History of Medicine and Allied Sciences* 33 (October 1978): 507–530.

108. Bulletin of the State University of Iowa, New Series, No. 418, August 27, 1927, "Mid-Summer Announcement of the School of Nursing."

109. Etta Rasmussen Papers, Folder 1, Account of Ida Hayes (May 1973), University of Iowa Archives.

110. Nancy Tomes, " 'Little World of Our Own,' " 517.

111. Ann Slater to L. B. Corder, no date (1928), MS File, Series I, M–N, School of Nursing–Miscellaneous, University of Iowa Archives.

112. See Charles Rosenberg, *The Care of Strangers,* "Healing Hands: Nursing in the Hospital," pp. 212–236.

113. Ibid.

114. Nursing Students to W. M. Middleton, May 21, 1901, Series I, M–N, School of Nursing–Miscellaneous, University of Iowa Archives.

115. Nursing Archive, Student Body of Nurses Minutes, University of Iowa Archives.

116. Lavinia L. Dock, "What We May Expect from the Law," *American Journal of Nursing* 1 (October 1900): 8–12.

117. Charles Rosenberg, *The Care of Strangers,* p. 222.

118. Bulletin of the State University of Iowa, New Series No. 182, April 1920, "Annual Catalogue of the School of Nursing, 1919–1920."

119. "Memorandum Relating to the Establishment of a College of Nursing in the State University of Iowa," MS File, Series I, M–N, School of Nursing–Miscellaneous, University of Iowa Archives.

120. Quoted in Bonnie K. Smola, "A Study of the Development of Diploma and Baccalaureate Degree Nursing Education Programs in Iowa from 1907–1978," Ph.D. Dissertation, Iowa State University, 1980, pp. 241–243.

121. The essential outline of the history of the University of Iowa Nutrition Department comes from Lee Anderson, *Internal Medicine and the Structure of American Medical Science: The University of Iowa, 1870–1990* (Ames: Iowa State University Press, 1996), pp. 72–77.

122. See Campbell Howard, "The Sphere of the Dietitian," *Journal of the American Dietetic Association* 2 (June 1926): 1–5.

123. See E. Neige Todhunter, "Ruth Wheeler," *Journal of the American Dietetic Association* 47 (December 1965): 465.

124. R. Wheeler to A. J. Lomas, April 6, 1923, File 1, 1922–23, W. A. Jessup Papers, University of Iowa Archives.

125. A. J. Lomas to L. W. Dean, April 9, 1923; Dean to W. A. Jessup, April 10, 1923, File 1, 1922–23, W. A. Jessup Papers, University of Iowa Archives.

126. R. Wheeler to W. A. Jessup, June 25, 1923, File 1, 1922–23, W. A. Jessup Papers, University of Iowa Archives.

127. L. W. Dean to W. A. Jessup, April 25, 1923, File 1, 1922–23, W. A. Jessup Papers, University of Iowa Archives.

128. R. Wheeler to W. A. Jessup, April 7, 1924; Wheeler to C. E. Seashore, May 27, 1924, File 74, 1923–24, W. A. Jessup Papers, University of Iowa Archives.

129. *Historical Statistics of the United States, Colonial Times to 1970* (Washington, DC: Department of Commerce, 1975), pp. 172, 374.

130. R. Wardall to L. W. Dean, January 20, 1926, File 73, 1925–26, W. A. Jessup Papers, University of Iowa Archives.

131. See E. Neige Todhunter, "Kate Daum," *Journal of the American Dietetic Association* 47 (November 1965): 434; Nelda Ross Larson, "Dr. Kate Daum," *Journal of the American Dietetic Association* 32 (March 1956): 229–230.

132. K. Daum to Mrs. Theo Stebbins, February 22, 1932, Dietetics Collection, University of Iowa Hospitals and Clinics.

133. From student evaluation documents contained in the Dietetics Collection, University of Iowa Hospitals and Clinics.

134. See Kathleen Wolf, *A History of the Iowa Dietetic Association, 1930–1970* (Iowa City: The Association, 1971).

135. See Hamilton Cravens, *Before Head Start: The Iowa Station and America's Children* (Chapel Hill: University of North Carolina Press, 1993).

136. Kate Daum, "Nutrition Is No Longer the Step-Child of Medicine," unpublished paper, no date; "Personnel and Organization of a Hospital Dietary Department," unpublished paper, no date, Dietetics Collection, University of Iowa Hospitals and Clinics.

137. Daniel M. Fox, "Abraham Flexner's Unpublished Report: Foundations and Medical Education, 1909–1928," *Bulletin of the History of Medicine,* 54 (Winter 1980): 475–96. Also, W. Bruce Fye, "The Origin of the Full-Time Faculty System," *Journal of the American Medical Association,* 265

(March 27, 1991): 1555–1562. Both papers draw heavily upon previously unpublished Flexner correspondence held in various archives.

138. Fye, "The Origin of the Full-Time Faculty System," 1558–1559.

139. *The Distribution of Physicians in the United States* (New York: General Education Board, 1924). Harrison visited Iowa City and the college of medicine to gather data for the study. See A. Flexner to W. A. Jessup, October 17, 1921, Folder 1F, 1920–21, W. A. Jessup Papers, University of Iowa Archives.

140. Abraham Flexner, *I Remember* (New York: Simon and Schuster, 1940), pp. 291–292; "Essential Documents on Iowa," pp. 91–93, Record Group 1.1, Series 218A, Box 1, Folder 4, Rockefeller Foundation Archives.

141. Abraham Flexner, "Medical Department, University of Iowa, Iowa City, Iowa. Visited December 8 and 9, 1920," December 12, 1920, Record Group 1.1, Series 218A, Box 1, Folder 4, Rockefeller Foundation Archives.

142. A wealth of correspondence is available in W. A. Jessup's papers; see L. W. Dean to Jessup, November 5 and December 27, 1920, File 1A, 1920–21; Dean and Jessup to A. Flexner, January 4, 1921, and Jessup to Flexner, February 16, 1921, File 1E; W. R. Boyd to Jessup, March 3, 1921, File 39C; Boyd to Jessup, April 20, 1921, Flexner to Jessup, May 25, 1921, Boyd to Flexner, May 28, 1921, and Jessup to Flexner, June 18, 1921, File 1C, 1920–21; Dean to Jessup, September 7, 1921, March 6, and May 10, 1922, Boyd to Jessup, May 13, 1922, and Flexner to Jessup, May 26, 1922, File 1F, 1921–22; Jessup to Boyd, October 20, 1922 (telegram); Jessup to General Education Board, October 28, 1922; Jessup to Henry Pritchett, October 31, 1922; Jessup to Pritchett, November 4, 1922; and Boyd to Flexner, November 6, 1922, File 39, Pritchett to Jessup, November 8, 1922, File 1, 1922–23, W. A. Jessup Papers, University of Iowa Archives.

143. The memo recounted the progress the University of Iowa had made in addressing the issues raised by Flexner's first report and detailed the physical expansion of the hospital since 1909. See File 1, 1922–23, W. A. Jessup Papers, University of Iowa Archives.

144. In W. R. Boyd to W. A. Jessup, March 5, 1921, File 39C, 1920–21, W. A. Jessup Papers, University of Iowa Archives.

145. Kendall's message to the philanthropic organizations, October 30, 1922, File 1, 1922–23, W. A. Jessup Papers, University of Iowa Archives.

146. See Lee Anderson, "'A Great Victory': Abraham Flexner and the New Medical Campus at the University of Iowa," *Annals of Iowa* 51 (Winter 1992): 231–251.

147. Ibid., p. 240. Also see Howard S. Berliner, *A System of Scientific Medicine* (New York: Tavistock Publications, 1985), chapter 12, and Stephen C. Wheatley, *The Politics of Philanthropy: Abraham Flexner and Medical Education* (Madison: University of Wisconsin Press, 1988), pp. 99–107.

148. Rosemary Stevens, *In Sickness and In Wealth: American Hospitals in the Twentieth Century* (New York: Basic Books, Inc., 1989), pp. 76–79.

149. Rothstein, *American Medical Schools and the Practice of Medicine*, p. 135. See also a review of internships included in *Journal of American Medical Association* 84 (March 28, 1925): 966.

150. See, for example, *Journal of the American Medical Association* 76 (April 16, 1921): 1083–1091. The survey provides a wealth of information on the types of hospital services available in each state, bed capacity and utilization, and other statistical data, but little or no qualitative analysis.

151. Stevens, *In Sickness and In Wealth*, passim. The brief account we present here does little to indicate the inter-organizational politics that characterized relations among the three bodies, a theme to which Stevens devotes considerably more attention. Stevens suggests, moreover, that the ACS's reform goals were designed to maintain the primacy of surgery—and surgeons—in the hospital setting.

152. See Medical Faculty Minutes, November 1914, University of Iowa Archives.

153. See Medical Faculty Minutes, September 1915, University of Iowa Archives.

154. Board of Education Minutes, January 17, 1920, University of Iowa Archives.

155. *American College of Surgeons Bulletin* 13 (December 1929): 4. Smaller hospitals were much less likely to meet ACS standards; for example, of the 547 hospitals of 25 to 49 beds surveyed in 1929, just 108, or 19. 7 percent, were approved.

156. Rothstein, *American Medical Schools and the Practice of Medicine*, pp.134–136.

157. *Journal of the American Medical Association* 90 (March 24, 1928): 911. On women in internships, see Mary Roth Walsh, '*Doctors Wanted: No Women Need Apply': Sexual Barriers in the Medical Profession, 1835–1975* (New Haven, CT: Yale University Press, 1977), pp. 219–225.

158. *Journal of the American Medical Association* 84 (March 28, 1925): 965.

159. The law is contained in the state-published *Acts of the 38th General Assembly* (1919), and thereafter appears in the *Code of Iowa*. In 1931 it was amended to formally integrate the Psychopathic Hospital with University Hospitals.

160. See, for example, "Organization with Reference to Related Institutions," in Gerhard Hartman, "Organization charts, University Hospitals, State University of Iowa," September 1949, Box 1, Gerhard Hartman Papers, UIHC Administrative Offices. Also, Beverly Benson, "SUI Hospitals Serve as Well as Teach," *The Daily Iowan*, May 27, 1947.

161. Adolph Meyer to L. W. Dean, October 17, 1916; Herman Adler to Dean, October 18, 1916; and Thomas Salmon to Dean, November 17, 1916, File 6, 1916–17, W. A. Jessup Papers, University of Iowa Archives. Meyer, a German immigrant, has been credited with placing American psychiatry "on a firm clinical basis." See George Mora, "The History of Psychiatry in the United States: Historiographic and Theoretical Considerations," *History of Psychiatry* 3 (June 1992): 187–202.

162. The board of education approved Byfield's appointment June 15, 1915; see Minutes for that date, University of Iowa Archives. For a larger perspective on pediatrics, see Sydney A. Halpern, *American Pediatrics: The Social Dynamics of Professionalism, 1880–1980* (Berkeley: University of California Press, 1988).

163. See A. L. Sahs, *History of the Department of Neurology, 1919–1974: The University of Iowa College of Medicine* (Iowa City, IA: The Department, 1985), p. 7.

164. Board of Education Minutes, July 23, 1919, and February 20, 1920, University of Iowa Archives.

165. Board of Education Minutes, August 31, 1921, University of Iowa Archives.

166. Board of Education Minutes, June 17, July 17, and August 24, 1924, University of Iowa Archives.

167. Board of Education Minutes, February 8, March 9, June 26, and July 9, 1926, University of Iowa Archives.

168. C. P. Howard to W. A. Jessup, January 9, 1923, File 1, 1922–23; L. W. Dean to W. A. Jessup, April 14, 1920, File 1(a), 1919–1920, W. A. Jessup Papers, University of Iowa Archives.

169. For a contemporary survey of developments, see G. M. Hanner, "American Inventive Genius Reflected in Hospital Equipment Today," *Hospital Management*, 21 (March 1926): 33–35.

170. Del T. Sutton, "Early Meetings of AHA," *Modern Hospital* 21 (November 1923): 470; "Committee on Training Reports," *Hospital Management* 13 (June 1922): 28; "US Stresses Hospital Needs," *Hospital Management* 17 (April 1924): 45.

171. See letters to Jessup from Schmidt, Gardner, and Martin; Marvin Biscoe; Ellerbe & Co.; and Egan Woodbury, dated April and May 1923, File 5, 1922–23, W. A. Jessup Papers, University of Iowa Archives.

172. Board of Education Minutes, January 11, 1923, University of Iowa Archives.

173. Board of Education Minutes, April 25, 1923, University of Iowa Archives.

174. S. S. Goldwater, "Preliminary Survey for Hospital Design," undated, File 5, 1922–23, W. A. Jessup Papers, University of Iowa Archives. Jessup's copy of the document is worn and shows clear evidence of frequent use.

175. "Preliminary Report of Building Committee of Medical Faculty," July 16, 1923, Medical Faculty Docket, University of Iowa Archives. The exact division of beds the report recommended was surgery, 240 beds (210 ward beds); head specialties, 190 beds (160 ward beds); internal medicine,

130 beds (100 ward beds); obstetrics and gynecology, 110 beds (90 ward beds); neurology, 50 ward beds; and dermatology, 20 ward beds.

176. L. W. Dean to W. A. Jessup, August 23, 1923, File 74, 1923–24, W. A. Jessup Papers, University of Iowa Archives.

177. Board of Education Minutes, November 22, 1923, University of Iowa Archives.

178. This description is taken from one published in *Hospital Management* 17 (March 1924): 43, 72–74. See also, Board of Education Minutes, December 3 and 5, 1923; and File 58, 1923–24, W. A. Jessup Papers, University of Iowa Archives.

179. Medical Faculty Minutes, February 5, 1924, University of Iowa Archives. See also, Board of Education Finance Committee Minutes, March 13, 1924, University of Iowa Archives.

180. See L. W. Dean to W. A. Jessup, December 5, 1923; W. Smith to W. A. Jessup, December 29, 1923, File 78, 1923–24, W. A. Jessup Papers, University of Iowa Archives.

181. See L. W. Dean to C. C. Burlingame, January 22, 1924, File 58, 1923–24, W. A. Jessup Papers, University of Iowa Archives.

182. Parnall had been recommended for superintendent of University Hospitals earlier in 1923, when that post was vacant, by Albert Barrett, director of the University of Michigan's Psychopathic Hospital. See A. Barrett to L. W. Dean, March 14, 1924, File 18, 1923–24, W. A. Jessup Papers, University of Iowa Archives.

183. See *Michigan Alumnus*, 32 (October 10, 1925), in the University of Michigan Historical Collections, Bentley Historical Library.

184. B. W. Caldwell to C. G. Parnell, March 19, 1924, File 58, 1923–24, W. A. Jessup Papers, University of Iowa Archives.

185. Memoranda of understanding between Parnall and Jessup are contained in File 74, 1923–24, W. A. Jessup Papers, University of Iowa Archives. Handwritten notes of the meeting can be found in File 58 of the same series.

186. C. G. Parnall, "Resume of Work," June 14, 1924, File 58, 1923–24, W. A. Jessup Papers, University of Iowa Archives.

187. The medical faculty's accession to the reduced version of the medical laboratories building is reflected in Medical Faculty Minutes, June 14, 1924, University of Iowa Archives.

188. B. W. Caldwell to C. J. Rowan, January 13, 1925, Medical Faculty Docket, University of Iowa Archives.

189. See Medical Faculty Minutes, January 20, 1925, University of Iowa Archives.

190. C. G. Parnall to O. H. Plant, February 19, 1925, File 57, 1924–25, W. A. Jessup Papers, University of Iowa Archives.

191. R. E. Neff to W. A. Jessup, March 16, 1923, File 18, 1923–24, W. A. Jessup Papers, University of Iowa Archives.

192. Caldwell's appointment on a six-month provisional basis was formally announced in Board of Education Minutes, April 25, 1923, University of Iowa Archives.

193. W. R. Boyd to W. A. Jessup, August 18, 1923, File 13, 1923–24, W. A. Jessup Papers, University of Iowa Archives.

194. Dean's letter to Caldwell regarding the alcohol fuss dated February 8, 1925, and Caldwell's reply, File 73, 1924–25, W. A. Jessup Papers, University of Iowa Archives.

195. B. W. Caldwell to W. A. Jessup, April 14, 1925; Caldwell to L. W. Dean, April 18, 1925; and Caldwell to Dean, June 1, 1925, File 73, 1924–25, W. A. Jessup Papers; Board of Education Minutes, May 5 and August 1, 1925, University of Iowa Archives.

196. These figures are extrapolated from the actual number reported for the first five months of the fiscal year; see B. W. Caldwell to W. A. Jessup, December 11, 1924, File 57, 1924–25, University of Iowa Archives.

197. B. W. Caldwell to C. J. Rowan, October 30, 1924, File 57; L. W. Dean to W. A. Jessup, May 16, 1925, File 73, 1924–25, W. A. Jessup Papers, University of Iowa Archives.

198. See Board of Education Minutes, March 6 and April 21, 1920, University of Iowa Archives. Even at this time, superintendent Herbert Collins sought to exert stricter oversight of indigent admissions to ensure that patients were indeed unable to pay for their care. The Finance Committee, however, denied his proposal to hire an admissions officer for the hospital.

199. B. W. Caldwell to C. J. Rowan, October 30, 1924, File 57, 1924–25, W. A. Jessup Papers, University of Iowa Archives.

200. Medical Faculty Minutes, December 16, 1924, University of Iowa Archives.

201. A review of how the indigent care deficit developed is contained in the Iowa State Board of Education Biennial Report, 1926–1928, pp. 10–25. Also, the report of the board's Special Committee on the Hospital of the College of Medicine, dealing substantially with this issue, is summarized in Board of Education Minutes, January 7, 1928, University of Iowa Archives.

202. See Board of Education Minutes, December 6, 1927, University of Iowa Archives. Also, "The University Hospital Waiting List of Indigent Patients, April 8th, 1929" (map showing number of people on waiting list from each of Iowa's 99 counties), File 57, 1928–29, W. A. Jessup Papers, University of Iowa Archives.

203. Board of Education Minutes, November 9 and December 6, 1927, University of Iowa Archives.

204. "Three Resign Posts on Iowa 'Medic' Staff," *Iowa City Press-Citizen*, May 5, 1927.

205. Ibid.

206. "Three Doctors Quit Posts at S.U.I College," *Des Moines Register*, May 5, 1927.

207. C. C. Clifton, "Strife Between Doctors and Dean Forced Iowa University Crisis," *Des Moines Sunday Register*, July 24, 1927. The full text of the letter the faculty wrote to Jessup, dated May 30, 1927, was reprinted in this report, which recapped the entire crisis in addition to the faculty letter that contained Jessup's point-by-point reply, as well as the text of the Board of Education committee's report on the matter.

208. "Charge Dean Used School for Own Gain," *Des Moines Register*, May 12, 1927.

209. Materials related to this incident are in File 73, 1927–28, W. A. Jessup Papers, University of Iowa Archives.

210. "Dean Resigns as Head of College of Medicine Here," *The Daily Iowan*, May 7, 1927.

211. Ibid.; "Doctor Gatewood, Miss McArthur to Leave University," *Iowa City Press-Citizen*, May 10, 1927.

212. "Dean Severs All Connections With Medical College," *The Daily Iowan*, May 12, 1927.

213. The text of the letter as drafted is in Medical Faculty Minutes, May 17, 1927, University of Iowa Archives.

214. Lee Wallace Dean, it should be noted, went to Washington University in St. Louis, where he gained some national recognition and concluded his long career in the 1940s.

215. C. C. Clifton, "Strife Between Doctors and Dean Forced Iowa University Crisis."

216. W. R. Boyd to W. A. Jessup, June 9, 1927 (telegrapher mistakenly identified sender as W. R. Bryce), and Boyd to Jessup, June 10, 1927, File 73, 1927–28, W. A. Jessup Papers, University of Iowa Archives.

217. File 104, 1926–27, W. A. Jessup Papers, University of Iowa Archives.

218. Orton was on the committee that drafted the faculty's response to Dean's letter of resignation; see Medical Faculty Minutes, May 17, 1927, University of Iowa Archives. It is worth noting that he may also have had other reasons for resigning. In September 1927, after Orton had left the faculty but while he was finishing work in Iowa City on a research project into the physiology of the brain—funded by $60,000 in Rockefeller money—he stood accused of diverting morphine from Psychopathic Hospital stocks to his own use. To this irregularity he confessed, citing chronic

"migrainous" headaches and residual pain from gastrointestinal surgery years before. Investigation of the matter was prompted by the dark and likely exaggerated claims of a fired male nurse who had had charge of Psychopathic Hospital's drug room. Deposed testimony by Orton, the nurse, and others is contained in a large envelope filed behind File 104, 1927–28, W. A. Jessup Papers, University of Iowa Archives.

219. W. R. Boyd to W. A. Jessup, June 14, 1927, File 73, 1927–28, W. A. Jessup Papers, University of Iowa Archives.

220. Numerous copies of the three-page letter, leaving blank the name of the doctor to whom Baker originally wrote, are in File 104, 1927–28, W. A. Jessup Papers, University of Iowa Archives.

221. W. R. Boyd to W. A. Jessup, June 14, 1927 (cable from New York), and Esther S. Bailey (secretary to Abraham Flexner) to Jessup, June 21, 1927, File 73, 1927–28, W. A. Jessup Papers, University of Iowa Archives.

222. W. A. Jessup to G. T. Baker, June 18, 1927, File 73, 1927–28, W. A. Jessup Papers, University of Iowa Archives. Jessup noted Alcock's and Beye's reservations and continued, "but they admit that the activities of the General Education Board and the Rockefeller Foundation in medical education throughout the world are so broad as to make it nearly impossible to find anyone who has not been under some such influence."

223. W. A. Jessup to Edwin R. Embree, July 5, 1927 (telegram); H. S. Houghton to Jessup, July 11, 1927; and Houghton to Jessup, August 27, 1927 (telegram), File 73, 1927–28, W. A. Jessup Papers, University of Iowa Archives. See also Board of Education Minutes, October 11, 1927, University of Iowa Archives.

224. Board of Education Finance Committee Minutes, February 2 and February 27, 1928, University of Iowa Archives.

225. Board of Education Minutes, November 4, 1927, and January 7, February 14, 1928, University of Iowa Archives.

226. Board of Education Minutes, August 25 and October 9, 1928, University of Iowa Archives.

227. Board of Education Finance Committee Minutes, October 8, 1929, University of Iowa Archives.

1. Mechanics Academy, 1877.

2. University Hospital, 1898. St. Mary's Church is in the background.

3. General Hospital, 1929.

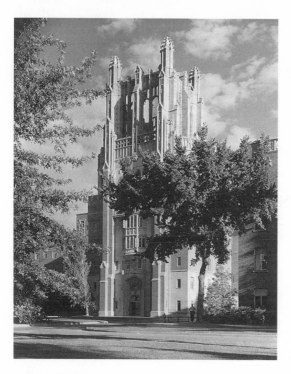

4. The Gothic tower.

5. The medical complex in 1956. General Hospital with its Gothic tower appears at upper right, and to its left is the Medical Laboratories building; between the two can be seen construction of the Medical Research Center, which opened in 1957. In the foreground at center is Psychopathic Hospital, and to its left is Children's Hospital.

6. Jennie Cottle, first superintendent of University Hospital, with members of the first graduating class of the training school for nurses, 1900.

7. Construction of the Pappajohn Pavilion begins in 1988 even as work on phases C and D of the Colloton Pavilion proceeds. For reference, General Hospital's Gothic tower stands in the background. In foreground at right stands the university Field House.

8. University of Iowa Hospitals and Clinics, 1996.

9. Children's Hospital in 1924 or 1925. Arthur Steindler's orthopeadic service occupied the building's east wings, to the right of the taller center section, while the Department of Pediatrics occupied the west wings. Construction materials for the Medical Laboratories building can be seen in the foreground.

10. The Iowa medical faculty, 1871. Standing, left to right: Gustavus Hinrichs, chemistry; John C. Shrader, obstetrics and gynecology; William B. Robertson, theory and practice of medicine; William D. Middleton, physiology; and Elmer F. Clapp, anatomy. Seated: Philo J. Farnsworth, materia medica; Washington Freeman Peck, dean and chair of surgery; and John H. Dillon, medical jurisprudence.

11. The orthopaedic brace shop, supervised for many years by P. G. Mott, at right. By the mid-1930s Mott and his seven assistants used the shop's lathes, presses, molds, and even a small forge to fabricate more than 4,000 appliances each year, including body and leg braces, splints, and special shoes.

12. Arthur Steindler, head of orthopaedics from 1915 to 1947, in 1928. (Kent Collection, University of Iowa Archives.)

13. Beds rolled onto the lawn at Children's Hospital so pediatric patients could enjoy the benefits of fresh air and sunshine.

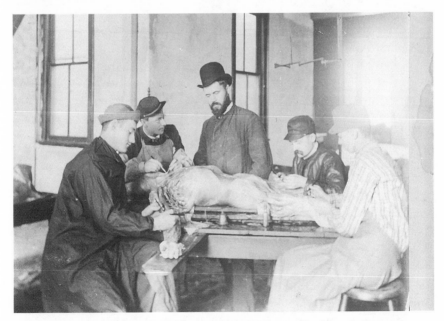

14. Anatomy professor Elmer F. Clapp with medical students and cadaver, probably 1880s.

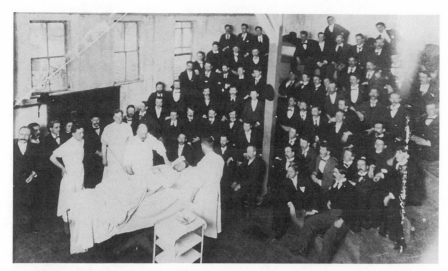

15. William D. Middleton gives a surgery clinic in Mercy Hospital's amphitheater, a remodeled carriage house, circa 1892.

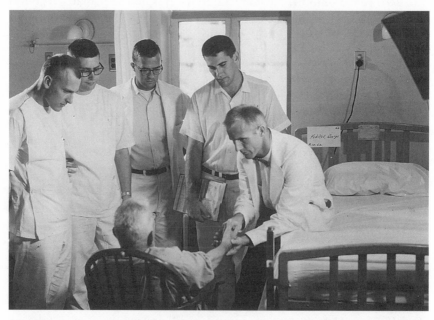

16. Robert Soper on rounds with residents and medical students in 1962. Soper, at that time a junior member of the surgery faculty, went on to head the department on an interim basis from 1992 to 1995.

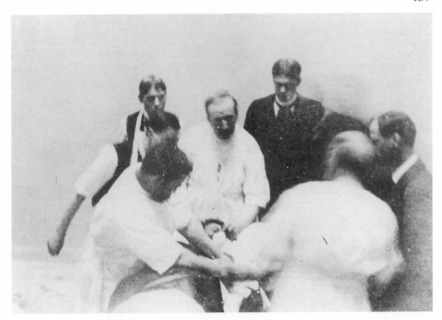

17. Surgery sometimes required brute force in the 1890s, before the advent of power equipment.

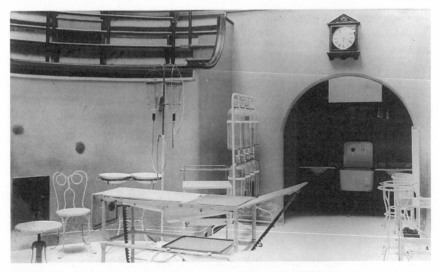

18. Surgical theater in University Hospital, early 1900s.

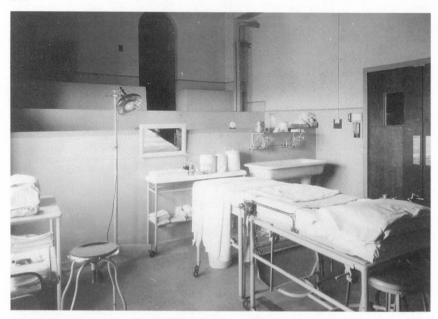

19. Operating room in General Hospital, 1929.

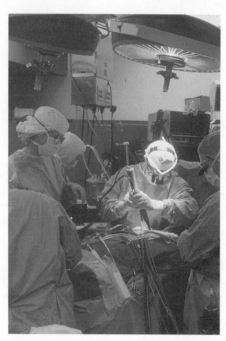

20. Open heart surgery, 1991.

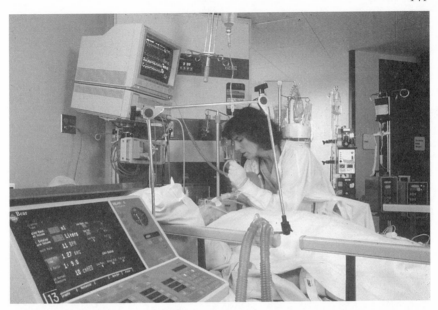

21. Surgical intensive care unit, 1991.

22. Department of Pediatrics head Frank Morriss checks on a baby in the neonatal intensive care unit, 1987.

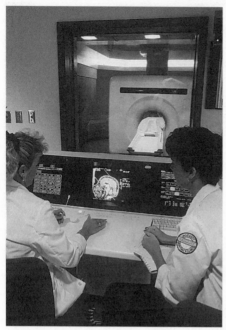

23. Magnetic resonance imaging, 1988.

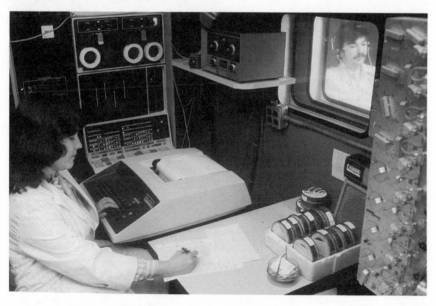

24. An otological examination, about 1990.

25. A laboratory in the Medical Laboratories building, possibly 1940s.

26. Researchers in the Medical
Research Center, circa 1969.

27. Ambulance fleet with drivers outside General Hospital, 1934.

28. The Air Care helicopter, inaugurated in 1979, prepares to land at the Carver Pavilion rooftop helipad. Though the helicopter does assist at crash sites and other emergencies, most of its flights are for the purpose of transferring critically ill indigent patients to the University of Iowa Hospitals and Clinics from other Iowa hospitals.

3

The University Teaching Hospital In Hard Times, 1929–1945

The much celebrated opening of the new General Hospital and Medical Laboratories Building in the fall of 1928 vaulted the University of Iowa to the front rank of academic medical centers, at least so far as physical facilities were concerned. However, the central importance of external funding in the planning and construction of the new medical campus left an important question unanswered. Could, or would, the economy and polity of Iowa provide the University Hospitals and the college of medicine with the means to sustain the new facilities and to utilize them to the fullest advantage? That meant not only an enlarged commitment to the indigent care programs that provided patients and operating revenues to the University Hospitals system; it also entailed a commitment to recruit the best available faculty and staff.

Coming on the heels of a nearly disastrous decade for Iowa's still largely agricultural economy, the Depression of the 1930s severely limited the university's ability to capitalize on its newfound opportunity. Between 1921 and 1933, more than half of Iowa's banks disappeared through closure or consolidation; by 1932, farm prices had fallen as much as 80 percent from highs achieved during World War I. In 1933 alone, nearly 10 percent of Iowa farms were subject to foreclosure, even as property taxes remained the principal source of state revenues.[1] Moreover, personal income in Iowa fell by nearly half between 1929 and 1933. One predictable result of economic hardship was deep cuts in state spending, with university appropriations suffering accordingly. By 1933, the university's appropriation had fallen 28 percent from its 1929 high of $2,500,000, and both the University Hospitals and the college of medicine bore their share of the reduction. The college's budget, for example, fell from $337,000 in 1929–1930 to $265,000 in 1933–1934. At the same time, state appropriations for indigent care dipped as low as $900,000 in 1934 and 1935, even as the Depression swelled the ranks of the indigent population.

In some respects, the results were hardly short of catastrophic for the academic medical center. The board of education set a 5 percent salary cut for university employees in 1931 and, pushed by the governor's Interim Committee on the Reduction of the Costs of Government, followed that with further cuts from 15 to 30 percent the next year. An effective freeze on hiring accompanied the salary cuts, with resultant staff shortages and labor unrest. Dean Henry Houghton saw his salary depleted by legislative mandate from $15,000 to $9,575; likewise, President Walter Jessup's salary fell from $18,000 to $10,000. Houghton warned that continued cuts "would necessitate return of all clinical chiefs to part time" and "would tend to lower scientific quality and prestige of the College of Medicine."[2] Jessup, in turn, warned of "sharp competition" from other institutions for valued personnel in technical fields.[3] Events confirmed much of Houghton's and Jessup's dire predictions, and the medical center did not recover from the trauma of the Depression until after World War II, emerging in 1945 a weakened institution, its prospects far dimmer than they had seemed in 1928.

Notwithstanding such setbacks, the hospitals continued to expand their service role through the 1930s and early 1940s, providing care to increasing numbers of both indigent and private patients. At the same time, in part because medical scientific research was not yet the capital-intensive enterprise it later became, medical science advanced in several directions in the 1930s and 1940s, from the discovery of antibiotics to the routinization of blood banking and transfusions, and University of Iowa faculty made significant scientific contributions of their own. The era likewise saw a continuation of the trend toward specialization in medicine, a trend exemplified in the institutionalization of the residency and the proliferation of specialty examining boards. Finally, the profession of hospital administration achieved a new level of maturity, in part at least the happy product of an otherwise disagreeable austerity. The skills of the hospital superintendent may have been, as their physician critics sometimes charged, chiefly those of a "hotel keeper"; but hard times placed a premium on just such skills.

The Indigent Care Conundrum

The University Hospitals was understood to exist chiefly to serve the needs of medical education; yet the hospitals' educational mission—as well as much of its political support—was critically contingent on indigent care programs funded by state government. For that reason, the issue of indigent care, considered in the context of a stubborn and paralyzing economic depression, absorbed a disproportionate share of administrators' time and energy in the 1930s. Moreover, the indigent care issue reopened festering divisions between the hospitals and the college of medicine and the Iowa State Medical Society, as well as with farm groups concerned over the burden of property taxes that, at the time, contributed the greater part of state revenues.

Because of the cap on state appropriations for indigent care instituted in 1925, some 125 beds in the new General Hospital were not put into service when the hospital opened in November 1928, leaving the entire fifth floor dark and vacant. In 1930, the number of empty beds more than doubled,[4] taking from service fully one-third of the new hospital's capacity. In January 1929, Superintendent Robert E. Neff wrote an open letter to the state's doctors, county officials, and social workers to explain the reduced indigent care service, "owing to the lack of State funds," and to note the considerable delay some state patients could expect before being admitted.[5]

The cap on indigent care payments, however, did not restrict the number of patients that county officials could commit for care at state expense. The result was a dilemma for hospital administrators. Their continued acceptance of all patients bearing state papers had led to a $238,000 deficit in fiscal year 1927. Officials then sought closer coordination of indigent care, by calculating the maximum number of state patients the hospital could afford to accept and apportioning those patients among the various clinical services on a monthly basis, with the extra beds removed from service.[6] Removing beds from service was, in some degree, a false economy, since the hospital's fixed operating expenses remained largely unchanged; also, the per diem charge for indigent patients failed to take into account extraordinary expenses involving specialized diagnostic services or appliances such as braces and casts. Earnings from higher charges to private and clinical pay patients (i.e., patients whose charges did not include physicians' fees) helped to cover the losses on indigent cases, but the number of paying patients declined as well during the depths of the Depression (Table 3.1).[7]

No matter how the costs were figured or the per diem rate set, the state's indigent care appropriation was too low to treat the number of patients obtaining commitment papers to University Hospitals, resulting

**Table 3.1   Patient Admissions, Patient-Days, and State Funding,
                    1929–1940**

Fiscal Year	Indigent Admissions	Indigent Patient-Days	Private Admissions	Private Patient-Days	Other Admissions*	Other Patient-Days*	Total Admissions	Total Patient-Days
1928–29	7,069	187,967	1,395	12,961	3,436	16,824	11,900	217,752
1929–30	8,590	200,513	1,400	14,779	2,810	19,116	12,800	234,408
1930–31	9,163	188,285	1,395	12,713	1,490	19,226	12,048	220,224
1931–32	11,011	195,419	1,275	12,052	1,251	14,747	13,537	222,218
1932–33	12,299	202,778	1,134	11,700	1,158	15,529	14,591	230,007
1933–34	13,028	217,146	1,281	13,041	1,474	20,178	15,783	250,365
1934–35	14,957	249,494	1,514	14,784	1,761	20,212	18,232	284,490
1939–40	15,063	223,723	2,307	22,931	2,316	28,418	19,686	275,072

Note: All categories include acute, newborn, and housed clinic patients.
*Includes clinical pay, county clinical pay, cost, student, staff, research, and State Services for Crippled Children patients.
Source: University of Iowa Hospitals and Clinics Annual Statistical Reports, 1929–40.

in a waiting list that grew at an alarming rate. First instituted in July 1927, the waiting list dipped to as low as 11 in November 1927, but thereafter it rose inexorably higher, reaching 1,000 in October 1929, 2,000 in early 1931, and a disconcerting 5,434 by April 1933.[8] At the same time, indigent admissions and indigent patient-days continued to grow.

The Iowa State Medical Society's Committee on Medical Education and Hospitals, in a 1930 report on the University Hospitals and the indigent care laws, attributed growth of the waiting list to several factors in addition to the reduced number of beds available for state patients. The report cited a general increase in indigency owing to economic conditions; both purposeful and unwitting abuse of the indigent care laws by physicians and county officials who interpreted the laws' provisions too broadly; incomplete investigation of individual cases by overworked county attorneys resulting in commitment of some patients who could probably afford care on their own; better roads that made travel to Iowa City from remote corners of the state easier and faster; emergency cases that received higher priority and thus delayed the admission of other patients; and changes of status among patients who, because of long hospital stays, acquired state indigent care commitment papers while already receiving treatment and thus delayed admission of other patients.[9]

The length of time that patients waited for admission depended on the clinical services to which they sought admission and on individual circumstances. The State Medical Society's 1930 report noted that typical waiting periods ranged from "weeks to months" and found wide discrepancies among the clinical services. The report cited the example of one doctor who examined two individuals, one of whom gained admission to the hospital within two weeks, while the other was still waiting after three months. Additional factors influencing the waiting period included the hospital's limited number of beds, patients' personal characteristics "such as color, sex, etc.," and the geographical distribution of patients.[10] According to an April 1933 analysis by the University Hospital superintendent, waiting periods of 3 to 15 months were typical, and 16- to 33-month delays were not uncommon.[11]

In the early stages of the crisis, Dean Houghton, Superintendent Neff, and other officials worried over the lengthening waiting list. "This brings us to a crisis in our hospital affairs which I have no authority to meet," Houghton wrote to Jessup as early as January 1930, when the patient waiting list contained only some 1,100 cases.[12] The problem was not only humanitarian and administrative; it also posed a potential political nightmare. Doctors and county officials around the state increasingly expressed dismay that residents they committed for care did not receive it promptly. Letters demanding immediate attention to particular cases arrived in Iowa City and in Des Moines at the board of education's offices, often from lawyers, newspaper publishers, or other prominent citizens, and each complaint generated its own flurry of paperwork.[13]

On occasion, there was political opportunity in responding to requests for emergency admissions. In one such instance, Samuel D. Whiting, an Iowa City attorney who represented Johnson County in the legislature, asked for an exception for a young girl on the waiting list. Writing to President Jessup on House of Representatives stationery, Whiting reported that an Ida County representative had approached him about a little girl on the waiting list.

> I told Mr. Aiken to send her on as an emergency case. I hope you will take this matter up at once and see that the child is admitted and given the best of care. Mr. Aiken has been one of the group always opposed to the University and I believe that if you give him a little attention in this matter that when the right time comes I can get his vote for whatever we want.

Penciled notations on the letter indicate that the girl was admitted as an emergency case the next day.[14]

Even more worrisome was a trend toward the use of emergency classification to circumvent the waiting list. In emergency cases, state law allowed for streamlining the commitment process and giving priority in admission, and physicians and county officials turned to this mechanism in ever greater numbers as waiting lists grew longer. In its 1930 report, the

Iowa State Medical Society observed that "the law defines cases of great emergency as, 'when the court or judge is satisfied that delay would be seriously injurious to the patient,' which, under a liberal interpretation, is broad enough to include a great number of cases, especially when 'delay' means weeks or months."[15] The superintendent himself reported that a flood of emergency cases in the last three months of 1930 had drastically reduced the number of patients called from the waiting list; indeed, of the 25 new patients admitted on average each day, just six came from the list.[16]

In part because of the resort to emergency classification, the cost of indigent transportation became a concern as well. Prompted by a spate of special ambulance trips, Houghton asked Jessup in early 1931 to make "some discreet and diplomatic inquiries . . . as to the propriety of this procedure in view of the urgent need of economy by the hospital." "Mr. Neff and I," he continued, "have been somewhat disturbed over the growing number who are being sent to the hospital in this fashion."[17] Cuts in rail service to rural areas also added to transportation costs, as did the continued growth in indigent patient numbers. The per patient transportation cost for the first six months of fiscal 1931 jumped to $22.21, up from $18.71 in fiscal 1930, bringing the total to just under $160,000 for the year, 16 percent of the indigent care budget.[18]

The University Hospitals, then, faced a series of interlocking crises as the Depression deepened. The state's limited indigent care appropriation forced operation of the hospitals at just two-thirds capacity; the limited bed capacity caused the patient waiting lists to grow to unmanageable proportions; long waiting periods, in turn, prompted county officials to designate more and more cases as emergencies; and the large number of emergency cases disrupted the orderly admission of patients and added to the cost of transportation. By early 1931, even some designated emergency cases were being turned away.[19] Early on in this self-perpetuating cycle, the waiting list was considered to be about 85 percent active—that is, most patients responded when called for admission. As the waiting period grew longer, however, more and more patients sought treatment elsewhere, gave up altogether, or died. The Iowa State Medical Society estimated the active portion of the list at barely 75 percent in 1930.[20] To an alarming extent, Iowa's indigent care system had broken down.

Political Challenges to the Indigent Care System

While university officials struggled in the face of declining budgets and growing demand for indigent healthcare services, they also faced political challenges to the University Hospitals' monopoly on indigent care. In late 1928, Mitchell County representative Brede Wamstad from Osage, supported by the Iowa State Medical Society and its legislative committee, prepared a new version of the amendment bearing his name for the upcoming 1929 legislative session. First introduced in 1927 and meant to allow state payment for indigent care at local hospitals, the amendment had been altered in committee, with Wamstad's concurrence, to require instead that county governments pay the cost of indigent care at University Hospitals. This altered amendment would have the same effect of increasing reliance on local facilities in the provision of indigent care.[21]

The revised amendment had nearly passed in 1927, clearing the house but failing by a single vote to come to the floor of the senate. With the same amendment again in prospect for the 1929 legislative session, university officials, medical faculty, and board of education members met repeatedly with Iowa State Medical Society officers in the latter half of 1928 to hammer out an agreement on indigent care policy, an effort made even more urgent by threats from agricultural forces to gut the indigent care system.[22] The dialogue forced each side to reassess, clarify, and defend its position, and the result was a workable compromise that, for the time being at least, left the indigent care system intact. More than anything else, it appears to have been the presence of Henry Houghton that pried the medical society from its alliance with the farm bloc. Houghton first met with the society's legislative committee in July 1928, when he aired his concern that Wamstad's proposal would reduce the number of indigent admissions to University Hospitals and threaten the integrity of the college of medicine's teaching programs. At the same time, however, the dean outlined procedural points on which the university was flexible and open to the medical society's concerns. Indeed, Houghton pointed out, some of Wamstad's proposed changes, such as limiting the term of commitment papers to two years and itemizing all indigent patients' bills, were already on record as board of education policy.

Most important, Houghton, unlike his predecessor in the deanship, established a tone of cooperation with the medical society that disarmed its earlier confrontational stance. Henry C. Shull, a board of education member who served on the liaison committee that worked with the medical society, reported that "the officers of the Medical Society expressed their extreme confidence in Dean Houghton and his ability to handle the situation in a manner satisfactory to them." For Shull, there was "no question" that Houghton's efforts at conciliation had "changed the entire situation and made the conference between the parties comparatively easy." Moreover, the medical society's legislative committee praised Houghton for injecting "a fine spirit of friendliness and a desire to cooperate."[23]

Nonetheless, there remained a major point of contention between the medical society and the college and hospitals, one only indirectly related to the question of indigent care. The medical society, holding that a state institution should not compete with doctors in private practice, sought to limit private service to 5 percent of the hospitals' beds. University officials, for their part, sought to assure the society's members that the hospitals did not wish or intend to compete with them for paying patients, so long as this did not entail a fixed limit on private service. In line with that, the board of education's liaison committee tentatively agreed to restrict the number of private patients at the hospital, provided that an adequate number of patients for teaching were available. However, the medical society's legislative committee refused to accept that rather vague assurance, leaving the matter unresolved.[24]

One final area of disagreement between the two sides was whether changes in indigent care policy should be enacted into law. The medical society wanted to change existing law in order to correct its flaws and prevent abuses, but university authorities and the board of education feared the worst from hostile lawmakers and hoped to forestall legislative action, preferring to enact policy changes through the board. At least one member of the society's legislative committee expressed to Houghton "a great deal of disappointment and resentment because of the apparent reluctance of the board to join with the State Medical Society" in seeking statutory changes in indigent care.[25] In December 1928 the board adopted some of the proposed policy changes, reaffirming the two-year limit on commitments and instituting more stringent measures to assure the indigency of state patients. But it deferred action on a formal rule restricting private practice to 5 percent of beds, while offering assurance that the University Hospitals did "not contemplate . . . expansion of private service beyond those [beds] already provided, which are now approximately 5% of the bed capacity."[26] Later, Houghton sought to convince medical society leaders that enacting policy through the board of education was more efficacious than changing the law. "It may be argued that the rulings of the board may be altered at any time in regular meeting, whereas modifications written into the law would crystallize them permanently—subject only to repeal by legislative action," Houghton wrote, apparently failing to recognize that statutory permanence was precisely what the society sought.[27] This issue, like the private practice issue, remained in dispute throughout the negotiations of late 1928.

Meanwhile, as expected, Brede Wamstad surfaced with his amendment in the 1929 legislative session. Introduced in January 1929 as House File 203, Wamstad's broad-ranging bill proposed to repeal state funding of indigent care in favor of the county financing plan just described, codify the two-year limit on indigent patient commitments, require examination of indigent patients by two local physicians prior to commitment, place liens equal to the value of hospital services on any property or earnings acquired by indigent patients within ten years after receiving care, and lower the fee paid physicians for court-ordered examinations.[28] The result of such legislation, Houghton had argued in autumn negotiations with the medical society, would be catastrophic for medical education. He pointed out that even with the current enrollment of about 200 in the mostly clinical third and fourth years, Iowa's ratio of students to beds was slightly higher than that of comparable schools, and projections of even larger entering classes forecast a greater, not lesser, need for teaching patients in the years ahead. Wamstad's amendment would authorize counties to impose a property tax levy of one dollar for each thousand dollars of assessed value to support indigent care, an amount calculated to provide roughly the same level of statewide funding as under current law. But the result, Houghton and others believed, would be a far greater reliance on local facilities and a sharp drop in the number of patients admitted to the University Hospitals. Houghton charged that similar plans in Indiana, Michigan, and Ohio had caused a dramatic loss of clinical volume and had forced officials "to open the [teaching] hospital as a pay clinic to the citizens of the State," thus bringing the state into competition with private physicians.[29]

To the relief of university officials, Wamstad withdrew his bill from consideration on March 22, citing for the record a "concerted effort" by the university, the board of education, and the medical society to "correct the abuses which have existed in the administration of the Perkins–Haskell-Klaus act in recent years."[30] Off the record, however, Wamstad said the bill fell victim to an effective campaign to isolate his and the bill's supporters. Specifically, Wamstad complained to the medical society's legislative committee that "the lobby opposing this measure" had created the impression that its support came not "from physicians of the entire state," but chiefly from "small groups in the larger centers, and particularly, Des Moines."[31] It was true that opposition to the indigent care system among physicians was largely confined to the Des Moines area. The medical society's December 1930 report on indigent care contained the results of a statewide survey in which the majority of responding physicians agreed that the indigent care law was working properly. The same majority also thought University Hospitals served indigent patients as intended by the law, that the local medical profession had not been harmed, and that they had not lost paying patients to the indigent care system. Across the board, it seemed, most doctors supported the Perkins and Haskell-Klaus acts as well as the University Hospitals' role in indigent care.[32] Whether or not the survey results were a surprise, they underlined the low priority most society members gave to indigent care reform.

There remained nevertheless a determined cell of opposition to the law and to the college of medicine and University Hospitals, opposition that, for lack of a more stable center, coalesced around the personal crusade of Elbert E. Munger of Spencer, Iowa, against the indigent care system in general and the University of Iowa College of Medicine in particular. In the context of the Depression, Munger's appeal engaged a far wider audience than would otherwise have been the case, as local governments struggled to maintain vital services and local taxpayers sought relief from their burdens. Importantly, despite the provisions of the Perkins and Haskell-Klaus laws, county expenditures by the early 1930s no doubt exceeded state expenditures for indigent health care, with counties forced to take responsibility for the cases turned away from the University Hospitals.[33]

An 1894 medical graduate and persistent critic of the medical school, Munger was, at his best, a gadfly whose barbs exposed the weaknesses in his targets; at worst, he was an irritable crank whose extreme positions alienated even his erstwhile supporters. Munger had long been an advocate of county hospitals, helping to formulate and pass a 1909 law allowing Iowa counties to organize local hospital boards and levy taxes to pay for modest facilities. His was a vision of community-based private healthcare within the reach of every citizen, a system of rural hospitals to counter the flight of doctors to urban centers and specialty practice, a promise of basic care, and "equal rights to all and special privileges to none."[34] However, few counties had taken advantage of the law, and passage of the Perkins law in 1915 and Haskell-Klaus in 1919 no doubt dampened enthusiasm for new county hospitals, leaving Munger's dream unrealized.

In 1931, Munger wrote a lengthy tirade against the indigent care laws for a local newspaper, and he fired off a series of letters to state and university officials calling for repeal of the indigent care laws and the dismantling of the University of Iowa College of Medicine.[35] More dangerous than the usual curmudgeon, Munger won appointment as chairman of a nine-member legislative task force (known also as the "committee of nine") created in 1933 to study the indigent care system and University Hospitals, a task force owing its origins to the worsening crisis in state finances and in indigent care. Created by a joint house and senate resolution early in the 1933 legislative session, the charge to the task force was to "seek the cause or causes of at least one of Iowa's present misfortunes, viz., unprovided for sick and suffering." Among the appointees were Oliver J. Fay of Des Moines, a medical society trustee who had been involved in the 1928 negotiations with the university; Arthur W. Erskine, a Cedar Rapids physician in favor of county financing and other reforms; and several members of the legislature, including Senator Morris Moore, a Walnut, Iowa, physician.[36]

The committee consulted a broad range of officials, including college of medicine faculty and University Hospitals staff, President Jessup and board of education members, members of the Iowa State Medical Society's legislative committee, the state health commissioner, and doctors and county officials from around the state. The committee also corresponded with top administrators at state medical colleges in Colorado, Illinois, Indiana, Michigan, Minnesota, Missouri, Nebraska, and Wisconsin; with the Association of American Medical Colleges' administrative secretary; and with the American Medical Association's Committee on Medical Education and Hospitals. Munger traveled east to speak personally with executives of the Rockefeller Foundation and the Brookings Institution, the latter then compiling a massive study on local and state government reorganization in Iowa, and with numerous federal officials, bureaucrats, and lawmakers.

The committee's preliminary report, entered into the house record on April 1, 1933, reflected the same principal objections to state-funded indigent care that had been aired in earlier debates over the Wamstad Amendment and included essentially the same reform proposals.[37] Most important, the task force recommended that the cost of indigent care at the University Hospitals be charged half to the state and half to the counties. Also, task force members still worried that the law enabled people able to pay for medical care to claim indigency, and they recommended making county boards of supervisors rather than district courts responsible for commitment proceedings. The committee reasoned, first, that counties had traditionally been responsible for providing relief to the poor in their jurisdictions and, second, that county supervisors would more adequately investigate the financial circumstances of prospective state patients. The committee, like Wamstad, also proposed that the county's share of the cost of each indigent patient's care be counted as a lien against whatever income or property the patient might acquire in the future.

The task force also addressed the necessary connection between indigent care at the University Hospitals and the needs of medical education. Noting that Iowa's physician-to-population ratio, at 1:928, was higher than the 1:1,200 considered adequate by the Association of American Medical Colleges, and citing Iowa State Medical Society statistics showing an average yearly loss of 71 physicians, compared to the approximately 95 medical graduates from the University of Iowa each year, the task force concluded, "your committe [sic] believes that a student body in the aggregate in the medical school of a number which would make available substantially 75 graduates each year, would fully and amply meet the needs of the State of Iowa insofar as its medical needs are concerned." The result, task force members reasoned, would be a corresponding reduction in "the quantity of clinical material for the teaching of the lesser number of students."

Thus, the 1933 task force report directly challenged the indigent care system and indirectly threatened the college of medicine and the University Hospitals by assuming that the medical center's mission was to replenish

Iowa's physician ranks at more or less the existing level. Of course, the report's discussion of medical education was naïve in many particulars, not least for ignoring the fact that the number of medical practitioners in Iowa was a function of the out-migration of at least half of each graduating class from the University of Iowa and the in-migration of varying numbers of graduates from other states. Perhaps more important, the report's authors ignored the political ramifications of setting an enrollment cap at the University of Iowa College of Medicine, thus limiting opportunities for the children of Iowa voters, a course contemplated by university and college of medicine officials from time to time but never successfully implemented.

The task force report did not mention another current objection to the state indigent care system: the unequal distribution of the benefits of indigent care among the state's counties. On the basis of population alone, assuming a rough correspondence between population and tax base, some counties received far more service than they paid for, and other counties far less. In fiscal year 1929, for example, 38 counties received a total of $500,000 in services from the University Hospitals while, judged on the basis of population, having paid only about $350,000 in taxes to support indigent care. Meanwhile, the remaining 61 counties received, in the aggregate, some $400,000 in services on about $625,000 in tax revenues. Not surprisingly, the counties receiving the greatest returns on tax revenues were Johnson, the home of the University of Iowa, and Linn and other contiguous counties. In fact, by this estimation, Johnson and Linn counties together paid in taxes only about a third of the value of the services they received. The counties receiving the least service for their tax money were those in central and western Iowa—farthest removed from Iowa City—and especially those with relatively large population centers such as Des Moines (Polk County), Council Bluffs (Pottawattamie County), and Sioux City (Woodbury County).[38]

Munger incorporated these statistics into his personal assault on the indigent care system and the college of medicine.[39] Outside the forum provided by the legislative task force, he also pressed arguments that struck deeper at the heart of medical education in Iowa. Having gathered a wealth of data on medical colleges in other states and finding that the University of Iowa operated the country's eighth largest medical school in one of the smallest cities among all of the AMA's class A medical colleges, Munger charged that such an enterprise was beyond the means of a depressed farm state economy. On the face of it, Munger's assertion had some merit; moreover, it had surfaced from time to time throughout the previous history of the college of medicine and remained long after Munger was gone. Noting that most small-town medical schools sent their students to larger cities for clinical instruction, Munger proposed moving the final years of Iowa's program to Des Moines, where teaching patients were more readily available, and he called for a reduction in the number of graduates to the range of forty to fifty per year. Munger suggested that the new General Hospital could be converted into a dormitory, perhaps combined with a student cafeteria and fraternity-sorority meeting house. Finally, he questioned not only the efficiency of transporting large numbers of indigent patients with common ailments long distances to receive care that was available closer to home; he also questioned the value of such patients for teaching.[40]

The fact that Munger's more extreme arguments and proposals did not appear in the legislative task force's preliminary report was an early signal of the divisions that ultimately split the group and left Munger isolated. For the time being, however, the task force received sanction to continue its work beyond the end of the regular legislative session and to report back to the special session that leaders expected to convene in August 1933. That special legislative session did not convene until November, however, and the task force had broken apart by that time, its members submitting majority and minority final reports. Moreover, within the seven-member majority—a majority that did not include Munger—three of the members were not in full accord with the final report and submitted a supplemental report. The majority essentially restated the task force's preliminary report and recommendations, proposing again that the cost of indigent care be shared one-half by the state and one-half by the counties, that commitment proceedings be carried out under the direction of county boards of supervisors, and that "the size of the Medical College be reduced by suitable entrance requirements, so that the average number of graduates will not exceed seventy-five per year."[41]

Events left Munger and Senator G. W. Patterson, a Republican farmer from Burt, alone in calling for the radical overhaul of state-funded indigent care and the University of Iowa College of Medicine. Their minority report, which Munger surely wrote, was laced with sarcasm and bitterness toward university officials, other supporters of the university, and fellow task force members alike, even labeling Thomas Burcham of the medical society's legislative committee a capitulator. Munger's minority report ran four times the length of the majority's report; the following passage suggests its tone:

> The minority is in complete accord . . . that "the Perkins-Haskell-Klaus law should not be modified." It should be repealed, the Perkins law restored to its original status and the adult indigent law forever scrapped. It is an abominable law—made up of incongruities, inconsistencies and impossibilities, incompatible with common sense. It makes possible, if it does not encourage and compel the perpetration of fraud; fraud upon the indigent and the tax payers, fraud upon the sick and well, fraud upon the reputable faculty of the college of

medicine, fraud upon the medical students, fraud upon the reputable medical profession of the state, fraud upon the patient with heart disease, who runs after advertised remedy, when he should be at home, quiet in bed; fraud upon the severely injured, especially skull fractures, whose lives are jeopardized or lost by reason of the long haul; fraud upon the aged and decrepit, who should be encouraged to die at home among comforting friends. Iowa's adult indigent law is the alpha and omega of all that is bad in legislation providing for the state care of sick indigents. There is no law in the United States to compare with it.

Whatever Munger's shortcomings, there was more to his cry than the ravings of an aging crank, particularly so in the deeply conservative philosophy behind his apparently quixotic fight against state indigent care. Above all, Munger saw in the state indigent system the dread specter of "State Medicine," an ill-defined force, subsidized by citizens' tax money, that threatened to undercut the practice of medicine by independent physicians. Such resistance to state-funded indigent care, and especially to state medicine, was not limited to Iowa; it was also evident in Michigan, where many doctors opposed that state's indigent care laws on the same grounds.[42] Nor, of course, was such resistance limited to the 1930s; state medicine was, under whatever label, long a cause célèbre of the American Medical Association as well.[43]

Finally, Munger's attack on the indigent care system and on the University Hospitals echoed a deep-seated fear and resentment of the way in which technology and institutionalized care, particularly for the terminally ill, already challenged traditional mores regarding sickness, death, and dying. Overall, Munger's minority report displayed a nostalgia for small-town, personalized healthcare and the right to die at home among friends and family, as opposed to the "industrial" reorganization of healthcare marked by the introduction of economies of scale, business management techniques, and technology, all of which threatened to dehumanize patients and marginalize the small-town, solo medical practitioner. In this instance, as in others, partisans of the college of medicine and the University Hospitals, consciously or not, helped to wrench control over medical science and practice from old-time physicians like Munger and to usher in a new era, confident that the advance of medical science and technology and the benefits of managerial efficiency far outweighed Munger's apparently obsolete views. Nonetheless, those views, far from obsolete, did not disappear with Elbert Munger.

The Great Depression and Austerity

As noted earlier, Iowa had scarcely recovered from the post–World War I farm crisis when the Depression began. By 1930, hard times had settled in across the state, and even islands of relative prosperity such as Iowa City felt the effects, as panicked depositors forced the closure of two local banks and gravely threatened a third.[44] For the University Hospitals, the result was a prolonged budgetary crisis spurred by increased demands for indigent care, reduced state appropriations, and declining revenues from private and clinical pay patients.

The gradual reduction in the state appropriation for indigent care coupled with a dramatic slump in income from paying patients—from $233,000 in fiscal 1930 to $230,000 in 1931 and to $172,000 in 1934[45]—forced Superintendent Robert Neff to cut the hospitals' payroll, laying off some employees, reducing others from full-time to part-time, and allowing vacancies to go unfilled. Nursing, business office, nutritional, and house-keeping staffs all suffered cuts.[46] The few new employees came, as President Walter Jessup explained to one correspondent, at a "considerably lower salary than the amount paid heretofore."[47] In the worst hard times of the Depression, when ten more nurses were needed to care for the greater number of state patients, Neff fired four half-time janitors and maids, two part-time painters, a seamstress, an elevator operator, and a housekeeper to offset the cost of the nurses' salaries.[48]

The hospitals staff was also subject to austerities imposed by the board of education on a university-wide basis. In September 1932, President Jessup reported that 300 positions had been cut or had gone unfilled throughout the university, and, in light of this and of the state's continuing economic crisis, the board of education determined to reduce its legislative askings by $500,000 per year and to implement across-the-board salary cuts.[49] However, in early 1933, the next General Assembly cut an additional $150,000 from the board's already reduced funding request. The result was a second round of deeper salary cuts—beginning at 15 percent for salaries of $2,000 or less and reaching 30 percent for salaries of $10,000 or more. Within the hospital, paid vacation was reduced by half and sick leave cut from fifteen days a year to seven.[50]

The fiscal problems of the early 1930s highlighted the administrative skills of Superintendent Robert E. Neff. Neff proved to be the institution's first genuinely effective manager, fulfilling Henry Houghton's stated need for an "expert hospital administrator." Neff's later reputation as a miserly enforcer of petty economies does scant justice to his managerial talent; indeed, Neff's practical administrative solutions to soaring indigent care problems helped, as described in the next paragraphs, to defeat the hospitals' political opponents in the legislative skirmishes of 1933 and 1934. Neff's peers recognized his accomplishments by electing him president of the Iowa Hospital Association at its formation in 1929, and, more important, the Iowa State Medical Society approved a resolution in 1931 praising Neff for the economies he had instituted at the hospitals.[51] Neff also proved to be a capable leader during a leave of absence by Dean Houghton in 1931–1932 and, later, when Houghton's resignation left the college of medicine without a dean from 1933 to 1935.

Neff's ingenuity in dealing with escalating budget problems was apparent in his handling of indigent transportation costs. As so-called emergency cases swelled transportation costs, Neff responded with a plan for a fleet of ambulances and drivers, a plan that not only saved on railroad and taxi fares but also eliminated much of the need for escorts, who received three dollars per day to accompany state patients to Iowa City. In March 1931, Neff requested $3,000 to buy an unspecified number of automobiles, hire drivers and a dispatcher, and pay for maintenance, garage rental, and insurance.[52] In June 1931, Iowa Attorney General John Fletcher, a Polk County Republican, held that the board of education did "not have the authority to purchase automobiles for the uses specified." However, Neff, Jessup, and the board persisted, and Fletcher reversed himself in March 1932, finding that since the law did not specify the means of transportation of indigent patients, Neff's plan to use state funds for the purchase and operation of an ambulance fleet was legal. In short order, the board of education finance committee authorized purchase of three ambulances, along with funds to pay drivers, maintenance, insurance, and depreciation. And, a year after presenting his original proposal, Neff bought the first University Hospitals ambulance, a seven-passenger Buick sedan, for $1,455. By October 1932, the modest ambulance fleet had extended its service area beyond the eastern counties Neff had originally proposed and carried passengers to and from most of the state's major population centers.[53]

Neff's office tallied the savings from ambulance operations over the estimated cost of providing equivalent rail service and made regular reports of those figures. As early as July 1932, Neff calculated savings of some $3,400, a figure equivalent to 623 patient-days of hospital care. A year later, Neff reported that the ambulance service, then up to four cars, had saved the institution nearly $44,000. Moreover, use of its own cars allowed the hospitals to better coordinate transportation needs, and each trip carried an average of more than five patients.[54] Neff also stepped up efforts to induce indigent patients to provide their own transportation, reducing to 58 percent the share of indigent patients requiring state-funded transport service in fiscal 1932. Overall, the cost of patient transportation dropped from a high of more than $166,291 in fiscal 1932 to $133,387 in 1934, a 20 percent reduction in just two years despite an 18 percent increase in the number of state patients.[55]

Few details of hospital operations escaped Neff's attention, particularly details with a bearing on operating costs. In August 1932, he suggested housing state patients receiving outpatient treatment in local boarding houses instead of in the hospitals. For example, cancer patients undergoing radiation therapy did not need hospital beds with full nursing service, Neff noted, and the hospital beds they occupied could serve additional patients. It would be cheaper, Neff concluded, to send patients to a local boarding house—which charged just fifty cents per night—than to have the hospital operate its own facility for ambulatory patients. Dean Houghton concurred, and the board of education approved the plan in November 1932.[56]

Neff also initiated an effort to collect private insurance claims paid to state indigent patients. "It seems grossly unfair in our opinion for patients to capitalize upon their hospital expense by obtaining hospital services at the expense of the State, and at the same time draw health or accident benefits under insurance policies," he wrote to Houghton, estimating the hospitals could recover "several hundred dollars per year" from such patients. An attorney general's opinion held that the hospital did not have the authority to make such claims unless the court committing a state patient specifically ordered proceeds from insurance claims to be paid to the hospitals; however, the board of education subsequently amended the forms used to commit state patients to make legal assignment of such insurance benefits to the hospitals.[57]

The waiting list of committed patients was by far the most difficult problem that Robert Neff and the University Hospitals faced. The lengthening waiting list prompted greater numbers of state patients to claim emergency status, which led, first, to longer waits for those not fortunate enough to gain emergency status; second, to increased transportation costs; and, third, to disruption of the equitable distribution of indigent service among Iowa counties, with the greater benefits flowing to those counties inclined to work the system to their advantage. By early 1933, an already serious situation worsened when the legislature sliced the indigent care appropriation for the second consecutive year, further weakening an already overloaded system. Moreover, as noted earlier, the indigent care system's political opponents had mobilized as well.

To meet the crisis, and especially to defuse its political overtones, Robert Neff devised a plan to establish an indigent patient quota for each county based on its proportion of the state's population. The idea was not new; in November 1930, Neff had referred to "the quota to which Jones County would be entitled on the basis of population" in reply to inquiries from county supervisors there regarding the indigent service.[58] Likewise, the state Medical Society's Committee on Medical Education and Hospitals, in its December 1930 report, had listed the theoretical quota for each county alongside the number of indigent patients actually admitted and the number placed on the waiting list.[59] However, a formal plan to implement the idea does not appear to have surfaced before 1933, when Henry Houghton unsuccessfully proposed it to the medical society's legislative committee. At that time, the committee was determined instead to win approval of partial county financing of indigent care.[60]

The quota plan was simple in concept: divide the state appropriation by the average cost per patient to arrive at the number of state patients the hospital could accept during the year and to apportion that number among all of the counties on the basis of population. In its final form, the plan in fact allowed counties to exceed their quotas by 10 percent, and it provided for the redistribution of unused quotas among the remaining counties.[61] To Robert Neff, the plan's biggest advantage was fairness. No longer would some counties receive disproportionate benefit at the expense of others, nor less service than their taxes paid for. Neff asserted that no form of direct county financing would address this problem. He noted also that larger counties, especially, could utilize local hospitals when they had filled their state quotas, diverting some of the indigent care "business" to the private sector. The quota plan would assure an adequate patient flow for teaching, Neff said, and regularizing this flow would allow the hospital to achieve better per patient economy. In addition to such efficiencies, Neff said the plan would eliminate certain direct costs, such as doctor examinations (at five dollars each) for patients never admitted to the hospital, which he estimated would save $10,000 a year.[62] Noting the "drastic decrease" in the state appropriation and "increased demand for hospital service," the board of education directed University Hospitals administrators in June 1933 to "prepare and administer a plan of apportionment of available service to the several counties based upon proportionate population," a plan calculated to fill 90 percent of available service "in order that there may be room for adjustments."[63]

Neff implemented the quota system beginning August 1, 1933, circulating a letter introducing the plan to physicians, county and court officials, and social workers, and in the fall he attended county medical society meetings across the state to sell the plan. Meanwhile, Neff and his staff culled more than 2,000 cases from the waiting list, reducing it to 3,052, by eliminating people who no longer needed or wanted service at University Hospitals.[64] In operation, the quota plan required meticulous record keeping and reporting, including monthly reports to every clerk of court in Iowa. The clerical burden prompted Neff to hire a half-time assistant to compile statistics and monitor the quota plan, a position that soon grew to full-time while another half-time position was added to handle paperwork.[65]

The quota plan, combined with Neff's other cost-cutting measures, quickly boosted hospital efficiency. In the first seven months of fiscal 1934 the per diem cost per state patient fell from $4.88 (including transportation and physicians' fees) to $4.26, a savings that Neff projected at $90,000 annually and one that would allow the hospital to treat 1,500 more patients with the same resources. The waiting list fell by 1,700 to 1,346, in the quota plan's first six months of operation. At the same time, the hospitals' average daily census rose from some 600 in fiscal 1933 to more than 656 in the first half of 1934, and total indigent patient-days for all of 1934 increased 7.1 percent over 1933 despite the cut in state appropriations.[66]

Neff's quota plan proved to be an attractive alternative to the more radical indigent care proposals that surfaced in and out of the state legislature. The board of education's approval of the plan in June 1933 presented the legislature with a fait accompli by the time of the November special session. Moreover, university partisans had by that time co-opted three legislative members of Elbert Munger's task force. In their minority supplement to the majority report, the three dissenters expressed their preference for continuing the quota plan, "at least for awhile," in lieu of enacting partial county financing of indigent care.[67] Furthermore, two of the three worked with University of Iowa law professor Clarence M. Updegraff in writing legislation to codify the quota plan and sponsored the resulting bill in the state house, while the third introduced it in the senate. Board of education secretary William H. Gemmill, in reporting these developments to President Jessup, concluded that prospects were "very good and satisfactory" for passage of the quota plan into law.[68] On a broader stage, the plan had also gained the endorsement of the Brookings Institution, which devoted a supplementary section of its state government study to the indigent care system; that appendix, written by A. F. Kuhlman of the American Public Welfare Association, recommended not only that the quota plan be permanently adopted but also that all indigent medical care in Iowa take place at the University Hospitals with funding sufficient to operate at full capacity.[69]

University partisans also mounted a vigorous lobbying effort against persistent opponents bent on enacting a county financing plan. From Chicago, Henry Houghton wrote to Arthur Erskine, the Cedar Rapids physician and Munger task force member who favored a county "half pay" plan; Houghton's letter criticized many provisions of the preliminary task force report as unsound and questioned the motives of the university's most ardent detractors. Kuhlman, author of the Brookings Institution's favorable report on the indigent care system, wrote to one of Munger's strongest remaining allies, recounting the hospitals' efforts to reduce the waiting list. President Jessup, meanwhile, pushed the quota plan bill in a characteristically understated manner. Disguising the fact that the bill had been written and orchestrated by university authorities, Jessup told one correspondent that the bill was "agreeable to the University authorities," and he wrote another that key state legislators were "supporting a bill in which the University is very much interested and wholly concurs."[70]

In the end, while county financing proposals languished in the special session, the quota plan passed by a 96–2 vote in the house on December 21 and easily cleared the senate by a 38–3 vote on February 13, 1934. Repeated efforts by opponents to amend the quota bill, particularly by inserting the county-pay plan, failed by wide margins despite attempts by the State Medical Society's legislative committee to mobilize support.[71] Governor Clyde L. Herring signed the quota plan into law on February 16, and it took effect immediately upon publication. In its final form, the law also significantly changed the commitment process, requiring county officials—before issuing a formal commitment order—to determine whether the University Hospitals could admit each patient within 30 days of the commitment hearing. If not, the law mandated counties to provide proper treatment at county expense, a provision meant to eliminate the extended waits for hospital service. Concomitantly, the law nullified the existing waiting list, stipulating that all patients with pending commitments re-qualify for state papers, those patients then receiving preference for admission. The law extended a similar preference to obstetrical and orthopædic cases. The bill also took note of the hospital's ambulance service, stipulating that the state would pay for private transportation of indigent patients only when hospital ambulances were not available.[72]

Passage of the quota law was a major milestone for the University Hospitals. Most obviously, it demonstrated once and for all that the university had enough political muscle to overcome challenges to the state-funded indigent care system centered in the University Hospitals. Moreover, throughout the affair, President Jessup, board of education secretary Gemmill, and Superintendent Neff displayed a political sense far keener than that of their rivals. Responding to bombast from opponents with calm and reasoned arguments, co-opting a faction from within the fractured legislative task force, and calling in heavy hitters such as Houghton and Kuhlman to lobby, university officials built a solid base of support in the legislature and effectively neutralized the opposition.[73]

In retrospect, however, the Depression-era crisis in indigent care and the debate over the University Hospitals' role in the indigent care system highlighted two unresolved problems. First, events reinforced, for better or worse, the hospitals' image as an indigent care institution. Of course, the importance of the hospitals' indigent care role to the state was indisputable, and it ensured ongoing state funding for the hospitals—no small concern through the Depression years. Yet the association of the hospitals with indigent care made it more difficult to promote the hospitals to paying patients, a problem of increasing importance in the post-World War II years.

Second, the reaffirmation of the hospitals' role in indigent care raised once again the issue of the hospitals' purpose. Did the hospitals exist primarily to serve the needs of an indigent patient population or the needs of medical education? Clearly, medical education had been the motivating force behind establishment of the indigent care system. Equally clearly, it was the needs of medical education rather than of indigent care that had won the good graces of Abraham Flexner and the Rockefeller philanthropies in the 1920s. Still, in 1933, President Jessup effectively captured public sentiment in observing that "the first objective in setting up this [indigent care] service was humanitarian, designed to bring relief to [the] crippled and indigent."[74]

The University Hospitals: A 1930s Snapshot

Despite the adverse effects of the Depression, the University Hospitals' operations continued to expand in size and complexity during the 1930s. The hospitals' north tower stood as a beacon of hope, a symbol of the very real accomplishments of medical science, and the most admired and photographed piece of architecture in the Iowa City area. By the mid-1930s, hospitals, especially teaching hospitals attached to academic medical centers, had truly become "temples of science," in Charles Rosenberg's memorable phrase, with technology progressively displacing the patient narrative and, to a considerable extent, the physician's own senses in the diagnosis of disease. Moreover, under the combined impress of science, technology, middle-class cultural ideals, and modern business management practices, rigid standards of decorum applied to hospitals staff—from physicians and nurses to housekeepers and cooks—and to patients and visitors as well. At the same time, the hospitals displayed a sharp division by social class, with private patients isolated in their private and semi-private rooms, often with private-duty nursing care. Overall, and in marked contrast to its late nineteenth- and early twentieth-century predecessors, the University of Iowa Hospitals in the 1930s presented a strictly disciplined environment that was, by turns, reassuring and intimidating to patients.

As noted earlier in Table 3.1, patient admissions at University Hospitals rose nearly 33 percent between 1928–1929 and 1933–1934, from 11,900 to 15,783. For comparison purposes, a 1933 survey of American and Canadian hospitals—based on 1931 data—reported 7,436 admissions at Boston's Massachusetts General Hospital and 61,430 at Chicago's Cook County Hospital. Massachusetts General reported an average patient census of 381 in 1931, and Cook County reported 2,483, compared to the University of Iowa Hospitals' 605. Massachusetts General recorded 65,410 indigent patient-days in 1931, compared to University Hospitals' 188,285 in 1930–1931;

Cook County recorded 907,295 total patient-days in 1931, compared to the University Hospitals' 220,724. Massachusetts General reported expenditures of $1.09 million in 1931; Cook County reported expenditures of $2.78 million; and University Hospitals' total expenditures in 1933–1934 stood at $1.19 million. Reduced to patient numbers and expenditures, Cook County Hospital in the early 1930s treated far more patients with—in proportional terms—far fewer resources than did the University Hospitals, while Massachusetts General treated far fewer patients than did the University Hospitals while deploying virtually identical resources.[75]

In the early 1930s, the University of Iowa Hospitals encompassed 16 wards of 20 beds each, plus 380 beds in smaller units of various kinds, 27 semi-private rooms, with daily charges of $4.50, and 47 private rooms, with daily charges of $6.00. However, because of budgetary restrictions and agreed upon limits on private patients, the occupancy rate in 1933–1934 was just 76.7 percent.[76] In the eighteen months from mid-1933 to the end of 1934, the University Hospitals' patient population included over 4,000 indigent children (15 years of age and younger), more than 1,600 of those receiving treatment in orthopædics, 1,100 in pediatrics, and 1,350 in the other clinical services.[77]

In 1933–1934, the department of orthopædics—located in the Children's Hospital—reported the largest number of patient admissions, with 2,276. The department of surgery—with four large patient wards—reported 2,234 admissions; the combined department of obstetrics and gynecology reported 2,151; the department of internal medicine reported 2,099; and the department of otolaryngology reported 1,970. Urology, ophthalmology, neurology, and pediatrics averaged just under 1,000 admissions each. The rank-order of clinical departments by private patient admissions was quite different, putting the department of urology at the top, with 292 private patients among its 1,138 admissions (25.6 percent), compared to 212 in surgery (9.5 percent), 207 in internal medicine (9.9 percent), 180 in otolaryngology (9.1 percent), and just 160 in orthopædics (7.0 percent). Private admissions were far smaller in number in the remaining services, for example, just 57 in neurology, 48 in ophthalmology, 39 in obstetrics, and 30 in gynecology. A ranking by outpatient visits changed the order once again, with orthopædics holding first place (6,745 visits), otolaryngology second (5,642), general surgery third (3,811), internal medicine fourth (3,370), and ophthalmology fifth (3,343). Overall, outpatient services were by far the fastest-growing component of the hospitals' operations. Total outpatient registrations swelled from 14,200 in 1928–1929 to 29,480 in 1933–1934, and total outpatient visits grew from 58,600 to 121,700.[78]

By the mid-1930s, the major clinical departments afforded a broad array of services for indigent and private patients on both inpatient and outpatient bases. The department of general surgery, headed by Howard L. Beye, consisted of two units, the first unit devoted to neck surgery and neurosurgery—the latter conducted in conjunction with the department of neurology—and the second unit accommodating chest and abdominal cases. Surgical procedures commonplace since the early twentieth century, such as appendectomies, hernias, and subtotal thyroidectomies, made up much of the overall caseload. The department had also developed "a special interest" in diseases of the lungs amenable to surgical intervention, much of that work done in collaboration with staff and patients from the state tuberculosis sanitarium at Oakdale. In the department of orthopædic surgery, headed by Arthur Steindler, the 1,092 surgical procedures in 1933–1934 included osteotomies to correct deformities of the arms and legs, various bone fusions, particularly of the ankles and spinal column, and tendon reconstructions and transplants—an area in which Steindler was a pioneer. In addition, department staff fitted orthopædic appliances, most of them produced in the orthopædic appliance shop, or "brace shop." In the department of otolaryngology, headed by Dean M. Lierle, surgical repair of cleft palates—some 100 cases in all—were a major focus, as were endoscopic examinations of the esophagus and bronchi, both for diagnosis and for removal of foreign materials. The department of urology, headed by Nathaniel G. Alcock, dedicated four rooms to cystoscopic examinations of the urethra and bladder and the diagnosis of prostate problems; common surgical procedures included transurethral resections for prostate cancer and lithotomies for the removal of stones from the bladder.

The department of obstetrics and gynecology, headed by Everett D. Plass, included 32 beds for gynecological patients, most of whom suffered from malignancies or pelvic inflammatory diseases; the most common procedures were dilatation and curettage and hysterectomy. The obstetric division maintained 63 beds for "waiting and delivered mothers" and a nursery accommodating 32 newborns; staff oversaw 858 births in three delivery rooms in 1933–1934. In the department of pediatrics, headed by Philip C. Jeans, the management of syphilitic children was a major focus, with an average census of some 80 patients receiving treatments, chiefly arsenicals, at any one time; a second major focus was the treatment of 100 or so children suffering from diabetes mellitus, with a regimen that included insulin—in use at the University Hospitals since the mid-1920s—and dietary guidelines. The department of internal medicine, headed by Fred M. Smith, exhibited a discernible movement toward specialization, particularly in cardiology and hematology, a trend reflecting both broader movements in internal medicine and the personal interests of Smith and his senior staff. In cardiology, the "heart station," in operation since the late teens, conducted hundreds of electrocardiograms annually by the mid-1930s; in hematology, the use of liver extracts in the treatment of pernicious anemia was one of the most important of then recent innovations. In the department of ophthalmology, headed by Cecil S. O'Brien, glaucoma and infectious diseases of the eye were the chief focus, many of the latter cases presenting in the outpatient clinic and referred from other clinical services; department staff performed nearly 500 surgical procedures in 1933–1934, including surgical intervention in glaucoma. The department of roentgenology had expanded substantially since its first organization some fifteen years before, offering its diagnostic services to other departments, notably the surgical specialties, as well as providing radiation therapy—particularly in the treatment of cancers, including an experimental program with urology in postoperative radiation therapy for prostate cancer.

Behind the increase in patient admissions and in the variety of patient services lay a sizable increase in medical staff at the University Hospitals. The 60 staff physicians and 31 interns and residents in 1928–1929 rose to 79 staff physicians and 67 interns and residents in 1933–1934. In the 1930s, interns and residents for the first time began to play larger roles in the care of indigent and private patients and in teaching—interns participating in the instruction of undergraduates and residents participating in the instruction of undergraduates, interns, and other residents. The lives of interns and residents were not easy. Interns received room, board, laundry, and an annual salary of $100 in return for round-the-clock service seven days per week. Similarly, residents received "full maintenance" in return for long hours of service and meager salaries—in internal medicine, for example, 20 dollars per month in the first year and 80 dollars in the second. Both interns and residents were monitored on and off the wards, not least by night charge nurses who scrutinized their comings and goings with special care.

Like the sharp increase in medical staff, the growth in the nursing staff did not halt in the face of Depression-era budget cuts, even though nursing salaries were a major component of the hospitals' overall budget. Nursing accounted for $124,936 of the $1,090,000 budget (11.5 percent) in 1933–1934, despite steep pay cuts in the early 1930s. The number of supervisory nurses increased only just over 11 percent, from 43 to 48 between 1928–1929 and 1933–1934; however, from the late 1920s, the hospitals began to employ increasing numbers of "general duty" graduate nurses, a measure of the need for a higher level of direct patient care than that afforded by student nurses. The hospitals' budget for 1929–1930 listed 20 such positions, a number that grew to 74 by 1935–1936. In addition, beginning in 1931, the hospitals' budget included as many as 30 graduate nurses who worked in return for just room, board, and laundry.

Meanwhile, nursing students still made up much of the hospitals' nursing contingent, a pool of labor less experienced but also less expensive, on average, than graduate nurses and no doubt more easily controlled. In 1933–1934, nursing enrollments totaled 139—46 seniors, 36 juniors, and 57 freshmen. At the University of Iowa as elsewhere, the prevailing notion of nursing education had changed little from the turn of the century, and nursing students were seen primarily as a source of cheap hospital labor. As testament to that, just 517 of the University Hospitals' nursing school's 977 graduates between 1900 and 1933 were still actively involved in nursing in 1933. Despite that, nurses in the 1930s were achieving a degree of specialization of their own; at the University Hospitals, for example, the department of general surgery introduced a concept of "group nursing" for critically ill patients.

One of the most striking changes in the early 1930s was the increase from six to thirteen in the hospitals' administrative staff, reflecting Robert Neff's more active policymaking role and the increase in administrative responsibilities associated with the growing complexity of the hospitals' operations.[79] By 1933–1934, the hospitals offered several new services in support of their clinical missions. For example, the fall of 1933 saw the inauguration of a milk pasteurization plant, contracting with two local milk producers—one holstein herd and one guernsey herd—whose facilities were subject to inspection by university authorities; in 1933–1934, the plant processed over 53,000 gallons of milk. In 1933, the hospitals also established an intravenous fluids laboratory that prepared normal saline and glucose solutions for parenteral nutrition and fluid replacement; in addition, the hospitals' budget included $14,677 in payments to blood donors— this just prior to the advent of blood banking. The hospitals also created the position of "hospitals hostess" in the fall of 1933, the hostess offering guidance to patients and their families. In the meantime, many established support services expanded considerably from the 1920s to the 1930s. In 1933–1934, the housekeeping department, responsible for general cleaning, laundry, and mending, counted 75 full-time employees. The social service department provided counseling and evaluation to nearly 7,000 patients, the bulk of them in orthopædics, pediatrics, and internal medicine. Kate Daum's department of nutrition, with a budget of $180,544 for food and $43,509 for salaries, comprised 74 full-time employees, including nine dietitians, responsible for dietary counseling of individual patients and for preparing and serving over 1.5 million meals annually to patients and staff.

Finally, the University Hospitals and the nearby Medical Laboratories Building nurtured the slowly expanding research interests of college of medicine faculty. Through the 1920s, research expectations for college of medicine faculty remained low, lofty pronouncements notwithstanding, but the 1930s brought a significant widening of participation by University of Iowa faculty in national scientific organizations as well as a smattering, at least, of important original research. The first small injections of external research funding helped to spur the research effort. In 1928–1929, the college of medicine reported receipt of $32,000 in external support, more than half of that devoted to training programs. The figure dropped dramatically during the early years of the Depression, reaching a low of $10,000 in 1932–1933 and standing at just $16,000 in 1933–1934. However, external support, especially for research, rebounded through the rest of the decade, peaking at $44,000 in 1938–1939. At the same time, internal support for research came from interest income accruing from the Rockefeller grants of the 1920s—funds converted to a Scientific Reserve Fund under Dean Houghton—and from departmental funds representing a portion of private practice fees. Total internal research support stood at $19,400 in 1928–1929 and grew to nearly $30,000 in 1930–1931 before tumbling to a low of just over $20,000 in 1933–1934.

Grants from corporations and from philanthropic foundations accounted for nearly all externally funded research projects in the 1930s. Examples were the $6,000 provided annually by the National Oil Products Company in the mid-1930s for metabolism research, the $2,500 received in 1935 from the S.M.A. Corporation for vitamin A research, the $6,000–$7,200 granted annually by Mead Johnson for pediatric metabolism research, the $2,000 annual contributions from Quaker Oats for calcium metabolism research, the $10,000 received in 1937 from the John and Mary Markle Foundation for research on blood clotting, and the $13,500 gift in 1939 from the National Foundation for Infantile Paralysis for poliomyelitis research.

The degree of research activity varied widely across departments and among individual faculty. A bare handful, like internal medicine's Willis Fowler, maintained formal research laboratories, occasionally, like Fowler, employing a laboratory assistant as well. The work of pathologists Emory D. Warner and Harry P. Smith on the blood clotting mechanism and the elucidation of the role of vitamin K was of major importance; in 1941, Smith won the American Society of Clinical Pathologists' Ward Burdick Medal for his work. Throughout the 1930s, the department of pediatrics, under the energetic leadership of Philip C. Jeans, was a major site of research, particularly in the area of pediatric nutrition and metabolism; studies by Jeans and his colleague Genevieve Stearns were widely published, and both were elected to membership in the American Institute of Nutrition in the late 1930s. Also important was the blood-banking work of Elmer DeGowin of internal medicine and Everett D. Plass of obstetrics and gynecology. DeGowin, Plass, and their associates published a series of articles addressing fundamental problems in the collection, storage, and transfusion of human blood, work that led in 1938–1939 to the establishment at the university of the first modern blood-banking system. That blood-banking research—

implemented by DeGowin's protegé Robert Hardin, who directed the Allied blood transfusion program in the wake of the D-Day invasion—was a crucial component of American military operations during World War II.

The Hospitals and Labor Relations

The Great Depression was the principal cause of a general decline in morale—and, to some extent, in the quality of care—at the University Hospitals. The university-wide salary and wage reductions of the early 1930s were scaled to affect least the lowest-paid employees, and top administrators took cuts along with everyone else. But even at the lowest pay scales those cuts amounted to 15 percent. Moreover, for a worker on a $1,000 annual salary, a cut of $150 was arguably more painful than a cut of, say, $3,000 applied to a $10,000 salary. In addition, salary cuts followed two years of layoffs and increasing workloads. The result was dissatisfaction among some groups of University Hospitals employees, many of whom gradually assumed a more militant stance toward the hospitals' management.

As the Depression wore on, continuing low-level complaints by janitors, housekeepers, and orderlies regularly demanded the attention of Superintendent Neff and President Gilmore, and employee complaints occasionally brought bad publicity for the hospital. A Christmas day 1935 article in a local newspaper, for example, quoted extensively from a letter by an unnamed source claiming that the pay cuts and working conditions in the University Hospitals were unfair, that there were not enough nurses, and that the hospitals' food was "putrid." Superintendent Neff himself had received a raise to $8,500 in July 1935, representing "a substantial restoration" of the cut he had taken in his pre-1933 salary of $9,000.[80] Responding to such charges, Neff acknowledged the nursing shortage to Gilmore, reporting that the more qualified nurses were going to institutions that paid more, forcing the hospital to hire nurses "who would otherwise be considered unacceptable."[81]

In 1937, prompted by complaints from a group of hospital employees, the state legislature "recommended" that the pay of those earning $1,200 a year or less—more than 80 percent of the hospital labor force—be restored to its pre-1933 levels. Neff and Gilmore had earlier considered restoring the wages and salaries of the lowest-paid employees, and university officials could hardly ignore the legislature's recommendation, particularly in light of the workers' restiveness and the legislature's command over the indigent care appropriation to University Hospitals. Under the new wage scale, female housekeepers, who worked 48-hour weeks on straight salary, saw their pay increase from $40 to $50 a month; male janitors' restored salaries amounted to $60 a month plus three meals a day; and male orderlies, many of whom worked more than 60 hours a week, saw their compensation rise to 25 cents per hour plus meals, up from 19 cents.[82]

The $24,000 the state legislature added to the indigent care appropriation was less than half of the $63,466 proposed in pay raises, and Neff paid for the unfunded portion of the wage and salary restoration by reducing the total state indigent patient quota and cutting 62 positions from the payroll,[83] a reduction in the labor force that surely added further to the workload of the remaining employees. Indeed, one housekeeper complained anonymously to Iowa Governor Nelson G. Kraschel about "all this extra work . . . heaped upon us."[84] In his response to the governor, Neff insisted that the housekeepers were not overworked, and he claimed, in fact, that there had been no effective reduction in staff. Neff's argument was, at the very least, disingenuous; perhaps the best that can be said is that he did transfer employees among departments in an effort to redistribute the reduced workforce.[85]

When the janitors in the hospitals complained that they still were paid less than janitors in other parts of the university, Neff responded that they had less responsibility than the "semi-custodians" on the east campus, and that their pay compared well with that of janitors in other Iowa hospitals. When orderlies complained that their raises had been offset by reductions in the number of hours they could work, Neff denied that their hours had been cut and said that each orderly had been given the choice of working either an 8-hour or 12-hour daily shift, although with the understanding "that no orderly work more than six days in each week."[86]

Neff, then, like any cash-strapped manager, looked first to reductions in labor costs to meet the shortfall in his budget; but, in his defense, the legislature had created a serious problem by effectively mandating raises but refusing to appropriate the necessary funds. In that 1930s version of "unfunded mandates," the superintendent's options were limited, and fewer employees undoubtedly meant more work and worse conditions for workers and patients alike. Hospital workers, already battered by five years of pay cuts and layoffs, understandably felt that their sacrifices were little appreciated, and the result was an outbreak of labor union activity at the University Hospitals. Despite the fact that workers had no legal right to engage in collective bargaining over pay and working conditions at state institutions, disgruntled hospital workers formed the "S.U.I. Hospital Employees Organization" and before long sought support from the American Federation of State, County and Municipal Employees.[87] The success of that early organizational effort is unclear; however, in early 1938, hospital workers pushed an eight-point program to standardize wage scales, hours, vacation, and sick leave, to determine the number of positions required in the hospital, and to obtain cost-of-living adjustments and a permanent pension fund.[88]

Robert Neff and the Profession
of Hospital Administration

Throughout his term as University Hospitals superintendent, and particularly so from the mid-1930s, Robert Neff enjoyed a far greater measure of authority over hospital operations than had any of his predecessors. In part that reflected Neff's smooth working relationship with Dean Henry Houghton. While Houghton exercised authority over medical affairs within the hospitals, he placed broad trust in Neff and showed little inclination to interfere in routine hospital operations or to contravene Neff's authority in areas apart from purely medical matters. At the same time, however, the formal line of authority between the dean and the superintendent remained clear, with Neff reporting to Houghton and Houghton reporting to President Jessup on behalf of the University Hospitals.

An administrative reshuffle in the college of medicine and in the university's central administration in the early 1930s enhanced Neff's position. Dean Houghton took a leave of absence for much of the 1931–1932 academic year, returning to China and to the Peking Union Medical College. During his absence, a committee composed of junior dean and physiology chair John T. McClintock, obstetrics and gynecology chair Everett D. Plass, and surgery chair Howard L. Beye handled the college's administrative affairs, with Beye serving as chief liaison to the University Hospitals.[89] Upon his return to Iowa City in August 1932, Houghton submitted his formal resignation effective January 1, 1933, having accepted the position as head of university clinics at the University of Chicago.[90] In the wake of Houghton's departure, the same committee as before took charge of the college of medicine.[91]

Walter Jessup, who had served as university president since 1916, resigned effective July 1, 1934, to become president of the Carnegie Foundation,[92] delaying the search for Houghton's successor. Jessup apparently preferred to give a new president the opportunity to participate fully in naming the new medical dean, and there were also financial incentives in leaving the deanship vacant. In any event, the board of education chose Eugene A. Gilmore to succeed Jessup as university president in the spring of 1934. A former University of Wisconsin law professor and vice governor in the U.S. occupation of the Philippines, Gilmore had come to Iowa City in 1928 as dean of the college of law. Although Gilmore was in the last years of his career by 1934, Walter Jessup found him to be "full of interest and enthusiasm" and undertook to brief him thoroughly on the inner workings of university administration. To bring Gilmore up to speed on the medical side of the campus, Jessup invited Henry Houghton to "come out [i.e., from Chicago] and pass the time of day with us," adding that Gilmore would "profit by a little education from you."[93]

In the interim, the search for a new dean of medicine languished. However, it did so now largely because of problems in the search itself. The difficulty was not a lack of promising candidates; rather the chief obstacle was the meager $8,000 salary offered by the board of education coupled with the resolute refusal of the medical faculty—the Lee Wallace Dean experience still fresh in mind—to extend private practice privileges to a new dean to make up the salary deficiency. It was not until the spring of 1935 that Ewen Murchison MacEwen, a Scottish immigrant and head of the department of anatomy since 1931, assumed the deanship.[94] MacEwen had been under consideration for the post since at least the previous summer,[95] suggesting that his selection was, in no small part, a matter of expediency.

Through the leadership transition in both the central administration and the college of medicine, Robert Neff remained as superintendent of the University Hospitals, a simple fact that helps to account for the practicing autonomy that Neff acquired during those crucial years. Beginning with Houghton's leave of absence in the fall of 1931, the seat of the college's authority over the hospitals was vacant for all but a few months until 1935, a period during which Neff began reporting directly to the president on matters pertaining to the hospitals' business and financial operations. It was during Houghton's leave of absence, for example, that Neff, working with Jessup and the board of education, initiated the hospital ambulance fleet, and it was after Houghton's resignation that Neff worked with the board to implement the quota plan.

By the time Eugene Gilmore assumed the presidency and Ewen MacEwen the deanship, this reporting relationship between the superintendent and the president was an established fact. Although perfectly aware that he should have some say in running the hospitals, MacEwen never managed to assert that authority fully; indeed, not being a clinician, MacEwen had a great deal of trouble asserting his authority over the clinical department heads. Overall, circumstances conspired to make MacEwen's twelve-year tenure as dean a troubled one and to vest in Neff a measure of the authority that both John A. Hornsby and Winford H. Smith had advised the university to place in its full-time hospital superintendent 20 years before. Thus, Robert Neff became, partly by intention and partly by default, an example of a slowly emerging corps of activist professional hospital administrators.

In the early decades of the twentieth century, the professionalization of hospital administration had lagged well behind that of medicine and even nursing. That lag reflected, first, the fact that even as late as 1930, relatively few hospitals had become enterprises, like the University of Iowa Hospitals, sufficiently large and varied to demand professional administrators. Second, the slow development of education for hospital administration generally reflected, as at the University of Iowa during Lee Wallace Dean's tenure as college of medicine dean, the reluctance of physicians to surrender authority over hospital operations. Third, hospital administration, as is true of most emerging professions, suffered from internal uncertainty and conflict over the scope and substance of its professional claims and, in turn, the scope and substance of its professional education.

Most of the early impetus behind the professionalization of hospital administration came from within the American Hospital Association (AHA), successor in 1907 to the Association of Hospital Superintendents founded in 1899. Among other things, the AHA sought standards for hospital equipment and supplies and the elaboration of efficient practices, concerns directly related to hospital administration. At the AHA annual meeting in 1910, Frederick A. Washburn and Joseph B. Howland—director and first assistant director at Massachusetts General Hospital—presented a paper on their hospital's methods of training administrators, and argued that large hospitals should establish formal training courses to serve both their own needs and those of smaller hospitals for trained administrative personnel.[96] Various papers and studies followed in subsequent years; however, the goal proposed by Washburn and Howland made little headway until the American College of Surgeons initiated its effort at national hospital standardization in 1918, a movement predicated to a considerable extent on shortcomings in hospital administration.

In 1922, a Committee on the Training of Hospital Executives, commissioned and funded by the Rockefeller Foundation, submitted a comprehensive report on administration in the nation's hospitals. Grounded in a thorough study of the organization and function of the hospital and emphasizing the hospital's expanding community roles, the committee's work was noteworthy, among other things, for presenting the first suggested curriculum for hospital administrators, a curriculum that aimed to produce administrators "with a broad vision of service and a broad educational background."[97] Still, the need of formal education for hospital administrators was far from universally accepted, and, in his discussion of the report before the American Hospital Association's 1922 annual meeting, the committee's executive secretary Willard C. Rappleye admitted that the recommended fifteen-month basic curriculum—encompassing nine months of academic work and six months of practical experience—included "a good many phases and activities that are possibly far-fetched."[98]

A second milestone occurred with the 1929 publication of Michael Davis's *Hospital Administration: A Career*, the result of another Rockefeller-financed study.[99] Based largely on extensive consultations with members of the AHA, Davis's program for the education of hospital administrators sought, as he later explained, to remedy two serious shortcomings in the profession: first, the lack of "broad basic objectives toward which administrators should be headed" and, second, administrators' weaknesses in both human relations skills and basic business methods.[100] Emphasizing training in business rather than medicine, Davis recommended a two-year university-based curriculum based on a graduate business model, with courses in accounting, statistics, organization and management, economics and social science, history and status of hospitals, business policy, public health, and legal relations. Reinforcing Davis's call for professional education, his study revealed that on-the-job training was still the norm among hospital administrators, 46 percent of whom were physicians, 20 percent nurses, 8 percent women in religious orders, 10 percent laymen, 11 percent laywomen, and 5 percent "unspecified," none of whom had received academic certification specifically for hospital administration.

Although one 1980 article lauded Davis's work as "the first book to significantly influence the education of hospital administrators,"[101] progress toward the professionalization of hospital administration continued to be slow. For example, an undergraduate training course begun at Marquette University in the mid-1920s was discontinued for want of students. Even at that late date, a major obstacle to the growth of a profession of hospital administration—a problem noted by many observers at the time—was the absence of a demand for trained administrators, suggesting the need to proselytize hospital board members and physicians on the virtues of professional administration. A second obstacle, ironically, lay in the American Hospital Association. On the one hand, the association was a major source of ideas on the proper training and role of the hospital administrator; on the other hand, association members were, by and large, more concerned with the development of the hospital itself, and particularly in updating the hospital to keep pace with the needs of modern medicine, than with the professional development of hospital administrators. In illustration, much of the program at AHA meetings centered on operational matters—for instance, how to maintain an efficient laundry service, how to establish a profitable radiology department, and how to hire graduate nurses.

Responding to a 1932 call from AHA President Paul Fesler, Matthew Foley, editor of *Hospital Management*, contacted J. Dewey Lutes, president of the hospital associations of Chicago and Illinois, to promote a professional association, and over the next several months Lutes solicited area hospital administrators as well as Malcolm MacEachern of the ACS for help. In February 1933, 18 administrators and 2 hospital magazine editors met at the Palmer House in Chicago and founded the American College of Hospital Administrators, an organization that, after a slow start, became an important voice in the professionalization of hospital administration.[102] At the time of the ACHA's inception, however, not very many hospital administrators yet had specific training in the field. According to American Medical Association data, physicians and nurses still held the vast majority of administrative positions in 1933. Of the AMA's 6,326 registered hospitals, 2,199, or more than a third, were headed by physicians; 2,542, or more than 40 percent, were headed by nurses; 767, or 12 percent, were headed by laymen; and 685, or 11 percent were headed by laywomen.[103]

The long-awaited report of the Committee on Costs of Medical Care, published in 1932, added further weight to the call for formal training programs for hospital administrators.[104] The first steps toward creation of such a program came at the University of Chicago, where Michael Davis, in collaboration with former Iowa medical dean Henry Houghton, then head of the University of Chicago Clinics, and William Spencer, dean of the school of business, established the nation's first graduate program in hospital administration in 1934, a program conducted under the auspices of the graduate school of business.[105] Funded by the Julius Rosenwald Fund from 1934 to 1937 and the Commonwealth Fund from 1937, the new course was headed by Director Arthur Bachmeyer with the assistance of Gerhard Hartman. It was open to students with a baccalaureate degree, an MD, or MPH, graduate status deemed essential to ensure that students possessed the requisite "background preparation" and sufficient maturity "to make conclusive decisions concerning their careers." The curriculum comprised a year of academic coursework—students choosing from a broad selection of courses, chiefly in business and some also in the health sciences— and a twelve-month administrative residency, culminating in the MBA. The program attracted disappointingly little interest from physicians; in general, according to those who conducted the course, the physicians who applied for admission were those with poor educational backgrounds or few prospects for success in private practice.[106]

The University of Chicago program served as a model for programs established at other universities during and immediately after World War II. One such program, described more fully in the next chapter, was at the University of Iowa, a project promoted by Dean Ewen MacEwen and Super- intendent Robert Neff. By the early 1940s, Neff had become a highly visible member of the emerging national community of hospital superintendents, having served as the ACHA's second president and also as president of the AHA. By the end of World War II, Neff compiled a well-rounded picture of the postwar healthcare system, noting the "inevitable expansion and improved distribution" of healthcare, the possibility of federal aid for grad- uate specialty training and facilities, and the likelihood and consequences of federal subsidies for community hospital construction. In light of those

changes, Neff counseled a fundamental reorientation of the University of
Iowa Hospitals, transforming the facilities into a regional medical center and
promoting relations with Iowa's community physicians to improve the flow
of patient referrals. In Neff's view, the task for the University Hospitals in the
postwar years would be to maintain its technological edge in the face of an
inevitable process of technology transfer that would, with federal aid, make
community hospitals increasingly competitive in high-technology areas.[107]

For Neff, and for MacEwen as well, graduate education in hospital
administration was part of an overarching strategy to accommodate the rapid
and far-reaching changes in the structure of American healthcare anticipated
in the postwar era. In addition, the Iowa Hospital Association, which Neff
had helped to found, urged creation of the program in anticipation of a
postwar boom in hospital construction.[108] Together, Neff and MacEwen,
with enthusiastic backing from university president Virgil Hancher, outlined
before war's end a graduate program to be taught by Neff, his assistant Harold
Smith, and professors from the college of business and the graduate college.
Approved by the board of education early in 1945 and initially scheduled
to open in the fall, the program was to include thirty semester hours of
classroom instruction followed by a nine-month hospital residency, and Neff
and MacEwen hoped to secure funding from the Kellogg Foundation to
subsidize operations. Neff's resignation in 1945 temporarily derailed the
project; however, the need for an administrator to carry through with the
plan for a graduate program in hospital administration was a major factor in
the choice of his successor.

The Development of Undergraduate Medical Education

In 1933, the American Medical Association's Council on Medical Education
and Hospitals, in conjunction with the Association of American Medical
Colleges and the Federation of State Licensing Boards, commissioned the
first comprehensive review of undergraduate medical education since Abraham Flexner's survey of 1908–1909. As part of that review, Herman G.
Weiskotten, dean of the Syracuse University College of Medicine, visited
89 medical schools in the United States and Canada in the years 1934–
1936, issuing confidential reports to each of the schools and publishing a
comprehensive report in 1940.[109] Weiskotten and his collaborators ranked
the schools in each of 96 categories covering organization, administration,
faculty, finances, physical facilities, libraries, and basic science and other
undergraduate programs.[110]

Based on detailed questionnaires as well as Weiskotten's April 1936
campus visit, the Weiskotten report dealt a blow to the University of Iowa
College of Medicine's self-image and to its standing among the nation's

medical schools. The principal deficiency noted in Weiskotten's report was the college's high ratio of students to faculty and to clinical cases, but those fundamental deficiencies led in turn to other problems. The report charged that at the University of Iowa, as at most other medical schools, instructors in the basic sciences taught too many sections and too many students, including large numbers of non-medical students—a problem whose origins lay in Flexner's "university department" vision to integrate the college of medicine into the larger university. In the fall semester of 1931, for example, faculty in the Department of Anatomy taught 332 students; the Department of Pathology counted 376.[111] Thus encumbered, faculty could devote little time to research and to participation in national scientific organizations, pushing the most promising young faculty, according to Weiskotten, toward clinical rather than basic science positions.

In the clinical years, meanwhile, Weiskotten found too many students in the University Hospitals wards in proportion to the number of clinical cases available for teaching, and, much like the situation in the basic sciences, he found that students received inadequate supervision from a too small staff. As a result of the unfavorable student-teacher ratio, clinical teaching relied too heavily on didactic instruction. More generally, the report charged that academic standards were low; the college permitted too many students to repeat courses they had failed; and the college used too many students as part-time instructors. Weiskotten's evaluation dropped the college of medicine from a ranking in the top 10 percent of medical schools to a middling position.[112]

MacEwen and the medical faculty took some immediate steps to address the points raised in the review. They reorganized clinical teaching in the senior year to give students more time in the wards and more contact with patients; yet there were still too few clinical faculty for adequate supervision. With an internal study showing that per capita costs of medical education had risen from $531 in 1927 to $815 in 1934,[113] even as college of medicine budgets fell, the only real solution to the high student-teacher ratio in clinical and basic science areas was to reduce the size of the student body. According to established standards, the college had preclinical facilities to teach not more than 100 first-year students and clinical facilities enough for not more than 65 seniors. In the early 1930s, entering classes averaged significantly above that level, and senior classes averaged near 90 (Table 3.2). Importantly, however, those numbers were substantially below the 152 first-year students accepted in 1929–1930, a figure dramatically reduced by the imposition of higher admissions standards in 1930.

Nationally, medical school enrollments peaked in the early 1930s and slumped later in the decade, although the number of graduates continued its steady rise, from 4,735 in 1931 to 5,377 in 1937.[114] At the University of

Table 3.2   College of Medicine Enrollments, 1930–1945

	First-Year	Second-Year	Third-Year	Fourth-Year	Total	Male/Female
1929–30	152	147	102	107	513	489/24
1930–31	97	106	102	95	402	380/22
1931–32	100	83	98	98	382	362/20
1932–33	127	81	72	93	378	365/13
1933–34	102	109	70	72	355	343/12
1934–35	112	90	97	65	373	361/12
1935–36	120	104	82	92	407	391/16
1936–37	113	109	86	80	404	388/16
1937–38	104	93	89	84	384	370/14
1938–39	56	93	72	88	328	318/10
1939–40	87	54	82	70	304	288/16
1940–41	88	71	47	82	288	274/14
1941–42	101	68	67	46	282	266/16
1942–43*	—	—	—	—	401	375/26
1943–44*	—	—	—	—	398	375/23
1944–45*	—	—	—	—	312	298/14

*Because of the accelerated program of instruction during the war years, the board did not report enrollments by class.
Source: Board of Education Biennial Reports.

Iowa, the question of reduced enrollments was politically sensitive, since, because the medical school was a public institution, national accrediting bodies were not its only constituency. In fact, university officials found it impossible to maintain a lower limit on entering classes, which averaged 112 from 1932 to 1937. Moreover, officials feared a glut of applications in advance of higher admissions standards in store for the 1938–1939 academic year, and Dean MacEwen asked the board of education to intervene, imposing a formal limit on the size of the entering class. In June 1937, the board specified 100 as the maximum number of first-year students and set the number of senior students at 80. The board also permitted the college to lower the limits to 90 and 75, respectively, "as rapidly as feasible."[115] As shown in Table 3.2, the combination of higher standards and the enrollment cap brought an extraordinary initial reduction (46.2 percent) in admissions between 1938 and 1939, but the numbers, as before, crept upward in subsequent years. Following the same pattern, total enrollments dipped significantly (26.6 percent) from 1938 to 1942, only to move steeply upward during the early war years before falling once more, this time reflecting the vagaries of wartime placement policies.

The tightening of admissions standards and the imposition of formal and informal enrollment caps significantly affected enrollments for women. In 1929–1930, women made up 4.7 percent of the student body, but that percentage slumped to a low of 3.2 percent in 1934–1935. Thereafter, female enrollments, like total enrollments, edged upward, peaking at 3.6 percent in 1937–1938 before the concerted effort to limit overall enrollments once again pushed female enrollments lower, to 3.0 percent in 1938–1939. Thereafter, as total enrollments rose into the war years, so, too, did the proportion of women students, achieving a maximum of 6.5 percent in 1942–1943. At the end of the war, however, largely as a consequence of military placement policies, women once again accounted for only 4.5 percent of the student body—a figure roughly equal to the long-term average. At the national level, meanwhile, female enrollments rose through the years of World War II, peaking at more than 14 percent in entering classes of 1945, with some schools, like Harvard University, admitting women for the first time.[116]

Graduate Medical Education

Nationally, the years from 1930 to 1940 saw the incorporation of fourteen medical specialty boards, each of which developed standards of training and education for its respective field. Previously, the American Board of Ophthalmology had organized in 1917 and the American Board of Otolaryngology in 1924. Together the burgeoning specialty boards formed the framework of a system to certify medical specialists, and this system in turn brought within its purview the graduate clinical training provided at the University of Iowa Hospitals. Under the emerging certification system, the various arrangements that constituted hospital internships, and what at University Hospitals were called "senior internships," crystallized into a more formal system of graduate medical education, the major feature of which was the standard hospital residency.[117]

As noted earlier, the University of Iowa had adopted a system of junior and senior internships by 1930, replacing what had previously been an ill-defined graduate experience that included the one-year internship required for medical licensure as well as advanced training in clinical practice and, occasionally, basic scientific research. In addition, the college sponsored increasing numbers of short courses and clinics for practicing physicians, offerings that today fall within the domain of continuing education. Prior to the 1930s, post-internship training in the specialties at Iowa chiefly reflected the personal preferences and idiosyncrasies of the clinical department heads. Arthur Steindler, for example, normally had several protégés in training who were variously referred to as interns, residents, assistants, research assistants, and instructors, all of them essentially apprentices with the most promising privileged to stay for as many as five years. In addition to room, board, and laundry service, they received small stipends for their work in the wards, operating rooms, laboratories, and lecture halls.

Designation of junior and senior internships was a step toward differentiating the two major categories of graduate medical education at the University Hospitals. The eighteen to twenty junior interns rotated through several clinical services during a one-year period that satisfied the legal requirements for medical licensure. Each senior intern, on the other hand, served under a single clinical chief on a renewable one-year appointment in order to gain the experience necessary for specialty practice. While junior interns, like interns in most other medical institutions, were largely unsupervised from a medical standpoint—MacEwen would later call them "lost sheep"—senior interns enjoyed a fuller relationship with their respective departments that often included advanced coursework in addition to intensive practical training. The senior internship itself, however, was only a transitional step toward the institution of a more formalized system of residencies.

The American Medical Association's Committee on Medical Education and Hospitals published its first list of approved residency programs in U.S. and Canadian hospitals in 1927, but the University of Iowa Hospitals did not make the list until 1933. That year the hospitals received AMA approval in 11 specialty fields, with obstetrics and gynecology counted separately.[118] With that change, the hodge-podge of senior internships became residencies, although with little apparent effect on the scope and substance of the training programs. By the end of the 1930s, however, residencies at the university had fallen in line with the certification standards established by the specialty boards then in existence—although in many cases those standards were still very much in flux. Ranging in length from one year (psychiatry) to five years (general surgery and otolaryngology), full-term residencies were comparatively few in number. No clinical department had more than two residents, while most had anywhere from one to seven "assistant residents"— in other words, they would accept up to seven first-year residents, of whom only one or two would eventually complete the full term (Table 3.3). Those who did not advance presumably either found other residency programs that would accept them or, more likely, left to enter general practice. This first effort to standardize residency programs at the University Hospitals, while uneven in some respects, had little effect on the number of residents in training across the clinical departments, with most departments showing only a slight gain or loss.

The elaboration of graduate medical education carried quite different implications for women than for men. As late as 1940, only 14.7 percent of

Table 3.3   University Hospitals Residency Programs, 1934 and 1938

	Residencies		Assistant Residencies	Length of Residency (Months)	
	1934	*1938*	*(1938)*	*1934*	*1938*
Internal Medicine	6	1	4	12–36	36
Neurology	2	1	1	12	24
Obstetrics-Gynecology	6	2	3	12–36	36
Ophthalmology	6	1	3	36	48
Orthopædics	3	1	7	12–36	36
Otolaryngology	8	2	5	27–60	60
Pathology	2	1	0	12	48
Pediatrics	3	1	2	12	24
Psychiatry	4	2	0	12–24	12
Radiology	3	2	2	24	24
Surgery	7	1	6	12–36	60
Urology	3	1	0	36	36
Total	**53**	**16**	**33**		

Source: *Journal of the American Medical Association* 103 (August 25, 1934): 597–608; 111 (August 27, 1938): 785–847.

hospital internship programs certified by the AMA (105 of 712) accepted female applicants, and just three programs in Iowa did so. In theory, the University Hospitals was one of those; however, a classic "catch-22" effectively precluded female appointments. Lacking women house staff, the hospitals made no provisions for housing them; without adequate housing, as Robert Neff patiently explained in 1939, there could be no female interns.[119] Although the General Hospital had originally reserved three rooms for female house staff, those rooms were, by the late 1930s, taken over for staff offices. The same argument applied to women residents as to interns, and a 1939 analysis in President Hancher's files showed that, aside from pediatrics and obstetrics-gynecology, the University Hospitals had trained no female residents in the 1930s.[120]

The University Hospitals in Wartime

World War II intruded on the University Hospitals and the college of medicine even before the United States' formal entry into the war in December 1941. First, medical supplies, especially those of European manufacture, became scarce and increasingly expensive as war spread across Europe and the western Pacific. Second, and perhaps more important, the cost of wages and salaries rose rapidly as wartime production and increased agricultural prices boosted the economy at last out of the Depression doldrums. Both factors put further strains on a hospitals' budget only just recovering from the worst effects of the Depression. In addition, the war effort ultimately imposed substantial burdens on an already severely strained college of medicine, as the selective service system siphoned non-tenure track faculty into the armed forces and medical school enrollments increased significantly.

Through the 1930s, Robert Neff had wrung every possible economy from the hospitals' operations,[121] and, from 1940–1941 to 1944–1945, total expenditures rose by 20.7 percent, from $1,483,000 to $1,790,000, compared to an increase of just 13.7 percent through the entire decade of the 1930s. From 1941 to 1945, the state appropriation for indigent care rose just 11.0 percent, from $1.00 million to $1.11 million. Under the circumstances, the hospitals' only recourse was to make cuts in the level of service to state patients, cuts that deepened after America's entry into the war (Table 3.4). The numbers of indigent admissions dropped 9 percent from 1940–1941 to 1941–1942, and slipped further in each succeeding year, for a total loss of 36.3 percent over the five-year period. At the same time, total indigent patient-days fell less sharply, at 31.4 percent, suggesting that the hospitals shouldered an increasing proportion of long-term patients with chronic illnesses. Meanwhile, reflecting the renewed agitation on the issue of private practice, private admissions rose 37.5 percent. With the increase in private patients, total admissions and total patient-days fell just 20.0 and 18.7 percent respectively, as private patient admissions rose from 11.2 to 19.3 percent of total admissions during the war years, signaling a major shift in the hospitals' patient base.

For the college of medicine, the effects of the war were also apparent before December 1941, reflecting a widespread mood of preparedness that affected medical education as it did the rest of American society. Facing a call for additional thousands of military physicians, the Association of American Medical Colleges urged its members in May 1941 to increase enrollments and to speed up their programs in order to graduate more doctors for both military and civilian service. The University of Iowa medical faculty's response was skeptical, perhaps based in part on memories from World War I, when a similar call had proved unwarranted. Faculty members maintained that "the emergency was not as great as was being stated and that in due course the Army would find that it did not need as many doctors as it first thought." Nonetheless, the college did admit 101 first-year students for the 1941–1942 session, 15 percent more than the previous year and a striking departure from the enrollment cap adopted by the board of education after the Weiskotten report. Moreover, contrary to its

Table 3.4   Admissions and Patient-Days by Payment Category, 1941–1945

Fiscal Year	Indigent Admissions	Indigent Patient-Days	Private Admissions	Private Patient-Days	Other Admissions*	Other Patient-Days*	Total Admissions	Total Patient-Days
1940–41	16,100	240,269	2,353	24,647	2,479	28,790	20,932	293,706
1941–42	14,647	205,627	2,595	27,876	2,890	34,092	20,132	267,595
1942–43	12,020	188,702	2,924	32,022	3,044	35,456	17,988	256,180
1943–44	10,620	164,240	3,031	31,851	3,405	38,736	17,056	234,827
1944–45	10,262	164,855	3,236	33,855	3,255	40,084	16,753	238,794

Note: All categories include acute, newborn, and housed clinic patients.

*Includes clinical pay, county clinical pay, cost, student, staff, research, and State Services for Crippled Children patients.

Source: University of Iowa Hospitals and Clinics Annual Statistical Reports.

initial misgivings, the faculty quickly adopted AAMC and War Department standards for accelerated medical education in December 1941.[122]

The accelerated program called for year-round instruction and the admission of a new first-year class every nine months instead of every twelve months. The plan, implemented at the University of Iowa in July 1942, meant that each entering class would complete its four-year course in three calendar years, a schedule that virtually eliminated vacations for faculty and instructors (leaving only four weeks between academic sessions). To boost enrollments, the AAMC plan also called upon medical schools to lower their admissions standards, reducing from ninety to sixty the number of undergraduate credit hours required of incoming students, a policy the University of Iowa adopted in January 1943. Just four months later, however, the board of education rescinded that action, possibly fearing a glut of ill-prepared students just as wartime staff reductions reached their most critical proportions.[123]

The loss of teaching staff began soon after the declaration of war, as the War Department ordered all reserve officers to active duty by April 1942. The War Department permitted medical instructors who filled "essential" teaching posts to avoid the callup by resigning their reserve commissions, and Willard C. Rappleye, chairman of the AAMC's Committee on Pre-paredness, urged medical deans to "persuade reserve officers . . . that they will be discharging their duty by continuing their present essential teaching activity."[124] However, many University of Iowa staff members chose military service, a loss that, by November 1943, totaled 33 faculty, instructors, and assistants for whom there were no replacements. In 1938–1939, the hospitals' clinical staff peaked in number at 88; in 1946–1947, the first full postwar year, the total recovered only to 62 even though, by that time, several younger faculty had returned from military service. Further compounding instructional shortcomings, the War Department's Office of Procurement and Assignment ordered a reduction in civilian resident and intern staffs beginning in January 1944.[125] Nationally, reduction of the medical teaching force soon had a noticeable effect on the quality of instruction. The AAMC released a study in October 1943 showing that a quarter of the 72 schools it surveyed reported fewer teachers than were needed to provide adequate instruction, while the remaining three-quarters were operating at bare minimum staffing levels. The study faulted the accelerated program for placing demands on the remaining staff "which can only be met for a limited time." In all, the study proclaimed "the danger signal of a breakdown" in medical education.[126]

The wartime regime worsened existing problems in the conduct of medical instruction at the University of Iowa, difficulties stemming from the cumulative effects of the Depression on the college of medicine—not least the relatively poor overall quality of the student body. Dean MacEwen complained in 1941 of the school's policy of drawing all of its students from Iowa, noting that superior applicants from out of state were routinely rejected in order to accommodate in-state applicants.[127] Just as important, as the war effort accelerated, local officials effectively lost control of admissions decisions to the army and navy, each of which conducted its own student placement and training programs and, together, reserved some 75 percent of available places in the nation's medical schools for military trainees.

The markedly increased teaching load for faculty and staff in the college added to an already gloomy state of affairs at University Hospitals. Not only was the teaching staff—meaning chiefly physicians—reduced in size, but the staff in nursing and non-patient service areas was reduced as well. The shortage of nurses was especially troublesome throughout the war, owing both to the need for nurses in military service and to the better salaries to be had elsewhere. Nurses were in short enough supply at the war's outset to drive MacEwen to urge higher standards for promotion and graduation in the school of nursing, but not higher standards for admission. "This will mean that certain girls may be able to take the course, but not graduated [*sic*]," he wrote. "We believe it sound under the present shortage,"[128] since, while students were enrolled, they would work on the hospitals' wards. At the same time, Neff raised salaries for nursing supervisors in a bid to keep them from leaving for other institutions. "This we considered quite essential in an effort to hold our key people as much as possible," he wrote Hancher.[129] Later in the war, Neff required private duty nurses, who registered with the hospital to work in the private patient area, to serve as general duty nurses for four weeks a year in return for private duty privileges.[130] Despite such draconian measures, the number of graduate nurses on duty at the hospitals fell by some 30 percent from 1940 to 1945.

Low wages also contributed to high turnover in the rest of the hospitals' labor force. Janitors and housekeepers could earn more money by working on the east campus of the university or in the war industries, and their positions went unfilled because the hospital could not attract enough applicants at the pay scales offered.[131] Labor relations were already problematic, as the Hospital Employees Organization had continued to agitate for better wages, sending a delegation to Des Moines in 1941 to meet with legislators and maintaining constant pressure on the administration.[132] But even when Neff attempted to adjust pay at the lower end of the wage scale in 1943, he encountered resistence from the university business manager, who feared that labor unrest on the east campus would reignite if hospital employees received raises. The need for a coordinated labor policy between the hospital and other units of the university prompted President Hancher to assign his business manager, along with Neff and administrative dean Allin Dakin, to this task, and eventually hospital workers received higher pay in exchange for the loss of meals that had been part of their compensation.[133]

Shortages of material also hampered hospital operations. Tire and gasoline rationing presented obvious difficulties for the ambulance fleet, notwithstanding the six-month supply of tires Neff had stockpiled by the start of the war. By 1942–1943, the ambulance fleet comprised 23 vehicles and traveled 7,500 miles monthly in transporting some 2,000 patients.[134] Neff sought special dispensation from state authorities to obtain needed supplies without regard to local quotas, only to learn that the hospital would have to present its requests to the county rationing boards just like everyone else.[135] As the war progressed, there was also a shortage of blood donors, which Neff ascribed to the decline in the number of civilian men on campus and the armed services' reluctance to permit uniformed men to donate blood.[136] Of course the rationing of steel, cotton and synthetic fabrics, sugar, coffee, and other goods nationwide also affected hospital operations.

The shortages of staff and supplies, the presence of more students in training, the longer hours and loss of vacations, the conflicts between labor and administration, the patriotic duty that many such as Neff felt to volunteer time for civilian contributions to the war effort, and the generally heightened tensions of wartime (officials even feared that saboteurs might plant bombs on campus) all meant unprecedented hardship for hospitals staff. Some participants in a May 1943 conference with Hancher openly expressed their weariness. In his memorandum on the conference Hancher wrote,

> I emphasized the fact that a continuous educational program, plus pressure for hospital service, has caused me grave concern. On several occasions doctors

have complained to me about the heavy loads they are carrying and that I feared that some of them might collapse under the strain. This would be a double tragedy in these times because there are no replacements. Furthermore there is no hope for more or better doctors or nurses, or even common helpers, as long as the war lasts. Dr. Plass, at this point, added that this was very noticeable in the Hospital and that his work was much harder than it used to be in many small ways that are hard to define. "Things just don't go as smoothly as they should," he added. Dr. Smith concurred emphatically. Dr. Alcock though[t] we ought not to take a defeatist view. This should be a challenge. Mr. Neff said that it might be a challenge, but that this was the first time in thirty years he had ever felt whipped. Dr. Alcock said you are never whipped until you think you are. Mr. Neff replied that was true and he proposed to carry on as best he could, but he certainly was as near to being whipped as he had ever been.[137]

The Private Practice Controversy

The combination of the Depression and wartime austerity helped to spark renewed conflict over private practice in the University Hospitals, an issue that had lain in wait since the 1927 imbroglio that had led to Dean Lee Wallace Dean's forced resignation. When the issue came to a head once again, it set at odds a university administration reluctant to change the 1928 policy limiting private practice at University Hospitals and a small number of part-time clinical chiefs who advocated an expanded private practice. Among the latter group, the most outspoken and committed to the cause of private practice was Nathaniel G. Alcock, who had since 1915 headed the department of genito-urinary surgery—which had become the department of urology in 1939 in line with specialty board certification standards.

Alcock and his supporters questioned the basis upon which the 1928 agreement with the Iowa State Medical Society stood, pointing out that private practice had never, in fact, been limited to 5 percent of the hospitals' beds. They also argued—plausibly enough—that there was now demand for more private beds and also that an expanded private practice could shore up the hospitals' uncertain finances. The chief battleground was the conversion of thirteen beds to private use on the second and third floors of the west wing of the General Hospital. Originally, those floors had contained 72 rooms with 99 beds for private patients; however, according to Robert Neff, demand for private beds "was far below these accommodations for a number of years." Consequently, ten of the rooms had been converted to other uses, including storage areas, a barber shop, and additional beds for state patients. In all, then, there were 83 beds for private patients in the General Hospital, rather than the 99 initially envisioned.[138]

Facing a deficit of $17,000 in his fiscal 1940 budget, Neff asked the medical faculty to approve raising the hospital fee charged to private patients. The faculty approved, but some accepted the rate hike only "under protest," as Dean MacEwen noted to President Gilmore on September 12, 1939. MacEwen noted further that the recent outbreak of war in Europe would worsen inflation in the cost of medical supplies, pharmaceuticals, and other materials, which would only exacerbate the hospitals' fiscal problems. He suggested converting thirteen of the west wing beds taken for other uses back to private patient service as a means to increase hospital revenues.[139]

Nathaniel Alcock had written President Gilmore several weeks earlier, "not as a member of the staff of the University Hospital or as a member of the staff of the University," but "as a tax payer of the state of Iowa." Alcock drew a paradoxical portrait of the hospital in which there existed on the one hand scores of empty ward beds that could not be filled because of a lack of state funding, and on the other hand a demand for private beds that could not be met because of the cap on private patients. He related the story of a private patient recently denied admission to the hospital, one "perfectly willing" to pay for a ward bed rather than a private or semi-private room. "I think it is a fine situation when I cannot get in," the patient had complained. Alcock continued,

> It is the private patients that are bringing in money to the hospital every day. It is money that the hospital needs in order to operate economically and efficiently. Yet there is not a day that we are not turning away private patients because we have not a vacant bed in a hospital that cannot be run economically and efficiently on account of the enormous number of vacant beds. Now, there is the situation in a nutshell and I think it is the most ridiculous thing I have ever heard of.[140]

In fact, by all accounts, demand for private beds was steadily increasing,[141] and Alcock's own patients, according to MacEwen, at times filled half of the available accommodations for private patients. In an improbable parallel to the indigent care crisis of a decade earlier, the demand prompted Neff to begin compiling a waiting list for private patients. In a further parallel to that earlier crisis, the hospital also admitted emergency private cases in excess of the available beds, placing such patients in ward beds until space in private rooms became available.[142]

A change in university administrations delayed any resolution of the private patient debate. Eugene A. Gilmore retired in July 1940 with a permanent successor yet to be named, and Chester A. Phillips, dean of the college of commerce, served as acting president until Virgil M. Hancher assumed the presidency that November. Hancher, who had earned his bachelor's and law degrees from the University of Iowa, practiced corporate law in Chicago for sixteen years before returning to Iowa as its president. During the July–November 1940 interregnum, Chester Phillips eschewed substantive policy changes, and when Hancher assumed the presidency, the question of the thirteen hospital beds was far from the top of his agenda.

Nonetheless, as circumstances worsened, Nathaniel Alcock and Dean M. Lierle, head of otolaryngology since 1927 and also one of the remaining part-time clinical chiefs, pressed the issue. At Alcock's and Lierle's initiative, the medical faculty voted in May 1941 to recommend returning the thirteen disputed beds to private service. In apprising President Hancher of the faculty's action, MacEwen added his own endorsement of the proposal and echoed the arguments Alcock and his supporters had made. Citing first the demand for private beds, MacEwen asked, "Should we deny the tax payer the quality of service furnished the indigent?" He noted, too, that the beds were originally intended for private service and, referring to the 1928 agreement limiting private practice at the hospital, asked, "Are the doctors of the state more important than the main supporters of the hospital [i.e., taxpayers and prospective patients]?" He concluded by asking that the question be put before the board of education for action.[143]

Hancher met with William Boyd, still head of the board of education's finance committee, and the two agreed broadly that adding thirteen beds to the private service would would not end complaints and might only "whet the appetite of the doctors for additional space." Boyd was particularly wary that expanding private practice could fuel "a wave of indignation against the staff" and endanger the indigent service, and he did not favor bringing the issue up to the full board of education.[144] Boyd, true to form, also wrote to Henry Houghton, now back in China, to apprise him of the situation. Houghton weighed in with dire warnings against changing the current balance of private and indigent service, calling the proposal "ominous" and the possible ramifications "calamitous" should it provoke revision of the indigent care law by the state legislature. "I cannot believe that the Board or President will sanction any change in the present ratio of private to service beds," he wrote back to Boyd.[145] Deference to Houghton doubtless reinforced Boyd's opposition to expanding private practice, and Boyd still occupied a central role in formulating board policy. As a result, the faculty recommendation went nowhere.

However, the private-to-indigent bed ratio, as mentioned above, was itself the subject of some confusion, as the number of private beds in the hospital had always exceeded 5 percent of the total. At the time of the original agreement in 1928, the full complement of private beds in the General Hospital and Children's Hospital amounted to more than 11 percent of the total; by 1941, even with fewer private beds in service, private patient-days still represented more than 8 percent of the hospital's service.

As Neff noted, "Only on a broad interpretation could this be considered as approximately '5%'."[146] In any event, Hancher continued to gather input on the matter, and later the Hospital Committee—made up of Neff, MacEwen, and the clinical department heads—formed a special subcommittee to study the issues surrounding possible expansion of private service.[147]

The lack of definitive action on the faculty recommendation contributed to an atmosphere of uncertainty about board policy, uncertainty that Alcock interpreted to his own benefit. Without naming names, Neff reported to the Hospital Committee in August 1942 that the number of private patients in public wards had averaged eight to ten per day over the course of several months, and Neff noted that those patients were "indicated as emergency cases by the various clinical services." Neff acknowledged that it was hospital policy "never to refuse any patient at any time who may present himself in distress or in need of medical care"; however, he warned that it might be necessary "to strictly insist that the physicians accept only *medical* emergencies and then only when patients are virtually 'dumped on our door step.'"[148] The medical council, a body composed of all college of medicine department heads and the dean, quickly endorsed Neff's appeal to restrict the number of private emergency admissions. The council instructed department heads to admit only those private emergency cases who were already in Iowa City and to stop the practice of calling in private cases whenever ward beds opened up.[149] In November 1942, the board of education went further, officially banning the admission of private patients to the hospitals' public wards, the only exception being true emergencies.[150]

At the same time that the use of ward beds for private patients was under scrutiny, Alcock antagonized Neff by threatening to subsidize the salaries of a male nursing supervisor and orderly in his department from his own private fee income. Despite Alcock's assertion, as quoted by Neff, that such an action was "'not illegal,' 'not immoral' and 'not dishonest,'" it clearly challenged the administrator's prerogative to establish the pay and working conditions for hospital staff. Alcock first asked Neff to raise the two employees' salaries from the hospital's payroll; when Neff refused, citing a $10-a-month raise pending for all nursing supervisors and his fear that raising the pay of a single orderly would cause "dissatisfaction among the other employees of this category," Alcock became hostile and threatened—in fact promised—to pay the employees on his own account. Neff felt strongly that he had the authority to prohibit Alcock from proceeding with his plan and sought backing from MacEwen and Hancher to do so. Both concurred, with MacEwen commenting, "The Department of Urology has been the source of a great deal of trouble." In fact, MacEwen continued, "It is in this department that most of the labor trouble started."[151]

Against this background of tension—not to mention the chaos and tension of wartime operations—the question of returning the thirteen beds to private service ground slowly toward a decision. In the spring of 1943, the Hospital Committee's special subcommittee on private practice recommended that the board of education reconsider its policy as stated in the 1928 agreement and allow the thirteen-bed expansion of the private service. To the previous arguments in favor of the expansion, the subcommittee now added the presumed shortage of medical services in some rural areas where physicians had been called away to active military duty. The full Hospital Committee then approved the subcommittee's recommendation. But when Hancher met with the subcommittee to discuss the proposal in detail, he found that of its five members—Alcock, Neff, H. Dabney Kerr, Everett D. Plass, and Fred M. Smith—only Alcock had any enthusiasm at all for the plan.

Kerr, Hancher wrote, was willing to go along with the proposal as a contribution to the war effort, but "was not keen about any increase." Hancher noted that Plass "took about the same position," while Smith "said he and his department had all the patients they needed." For his part, Neff promised to "administer whatever policy is approved." That left only Alcock, who "favored no limitation whatever" on private practice at the hospital. Hancher concluded that the subcommittee's recommendation did not appear to satisfy his desire that any change be "temporary or limited in character," that it "not involve a greater load than the staff could carry," and that "no one should profit as a result of the [war] emergency." Under the circumstances, he was inclined to think "the present policy would have to stand unless it could be shown to be clearly wrong." Hancher told the subcommittee that "the proposal would be greatly strengthened *if it could be said that no one proposed to profit by the emergency*" [emphasis in original]. Moreover, he thought it "unfair to ask the full time men to carry an added load without increased compensation while the part time men would increase their earnings from the increased load." In that vein, "Dr. Alcock did not offer to waive the fees from private patients, nor did he offer to ask his part time colleagues to do so."[152]

A month later Hancher held another conference on private practice, this time meeting only full-time faculty members, some of whom served under part-time department heads. On that occasion, most participants were distinctly opposed to the part-time clinical chiefs' conduct of their private practices in the hospital. Most, such as neurology head Clarence Van Epps and internal medicine's James A. Greene, felt that the part-time department heads were too absorbed in private practice, and both Van Epps and Greene suggested that part-timers tended to forget the institution's educational mission. Everett Plass, who now came out against adding any private beds in the hospital, favored allowing university doctors to supplement their salaries with private fees up to an established ceiling, above which the income would revert to the college of medicine.[153]

Alcock, however, had not given up. In October 1943, bypassing normal lines of authority, he wrote to William Boyd, asserting that two recent resignations from the medical faculty resulted from the denial of private practice privileges. Boyd, of course, passed the information to Hancher, who met with one of the individuals and wrote the other to ask if Alcock's charge was true. Both denied it, one stating "categorically that he was not leaving on account of a denial of part time arrangement," and the other—James Greene—citing the opportunity he had received to head a department and receive a significantly higher salary at Houston's Baylor University.[154] Alcock's letter to Boyd was part of a renewed push that he, Lierle, and department of surgery head Frank R. Peterson were undertaking to gain approval for the thirteen-bed expansion. The three pressed Robert Neff for an answer on the expansion proposal, but Neff, like Plass, was now opposed. Hancher noted that Neff "felt that, with the pressure of the increased teaching load [because of higher wartime enrollments and the accelerated teaching program], and the shortage of medical and non-medical personnel, it would be a complete answer to say that an increase could not be made at this time without a decline in quality of instruction."[155] MacEwen later added to the arguments against the expansion, citing wartime shortages of hospital medical staff caused by reductions in residency and internship programs.[156] Hancher presented the plan, "together with detailed arguments for and against," to the board of education—along with his recommendation that the expansion be denied. The board, after deferring action in November, finally ratified Hancher's position in December 1943—two-and-a-half years after the expansion proposal first was formulated.[157]

The question of the thirteen additional private beds was only one part—and perhaps not the most important part—of the troublesome private practice issue to surface in the early 1940s. The proposal to add thirteen beds to the private service was not a long-term solution to the problem of growing demand for service from paying patients; nor did it address the question of the proper ratio of private-to-indigent service at University Hospitals. In the same way, the board of education's rejection of the proposal resolved neither the looming issues of a changing private-to-indigent patient base nor the increasingly unworkable compromise between full-time and part-time faculty systems in the college of medicine.

During the Depression years and, it seemed, even more so during the war years, the existence of two classes of medical staff with two sets of privileges and wide discrepancies in income potential worsened the impact of hard times on staff morale. In 1940, eight clinical chiefs—all of the surgical specialties plus internal medicine—still retained part-time status and held a virtual monopoly on the lucrative and growing private service within the University Hospitals. In addition, and partly as a result of their devotion to private practice and the returns they derived from it, those chiefs operated their departments to a greater or lesser extent as private fiefdoms, with some of them, like Nathaniel Alcock, conspicuous in ignoring institutional policies regarding faculty responsibilities in undergraduate and graduate teaching, research, and the care of indigent patients.

The part-time clinical chiefs' relative autonomy was a significant source of tension between them and the rest of the college, particularly full-time junior faculty, full-time department heads, basic sciences faculty, and the dean. Simmering since the traumatic events of the late 1920s, the question of the part-time chiefs' position crystallized after the curricular reorganization of the late 1930s. One effect of this was to place greater teaching demands on the faculty and house staff. Some clinical chiefs tended either to ignore their added teaching duties or to shift the responsibility of teaching down the line to their assistants and house staff. The exigencies of wartime—accelerated schedules, large classes, fewer personnel—further heightened the conflict both within and among the clinical departments. With the steady expansion in the hospitals' private service during the 1930s and early 1940s, notwithstanding the board of education's agreement to limit private practice, some of the department heads reportedly earned $40,000–$75,000 per year in private patient fees. At the time, the average salary for a full-time assistant professor was no more than $4,000, with no more than twice that amount for a full professor.[158]

Dissatisfaction was often especially acute among the assistants of these part-time heads, assistants who treated the chiefs' private patients as well as indigent cases, did the largest share of the teaching, and had little security in pay or position in return. It was there that, in President Hancher's estimation, the discrepancy between part- and full-time status was "the widest and most unfair."[159] That inequitable distribution of responsibilities and rewards was, of course, a carryover from the nineteenth century, and even in the first decades of the twentieth century most clinical departments still consisted of a department head and a small group of assistants, few of those in tenure track positions. By 1940, however, the number of tenure track, full-time faculty—thus, the reservoir of frustration—had expanded considerably, and department heads had become a decided minority.[160]

Assistants might receive some compensation for treating their chiefs' private patients, but such compensation was a personal matter, and Dean MacEwen criticized the practice as "a form of modified fee-splitting" that, although reportedly commonplace in all of the surgical services, was "unsound and very dangerous."[161] A one-month sample of private cases in the department of urology in 1941, for example, revealed that the majority of procedures done on Alcock's patients were performed in whole or in part by associate professor Ruben Flocks. When Alcock demanded to MacEwen that Flocks join him as a partner in private practice, and he in fact began paying Flocks an annual salary despite Flocks' full-time appointment, MacEwen and Hancher decided that they would sooner part with the chief than with Flocks. The latter they regarded as the equal of Alcock; yet they could not approach the combined salary that he already was receiving under Alcock's aegis. Even worse, few formal regulations had been established regarding promotion, job security, salary, or workload for assistant and associate professors; advancement in pay and rank was, according to one faculty member, "a hit-and-miss affair."[162]

Hancher and others worried, rightly enough, that the uproar caused by part-timers such as Alcock undermined collegiality among the faculty, detracted from the academic environment of the college, and stunted efforts to foster research. At the same time, by the 1940s, the longstanding plan to convert the remaining part-time positions to full-time had grown obviously unrealistic. It was clear—to Hancher at least—that some solution to the private practice conundrum was imperative, and the approaching retirement of the most illustrious of the part-timers, Arthur Steindler, appeared to open a window of opportunity. Hancher also learned that, apart from Alcock, the part-time clinical chiefs recognized the danger of the situation, and some appeared ready to accept a radical restructuring of the private practice system.[163] Realizing that the college could not hope to sustain the existing double standard once wartime restrictions on faculty movement ended, Hancher set his sights on a radical postwar restructuring of the private practice system to avoid a "mass exodus" that would wreck the college.[164]

Conclusion

Events from 1928 through mid-1945 provided a stiff test for the University of Iowa Hospitals, with the tight budgets and staff shortages of the Depression and the war years projecting an unwelcome contrast to the exuberant expansion of the teens and twenties. In some respects at least, the University Hospitals survived the test as well as, or perhaps better than, might have been expected. For example, the period saw a substantial expansion in the hospitals' clinical services, marked by a one-third increase in patient admissions between 1930 and 1945. Likewise, the hospitals survived serious political challenges to the indigent care system, a system vital to the hospitals' existence and essential to their educational mission. The hospitals also made significant strides in the area of administration, as Robert Neff occupied a far more important place in both operations and policy than had any of his predecessors. Under the circumstances, those were no small accomplishments.

Yet, in 1945, the hospitals emerged from long years of hardship and discontent with serious faults, the most important of them obvious even to then-contemporary observers. First, the hospitals' stature as a teaching institution had declined markedly since the buoyant days of the late 1920s, reflecting slowly worsening inadequacies in both teaching staff and facilities. Second, the endlessly divisive and seemingly intractable dilemma of private practice threatened to erupt into open warfare in the postwar years, pitting part-time faculty against their full-time colleagues and against the administration of the college of medicine, the hospitals, and the university as well. Third, the hospitals suffered severe limitations from their dependence on indigent care—and, thus, on state appropriations—for their survival, a lifeline that had proved to be tenuous indeed during the Depression and one that detracted from the hospitals' overall appeal to private patients.

Moreover, the likelihood of major changes in the American healthcare system and in American medical education in the immediate postwar era further complicated the outlook for the University Hospitals. The growth of private health insurance during the war—in part a result of wage and price controls that encouraged organized labor to seek health benefits in lieu of wage increases—promised to create a new class of healthcare consumers, a promise further enlarged by the very real possibility of a postwar national health insurance program. At the same time, a federally subsidized postwar explosion in community hospital construction, coupled with federal aid for specialty medical training, threatened to increase the competition for those consumers. Meanwhile, the marriage of the federal government and scientific research, also a product of wartime experience, held the prospect of a major transformation in the academic medical center with important consequences for teaching hospitals.

However, if the University of Iowa Hospitals' problems were reasonably clear in 1945, the solutions to those problems were far less plain. Similarly, while Robert Neff and others were well aware of the lessons to be learned from the combined experience of Depression and war and were, to some extent at least, also attuned to the many changes that lay ahead, the University Hospitals' responses to the opportunities and risks of the postwar world were uncertain at best. In fact, as the next chapter details, those responses came not as part of an overarching pattern but in piecemeal fashion, forged in the sometimes intense give-and-take of legislative and institutional politics over the course of two decades and more.

Notes

1. For an overview of the depression in Iowa, see Leland L. Sage, *A History of Iowa* (Ames: Iowa State University Press, 1974), pp. 269–308.

2. H. S. Houghton to O. J. Fay [telegram], February 11, 1933, File 73, 1932-33, W. A. Jessup Papers, University of Iowa Archives.

3. W. A. Jessup to Cliff Millen, August 4, 1931, File 67, 1931-32, W. A. Jessup Papers, University of Iowa Archives.

4. The 125-bed figure is from R. E. Neff, "To the Physicians, County Officials, and Social Workers of the State of Iowa," January 7, 1929, Folder 57, 1928-29; see also Minutes of the Medical Faculty Hospital Committee, September 27, 1928, File 57, 1928-29, W. A. Jessup Papers, University of Iowa Archives. The 266-bed figure is from an untitled report dated July 30, 1930, showing growth of the indigent patient waiting list from July 1929 to July 1930, File 57, 1930-31, W. A. Jessup Papers, University of Iowa Archives.

5. Neff, "To the Physicians, County Officials, and Social Workers of the State of Iowa."

6. "University Hospital Finances," a memo prepared by President Jessup's office, October 1928, detailed the hospital's financial predicament and the steps taken to deal with it. See File 57, 1928-29, W. A. Jessup Papers, University of Iowa Archives.

7. See Board of Education Minutes, January 29, 1929, University of Iowa Archives.

8. "State Patient-Clinical Service," unsigned memo, January 1930, tabulated the waiting list as of the first and last day of each month from August 1927 to December 1929. See File 57, 1929-30, W. A. Jessup Papers, University of Iowa Archives. Erwin C. Pohlman to W. A. Jessup, April 30, 1931, numbered the waiting list at 2,277, File 57, 1930-31, W. A. Jessup Papers, University of Iowa Archives. The 5,434 figure is from the preliminary report of a joint legislative committee appointed to investigate the status of indigent care; the report appeared in *Journal of the House* (Des Moines: State of Iowa, 1933): 1130–1136. One should note that the committee's chairman, Dr. E. E. Munger of Spencer, Iowa, was an implacable foe of University Hospitals and the college of medicine, and used his position to foster opposition to the institution.

9. Iowa State Medical Society Committee on Medical Education and Hospitals, "A Study of the Laws Relating to the Commitment of Patients to the State University Hospitals and the Operation Thereof," December 1930 (Des Moines, IA: The Society), pp. 45–46.

10. Ibid., pp. 47–48.

11. Detailed tables analyzing the waiting list by county, by clinical department, by diagnosis, and so forth are contained in a large envelope labeled, "Waiting list statistics," File 57, 1932-33, W. A. Jessup Papers, University of Iowa Archives.

12. H. S. Houghton to W. A. Jessup, January 29, 1930, File 57, 1929-30, W. A. Jessup Papers, University of Iowa Archives.

13. A typical exchange involved Ray P. Scott, a Marshalltown attorney, to W. A. Jessup, January 28, 1931; R. E. Neff to Scott, January 29, 1931; Jessup to Scott, January 31, 1931; and Scott to Jessup, February 2, 1931, File 57, 1930-31, W. A. Jessup Papers, University of Iowa Archives. The result was the immediate admission of the patient—a Marshalltown police officer—on whose behalf Scott acted.

14. S. D. Whiting to W. A. Jessup, January 29, 1931; also R. E. Neff to W. A. Jessup, January 30, 1931, File 57, 1930-31, W. A. Jessup Papers, University of Iowa Archives.

15. Iowa State Medical Society, "A Study of the Laws Relating to the Commitment of Patients to the State University Hospitals and the Operation Thereof," p. 45.

16. R. E. Neff to H. S. Houghton, January 13, 1931; Houghton to W. A. Jessup, January 13, 1931, File 57, 1930-31, W. A. Jessup Papers, University of Iowa Archives.

17. H. S. Houghton to W. A. Jessup, January 15, 1931, File 57, 1930-31, W. A. Jessup Papers, University of Iowa Archives.

18. R. E. Neff to H. S. Houghton, January 13, 1931; Neff to Houghton, March 31, 1931, File 57, 1930-31, W. A. Jessup Papers, University of Iowa Archives; Gerhard Hartman, "Current expenditures by function," a statistical resume of financial data compiled by Hartman in 1946, Gerhard Hartman Papers, UIHC (University of Iowa Hospitals and Clinics) Administrative Offices.

19. H. S. Houghton to W. A. Jessup, January 13, 1931, File 57, 1930-31, W. A. Jessup Papers, University of Iowa Archives.

20. Iowa State Medical Society, "A Study of the Laws Relating to the Commitment of Patients to the State University Hospitals and the Operation Thereof."

21. *Journal of the House* (Des Moines: State of Iowa, 1927). Introduced on February 25, 1927, the bill went to the committee on public health whose members adopted the extensive revisions introduced by Wamstad himself at the behest of Iowa State Medical Society members from Polk County. The bill passed the House on April 8; however, the Senate sent the bill to its sifting committee (a committee to reduce the number of bills pending near the end of a legislative session), where opponents refused to consider it. An attempt to remove the bill from committee failed by a single vote in the full Senate. See also, "Transactions, House of Delegates, Iowa State Medical Society," *Journal of the Iowa State Medical Society* 17 (July 1927): 247–263 especially 258–260, "Report of Committee on Public Policy and Legislation."

22. "Joint meeting of the legislative committee and state university officials," September 15, 1928, File 73, 1928-29. W. A. Jessup Papers, University of Iowa Archives. That the medical society had broken with the farm bloc and now wished to cooperate with the university on the matter of indigent care is made clear by numerous comments in this meeting.

23. H. C. Shull to G. T. Baker, November 13, 1928, File 57, 1928-29, W. A. Jessup Papers, University of Iowa Archives; *Journal of the Iowa State Medical Society,* 19 (July 1929): 343.

24. The medical society's legislative committee and the board of education's liaison committee met in November 1928 to present their respective positions and exchange views. See H. C. Shull to G. T. Baker, November 13, 1928, op. cit.

25. H. S. Houghton to W. A. Jessup, December 20, 1928, File 73, 1928-29, W. A. Jessup Papers, University of Iowa Archives.

26. Board of Education Minutes, December 11, 1928, University of Iowa Archives.

27. Ibid. See also, "Report of Committee on Public Policy and Legislation," *Journal of the Iowa State Medical Society* 19 (July 1929): 341–346. The committee reported, 345, that "[a]fter a careful analysis of the resolutions from the board of education, one is convinced that the board does not feel inclined to use its influence in any way to have the present Perkins, Haskell-Klaus Laws changed in any manner. Although they agree that certain changes should be made they are unwilling to consent to such changes being made in the laws, preferring that the changes be a policy of the Board."

28. *House Bills and Resolutions, 1929* (Des Moines: State of Iowa, 1929).

29. H. S. Houghton to W. A. Jessup, September 27, 1928, File 73, 1928-29, W. A. Jessup Papers, University of Iowa Archives. Also see Wamstad's proposed legislation, identified as House File 203, in *House Bills and Resolutions* (Des Moines: State of Iowa, 1929).

30. *Journal of the House, 1929* (Des Moines: State of Iowa, 1929): 995.

31. "Report of Committee on Public Policy and Legislation," p. 345.

32. Iowa State Medical Society, "A Study of the Laws Relating to the Commitment of Patients to the State University Hospitals and the Operation Thereof," p. 14.

33. See *Journal of the Iowa State Medical Society* 24 (January 1934): 50.

34. E. E. Munger, "Hospitals and the health problem with special reference to rural America," *Report of the Board of Health of the State of Iowa* (Des Moines: State of Iowa, 1912), p. 282. See also, *Acts and Joint Resolutions Passed at the Regular Session of the Thirty-Third General Assembly of the State of Iowa* (Des Moines: State of Iowa, 1909), pp. 24–28. The phrase quoted here is contained in the law's enacting clause.

35. This and other Munger materials are in File 57, 1930-31, W. A. Jessup Papers, University of Iowa Archives.

36. The most comprehensive source for information on the joint resolution that created Munger's task force is *Journal of the Iowa State Medical Society* 23 (July 1933): 407–414; texts of the resolution, the committee's preliminary report and proposed bills to implement its recommendations, and some of its correspondence are reprinted therein. Erskine's views are known from a paper he delivered to the Buchanan County Medical Society on December 12, 1932, "Problems of Medicine and Medical Care in Iowa," File 57, 1932-33, W. A. Jessup Papers, University of Iowa Archives.

37. "Preliminary Report of the Committee Acting Under Joint Resolution No. 7," *Journal of the House* (Des Moines: State of Iowa, 1933), pp. 1130–1136.

38. An International News Service report summarizing these findings, dated April 15, 1930, File 57, 1929-30, W. A. Jessup Papers, University of Iowa Archives.

39. "Inquiry in indigent law shows abuse," *Spencer News Herald,* April 8, 1933.

40. E. E. Munger to H. S. Houghton, March 16, 1933, File 57, 1932-33, W. A. Jessup Papers, University of Iowa Archives.

41. The committee's reports appeared in the Senate record, November 21, 1933, *Journal of the Senate of the Forty-fifth General Assembly Extraordinary Session* (Des Moines: State of Iowa, 1934): 122–131; reprinted in *Journal of the Iowa State Medical Society* 24 (January 1934): 47–70.

42. Isabel Campbell Bruce and Edith Eichoff, *The Michigan Poor Law: Its Development and Administration with Special Reference to State Provision for Medical Care of the Indigent* (Chicago: University of Chicago Press, 1936), pp. 88–118.

43. See, for example, Rosemary Stevens, *American Medicine and the Public Interest*, pp. 142–145.

44. W. A. Jessup to H. C. Shull, October 10, 1931, reports the closure of the Johnson County Savings Bank and Citizens Savings Bank in Iowa City. "The First National withstood a run of several days," saved by its substantial investment in government bonds, Jessup wrote. See File 57, 1931-32, W. A. Jessup Papers, University of Iowa Archives.

45. Figures are from a table, "Proportionality of support of total expense budget appropriation versus paying patient income 1927-28 to date," compiled by University of Iowa Hospitals and Clinics and dated February 1, 1994, University of Iowa Hospitals and Clinics Administrative Offices.

46. See Board of Education Finance Committee Minutes, February 18, 1931, University of Iowa Archives.

47. W. A. Jessup to E. J. Feuling, March 17, 1933, explained the policy of filling positions at lower salaries, File 57, 1932-33, W. A. Jessup Papers, University of Iowa Archives.

48. See Board of Education Finance Committee Minutes, February 24, 1933, University of Iowa Archives.

49. See Board of Education Minutes, September 27, 1932, University of Iowa Archives.

50. See Board of Education Minutes, May 18, 1933, and Finance Committee Minutes, May 22, 1933, University of Iowa Archives.

51. "Iowa Hospital Association Organized," *Journal of the Iowa State Medical Society* 19 (July 1929): 320. "Transactions House of Delegates," *Journal of the Iowa State Medical Society* 21 (July 1931): 409.

52. R. E. Neff to H. S. Houghton, March 31, 1931, File 57, 1930-31, W. A. Jessup Papers, University of Iowa Archives.

53. Earl F. Wisdom to Iowa State Board of Education, June 29, 1931, Board of Education Minutes, July 3, 1931; Wisdom to Board of Education, March 7, 1932, Board of Education Minutes, March 8, 1932. The finance committee voted to authorize ambulance purchases and related expenses on April 13, May 23, and September 26, 1932; a special account was set up to handle these expenses. For a summary, see File 57, 1932-33, W. A. Jessup Papers, University of Iowa Archives. After the first attorney general's opinion, Jessup and others thought they might have to obtain legislative

approval of the ambulance plan; see Jessup to H. C. Shull, October 10, 1931, File 57, 1931-32, W. A. Jessup Papers, University of Iowa Archives.

54. Neff's steady stream of monthly reports on ambulance service operations begins with May 22 to June 21, 1932, in which he estimates savings of $1,747.97; in the period January 22 to February 21, 1933, in which a fourth car was initiated into service, Neff reported a total cost of $1,794.58, compared with an estimated $6,543.48 for equivalent rail service, for a savings of $4,748.90. See also the memo by Erwin C. Pohlman dated July 15, 1932. All in File 57, 1931-32, 1932-33, 1933-34, 1934-35, W. A. Jessup Papers, University of Iowa Archives.

55. By October 1945, the hospitals fleet numbered 26 cars, some showing obvious signs of wear, and the transportation service had logged almost ten million miles. An unsigned, undated manuscript detailing economy measures by the hospital and containing information on the ambulance service, is in File 57, 1932-33, W. A. Jessup Papers, University of Iowa Archives. Figures showing yearly expenditures for various categories of expense, including patient transportation, were obtained from Gerhard Hartman's "Historical Binder" in College of Medicine Storage.

56. R. E. Neff to W. A. Jessup, August 20, 1932; H. S. Houghton to Jessup, October 20, 1932; Neff to Houghton, October 25, 1932; Houghton to Jessup, October 31, 1932, File 57, 1932-33, W. A. Jessup Papers, University of Iowa Archives. See also Board of Education Minutes, November 9, 1932.

57. R. E. Neff to H. S. Houghton, October 17, 1932; Houghton to W. A. Jessup, October 21, 1932; E. F. Wisdom to Iowa State Board of Education, December 31, 1932, File 57, 1932-33, W. A. Jessup Papers, University of Iowa Archives. See also Board of Education Minutes, January 12, 1933, University of Iowa Archives.

58. R. E. Neff to H. S. Houghton, November 28, 1930, File 57, 1930-31, W. A. Jessup Papers, University of Iowa Archives.

59. Iowa State Medical Society, "A Study of the Laws Relating to the Commitment of Patients to the State University Hospitals and the Operation Thereof," Table XXXIII, p. 47.

60. R. E. Neff to W. A. Jessup, March 17, 1933, File 57, 1932-33, W. A. Jessup Papers, University of Iowa Archives. Houghton by that time was director of clinics at the University of Chicago.

61. Ibid.

62. R. E. Neff Memorandum, March 25, 1933, File 57, 1931-32, W. A. Jessup papers, 1931-32, University of Iowa Archives. (Misfiled under the wrong year.)

63. Board of Education Minutes, June 28-29, 1933, University of Iowa Archives.

64. R. E. Neff and J. T. McClintock, August 1, 1933; Neff to W. A. Jessup, February 10, 1934, File 57, 1933-34, W. A. Jessup Papers, University of Iowa Archives.

65. The board of education's finance committee approved the original position, which was intended to be temporary, on October 21, 1933; the job became full-time after finance committee action on April 6, 1934, and a half-time stenographer's job received approval on April 25, 1934. See Board of Education Minutes for those dates, University of Iowa Archives.

66. R. E. Neff to W. A. Jessup, February 10, 1934; Neff to Jessup, October 7, 1934, File 57, 1933-34, W. A. Jessup Papers, University of Iowa Archives. Figures for patient-days are from annual statistical reports compiled by the hospital, courtesy UIHC Office of Financial Management and Control.

67. *Journal of the Iowa State Medical Society* 24 (January 1934): 51.

68. W. H. Gemmill to W. A. Jessup, November 20, 1933, File 67A, 1933-34, W. A. Jessup Papers, University of Iowa Archives.

69. A typewritten summary of Appendix C of the Brookings Institution report, "Medical Care of the Indigent Sick in the Hospitals of the State University of Iowa," File 13 B, 1933-34, W. A. Jessup Papers, University of Iowa Archives.

70. H. S. Houghton to A. Erskine, November 23, 1933, File 67A, 1933-34; A. F. Kuhlman to G. W. Patterson, November 18, 1933, File 13B, 1933-34; Jessup to C. F. Kuehnle, December 6, 1933, File 67A, 1933-34; Jessup to O. E. Klingaman, November 22, 1933, File 67, 1933-34, W. A. Jessup

Papers, University of Iowa Archives. In his letter to Kuehnle, Jessup also cited support for the quota plan from William Jepson of Sioux City, the former head of surgery at University Hospital.

71. The legislative history of the competing bills can be traced through the House and Senate *Journals* for the special legislative session of 1933-34 (45th General Assembly). The county part-pay bill, House File 67, was sponsored by Representatives William J. Dreesen and John H. Schroeder. For medical society involvement, see Thomas Burcham to members of the Iowa State Medical Society, January 2, 1934, File 67A, 1933-34, W. A. Jessup Papers, University of Iowa Archives.

72. The bill as originally written appeared in *House Bills and Resolutions 1933-1934, Part 1* (Des Moines: State of Iowa, 1934); refer to House File 112. For the law as passed, see *Acts and Joint Resolutions Passed at the Extraordinary Session of the Forty-fifth General Assembly of the State of Iowa* (Des Moines: State of Iowa, 1934), pp. 80–83. The entire indigent care law as amended appears in the revised *Code of Iowa, 1935* (Des Moines: State of Iowa, 1935); refer to chapter 199.

73. They had even taken care to plant a political bombshell against the possibility of the indigent care system being gutted. Joint Resolution 2, drafted, like the quota bill, by university law professor Clarence M. Updegraff, would have removed restrictions on "public use and patronage" of the hospital—in effect opening it to any and all patients despite the policy of limiting private practice to 5 percent of beds. The resolution came out of the House public health committee with a recommendation for approval, but was never acted on by the full House.

74. W. A. Jessup draft memorandum, November 5, 1933, File 67A, 1933-34, W. A. Jessup Papers, University of Iowa Archives.

75. James Clark Fifield, *American and Canadian Hospitals* (Minneapolis, MN: Midwest Publishers Company, 1933).

76. This information and much of what follows is taken from "Annual Report of the University Hospitals, State University of Iowa, June 30, 1934," *Bulletin of the State University of Iowa* (December 22, 1934).

77. "A Journey Through the State University of Iowa Hospitals," February 1935, Hospital Records Group 27, University of Iowa Archives.

78. All figures from University of Iowa Hospitals Annual Reports, University of Iowa Archives.

79. *State University of Iowa Catalog, 1929*, University of Iowa Hospitals Annual Report, 1933-34, University of Iowa Archives.

80. R. E. Neff to E. A. Gilmore, June 12, 1935, File 57, 1934-35, E. A. Gilmore Papers, University of Iowa Archives, calculated the cost of raising certain hospital salaries 10 percent. Gilmore to Neff, July 27, 1935, File 57, informed Neff that his salary had been adjusted upward.

81. See File 57, 1935-36, E. A. Gilmore Papers, University of Iowa Archives; see also R. E. Neff to E. A. Gilmore, September 18, 1936, File 57, 1936-37, E. A. Gilmore Papers, University of Iowa Archives.

82. R. E. Neff to E. A. Gilmore, July 9, 1937, File 57, 1937-38, E. A. Gilmore Papers, University of Iowa Archives.

83. Ibid.

84. A copy of the letter to Governor Kraschel, dated August 9, 1937, and signed "An Employee," File 57, 1937-38, E. A. Gilmore Papers, University of Iowa Archives. The letter prompted an exchange between Governor Kraschel and Neff regarding employment policies and labor relations at the hospital.

85. R. E. Neff to N. G. Kraschel, August 20, 1937, File 57, 1937-38, E. A. Gilmore Papers, University of Iowa Archives.

86. R. E. Neff to E. A. Gilmore, July 9, 1937, File 57, 1937-38, E. A. Gilmore Papers, University of Iowa Archives.

87. An undated letter from the American Federation of State, County and Municipal Employees to A. L. Doud, a newly elected legislator from Douds, Iowa, reviewed the salary history at University Hospitals, stating that the hospital employees' union had been active since about 1937. For the

letter, on AFSCME letterhead, see File 57, Part 1, 1942-43, V. M. Hancher Papers, University of Iowa Archives.

88. See "Inaugurate move to place all state employees under civil service regulations," *Iowa City Press-Citizen*, March 30, 1938.

89. An undated memorandum by Houghton spelling out the responsibilities of each committee member from File 57, 1932-33, W. A. Jessup Papers, University of Iowa Archives. McClintock was to serve as liaison to the president and oversee student affairs and first- and second-year curriculum; Plass was to oversee extracurricular activities and relationships of the college; and Beye, in addition to serving as hospital liaison, was to oversee third- and fourth-year curriculum.

90. Liked and respected even by those with whom he disagreed, Houghton continued, at the invitation of university officials, to play a role in the university's political and academic affairs for more than a decade. In 1933-34, Houghton helped Jessup, Neff, and board of education secretary Gemmill to lobby members of the legislature, and Houghton even met with Elbert Munger on more than one occasion. In later years, he would be called upon to help evaluate the role of the board of education's finance committee; more important, Houghton was to mediate a bitter dispute among medical faculty over private practice, a dispute that led to adoption of the Medical Service Plan in 1946. On Houghton and the quota plan, see R. E. Neff to W. A. Jessup, March 17, 1933, File 57, 1932-33, W. A. Jessup Papers, University of Iowa Archives. On Houghton's communications with E. E. Munger, including his letter of introduction to General Education Board Secretary Alan Gregg, see *Journal of the Iowa State Medical Society* 24 (January 1934): 54–70. See also Houghton to A. Erskine, November 28, 1933, File 57, 1933-34, W. A. Jessup Papers, University of Iowa Archives. Houghton's appointment to a committee to evaluate the role of the finance committee is recorded in Board of Education Minutes, October 10, 1939, University of Iowa Archives.

91. Houghton's intentions were known at least as early as November 25, 1932, when Abraham Flexner wrote Jessup to suggest a candidate for the Iowa deanship. Strangely, it was not until February 8, 1933 that the board of education officially accepted Houghton's resignation. See Board of Education Minutes for that date. Also see Flexner to Jessup, November 25, 1932, and Flexner to Jessup, January 26, 1933 (cable), File 73, 1932-33, W. A. Jessup Papers, University of Iowa Archives.

92. A *Pittsburgh Post-Gazette* newspaper article reporting Jessup's plans, December 13, 1933, File 7, 1933-34, W. A. Jessup Papers, University of Iowa Archives. Jessup's official resignation was recorded in Board of Education Minutes, April 24, 1934, University of Iowa Archives.

93. W. A. Jessup to H. S. Houghton, May 29, 1934, File 73, 1933-34, W. A. Jessup Papers, University of Iowa Archives. See also Board of Education Minutes, June 5, 1934, University of Iowa Archives.

94. E. A. Gilmore to Board of Education, May 21, 1935, File 73, 1935-36, E. A. Gilmore Papers, University of Iowa Archives.

95. H. S. Houghton to E. A. Gilmore, August 30, 1934, File 73, 1934-35, E. A. Gilmore Papers, University of Iowa Archives.

96. Matthew O. Foley, "A.H.A. Interest in Training of Executives Noted in 1910," *Hospital Management* 33 (April 1932): 27–29.

97. See *The Report of the Committee on the Training of Hospital Executives* (Chicago: The Committee, 1922).

98. *Transactions of the American Hospital Association, 1922*, pp. 212–231.

99. Michael Davis, *Hospital Administration: A Career* (New York: The Rockefeller Foundation, 1929).

100. Michael Davis, "Development of the First Graduate Program in Hospital Administration," *The Journal of Health Administration Education* 2 (Spring 1984): 122.

101. George Wren, "An Historical View of Health Administration Education," *Hospital and Health Services Administration* (Summer 1980): 31.

102. Ira Kipnis, *A Venture Forward: A History of the American College of Hospital Administrators* (Chicago: American College of Hospital Administrators, 1955), pp. 12–13.

103. Michael M. Davis, "The Nurse in Hospital Administration: Her Significant Place as Shown by a Study," *American Journal of Nursing* 36 (1936): 561–563.

104. Fletcher Havens Bingham, *Graduate Education for Hospital Administration: A Critique and a Program* (Iowa City: The University of Iowa Graduate Program in Hospital and Health Administration, 1967), p. 65.

105. See Michael Davis, "Development of the First Graduate Program in Hospital Administration"; Gerhard Hartman, "Graduate Education in Hospital Administration, 1934–37," *Journal of Business* 11 (October 1938): 1–13.

106. Hartman, "Graduate Education in Hospital Administration," p. 1.

107. See, for example, R. E. Neff to V. M. Hancher, June 15, 1945, File 58, 1944–45, V. M. Hancher Papers, University of Iowa Archives.

108. For a copy of the IHA resolution, see V. M. Hancher to E. M. MacEwen, March 28, 1945, "Presidents" File, E. M. MacEwen Papers, College of Medicine Archives.

109. Herman G. Weiskotten, et al., *Medical Education in the United States 1934–1939* (Chicago: American Medical Association, 1940). See also *Journal of the American Medical Association* 108 (March 27, 1937): 1026–1029. Weiskotten's collaborators were Alphonse M. Schwitalla, dean of the St. Louis University School of Medicine; William D. Cutter, secretary of the AMA Council on Medical Education and Hospitals; and Hamilton H. Anderson, a council staff member.

110. Weiskotten, et al., *Medical Education in the United States 1934–1939*, Appendix A, pp. 212–227.

111. H. S. Houghton to W. A. Jessup, April 7, 1931, File 73, 1930–31, W. A. Jessup Papers, University of Iowa Archives.

112. E. M. MacEwen to E. A. Gilmore, January 9 and June 4, 1937, File 73, 1936–37, E. A. Gilmore Papers, University of Iowa Archives.

113. "Statement Showing Per Capita Cost of Medical Students for the Year 1934-35 Compared to 1927-28," File 73, 1934-35, E. A. Gilmore Papers, University of Iowa Archives.

114. *Journal of the American Medical Association* 109 (August 28, 1937): 671.

115. Ibid. Also see Board of Education Minutes, June 17, 1937, University of Iowa Archives.

116. Mary Roth Walsh, *'Doctors Wanted: No Women Need Apply': Sexual Barriers in the Medical Profession, 1835–1975*, p. 230.

117. A helpful summary of American Medical Association efforts to organize and implement a system of specialty boards is contained in Ray L. Wilbur, "Progress in Graduate Medical Education," *Journal of the American Medical Association* 114 (March 30, 1940): 1141–1146; Wilbur was then chairman of the AMA's Committee on Medical Education and Hospitals.

118. *Journal of the American Medical Association* 101 (August 26, 1933): 708–712. The eleven fields were gynecology, internal medicine, obstetrics, ophthalmology, orthopedics, otolaryngology, pathology, pediatrics, psychiatry, radiology, and surgery.

119. R. E. Neff to M. E. Nelson, September 13, 1939, File 107, 1940-41, V. M. Hancher Papers, University of Iowa Archives.

120. File 107, 1940-41, V. M. Hancher Papers, University of Iowa Archives.

121. See R. E. Neff to V. M. Hancher, December 7, 1940, File 57, 1940-41, V. M. Hancher Papers, University of Iowa Archives.

122. See Medical Council Minutes, June 9 and December 21, 1941, University of Iowa Archives. Finally, in October 1940 the AAMC appointed a committee to work with military authorities in the procurement of additional doctors; by May 1941, the committee was convinced of the need for more doctors in both military and civilian service, leading to the AAMC Executive Council's recommendation to medical schools throughout the country. The Pearl Harbor attack on December 7, 1941, hastened planning for accelerated medical education, and a special session of the association adopted the program in February 1942. The AMA Council on Medical Education and Hospitals and the Federation of State Boards of Licensure also supported the plan. See Ewen M.

MacEwen, "The Accelerated Program in Medicine," *Journal of the Association of American Medical Colleges* (May 1944). The article is the text of an address MacEwen delivered as president of the AAMC to the fortieth Annual Congress on Medical Education and Licensure in Chicago on February 15, 1944, File 109, 1943–44, V. M. Hancher Papers, University of Iowa Archives.

123. See Board of Education Minutes, January 14 and May 11, 1943, University of Iowa Archives.

124. Rappleye, "Memorandum to deans of medical schools," March 11, 1942, File 108, Part 1, 1941–42, V. M. Hancher Papers, University of Iowa Archives.

125. E. M. MacEwen to V. M. Hancher, November 2, 1943, File 109, 1943–44, V. M. Hancher Papers, University of Iowa Archives. Of the 33, four were from the faculty, eleven were instructors, and eighteen were assistants. In addition, three faculty had left the college for other civilian positions.

126. William L. Laurence, "Medical schools feel war strain," *New York Times,* October 26, 1943.

127. College of Medicine Report, September 20, 1941, File 108, 1941–42, V. M. Hancher Papers, University of Iowa Archives.

128. Ibid.

129. R. E. Neff to V. M. Hancher, January 12, 1943, File 57, Part 1, 1942–43, V. M. Hancher Papers, University of Iowa Archives.

130. R. E. Neff to B. B. Hickenlooper, February 16, 1944; Neff to V. M. Hancher, February 25, 1944, File 57, 1943–44, V. M. Hancher Papers, University of Iowa Archives.

131. R. E. Neff to V. M. Hancher, January 12, 1943, File 57, Part 1, 1942–43, V. M. Hancher Papers, University of Iowa Archives..

132. See, for example, E. M. MacEwen to V. M. Hancher, August 27, 1941; R. E. Neff to Hancher, August 29, 1941; and Neff to Hancher, September 3, 1941, File 58, 1941–42, V. M. Hancher Papers, University of Iowa Archives. Representatives of the employees' organization met with an interim legislative committee in September 1941 about the hospital budget; Neff had earlier urged the employees not to meet with legislators, but to work through the board of education instead. The union would later claim that the hospital had not fully restored wage cuts in 1937, but had pocketed the extra money the legislature appropriated for this purpose. See Hancher Memorandum, July 25, 1942, File 57, Part 2, 1942–43, V. M. Hancher Papers, University of Iowa Archives.

133. See V. M. Hancher to R. E. Neff, April 20, 1943, and Neff to W. H. Cobb, April 12, 1943, File 57, Part 1, 1942–43; Hancher to Board of Education, January 3, 1944, File 57, 1943–44, V. M. Hancher Papers, University of Iowa Archives.

134. "A Journey Through the State University of Iowa Hospitals," 1942–43, Hospital Records Group 27, University of Iowa Archives.

135. See V. M. Hancher Memoranda, December 31, 1941, and March 4, 1942, File 58, 1941–42, V. M. Hancher Papers, University of Iowa Archives.

136. V. M. Hancher Memorandum, January 13, 1944, File 57, 1943–44, V. M. Hancher Papers, University of Iowa Archives.

137. V. M. Hancher Memorandum, May 28, 1943, File 57, Part 1, 1942–43, V. M. Hancher Papers, University of Iowa Archives.

138. R. E. Neff to V. M. Hancher, June 23, 1941, File 57, 1940–41, V. M. Hancher Papers, University of Iowa Archives. It should be noted that by 1943, when the conflict came to a head, a special subcommittee of the Hospital Committee calculated there were eighty private beds in General Hospital, not eighty-three. Likewise, Neff originally figured that fifteen beds, not thirteen, could be reconverted to private use. It should be noted, too, that the four private rooms with a total of eight beds at Children's Hospital never figured into the ongoing debate.

139. E. M. MacEwen to E. A. Gilmore, September 12, 1939, File 57, 1939–40, E. A. Gilmore Papers, University of Iowa Archives.

140. N. G. Alcock to E. A. Gilmore, August 4, 1939, File 57, 1939–40, E. A. Gilmore Papers, University of Iowa Archives.

141. Both Neff and MacEwen attest to the rising demand for private beds. In addition to R. E. Neff to V. M. Hancher, June 23, 1941, see E. M. MacEwen to Hancher, June 23, 1941, File 57, 1940-41; MacEwen to Hancher, July 16, 1941, File 57, 1941-42; and Robert Neff, "Private Room Situation," September 5, 1942, File 57, 1942-43, V. M. Hancher Papers, University of Iowa Archives.

142. See R. E. Neff to V. M. Hancher, June 23, 1941; E. M. MacEwen to Hancher, June 23, 1941, File 57, 1940-41, V. M. Hancher Papers, University of Iowa Archives.

143. E. M. MacEwen to V. M. Hancher, July 16, 1941, File 58, 1941-42, V. M. Hancher Papers. See also, O. N. Elliott to J. C. Reid, June 17, 1941, File 57, 1940-41, V. M. Hancher Papers, University of Iowa Archives. Elliott, a close friend of Alcock, was writing Reid, a board of education member, to complain about the lack of adequate private patient services at the hospital. The letter can be understood as stating the arguments Alcock and his supporters used to support their position.

144. V. M. Hancher memo, July 17, 1941, File 58, 1941-42, V. M. Hancher Papers, University of Iowa Archives.

145. H. S. Houghton to W. R. Boyd, September 10, 1941, File 58, 1941-42, V. M. Hancher Papers, University of Iowa Archives.

146. R. E. Neff to V. M. Hancher, June 23, 1941, File 57, 1940-41, V. M. Hancher Papers, University of Iowa Archives.

147. See, for example, V. M. Hancher memo, January 31, 1942, in which he recounted a discussion with MacEwen about private practice, File 108, Part 1, 1941-42, V. M. Hancher Papers, University of Iowa Archives. The subcommittee mentioned here was composed of Neff; Alcock; R. Dabney Kerr, the full-time head of Radiology; E. D. Plass, full-time head of Obstetrics and Gynecology; and Fred Smith, head of Theory and Practice of Medicine and a part-time member of the faculty.

148. R. E. Neff, "Private Room Situation," September 5, 1942, File 57, 1942-43, V. M. Hancher Papers, University of Iowa Archives. That Alcock's patients made up the largest proportion of the private cases placed in the public wards must be inferred from data showing that the Urology Department had the highest daily census and greatest number of patient-days in July and August 1942; the department also had the highest percentage of private patients in its case mix, at 41.3 percent in July and 40 percent in August 1942—compiled by Neff and reported to Hancher in E. M. MacEwen to Hancher, October 8, 1942, File 57, Part 2, 1942-43, V. M. Hancher Papers, University of Iowa Archives.

149. Medical Council Minutes, September 21, 1942, University of Iowa Archives.

150. Board of Education Minutes, November 6, 1942, University of Iowa Archives.

151. R. E. Neff to E. M. MacEwen, October 20, 1942; MacEwen to V. M. Hancher, October 22, 1942; Hancher to MacEwen, November 12, 1942, File 57, Part 1, 1942-43, V. M. Hancher Papers, University of Iowa Archives.

152. V. M. Hancher Memo, May 28, 1943, File 57, Part 1, 1942-43, V. M. Hancher Papers, University of Iowa Archives.

153. V. M. Hancher Memo, June 26, 1943, File 57, 1942-43, V. M. Hancher Papers, University of Iowa Archives.

154. N. G. Alcock to W. R. Boyd, October 10, 1943; V. M. Hancher to J. A. Greene, October 26, 1943; Greene to Hancher, November 1, 1943; Hancher Memorandum, October 26, 1943, File 57, 1943-44. See also E. M. MacEwen to Hancher, November 29, 1943, File 109, 1943-44, V. M. Hancher Papers, University of Iowa Archives.

155. V. M. Hancher Memorandum, October 12, 1943, File 57, 1943-44, V. M. Hancher Papers, University of Iowa Archives.

156. E. M. MacEwen to V. M. Hancher, November 1, 1943, File 57, 1943-44, V. M. Hancher Papers, University of Iowa Archives.

157. See Board of Education Minutes, December 14, 1943, University of Iowa Archives.

158. Although no definitive figures exist for the actual income of the part-timers, Executive Committee Chairman Willis Fowler told the *Des Moines Sunday Register*, in "SUI Wage System Aids Medical Research," February 10, 1942, that the part-timers had been making $40,000–$75,000 per year.

159. V. M. Hancher to W. R. Boyd, December 10, 1943, File 109, 1943-44, V. M. Hancher Papers, University of Iowa Archives.

160. For general discussion, see also Stow Persons, *The University of Iowa in the Twentieth Century*, p. 227.

161. E. M. MacEwen to V. M. Hancher, August 29, 1940, File 107, 1940-41; October 11, 1941, File 108, 1941-42; November 21, 1945, File 109, 1945-46, V. M. Hancher Papers, University of Iowa Archives.

162. Statement from John McClintock, included in E. M. MacEwen to V. M. Hancher, December 18, 1945, "Presidents" File, E. M. MacEwen Papers, College of Medicine Archives.

163. Hancher Interviews, July 1943, File 109, 1943-44, V. M. Hancher Papers, University of Iowa Archives.

164. V. M. Hancher to G. H. Scanlon, April 2, 1948, Medicine File, University of Iowa Archives.

4

Postwar Expansion of the University Teaching Hospital, 1946–1965

In retrospect, the formal Japanese surrender of early September 1945, greeted with much fanfare on the University of Iowa campus as it was elsewhere, was a major milestone in the history of the University Hospitals. Wartime shortages and rationing programs soon ended, and the demobilization of military personnel boosted the hospitals' staff numbers to prewar levels. Yet the end of the war did not itself resolve the most worrisome of the University Hospitals' problems. For example, the 1945–1946 state appropriation for indigent care rose only ¹⁄₁₀th of 1 percent from the year before and was barely 10 percent above the figure for 1939–1940—comparisons made even worse by wartime inflation that drove per diem costs at the hospitals from $4.58 in 1940 to $6.57 in 1945.[1] Meanwhile, other problems—not least the controversy over private practice, the inadequacies in undergraduate and graduate medical education, and the hospitals' dependence on indigent care—only grew more acute in peacetime.

In January and February 1946, following Robert Neff's December 1945 resignation to return to Indianapolis to head Methodist Hospital, Dean Ewen MacEwen and several of the clinical chiefs escorted Neff's would-be successors on tours of the General Hospital. What they saw was a much diminished enterprise. Years of stagnant funding, the more recent spate of high inflation, and chronic personnel shortages had cut deeply into hospitals' operations and especially into the hospitals' indigent service. Nursing salaries alone rose nearly 20 percent from 1940 to 1946. As wartime inflation eroded the state appropriation for indigent care by one-third and the per diem operating costs rose steadily, Robert Neff and the board of education had repeatedly cut the county quotas for admission. By 1944–1945, as discussed later in this chapter, indigent admissions were 35.9 percent below the 1940–1941 level, and indigent patient-days were down by 31.4 percent. In just five years, from 1940 to 1945, the University Hospitals' indigent care programs dropped from 18.8 percent to 7.9 percent of all patient-days in Iowa hospitals; overall, the University Hospitals' share of total patient-days in all patient classifications slumped from 21.8 percent to 11.7 percent between 1935 and 1945.[2] The dramatic decline in patient numbers also endangered the hospitals' teaching mission. In 1945, the board of education warned that only a significant infusion of funds to cover the higher costs for food, drugs, and equipment and further cuts in medical student enrollments could prevent the devastation of clinical teaching.[3]

Of course, the University of Iowa Hospitals, like most teaching hospitals, stood at the threshold of a new era in the fall of 1945, an era defined in part by relatively simple epidemiological and demographic trends more or less obscured during the long years of depression and war. As recently as 1920, deaths from infectious diseases had accounted for two-thirds of the total mortality in American society, but by 1945, deaths from chronic diseases—the consequences of increased longevity, more effective public health programs, and slowly rising standards of living—accounted for two-thirds of total mortality.[4] Moreover, the much publicized triumphs of medical science in the previous half-century, along with the ongoing urbanization of the American landscape and a remarkable postwar economic boom, made professional healthcare services more valued and more sought after than ever before, a trend bolstered by the expansion of private health insurance.

A new consensus regarding the role of the federal government in American society in general and in health care in particular was a second important factor shaping the postwar era. The federal government's role in scientific research and development expanded enormously during the war—as important, for example, in the commercial production of penicillin as in the development of the atomic bomb.[5] At the same time, wartime experience provided dramatic evidence of the link between medical science and the public health. For example, new techniques and new drugs helped to lower the death rate among American servicemen and women from 35.5 per 1,000 in World War I to 11.6 per 1,000 in World War II; perhaps more important, rates of non-battle deaths fell from 18.4 per 1,000 to 3.0 per 1,000.[6] At the same time, medical data compiled by the Selective Service

System highlighted the deficiencies of the prewar healthcare system. Taken together, that experience, publicized by a highly effective political lobby, pointed the way to a new postwar relationship among government, research universities, and the healthcare industry, including an unprecedented commitment of federal funds to scientific research, construction, and education at the nation's academic medical centers and teaching hospitals.

The Postwar University Hospitals

The University of Iowa Hospitals in the early postwar years bore little resemblance to today's gleaming facilities but existed, in the memory of one administrator, in "a gloomy state of disrepair and ineffectiveness."[7] Similarly, the clinical staff complained as late as 1951 that the General Hospital's cramped main lobby tended to induce "depression and claustrophobia" in new patients and visitors.[8] Although such criticisms were no doubt overblown and could apply equally to most other hospitals of the time, it was nonetheless true that the University Hospitals made little effort to cater to the human needs of its clientele—a clientele that had been, throughout the hospitals' history, largely a captive one.

It was also true that existing conditions contrasted with emerging standards in hospital design meant to cater to an increasingly middle-class patient population. By those standards, as well as by today's expectations, the University Hospitals' wards in 1945 were crowded, noisy, bare, and drab.[9] For want of space, corridors and stairwells often became ad hoc waiting, conference, and classroom areas, in competition with the normal flow of service carts, beds, staff, and visitors. Likewise, during the regime of Robert Neff—known to some as "Economy" Neff—walls and ceilings throughout the hospitals were coated in shades of grey for ease of maintenance, a choice that also reflected earlier opinion that patients in need of rest and recuperation should be shielded from sensory stimulation.[10] Perhaps worst of all, the University Hospitals suffered in the eyes of many Iowans, especially middle-class Iowans, from an association with the teaching of clinical medicine upon an indigent population.

The hospitals' eleven operating rooms suffered from a lack of temperature and humidity controls that left the rooms drafty and cold in the winter and stifling in the heat of summer. In the late 1930s, WPA funds paid for the installation of air-conditioning equipment in the Iowa Memorial Union and the university theater, but not the hospitals. In addition, there were no post-operative dressing areas; staff and students dressed wounds in the open wards, sometimes amid "the curious and distressed glances of [the patients'] neighbors." Likewise, there were no post-anesthesia recovery areas, no intensive care units, and an emergency treatment capability that the head of surgery dismissed as "little short of disgraceful!"[11] The waiting list for surgery extended at times into months,[12] even though the average length of hospital stay for common surgical procedures—for example, the department of surgery's most common procedure, the repair of hernias— had fallen by half or more since the 1920s and carried lower risks of complication. Static electricity from the old and overtaxed electrical system in the operating rooms made the use of cyclopropane, an explosive anesthetic agent, a constant danger.[13]

By the end of the war, the epidemiological shift from primary care, especially of infectious diseases, to secondary care for advanced cases of chronic diseases had substantially transformed the University Hospitals' indigent patient base and, to a lesser extent, the private patient base. For example, penicillin, just becoming readily available to the public in 1946, drastically simplified the treatment of a broad range of infectious diseases— from bacterial endocarditis to pneumonia and syphilis—and brought amazing reductions in death rates. From the mid-1930s to the mid-1940s, Iowa's death rate from pneumonia dropped by two-thirds, with the average hospital stay for pneumonia patients falling by some 75 percent.[14] Nationally, the advent of antibiotic therapy cut the percentage of fatal pneumonia cases from one in four to one in one hundred.[15]

Other developments contributed also to the long-term trend toward more complex care and toward an aging patient base at the University Hospitals. First, the county quota plan implemented in 1934 apportioned patient admissions, rather than patient-days, among the counties, encouraging local officials to refer their lengthiest, costliest cases to the University Hospitals, to the detriment of the hospitals' budget and its medical education mission. Second, the lack of convalescent homes in local communities kept some recovering patients in the hospitals longer than would otherwise have been necessary. Third, State Department of Health cancer clinics established throughout Iowa in the late 1930s served patients with cancer in earlier, more treatable stages, tending to leave to the University Hospitals those patients in the final stages of the disease. Frank Peterson, head of surgery from 1936 to 1947, wrote that he had observed, as early as 1938, a "strong tendency of physicians to send in patients affected by the more critical type of diseases." In Peterson's view, "the quota system has, undoubtedly, been influential in bringing about this result." More broadly, he charged that the quota system lay behind "a concerted effort on the part of physicians to send in particularly difficult and complicated fractures and patients with chronic debilitating diseases," a pattern that had led Peterson's department and some others to refuse hospitalization to any patient whose condition would not benefit by a prolonged stay.[16]

The Arrival of Gerhard Hartman

In the winter of 1945–46, the leading candidates in the search for Robert Neff's replacement as hospitals superintendent were Russell Nye, administrator of the Dallas City-County Hospital; George Buis, a University of Iowa alumnus who later became director of Yale University's program in hospital administration; and Gerhard Hartman, a classmate of Buis's from the University of Chicago and the director of Newton-Wellesley Hospital in Newton Lower Falls, Massachusetts, an institution affiliated with Tufts University.[17] After campus interviews, the college of medicine's Medical Council expressed its preference for either Nye or Hartman, and Hartman's subsequent selection reflected chiefly the preference of President Virgil Hancher and, to a lesser extent, Dean Ewen MacEwen.[18]

A tall charismatic figure, Hartman impressed Hancher as "strong physically, a fine-looking person."[19] Hartman had earned a master's degree in business administration from the University of Buffalo in 1935 and had enrolled the following year in the University of Chicago's school of business as a Ph.D. student. Within two years, he had become assistant professor and associate director of Chicago's pioneer program in hospital administration.[20] Hartman studied under and published with Arthur C. Bachmeyer, a physician-administrator who was himself one of the pioneers in professional hospital administration and successor to Henry Houghton as director of the University of Chicago Clinics. Hartman was also a protegé of sociologist Michael Davis and of Malcolm MacEachern, who had taken a leading role in organizing the successful American College of Surgeons hospital standardization program.[21] While still studying for his doctorate, Hartman also served as the American College of Hospital Administrators' first full-time executive secretary from 1937 to 1941.[22]

In 1942, with Ph.D. fresh in hand, Hartman became director of the 250-bed Newton Hospital; later, he managed the merger with Wellesley Hospital, forming the Newton-Wellesley Hospital.[23] Hartman was also a member of the American Hospital Association's Council on Government Relations, which in 1943 formulated a resolution calling on the federal government to begin planning a massive postwar hospital construction program. Moreover, Hartman displayed obvious academic potential, writing *Problems and References in Hospital Administration* while still at Chicago, and later editing, with Arthur Bachmeyer, *The Hospital in Modern Society* and *Hospital Trends and Developments, 1940–46.* By his early thirties, then, Gerhard Hartman seemed the personification of a new generation of energetic and highly trained hospital leaders, "an ambitious breed (of) hospital administrator . . . without medical degrees."[24] Some within the AHA foresaw a bold future for Hartman and his peers, hospital administrators prepared by training and temperament to exercise broad authority over America's teaching hospitals.[25]

One of the University of Iowa's attractions for Hartman was the already approved, but not yet organized, graduate program in hospital administration, a program that was part of a major national expansion of the field. By the time of the new superintendent's arrival in Iowa City, programs at Northwestern University, Columbia University, the University of Minnesota, Washington University, and St. Louis University had joined programs already established at the University of Chicago and Cornell University. As was the case at the University of Iowa, where both masters and Ph.D. programs—the latter the first in the nation—formally began in 1950, most of the early postwar programs were established either in colleges of medicine or in schools of public health, rather than, as in the University of Chicago program, in schools of business.

With the growth in hospitals and in training programs for hospital administration, both the nature of the profession and, in turn, the nature of the professional curriculum came under increasing scrutiny. A 1948 study funded by the W. K. Kellogg Foundation and sponsored by the Joint Commission on Education of the American College of Hospital Administrators and the American Hospital Association delineated the most pressing problems facing hospital administrators—the first, not surprisingly, was working with medical staff—and made several recommendations regarding course organization and curriculum to address the administrator's broad responsibilities in areas as diverse as patient care, financial management, physical plant maintenance, and planning.[26]

In light of the rapid development of the field of hospital admin-istration and of the generally unpromising situation at the University of Iowa, President Hancher and Dean MacEwen were aware that the $10,000 offered for the superintendency was hardly sufficient inducement for a candidate of Gerhard Hartman's credentials. Still, the University of Iowa Hospitals were among the nation's largest teaching facilities and would, in combination with the nascent graduate program in hospital administration, afford Hartman considerable professional visibility. Also, the University Hospitals carried a special cachet for Hartman because of their status as a Rockefeller-assisted, "rural-focused social experiment,"[27] one whose chief mission lay in the delivery of indigent care, an area in which Hartman expressed a special interest.[28] And Hartman was already well acquainted with University Hospitals through student field trips during the course of his doctoral studies at Chicago. Overall, the University Hospitals seemed ripe for an infusion of strong leadership, and success at the University of Iowa would unquestionably establish Hartman's prominence in what was then a rapidly developing field. With all of that in mind, Hartman accepted the position on April 19, 1946, and agreed to begin work July 1.

Thanks to his training and his associations with some of the major figures in the developing world of hospital administration, Gerhard Hartman came to the University of Iowa Hospitals with a well-developed set of ideas about the role of hospitals in society and about the administrator's role in the hospital. Hartman had imbibed the notion, current in the 1930s, of the hospital as a broad-based community institution. Given that concept, the work of physicians, even in a university teaching hospital, was only a small portion of the facility's overall mission and the physicians' voice, therefore, was only one among many within the hospital structure. Each voice had its legitimate, if limited, agenda and vision; only the superintendent's vision encompassed the whole. Thus, the superintendent's role was one of coordination and integration, managing the many interests within the hospital and the hospital's links with the community at large.

Hartman's view of the evolution of the American hospital, like that of his mentors, rejected the prevailing assumption that the modern hospital owed its existence to the many remarkable advances of medical science over the previous half-century. On the contrary, Hartman insisted that the modern hospital, emerging in the late nineteenth and early twentieth centuries, had provided the stage for medical advances, a view that put the future of healthcare firmly in the hands of hospital administrators and put physicians in their service as well. "Under whatever type of management a hospital operates," Hartman lectured his graduate students, "it must serve the public if it is to be an effective public service institution." Moreover, the diverse relationships within the hospital and the complexities of its business dealings "make it essential that there be an administrative organization which will coordinate all phases of hospital service." In short, "hospital administration today has become a highly specialized field of endeavor and can no longer be filled by the untrained, inexperienced individual [i.e., the physician]."[29] In the hospital context, Hartman defined medical care as "the organized provision of personal health services by physicians, dentists, nurses and auxiliary personnel, utilizing clinics, hospitals and related facilities for the purpose of promoting positive health, prevention of ill health, curing or mitigating disease, rehabilitating the patient and reducing the economic insecurity and dependence associated with illness." That definition pointedly denied physicians the central role in healthcare that they had long claimed, viewing them as one among many elements in a wide-ranging healthcare enterprise coordinated by the hospital administrator.[30]

An organization chart compiled by Gerhard Hartman in September 1949 effectively captured his view of the superintendent's position (see

Figure 4.1). It is clear from the chart that, in Hartman's view, the superintendent held primacy over virtually all operational areas in the University
Hospitals. In this scheme, not only did the hospitals sit on an equal plane with
the college of medicine; the superintendent claimed direct authority over the
hospitals' professional services. Meanwhile, the authority of the dean of the
college of medicine filtered through the hospital committee, a committee
blending medical and administrative interests and existing in practice at
the sufferance of the superintendent. In any event, even the committee's
connection to professional services was not one of "administrative authority"
but only a "line of communication" in Hartman's outline. As the next
section demonstrates, Hartman's view of the superintendent's role provoked
stiff resistance from a medical faculty steeped in a far different tradition and
jealous of its assumed prerogatives.

Administration Theory versus Practice

Prior to Gerhard Hartman's acceptance of the superintendency, President
Hancher offered his hope for "close working relations" between the superintendent and the dean of the college of medicine. "Dean MacEwen,"
Hancher assured Hartman in April 1946, "will do his part in making the
relationship a pleasant and cooperative one."[31] Although MacEwen had indeed supported Hartman's selection, the dean harbored serious reservations
regarding Hartman's vision of the superintendent's role, and disagreement
on that score clouded the relationship between the two men from the
outset. Of course, Hartman's predecessor, Robert Neff, had enjoyed much
of the authority that Hartman claimed; however, Neff's relative autonomy, as
explained in the previous chapter, was the chance result of circumstances and
personalities. Moreover, the dean had chafed under that previous regime,
one that he had inherited in 1935 and, in part because he was not himself
a clinician, had been unable to change.

From the first, Gerhard Hartman insisted on the "perfectly clear" condition, as Hancher called it, that he not "work under the Dean."[32] Hartman's
position was largely in accord with Hancher's own contention—grounded
in the hospitals' extensive service mission and in his own experience during
his tenure as president—that the superintendent should have control of
the hospitals budget and report directly to the president and the board of
education. In Hancher's view, only decisions pertaining directly to medical
service and medical education properly fell to the dean in his capacity as
hospitals medical director. That, Hancher noted unequivocally, was how the
previous superintendent had operated; moreover, he thought it a standard
arrangement in most hospitals, "even teaching hospitals." Although he was

Figure 4.1   Gerhard Hartman's Organizational Table, September 1949

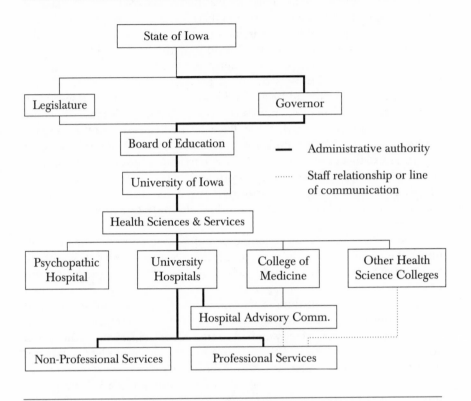

Source: Hartman Papers, Offsite Storage, Oakdale Campus.

prepared, he said, to listen to alternatives, the president clearly preferred that such an arrangement apply to the new superintendent, who might otherwise "be unwilling to come to Iowa."[33]

MacEwen maintained quite a different idea of the superintendent's proper jurisdiction, a view shared by many of the medical faculty as well. In late 1945, MacEwen noted that the hospitals superintendent had originally been, "like the head of any other department [i.e., in the college of medicine]," under the dean's authority, but that Robert Neff had arrogated authority over business matters during the 1933–1935 interregnum and "had never returned them to the routine of this office."[34] In a letter to President Hancher one week after Gerhard Hartman's second interview, MacEwen again referred to the hospital superintendent as "a member of the College of Medicine staff," implying a position subordinate to that of the dean.[35]

Of course, MacEwen had very practical reasons for claiming ultimate authority over the hospitals. The first was budgetary oversight, the lack of which, he said, had become a "rather embarrassing administrative problem" as well as a "constant source of irritation."[36] MacEwen had been unable, for example, to stop Robert Neff's "devious method" of servicing indigent care deficits with higher private patient fees.[37] MacEwen also sought to buttress his position vis-à-vis the most powerful members of his clinical faculty, with whom he had been at odds for a decade over the question of private practice and all of the ramifications attached to it. Because of private practice, MacEwen charged, the college of medicine was not a cohesive academic unit but "an accumulation of relatively autonomous, independent departments" that each controlled "space, curriculum hours, and policies of all types" within its own bailiwick. To strengthen his position in that contest, MacEwen sought to regain control over space allocations, private patient charges, the hospital committee, and other administrative tools usurped, in his view, by Robert Neff.[38]

Not all clinical faculty, it should be noted, wanted to see the hospitals under the control of the dean. Urology chief Nathaniel Alcock was more than content with a weak dean. Alcock maintained the largest private patient service of any department, an operation that earned him several times more money than a full-time salary and allowed him to flout hospital and college policies against employing or subsidizing his assistants, nurses, and orderlies. Despite that, MacEwen had named Alcock chairman of the search committee charged with selecting a new hospitals superintendent, a decision perhaps intended to appease one of the dean's most vocal opponents. Whatever the case, the choice of Alcock to head the search committee was unlikely to further the dean's cause, and, according to testimony from long-time faculty member John McClintock, Alcock told Gerhard Hartman during one of his campus visits that he could have control over the hospitals' budget if he desired. The search committee, in turn, concurred,[39] in effect simply reiterating President Hancher's clear position.

The situation confronting MacEwen, then, was not a happy one when the new superintendent arrived in the summer of 1946. Not only did Gerhard Hartman bring with him an ambitious professional agenda; President Hancher had also enunciated a clear policy at odds with the dean's designs, conceding to Hartman "the same roles and relations" that Neff had enjoyed.[40] In all, it appears that matters were ripe for conflict, and within a few months there were signs of tension. Early in 1947, MacEwen lodged complaints over Hartman's frequent absences on consulting trips, a perquisite granted the superintendent perhaps in part as compensation for his comparatively low university salary. Whether or not because of those complaints, President Hancher advised the superintendent in February to notify him in advance of such trips.[41] In turn, when the dean sought, as he had during Robert Neff's superintendency, to exert his influence through the hospital committee, Hartman effectively disbanded it, much as his predecessor had done in the early 1940s and for much the same reason.[42] In May 1947, friction between MacEwen and Hartman flared over conditions at the hospitals' convalescent home. After reviewing problems at the home, MacEwen demanded that Hartman take "some definite action . . . on reorganization" of the facility and also demanded a statement "concerning the basis on which you can run this home as a real convalescent home."[43] A few weeks later, in a *Daily Iowan* interview, MacEwen once again claimed that the hospitals belonged to the medical school and that the superintendent's only responsibility was to run the hospitals at peak efficiency, implying that important decisions regarding space and budget allocations fell rightly within the dean's province.[44]

In the spring and summer of 1947, two major administrative developments further complicated relations between the hospitals administration and the college of medicine. First, the board of education, at Hancher's request, adopted a plan in May 1947 to organize the medical campus into a division of health sciences and services. Hancher's plan, which was promoted by Alan Gregg of the Rockefeller Foundation and already in place at several universities, created a unified medical center administrative structure in the charge of executive dean Carlyle F. Jacobsen. Jacobsen, with no background in either the health sciences or hospital administration, now stood between the president and both the hospitals superintendent and the college of medicine dean. Second, on September 1, 1947, Ewen MacEwen suffered a heart attack and died. Personal feelings aside, MacEwen's death did "make things easier" for President Hancher and Dean Jacobsen, who were frustrated by the dean's inability to control his part-time clinical chiefs;[45] however, the dean's death also gave the medical faculty an opportunity to vent their frustrations regarding administration of the hospitals.

On September 23, while Gerhard Hartman was away on a consulting assignment, the medical council discussed at length "the situation in the Hospital." Noting that "the Hospital exists for purposes of education," council members questioned executive dean Carlyle Jacobsen, now de facto acting dean, regarding the superintendent's responsibilities and his relations with the clinical staff, specifically demanding that Hartman consult with them before making decisions affecting clinical or educational services. In turn, Jacobsen defended Hartman, conceding that the superintendent had in fact made decisions on a unilateral basis but maintaining that he had done so as a matter of expediency and with the dean's concurrence. Nonetheless, Jacobsen agreed to encourage better communications between hospitals administration and the clinical staff and to have Hartman hew scrupulously to the same guidelines that had applied to his predecessor. Asked whether or not the hospital committee would be revived, Jacobsen said that he had discussed the matter with Hartman and that he would recommend action. "Mr. Hartman," the council minutes concluded, "sees his opportunity and need for advice." Should that prove not to be the case, the council added, "we will have to take other steps."[46]

In apprising Hartman of the proceedings, Jacobsen urged the superintendent to accede to the "old established relationship" in which the superintendent was part of a "family council," a relationship, according to Jacobsen, that Neff had followed in his dealings with the clinical faculty. The dean also suggested establishment of a new Hospital Advisory Committee to replace the old hospital committee, assuring Hartman that "the more insightful of faculty members" appreciated his frustrations with the old committee, particularly Dean MacEwen's attempts to seize control over it. Moreover, Jacobsen acknowledged that "the period of reorganization" during Hartman's first year had justified unilateral decision making, but that Hartman might now want "to review this policy." With Dean MacEwen's death, Jacobsen saw the chance "to establish a clearly understood relationship" between the superintendent and a new dean and between the superintendent and the clinical staff.[47]

Matters did not proceed as smoothly as Jacobsen had hoped. While Hartman inaugurated the Hospital Advisory Committee as requested, his reorganization plans were soon bogged down in discord with the college of medicine and the school of nursing over staff appointments and salaries. In December 1948, Dean Jacobsen notified President Hancher of Hartman's desire "to define and draw a sharp line between the operation of the University Hospital as a service undertaking and the educational functions which are to be performed in that hospital." In particular, Hartman claimed "complete control" over individuals—not excluding interns and residents—on the hospitals' payroll, rejecting claims of "direction from people in an educational undertaking."[48]

In the meantime, the search for Ewen MacEwen's successor in the winter of 1947–48 was frustrating, with few candidates willing even to consider the position. Indeed, the deanship was, if possible, less attractive in 1947 than it had been a dozen years earlier, when a selection committee had reluctantly offered the job to MacEwen. Eventually, Mayo Soley, an assistant dean from the University of California–San Francisco—who ranked only sixth on a short list of seven candidates—accepted the deanship effective July 1, 1948. Born in 1907, Soley was a descendant of Charles J. Mayo and a 1933 graduate of Harvard Medical School. A pharmacologist and internist specializing in the use of radioactive iodine in thyroid disease, he had begun as an instructor at UCSF but had risen to the position of an assistant dean before he was appointed dean and research professor in internal medicine at the University of Iowa.

Before coming to Iowa, Soley inquired of Jacobsen about stories he had heard of the superintendent's troubled relationship with the clinical faculty and the former dean. While it was not an easy matter, Jacobsen responded, to delineate the dean's and superintendent's respective jurisdictions, he was determined "to see that all decisions are centered around the question— What is best for medical education?—since the only reason the Hospital exists at the University is for its role in education."[49] The question of the appropriate balance between patient service and medical education was, of course, precisely the point at issue between the superintendent and his faculty critics. That issue did not subside with the coming of a new dean, and Mayo Soley's brief tenure in the college of medicine deanship from July 1948 to June 1949 brought no significant improvement in relations between the hospitals and the college of medicine.

Pressured by problems on several fronts, some of them discussed later in this chapter, Mayo Soley shot himself to death on June 21, 1949. Soley's death stunned the college of medicine and the university community at large. Two days later the medical faculty convened to discuss the problems facing the college and adopted a resolution, drafted by Stuart Cullen of anesthesiology, calling for a full review of the dean's responsibilities before opening the search for a successor.[50] In a rare address to the medical faculty, President Hancher concurred, noting "the risks involved in placing another single individual in the position [i.e., the deanship] . . . are so great as to make questionable the appointment of an Acting Dean."[51] In addition, one faculty correspondent advised Hancher that he and his colleagues viewed Carlyle Jacobsen's previous stint as acting dean a "calamity" and did not want to see it repeated.[52] Instead, Hancher the next day distributed a questionnaire to the medical faculty soliciting their confidential opinions on the composition of an interim executive committee to oversee the college.[53] Hancher then selected a five-member committee, chaired initially by Robert Tidrick of surgery and later by Willis Fowler of internal medicine, that governed the college and assumed authority over medical services in the hospitals through an extended interregnum lasting until the arrival of Norman Nelson in 1953.

In contrast to the case in 1933–1935 when Dean Henry Houghton's resignation had allowed Superintendent Robert Neff to broaden the powers of his office, the vacancy in the dean's office in 1949—accompanied by the creation of an aggressive college of medicine executive committee— provided rebellious faculty an opportunity to take the offensive against the hospitals' administration. Twenty-six respondents in Hancher's June 1949 faculty survey, including most department heads, offered the unsolicited observation that the relationship between the college and the hospitals was the most important problem facing a new dean. Moreover, in the summer of 1949, Henry Houghton added his name to the growing list of critics. While vacationing in California, Hancher's administrative dean and chief assistant Allin Dakin visited Houghton in Carmel to ask his thoughts on the question of administrative authority in the University Hospitals. After his conversation with Dakin, Houghton wrote Hancher directly, expressing his shock that the divisional dean (Jacobsen) was not a physician and that the hospitals, "as an instrument of clinical instruction," were not under the authority of the dean of the college of medicine. In Houghton's recollection, there had never been any doubt about his authority over the hospitals during his own term as dean. Yet he and Robert Neff had "worked together in complete good will," with Neff taking charge of "the service aspects" of hospitals operation and the dean assuming responsibility for "all teaching relationships." "It appears to me," Houghton warned in closing, "that a lay hospital director should not have the final authority in a teaching hospital."[54]

In the meantime, serious fiscal problems in the hospitals further strained relations. These were problems that had begun as early as the fall of 1947, when Hartman, despite dean Jacobsen's reservations and despite having been cautioned earlier by President Hancher to exercise more care in personnel recruitment,[55] had promoted an accountant of questionable credentials to the position of controller in the hospitals' business office. Within weeks of the appointment, complaints of incompetence surfaced, both from within the hospitals' business office and from the university's central administration,[56] and in the spring of 1948, an audit of hospitals accounts led to the transfer of accounting responsibility to the university business office. Subsequently, however, the hospitals' fiscal position grew increasingly worrisome. In April 1949, President Hancher worried that a new billing system instituted by Hartman shortly after his arrival—in which each clinical department billed its non-indigent charges separately—had contributed to "a growing lack of confidence in the University Hospitals,"[57] reflected in diminished private patient numbers. In July and August 1949, in part because of the declining private patient census, hospitals expenses exceeded revenues by more than $120,000,[58] and tempers grew short as efforts by Hartman's administration to stanch the flow of red ink proved ineffectual. Both the medical council of department heads and the newly created executive committee took the hospitals' management to task, and Hartman responded that he had been asked to deal with the situation but was not given requisite authority to do so. Hartman also claimed, no doubt rightly, that some of the problems—for example, the decrease in private patient numbers as well as a nursing shortage—were beyond his control and were, in any event, self-limiting and would soon correct themselves.[59]

Fiscal year–end results, in fact, bore out Hartman's forecast, thanks in part to concerted economies in purchasing and staffing, but not before a rancorous confrontation occurred in late 1949 between Gerhard Hartman and the newly energized medical faculty. At a meeting of the medical council on November 30, 1949, with Dean Carlyle Jacobsen presiding, Hartman announced that President Hancher, eschewing an appeal to the legislature's interim committee, had charged him with responsibility for eliminating a $30,000 deficit in the hospitals' budget prior to the board of education finance committee meeting scheduled just two days later. Under the circumstances, Hartman told Jacobsen and the council members, the only practicable, short-term solution was either to cut the stipends and maintenance costs of residents by one-third or to eliminate one-third of residency positions. He had, he said, chosen the latter course.[60]

This aspect of the story, too, had a previous history. In 1945, pursuant to the recommendation of the college of medicine's committee on postgraduate medical education, Robert Neff had accepted transfer of the house staff budget—that is, "all of the house officers needed to care for the [indigent] service"—from the college to the hospitals, a move meant to loosen the hold of part-time clinical chiefs on the services of house staff and to force faculty to take more responsibility for graduate teaching.[61] The political ramifications of that transfer had apparently escaped notice in 1945 but became clear enough in November 1949, in the midst of the enormous postwar expansion of residency programs nationwide and the increase in the costs of graduate medical education at the University of Iowa Hospitals.

Denied the opportunity for input or even discussion, clinical faculty were outraged at Hartman's action. Just as important, Carlyle Jacobsen sharply criticized the superintendent for his handling of the affair, reminding him that President Hancher had authorized him only to make recommendations and had, in addition, counseled the use of common sense in doing so. Jacobsen also charged that Hartman had misled the medical council about important facts relating to Hancher's position regarding the budget shortfall and warned that he would personally intervene to ensure that the council had the opportunity to act on the residency cutback before the matter reached the board of education finance committee. Further, Jacobsen pinned responsibility for the deficit itself squarely on Hartman. "The primary responsibility," he said, "rests in your failure to have presented a budget that was realistic in the first instance," a particularly egregious failure in light of efforts on the part of the clinical departments in "reducing their budget[s] to meet the available funds."[62]

For reasons of his own, President Hancher as yet showed little inclination to intervene in the worsening jurisdictional dispute between the college of medicine and the hospitals. First, Henry Houghton's description

of the Neff-Houghton-Jessup relationship of the early 1930s—the arrangement preferred by most clinical faculty—differed sharply from the Neff-
MacEwen-Gilmore relationship that Hancher had observed when he took
over the presidency in 1940 and had subsequently continued. Again and
again in the intervening years, Hancher had reiterated his support for a
college-hospitals relationship that, in the eyes of the medical faculty, bore an
uncomfortable similarity to the position Hartman had staked out. Second, in
the wake of Dean Soley's suicide, Hancher was deeply involved in a broader
debate with the medical faculty in general, and a few outspoken part-time
clinical heads in particular, over the governance of the college of medicine
and the divisive issue of private practice.

For the president, to back down on any one of those issues would
undermine his positions on the other two; yet the problem of college of
medicine–hospitals relations simmered on. In January 1950, the college's
executive committee released its "Prospectus on Reorganization of the
Deanship," which proposed to grant the dean, operating through an associate
dean and a system of committees, ultimate control over the hospitals' service
and educational functions and budget. Differing with Henry Houghton
and the executive committee, Hancher responded to the prospectus by
denying that "Mr. Neff had been subordinate to the Dean of Medicine."
The situation he found upon his arrival in 1940, Hancher noted once more,
was one in which "the administration of the College of Medicine and the
administration of the Hospital were quite independent of each other," with
Neff reporting "directly to the president in a coordinate relationship with the
Dean." Any change in that relationship would, Hancher claimed, have led
to "dissatisfaction on Mr. Neff's part and very probably to his resignation."[63]

Nonetheless, in March 1950, when Hancher surveyed faculty opinion
for a second time on the deanship search and asked for comment also on the
relationship of the hospitals to the college of medicine, 26 of 60 respondents
maintained that the superintendent should be subordinate to the dean,
while most of the remainder expressed no opinion and only a handful were
opposed. In a letter distributed to each of the 26 faculty demanding the
subordination of the superintendent, Hancher raised practical objections.
If the dean were "to assume responsibility for the fiscal operation of the
Hospital," would he not be "in effect the Superintendent"? How could he
find the time to fill that dual role? In addition, echoing a question raised
in the Lee Wallace Dean era, Hancher asked, "Why would any competent,
self-respecting man serve as superintendent in a situation where he has the
responsibility and another the authority"?[64]

Faculty responses were swift and sharp. "It should constitute no blow
to a man's self-esteem to be guided" by the dean of the college of medicine,
one faculty member wrote.[65] Another contended, "It is equally difficult for

me to visualize a competent, self-respecting Dean serving in a position in which he has no authority over the laboratory in which half the teaching in the College of Medicine [is done]."[66] John McClintock, an elder statesman and one with a long, if not altogether reliable, memory, said, "I do not know that any of the past superintendents lost face or 'their self-respect' by working under this rule." Elmer DeGowin, a twenty-year faculty veteran, dismissed the superintendent's functions as most nearly like "those of a hotel keeper." Moreover, DeGowin saw no way that a superintendent could "aspire to anything more, much less on a par with the dean of an educational division of a great university."[67] Another correspondent, adopting a more plaintive tone, noted that "the College of Medicine as such now has no decisive voice in the affairs of the University Hospital." With no hospital committees functioning, this writer worried that "unless this ominous situation is reversed, the University Hospital will shortly be in reality only an affiliated hospital."[68]

Some respondents clearly carried considerable residual enmity toward Gerhard Hartman because of his November 1949 proposal to cut residency positions. Neurosurgeon Russell Meyers, for example, described that plan as "a rather elementalistic administrative solution to a problem which by nature is highly complex." Cutting residents across the board, in Meyers' estimation, would seriously impair the ability of some departments to care for their patients, while other departments could just as easily spare half their residents. In addition, Meyers charged that Hartman had delayed informing the faculty of a problem that had surely been weeks in gestation and had done so in order to create an emergency situation in which the superintendent could impose his will.[69]

In July 1950, in a speech to the college of medicine executive committee, a perplexed President Hancher conceded that relations between the college of medicine and the hospitals constituted "a continuing enigma in some respects." Still, the president made yet another effort to achieve an accommodation between the opposing camps, announcing that his new university-wide provost, Harvey H. Davis, would review all of the issues raised in the executive committee's prospectus, including the relationship between the college and the hospitals.[70] When the provost issued no formal decisions on any of the issues in the following months, the medical faculty adopted a resolution on May 17, 1951, reiterating its stand on the issue of hospitals governance and voting to send the controversial 1950 prospectus on the deanship to Hancher once again.[71] For the moment, however, the faculty's determination to see the dean of the college of medicine vested with ultimate authority over the hospitals foundered on the simple fact that the dean's office was vacant, had been so for the two years since Mayo Soley's death, and would continue so for nearly two more years.

The dispute between the medical faculty and Gerhard Hartman reached a flash point again in the summer of 1952, when Elmer DeGowin—a member of the search committee that had first recommended Hartman for the superintendency in 1946—submitted his resignation over the superintendent's refusal to underwrite an expansion of DeGowin's blood banking operation. This incident, like most others, was in fact part of an ongoing conflict, in this instance over the superintendent's control over space allocation and especially over funds for repair and renovation of hospitals facilities. The executive committee, headed then by Willis Fowler, DeGowin's colleague in internal medicine, endorsed DeGowin's position and notified President Hancher that DeGowin would retract his resignation only if the hospitals met his request for facilities and personnel.[72]

This latest blowup at last forced Virgil Hancher's hand. While the president had objected more than once to Hartman's extensive consulting commitments (to the point in July 1948 of requesting specific information concerning the extent and terms of all of the superintendent's current consulting projects), he had stood apart from the squabbles between the hospitals and the college. Moreover, Hancher had consistently held to much the same view of the superintendent's authority as had Hartman, envisioning the dean and the superintendent as "coordinate" powers. In addition, Hancher appears, by and large, to have held Hartman in high regard. But on this occasion Hancher reversed himself and dispatched a devastatingly blunt letter to his superintendent. "At an early date," Hancher wrote, "Provost Davis and I would like to explore with you your relation to the University Hospitals, the College of Medicine, and the University generally." "It seems to us," the president continued, "that the relationship is not satisfactory." Repeated eruptions had left little hope in the president's mind that "a permanently satisfactory solution is at hand." For that reason, Hancher concluded, "I have requested that you be continued on a temporary basis with your present rank and salary without prejudice to a reconsideration at an early date."[73]

By the time new college of medicine dean Norman Nelson arrived in July 1953, Hancher and Davis had informally implemented parts of the executive committee's prospectus on the deanship, at least as it related to governance of the hospitals, a condition that Nelson later claimed to have been "a requirement of my acceptance [of the deanship]."[74] Through that arrangement, Nelson gained authority over budgetary recommendations for the hospitals and also became the hospitals' medical director, a position that gave him authority over medical education and medical service functions.[75] The results, at least to President Hancher, were exemplary. In December 1953, Hancher expressed to Gerhard Hartman his pleasure "with the way in which everyone seems to be cooperating to make this a great medical center."[76] Outside the president's view, however, the transition to the new dean was not without incident, as Norman Nelson established his authority to head the Hospital Advisory Committee and, overall, established tighter control over the hospitals.

Events of the late 1940s and early 1950s, culminating in the reorganization of 1953, left the bold vision of the new breed of hospital administrator advocated by Gerhard Hartman and his like-minded colleagues in the field more than a little tattered. Clearly, the notion that a strong superintendent could circumscribe the authority of the medical staff had faltered in this test at the University of Iowa Hospitals. Just as clearly, however, that failure was not entirely, or perhaps even chiefly, Gerhard Hartman's. Admittedly, the superintendent was occasionally confrontational, perhaps unnecessarily so, in his dealings with the college of medicine; yet Hartman rarely acted without provocation. In retrospect, regardless of how events might have appeared to the principals, Hartman's failure to achieve his goal of autonomy as hospitals superintendent was primarily a consequence of the hospitals' continued dependence on indigent care and the state appropriations that funded indigent care, a condition that severely limited the superintendent's real power vis-à-vis the clinical faculty. In contrast, as detailed in the next chapter, the advent of Medicare in the mid-1960s, buttressed by the continued spread of private health insurance, afforded the hospitals' administration the opportunity to accomplish much of what Hartman had sought.

Hospitals Expansion, 1946–1955

Notwithstanding the sometimes bitter conflict between the hospitals administration and the college of medicine in the first postwar years, the hospitals saw significant growth and improvement in several areas during the early years of Gerhard Hartman's leadership. For example, on returning to the General Hospital in 1948, one former nursing student remarked on the startling change in appearance from former years. "The whole hospital has taken on a new look," she exclaimed. "[I] couldn't believe it was SUI," she added, noting especially the "pretty and bright" color schemes that had displaced the tiresome greys.[77] Meanwhile, Hartman was instrumental in winning substantial increases in state appropriations, and he implemented several improvements in operations, ranging from the creation of a centralized mail delivery system and the rationalization of nursing services to the installation of an emergency lighting plant and automatic thermostats on the heating system. At the same time, the hospitals' medical staff increased more than 50 percent in the first postwar decade, and total hospitals' staff nearly doubled.

Total patient admissions rose 22.7 percent from 1945–1946 to 1954–1955 (Table 4.1), significantly below the 50.0 percent increase in the 1930s. Likewise, indigent admissions in 1954–1955 were 22.1 percent above the level at the end of the war, compared to an increase of 75.4 percent in the 1930s. The total of indigent patient-days was in fact below the levels of the early 1930s. Reflecting the shifting nature of the indigent caseload, indigent patients' average length of stay rose from 16.7 days in 1945–1946 to a peak of 17.5 days in 1951–1952 before retreating to 16.2 days in 1954–1955. Meanwhile, the average length of stay for all patient classifications dipped from 14.4 days in 1945–1946 to 13.3 days in 1954–1955, as total patient-days increased 13.7 percent in the period. Importantly, private admissions continued the climb begun in the years just prior to World War II, more than doubling in the fifteen years from 1939–1940 to 1954–1955, while the length of stay for private patients dropped from 9.67 to 8.35 days, a striking contrast to the figure for indigent patients.

In 1945–1946, orthopædics led all clinical departments in patient admissions with 2,797, accounting for 16.3 percent of all hospitals' admissions. Internal medicine followed with 2,655; surgery counted 2,596, otolaryngology 1,993, obstetrics/gynecology 1,762 (including 709 births), pediatrics 1,723, urology 1,655, ophthalmology 1,160, neurology 1,041, and dermatology 377. By 1954–1955, the rank order by admissions had changed significantly, as surgery held first place with 3,282, or 16.3 percent of all admissions. Internal medicine maintained its hold on second place, counting 3,049 admissions, and pediatrics stood third with 2,997 admissions. Rounding out the list, obstetrics/gynecology admitted 2,548 patients (including 1,338 births), otolaryngology 2,291, orthopædics 2,133, urology 1,938, ophthalmology 1,474, neurology 1,027, and dermatology 305. In percentage terms, pediatrics showed the largest gain in admissions over the period at 73.9 percent, followed by obstetrics/gynecology at 44.6 percent, ophthalmology at 27.1 percent, surgery at 26.4 percent, urology at 17.1 percent, otolaryngology at 15.0 percent, and internal medicine at 14.8 percent. In the same period, admissions in orthopædics dropped 23.7 percent, and admissions in dermatology fell 19.1 percent.

Outpatient registrations varied widely from year to year, beginning at 32,374 in 1945–1946, peaking at 39,434 in 1946–1947, falling to 27,462 in 1951–1952, and ending the period at 31,407 in 1954–1955. Ophthalmology counted the largest number of outpatient registrations, 4,884, in 1945–1946, followed by otolaryngology with 4,864, surgery 4,227, internal medicine 3,743, orthopædics 3,687, dermatology 3,010, pediatrics 2,886, obstetrics/gynecology 2,328, urology 1,363, and neurology 1,326. Like patient admissions, the distribution of outpatients among the clinical departments changed significantly by 1954–1955. In that year, otolaryngology

Table 4.1   University Hospitals Admissions and Patient-Days, 1946–1955

Fiscal Year	Indigent Admissions	Indigent Patient-Days	Private Admissions	Private Patient-Days	Other Admissions*	Other Patient-Days*	Total Admissions	Total Patient-Days
1945–46	9,938	165,741	3,506	34,384	3,689	46,531	17,133	246,656
1946–47	9,146	160,428	3,976	35,763	4,193	53,344	17,315	249,535
1947–48	11,324	180,969	3,785	33,196	3,979	45,033	19,088	259,198
1948–49	11,797	195,989	4,046	32,901	3,748	42,545	19,591	271,435
1949–50	11,392	192,476	3,963	30,537	3,970	45,992	19,325	269,005
1950–51	11,361	187,558	4,139	35,693	3,918	51,077	19,418	274,328
1951–52	11,376	198,585	4,458	38,053	3,236	32,186	19,070	268,824
1952–53	11,052	190,090	4,521	37,922	3,916	41,086	19,489	269,098
1953–54	11,840	195,147	4,890	41,063	3,471	34,553	20,201	270,763
1954–55	12,139	196,939	4,962	41,435	3,925	42,124	21,026	280,498

Note: All categories include acute, newborn, and housed clinic patients
*Includes clinical pay, county clinical pay, cost, student, staff, research, and State Services for Crippled Children patients.
Source: University of Iowa Hospitals and Clinics.

totaled 4,870 outpatient registrations, orthopædics 4,857, ophthalmology 4,800, dermatology 3,981, surgery 3,468, pediatrics 2,639, internal medicine 2,407, obstetrics/gynecology 1,932, urology 1,723, and neurology 616. Neurology experienced a 53.5 percent decline in outpatient registrations in the period, internal medicine saw a 35.7 percent decline, and surgery 18.0 percent. Meanwhile, dermatology saw an increase of 32.3 percent, orthopædics 31.7 percent, and urology 26.4 percent.

Contrary to the small growth in overall patient numbers, hospital revenues increased sharply between 1946 and 1955 (Table 4.2). Net revenues rose 190 percent, including revenues from state, private, and clinical pay patients and other sources. For the first time in two decades, state appropriations for indigent care rose substantially, increasing 240 percent between 1945–1946 and 1954–1955. Two years were keys to that growth in state funding: in 1947 a 35.5 percent increase was approved after several weeks of contentious debate, and in 1951 a 37.8 percent increase was approved after an equally contentious debate, this time over expanded enrollments in the college of medicine. Overall, the average cost per indigent admission rose nearly threefold, from $110.41 in 1945–1946 to $316.64 in 1954–1955. Meanwhile, private patient revenues rose 156 percent, surpassing the $1 million mark in 1955. The average cost per private admission rose 85.6 percent, from $110.40 in 1945–1946 to $204.81 in 1954–1955, an increase far smaller than the comparable figure for indigent patients but suggestive in part of the shift toward chronic cases among the indigent caseload.

Clinical faculty numbers grew dramatically in the first postwar decade, a measure of growth in both the college of medicine and the hospitals. Jumping from 60 to 106 tenure track faculty and from 107 to 167 total clinical faculty (Table 4.3), the largest growth, in absolute numbers and in percentage terms, came in the first five years after the war, as the college of medicine and the hospitals worked to replenish depleted staff ranks. Overall, the figures show a trend to replace non-tenure track with tenure track faculty, the proportion of the former falling from 43.9 percent of all clinical faculty in 1945 to 36.5 percent in 1955—a product in part of the Medical Service Plan discussed in a later section of this chapter. The greatest gains and percentage gains in tenure track faculty came in two of the largest clinical departments: internal medicine increased 250 percent from six to twenty-one and pediatrics gained 240 percent from five to seventeen. Meanwhile, the expansion of clinical faculty brought a decline in the proportion of females, from 13.1 to 8.4 percent, reflecting the very small numbers of women in tenure track positions.

Like the clinical areas, other hospitals departments also grew dramatically. In 1945–1946, total hospitals staff stood at 714; in 1954–1955, the number reached 1,326. As the medical staff declined slightly as a percentage

Table 4.2   University Hospitals Revenues, 1946–1955

	State Appropriations ($000)	Private Patient Revenues ($000)	Total Revenues ($000)
1945–46	1,111	396	1,931
1946–47	1,363	482	2,505
1947–48	1,847	484	3,032
1948–49	2,372	552	3,498
1949–50	2,578	524	3,688
1950–51	2,558	628	3,846
1951–52	3,525	744	4,837
1952–53	3,276	765	4,857
1953–54	3,692	854	5,347
1954–55	3,782	1,013	5,604

Note: Total Revenues column includes income from sources not shown in table, such as ward charges from clinical, county clinical, student, staff, and State Services for Crippled Children patients, as well as laboratory fees, visitor cafeteria receipts, and the like.
Source: University of Iowa Hospitals and Clinics; University of Iowa Financial Reports.

of all hospitals staff, the graduate nursing staff increased 176 percent, from 101 to 279 and from 14.1 to 21.0 percent of total staff numbers. Moreover, numbers of nurse aides and, later, licensed practical nurses rose substantially also, from 105 to 234, an increase of 123 percent. Total nursing staff, then, increased from 206 in 1946 to 513 in 1955 and made up 38.7 percent of all staff at the hospitals in the latter year. The overall growth in nursing staff to some extent reflected the larger trend toward specialized care in the University Hospitals, and the ratio of total patient-days to total nursing staff dropped precipitously from 1197.4 in 1946 to 546.8 in 1955. The growth in salaried nursing staff also reflected the inauguration of the baccalaureate program in nursing begun in 1949, a milestone that gave nursing education an independent base and reduced the hospitals' claim to the labor of student nurses. By the early 1950s, the opening of the Veterans Administration Hospital, which offered a 40-hour work week and significantly higher salaries, along with the rapid expansion of community hospitals throughout Iowa, prompted a serious nursing shortage and an extraordinary turnover rate among nurses at the University Hospitals. The superintendent responded by closing two General Hospital wards, and he appealed to inactive nurses, many of whom were married, to rejoin the workforce, offering a daycare center as an added inducement. When that strategy failed to fill the gap, the University Hospitals, too, adopted the forty-hour week and higher salaries for nursing staff.

Table 4.3 College of Medicine Faculty By Department and Gender, 1945–1955

	1945					1950					1955				
	Tenure Track	Other	Total	Male	Female	Tenure Track	Other	Total	Male	Female	Tenure Track	Other	Total	Male	Female
Anatomy*	8	0	8	7	1	12	0	12	9	3	12	0	12	10	2
Biochemistry*	5	0	5	5	0	7	0	7	6	1	10	0	10	9	1
Dermatology	1	0	1	1	0	2	0	2	2	0	3	0	3	3	0
Internal Medicine	6	6	12	10	2	18	2	20	17	3	21	11	32	27	5
Microbiology*	4	0	4	3	1	4	0	4	3	1	7	0	7	6	1
Neurology	3	0	3	3	0	5	1	6	6	0	3	3	6	5	1
Obstetrics-Gynecology	5	4	9	7	2	4	2	6	6	0	4	2	6	6	0
Ophthalmology	3	7	10	10	0	5	6	11	10	1	4	5	9	7	2
Orthopedics	3	4	7	7	0	4	0	4	4	0	6	4	10	9	1
Otolaryngology	4	6	10	7	3	6	6	12	12	0	7	5	12	10	2
Pathology	5	0	5	5	0	6	3	9	9	0	6	4	10	10	0
Pediatrics	5	8	13	8	5	9	5	14	10	4	17	3	20	18	2
Pharmacology*	3	0	3	3	0	4	0	4	4	0	5	0	5	5	0
Physical Therapy-Rehabilitation*	—	—	—	—	—	—	—	—	—	—	5	1	6	3	3
Physiology*	8	0	8	7	1	18	0	18	16	2	14	0	14	12	2
Preventive Medicine*	10	0	10	7	3	12	0	12	9	3	15	0	15	13	2
Program in Hospital Administration*	—	—	—	—	—	1	0	1	1	0	1	0	1	1	0
Psychiatry	5	4	9	7	2	9	1	10	8	2	11	2	13	11	2
Radiology-Radiation Research	3	3	6	6	0	5	0	5	5	0	8	4	12	12	0
Surgery	15	1	16	16	0	16	3	19	18	1	18	13	31	30	1
Urology	2	4	6	6	0	3	0	3	3	0	3	6	9	8	1
Clinical Totals	60	47	107	93	14	92	29	121	110	11	106	61	167	153	14
Basic Science/Other	38	0	38	32	6	58	0	58	48	10	69	1	70	59	11
Grand Totals	**98**	**47**	**145**	**125**	**20**	**150**	**29**	**179**	**158**	**21**	**175**	**62**	**237**	**212**	**25**

*Basic science and other departments.

Source: University of Iowa College of Medicine annual staffing lists.

With the hospitals operating at near capacity in the late 1940s and with increasing pressures for staff and teaching space, Gerhard Hartman reclaimed space for patient care that had been abandoned to other functions in previous years. For example, Hartman removed the part-time employees who had lived in the General Hospital, reclaimed two 30-bed wards vacated by army and navy personnel, and moved the student infirmary out of the General Hospital. Hartman also procured eight war surplus quonset huts at a cost of $70,000—financed from private patient fees—and installed the temporary buildings accommodating 151 beds immediately south of the General Hospital.[78] Outpatients who had filled wards while waiting for diagnostic tests and treatment were among the patients who occupied what was euphemistically known as the "Hotel Annex." Confident that the hospitals would soon receive federal funds for expansion, Hartman insisted that the quonset buildings—which clinical staff called an embarrassment—were only temporary; in fact they remained in use for some fifteen years.[79] The quonset huts allowed the hospitals to serve some ninety additional ward patients at any one time, increasing annual service by more than 30,000 patient-days and holding in check per diem costs, which had grown 63 percent between 1940 and 1946. Through such expedients, the General Hospital had 669 inpatient beds in service from 1947, and the Children's Hospital counted 215.[80]

Hill-Burton and the Growth of Community Hospitals

Developed and promoted by the American Hospital Association, endorsed by the American Medical Association, and the beneficiary of strong bipartisan support in Congress, the Hill-Burton Hospital Survey and Construction Act of 1946—named for Senators Lister Hill of Alabama and Harold Burton of Ohio—fueled the construction of community hospitals in underserved areas of the United States. The act required state-by-state surveys of the availability, quality, and potential viability of hospitals, and it allocated to the states federal funds equal to one-third of the cost of constructing hospitals to meet the assessed demand, with the proviso that construction conform to U.S. Public Health Service standards. The act also required state departments of health to license all hospitals, whether old or new. Finally, Hill-Burton called on medical schools and their teaching hospitals to take up the role of regional specialty—or, in the parlance of the time, "secondary care" facilities—serving both as training grounds for specialized personnel and as places for caring for the advanced cases that local hospitals were not equipped or staffed to handle. In all, Hill-Burton was, as Rosemary Stevens notes, a "major landmark" in the history of American hospitals, sponsoring nearly 5,000 construction projects in the next twenty years and, just as important, injecting federal agencies and standards into state and local healthcare decisions.[81]

In Iowa, 13 percent of AMA-registered hospital beds had disappeared from service between 1929 and 1941, and 12 percent of the remainder fell out of service during World War II.[82] In anticipation of federal legislation, the Iowa General Assembly passed the Iowa Hospital Survey and Construction Act and the companion Hospital Licensing Act in 1945 charging the State Department of Health with licensing all hospitals and creating a State Hospital Survey Committee to determine the condition and supply of beds throughout the state.[83] Headed by Walter Bierring, president of the State Board of Health, the survey committee's preliminary results showed that in 1945 Iowa had 500 institutions that passed as hospitals, but most of those were small enterprises run by one or a few physicians and comprising only a few beds. The final report, completed near the end of 1947, identified only 145 hospitals, and many of these, such as Des Moines General Hospital and Booth Memorial Hospital, were filled entirely with "unacceptable" beds. To bring the state up to the U.S. Public Health Service standard of 4.5 beds per 1,000 population would, Bierring calculated, require the addition of more than 4,000 general hospital beds at a cost of some 40 million dollars.[84] By the time Hill-Burton became law in 1946, 39 Iowa counties and communities had already amassed $6.7 million for hospital construction.[85]

Behind the concern for adequate hospital facilities lay the issue of physician numbers and distribution. In 1947, the American Medical Association claimed that only 32 of Iowa's 99 counties had an adequate number of physicians—that is, fewer than 1,000 residents per physician. Forty-two counties had population-to-physician ratios between 1,000 and 1,499, and the remaining 25 counties had ratios of 1,500 or more.[86] The consensus among civic leaders, as well as within the state medical society, was that new physicians would locate only in communities with adequate hospitals. The key to attracting physicians, therefore, and particularly younger ones, lay in providing them with a modern hospital in which to practice. "The costs of carrying on a medical practice now are such that a physician cannot equip and maintain an office in a town of 500 people," the *Journal of the Iowa State Medical Society* warned. The physician must either locate in an urban area, the journal stated, "or he must be where he has access to those facilities in either a hospital or a laboratory."[87]

Walter Bierring submitted the Iowa Hospital Plan, as it was called, to the Public Health Service at the end of 1947. Bierring's plan established a priority system serving those communities most in need, provided they could both afford their share of the construction costs and possessed the means to operate the facilities. In many counties, those guidelines limited construction to small hospitals, and, despite Public Health Service guidelines recommending at least fifty beds per facility, Bierring's plan included the construction of nine community hospitals with fewer than 35 beds. Bierring targeted some of Iowa's larger cities for new hospital construction as well, including Cedar Rapids and Des Moines.[88] Through 1954, Hill–Burton provided $11 million in federal funding for 49 projects in Iowa, increasing the state's acceptable hospital beds from 6,689 in 1946 to 9,383 in 1954, while leaving the number of hospitals unchanged. Partly in response to the expansion of hospital beds and partly in response to the rapid spread of private insurance coverage, hospital admissions in Iowa climbed dramatically in the early postwar years, rising 26 percent from 1946 to 1950 alone and far outpacing population growth.[89]

For the University of Iowa Hospitals, the Iowa Hospital Plan and subsequent Hill–Burton projects meant significant change, quite apart from the increased competition from community hospitals. Most important, university officials and the state board of education worked hard to win formal recognition for the University Hospitals as the linchpin of an expanded and coordinated statewide hospital system, an idea opposed—initially, at least—by Walter Bierring and the hospital survey committee.[90] In April 1948, two months after the Public Health Service approved Walter Bierring's hospital plan, Gerhard Hartman announced in the *Journal of the Iowa State Medical Society* that the University Hospitals would lead the state into a "rapid period of growth and metamorphosis." As Hartman saw it, the University Hospitals would fulfill several distinctive functions in an emergent statewide healthcare system, including indigent care, medical education, medical research, "statewide consultation services (from) renowned specialists," and the provision of "diagnostic and therapeutic facilities not feasible except at a hospital center of large size."[91] In Hartman's view, the growth of community hospitals and the explosion in private patients would not render the University Hospitals redundant. Indeed, the hospitals would be the heart of the new hospital system, emphasizing advanced care over primary care, the latter conceded as a matter of necessity to community hospitals. The resulting spiral of increasingly specialized patient services and training programs profoundly influenced the hospitals' postwar history.

The hospital licensing provisions of the Hill–Burton Act were likewise significant for the University Hospitals. Initially, the board of education and university officials argued that their facilities should be exempt from state licensure requirements and sought an opinion to that effect from the state attorney general.[92] To the surprise of Gerhard Hartman and Carlyle Jacobsen, the attorney general ruled to the contrary,[93] and university officials then reluctantly looked into complying with state licensing requirements. After the first licensing inspection was completed in early 1950, resulting in many suggestions regarding procedural and structural alterations, the regents instructed the university business manager to apply for the requisite license with the understanding that the university would comply with those items for which funds were available but would not respond to all of the points raised. However, the university's general counsel advised against ignoring the law, warning that state law empowered regulators to close the hospital for noncompliance; instead, he suggested that the university seek an exemption from the legislature, a tactic that also failed.[94] In the end, the University Hospitals, however grudgingly, accepted state licensing, and the licensing board's annual reports, with their extensive lists of recommendations for improved services and facilities, were discovered to be useful tools for University Hospitals administrators in seeking funds for various capital improvements.

The University Hospitals also became subject to the standards of the Joint Commission on Accreditation of Hospitals (JCAH), a group formed in 1952 that joined together the review and accreditation programs of the American Hospital Association, the AMA's Council on Medical Education and Hospitals, and the American College of Surgeons.[95] The University Hospitals secured JCAH accreditation in 1953, one of only 34 of the state's 100 hospitals to do so. After the first full-scale site review in 1955, the hospitals won the maximum three-year accreditation, with just four recommended improvements, all having to do with patient records. The hospitals repeated that success in 1958, 1961, and 1964, each time with few suggested improvements,[96] although that exemplary accreditation record rested to some extent on the cursory nature of review procedures as well as the bias of the survey instruments, which, for example, placed little emphasis on the condition of the physical plant.

Private Practice and the Medical Service Plan

As noted in the previous chapter, hard times during the Depression and World War II exacerbated preexisting tensions caused by the full- and part-time division within the college of medicine faculty. In President Hancher's blunt estimation at the dawn of the postwar era, "The disparity in income between members of the staff is generally regarded as greater than the disparity in the ability, skill, and energy of the same individuals." Furthermore, Hancher observed, "there is dissatisfaction because the absorption of certain senior members of the staff in private practice, from which they obtain their disparate income, throws an undue burden of teaching, research, and clinical care of the indigent upon junior members of the staff."[97] Some of his critics, Hancher later noted, seemed to think "that you can have a single man at the head of a department and a lot of flunkies running around doing his bidding," but modern medicine, he noted, "is far too complicated for that arrangement." Without strong remedial action, Hancher later maintained, "we would have had no medical school worth rating."[98]

In August 1945, the abrupt termination of the war brought the private practice issue "suddenly into focus." Warned that the college was "seething with unrest, uncertainty, bitterness and resentment,"[99] Hancher undertook a series of interviews with faculty members, who confirmed an "impending blow-up" in the college.[100] He also dispatched administrative dean Allin W. Dakin to study the Mayo Clinic's new full-time system, and he wrote to Alan Gregg at the Rockefeller Foundation to follow up on advice Gregg had dispensed two years before.[101] The question now was not whether or when to abolish the remaining part-time system, but how it would be done. Hancher charged Dean Ewen MacEwen "to undertake a survey of the College of Medicine and the University Hospital with respect to full-time and part-time appointments to the medical staff." Such a survey, Hancher continued, should focus on the college's teaching, research, and indigent care missions; in contrast, private practice should be "definitely secondary." He had already promised the board of education, he said, to have a plan completed by January 1, 1946.[102] However, MacEwen held back, wary of already strong opposition to his leadership within the medical faculty and reluctant to try to impose drastic solutions from above. Hancher then instructed the dean to form a committee, but MacEwen did nothing, prompting the president to urge him to "get busy" and have a plan ready by the stated deadline or face a plan installed by presidential fiat.[103]

The previous autumn, at the 56th annual meeting of the AAMC, the subject of the association president's address was precisely the issue faced by the University of Iowa College of Medicine. Hancher had accompanied MacEwen to Pittsburgh for the meeting and had heard A. C. Furstenberg, dean of the University of Michigan Medical School, announce that while the subject of private practice had long been a troublesome point at a number of medical schools, the time was right for action. "Improved economic conditions," Furstenberg noted, along with reconversion to a peacetime regime meant "that the optimum time has been reached for long needed reforms."[104]

Furstenberg then outlined five types of faculty practice plans, each of which entailed all too familiar problems. First, the speaker conceded that economic realities had proved the strict full-time system to be unsustainable. A second plan, known as departmental fee-funding, placed patient fees in a departmental fee fund, from which money was then distributed to staff members to supplement salaries; however, according to the Michigan dean, such plans tended to create sizable disparities in income from one department to the next and were potentially divisive on that count. A third plan was geographic full-time, which in Furstenberg's formulation, paralleled existing practice at the University of Iowa, with part-time clinical heads maintaining private practices within the confines of the teaching hospital. By far the most common plan in 1945, geographic full-time, assumed "the loyalty, honesty, and integrity of the man and his devotion to duty," a problematic assumption in Virgil Hancher's view.[105] Regulated or limited private practice was a fourth alternative, a system in which department heads and perhaps one or two of their assistants received fees from patients, up to a specified percentage of full-time salaries. In Furstenberg's estimation, the chief weakness in regulated private practice was that "clinicians who have operated under this plan devoted so much time to the practice of medicine . . . that they neglected their teaching duties and research programs," another problem all too familiar to Hancher. The final option was the limited full-time or Michigan system in which each faculty member had the privilege of requesting a part-time appointment, but here, too, the effect upon teaching and research was problematic at best.[106]

The departmental fee-funding system described by Furstenberg echoed, at least in outline, a system that Everett Plass and Alan Gregg had proposed to Hancher three years earlier. That system, which Plass and Gregg called a "modified fee fund," envisioned all staff members as full-time, paid them viable but modest salaries, and allowed them to boost their income by substantial margins, within limits and according to their rank, through private practice. Under such a plan, practice fees would be collected by the university and redistributed either directly to clinical faculty or through their department heads in proportion to either individual or departmental earnings.[107] In some respects, the Plass-Gregg plan resembled the long-standing practice at the University of Iowa by which practice fees, aside from moneys accruing to part-time faculty, were given over to department heads for distribution within the department for a variety of purposes.

When the drafting committee appointed by Dean MacEwen had produced no planning report by early January 1946, Hancher sent a draft of a "Statement of Policy" to MacEwen for his review. Taking the advice and much of the wording of a letter written by John McClintock, Hancher proposed the Michigan system, allowing faculty to apply for a part-time appointment, provided that private practice be closely regulated and limited to one-third of their time; meanwhile, other faculty members would devote themselves full-time to teaching, research, and care of the indigent. Hancher also expressed his willingness to accept a different plan, so long as it reached the same objectives of equity in income, security, and equitable promotion and fostered an emphasis on teaching, research, and indigent patient care.[108] MacEwen's committee, headed by Dabney Kerr of radiology, took no action on Hancher's statement, and two weeks later, on January 18, Hancher met with the committee and delivered an ultimatum to "formulate the terms of a uniform faculty appointment in order to achieve the closest possible approximation to full-time." Stalled by "considerable discussion and doubt as to just what its function was," including threats of resignation from two of its members, the committee made no headway, and, after several fruitless sessions, Nathaniel Alcock recommended bringing in former dean Henry Houghton as a consultant and negotiator.[109] Hancher approved the suggestion, noting that Alcock was a "hero worshipper" and that "Houghton was his hero."[110]

It may be that Alcock recommended Houghton as arbiter with the expectation that the former dean would temper Hancher's reform bent; if so, he was disappointed. The Medical Service Plan that emerged under Houghton's guidance granted private practice privileges to any faculty member with the rank of assistant professor or above, distributing the proceeds as salary supplements ("commutation fractions") to all tenure track clinical faculty. Incorporating increases in base salaries as well, the plan made assistant professors eligible for supplements up to 50 percent of their new salaries of $4,000 to $6,000. The plan allowed associate professors to boost their salaries of $5,000 to $8,000 by 75 percent, while full professors, with salary ranges of $7,000 to $9,500, and department heads, with salaries of $8,000 to $10,000, could receive commutation fractions up to the amount of their salaries. Existing part-time heads received an added $5,000 allowance. The plan applied excess funds to other departmental needs, including equipment and research programs, with a portion allotted to the college's Central Scientific Fund. The plan included a compensation committee vested with responsibility for the plan's operations, and, because the higher base salaries prescribed in the plan would result in a budget deficit, it called for an additional state appropriation of $175,000 for salaries. Finally, calling on the state to allocate funds specifically to support research, Houghton's plan noted that "the national reputation of the College is dependent upon the character of [its] research" and recommended that all faculty members be allowed to devote up to one-third of their time to research, that department heads encourage and facilitate research, and that the college give preference to research-oriented physicians in hiring.[111]

In their minority report, Alcock and the other part-timers on the committee rejected the fundamentals of the plan unless Houghton were hired to oversee it during a two-year trial period, a condition that, among its other flaws, implied the firing of Dean MacEwen. The board of education ignored that condition, apparently hoping that Alcock would resign, as two other opponents—surgery head Frank Peterson and ophthalmology head Cecil O'Brien—were about to do. However, Alcock opted to stay and fight. "To put it very bluntly," Alcock wrote to the full-timers, "there will be much work to be done after 5 p.m. and before 8 a.m.," implying that full-time faculty were not accustomed to the long working hours of their part-time colleagues. "We can promise you much sweat but we hope with no blood," he continued; nonetheless, "we can also visualize that there will be complications that may come close to causing the shed [*sic*] of blood." Alcock hoped to see the demise of the plan after the two-year trial that all concerned had been "wise enough to place upon it."[112] Taking the side of Alcock and other critics, the Iowa State Medical Society labeled the Medical Service Plan "a form of socialized or communistic medicine." Although acknowledging the problems in the college, the society argued that the plan would create problems of its own, predicting that the higher salaries would cause resentment in the rest of the university and that private practice income would be exploited by state legislators, leading to lower appropriations for faculty salaries. The plan, the society cautioned, "may work while times are good and plentiful, but when and if the anticipated period of readjustment [to a lower level of economic activity] comes, we question if men of high caliber can be maintained."[113]

Objections notwithstanding, the board of education approved the Medical Service Plan in January 1947 and set its implementation for July,[114] a watershed in the college of medicine's history and in that of the University Hospitals as well. Most important, the plan provided a working accommodation to balance the demands of patient service, teaching, and research, and it resolved much of the mounting friction surrounding private practice. No doubt, too, the plan made possible the recruitment of such high-caliber faculty as surgery head Nathan Womack, internal medicine head William Bean, and ophthalmology head Alson Braley, and it boosted the place of research in the college.[115] For the hospitals, the plan ensured an expanding private practice, providing not only additional much needed income but also a broader range of patients for teaching purposes. In 1948, President Hancher agreed to raise the 5 percent quota on private patient beds "slightly" if necessary "to recruit and keep a good, well-balanced staff."[116] Less obvious but just as important, the Medical Service Plan was a major step in the transition from an autocratic, hierarchical system of governance in the college of medicine toward a more democratic one. By 1954–1955, Medical Service Plan income for all clinical departments reached just over $1 million, with surgery commanding more than 18 percent of the total, otolaryngology and internal medicine generating more than 12 percent each, and ophthalmology just under 12 percent.

At the same time, the plan's critics, notably Nathaniel Alcock, made some telling points, arguing that in order for the plan to work, more money will have to be earned and therefore more private practice will have to be done. This brings us to the ridiculous position of embarking on a policy that increases the very thing that is said to have created our ills. . . . This plan is built upon the assurance that the next legislature and legislatures in the future will appropriate enough money to increase the basic salaries quite handsomely. . . . Are you not gambling and putting your money on a rather long shot? . . . [D]o you think the legislature will be sympathetic in appropriating large sums of money to men who are permitted to have the proposed incomes? It would seem to us in these rather pessimistic days that you men are quite optimistic.[117]

While few contest the claim that the Medical Service Plan was a major success and played a substantial role in subsequent expansion in the college of medicine, the weaknesses that Alcock identified were real enough. Indeed, they surfaced again and again in subsequent decades, raising concerns within the college of medicine administration and among the medical faculty.

Mandated Growth in Medical Education

By the late 1940s, the long simmering and very public issue of the shortage of doctors in Iowa's small towns reached a crisis stage, resulting in a mandate from the Iowa General Assembly to expand undergraduate medical student enrollments by 30 percent. In part, the legislature reacted to the fact that the college of medicine's budget had risen from $652,000 in 1945–1946 to more than $1.7 million in 1948–1949; yet total undergraduate enrollments, marking a resumption of the scale-down of the late 1930s, held stubbornly in the range of 300. The postwar years had brought a strong surge in applications for admission to the college of medicine, as was the case at medical schools across the United States; however, the college's admissions committee was rejecting greater numbers of qualified applicants rather than accommodating more students.[118] Where, many legislators wondered, was the additional money going? To make matters worse, a 1947 study published in the *Journal of the Iowa State Medical Society* indicated that more than half of Iowa's general practitioners were 60 years of age or older[119]—a serious problem when Hill-Burton construction would soon add hundreds of hospital beds to Iowa's healthcare infrastructure and few new physicians were choosing general practice in Iowa's smaller communities.

When he took office on July 1, 1948, new college of medicine dean Mayo Soley stepped into a hornets' nest of problems, most importantly the jurisdictional contest, described earlier, between the dean and the hospital director and the legislative pressures to expand medical enrollments. A correspondent later told President Hancher that Soley had confided to him "that he did not know or even dream that he was getting into the kind of situation which he faced," and, had he known, "he would not have come."[120] In November 1948, just four months after taking office, Soley and Gerhard Hartman submitted an estimate of the additional costs of expanding student enrollments as the legislature had demanded. According to that estimate, a 10 percent increase in entering classes entailed $108,000 in additional operating costs; a 20 percent enrollment increase added $190,000; and a 30 percent increase added $270,000. The largest expenditures, as Soley reported to an interim committee of the General Assembly in January 1949, would be for adjustments to the physical plant, especially in the pathology/bacteriology laboratory, facilities for obstetrics training, and extensive changes to the operating rooms, outpatient clinics, offices, other laboratories, and the library.[121]

Soon after, the Iowa House of Representatives approved a mandated 30 percent increase in the freshman class size—to 120—at the earliest possible date. Virgil Hancher, Carlyle Jacobsen, and Mayo Soley asked the senate to quash the mandate, but succeeded only in winning a softening of the language, making the 30 percent target a "request" and seeking the "cooperation" of the university in achieving the goal. In response, Hancher and Soley issued a joint press release claiming that the doctor shortage was a problem of distribution rather than aggregate numbers. Soley also announced that the medical school had begun actively encouraging students to enter general practice preceptorships. After the war, Hancher and Soley maintained, many returning physicians understood that specialization was an inexorable trend and, as a result, the popularity of general practice had diminished. Moreover, the college of medicine was graduating more than enough physicians to meet the state's replacement needs; Soley noted that the medical school had graduated 524 physicians since 1941, while only 474 Iowa physicians had left practice. The problem was that new graduates were not entering general practice, as had the majority of their elders, and many were leaving the state. In any event, Hancher and Soley argued, enrolling fewer but better-quality students was a more efficient use of state money, contrasting the graduation rate of just 47.8 percent from the class of 142 admitted in 1929 with the 84 percent rate of graduation among the 87 medical students admitted in the last prewar class of 1941.[122]

Along with the "request" for expanded enrollments, the Iowa General Assembly in 1949 approved a capital expansion allowance of just $560,000 for the entire university, at a time when most colleges and departments were staggered by the influx of new students, many of them receiving benefits under the GI Bill, and more than two dozen university departments and offices were functioning out of temporary structures left over from the war. The General Assembly specifically withheld funds for capital improvements needed in the college of medicine, promising appropriations only when the college achieved stated enrollment targets.[123] At the same time, President Hancher was not disposed to favor the college of medicine over other areas of the university facing equal or greater enrollment pressures; indeed, Hancher was inclined to grant the liberal arts campus priority in capital funding because of a 60 percent enrollment increase since the 1920s. Making matters worse, some liberal arts faculty already complained of physicians "milking" the rest of the university for their own benefit.[124] Overall, Provost Harvey Davis said, the needs of the medical campus ranked fourteenth on the university's list of priorities.[125]

As early as the fall of 1948, the university's business office notified Dean Soley that most of the college of medicine's departmental accounts, including the dean's office account, were seriously depleted. Six weeks later, with more than half of the fiscal year remaining, roughly half of those accounts were overdrawn.[126] Facing the added burden of expanded enrollments, Hancher, Soley, Jacobsen, and Hartman pressed their case on the General Assembly in the spring of 1949, presenting plans and requesting funds, only to be rebuffed. On June 7, Soley reluctantly informed the medical faculty of his failure "to impress upon the General Assembly the needs and requirements of the College in carrying out the task now assigned to it." He had, Soley said, just one chance remaining, a meeting with legislative leaders set for June 13.[127]

On June 8, 1949, the dean received discouraging news in the form of a report on physician distribution in Iowa. Starting from the existing ratio of 1 physician per 1,200 Iowans, and assuming only a negligible in-migration of physicians from outside the state, the college would need each year to graduate 79 physicians who would stay in Iowa to practice. Nothing but those 79 new doctors would bring the state's physician-to-population ratio in line with the national average. Given the historic 45 percent retention rate of University of Iowa graduates in practice in Iowa, even a doubling of enrollments clearly would not satisfy the state's need for doctors. "It is very doubtful," the report concluded, "that the plan [i.e., a one-third expansion of enrollments] will supply Iowa with enough doctors, even if the trend to leave the state is ameliorated."[128]

At the June 13 meeting, Hancher told legislators that the mandated expansion in the college of medicine would easily consume the entire sum allotted to the university for capital improvements during the upcoming biennium. He threatened that the press and public would not be pleased to learn that their "favorite campus projects were being deprived of funds in order to provide more doctors." Soley's presentation at the same meeting, a presentation Hancher found to be "clearly and carefully arranged," took up most of the meeting and began with the frank statement that the goal of 120 freshmen by the fall of 1950 was impossible. The time required to secure bids on the needed construction would be nearly two years, Soley explained, and alterations by department would have to be done sequentially and not simultaneously, so tight was space in the hospitals. Such work could not be completed before the fall of 1952, and the effects of expanded enrollments would not be felt in Iowa medicine until 1957, when members of the first enlarged class completed their internships. The delegation presented a staggering bill—one much inflated from previous estimates—including $600,000 for a new hospital wing, $400,000 in various other capital improvements, more than $300,000 for equipment, and $200,000 in additional operating costs.[129]

Soley left the meeting with legislators promising to devise a less expensive plan, and, after several days of intensive work, he informed his colleagues that he had devised new solutions. But Soley's suicide on June 21, 1949, cast this, as it did many other issues, into limbo. Hancher remarked that "all of the threads of our planning were in [Soley's] hands" when he died, and that he had left little trace of his most recent planning behind.[130] Finally, two months later, the college of medicine presented a budget to meet the first two years of expanded enrollments, a budget that included no new construction, just $69,700 in renovations and alterations, and $162,290 for equipment, additional staff, and higher operating expenses. The university and the state legislature eventually provided the money.[131] Meanwhile, the University Hospitals would not be affected until the larger classes began their junior and senior clerkships. Although Gerhard Hartman had earlier presented legislators with a thinly detailed $200,000 proposal for improvements, most of the discussion over hospital changes lay ahead and chiefly involved negotiations between Hartman's assistant, Glen Clasen, and the medical staff.

By the fall of 1951, undergraduate enrollment at the University of Iowa College of Medicine exceeded the targeted one-third expansion in entering classes (Table 4.4), total enrollment having already risen 39.6 percent since 1948–1949. By the mid-1950s, average enrollments had increased more than 40 percent over 1948–1949. Aside from the increase in overall numbers, perhaps the most striking feature of postwar enrollment patterns—at the University of Iowa and elsewhere—was the dramatic decline in women students, both in absolute numbers and as a proportion of the total student body. Reversing the 1930s pattern, which saw the percentage of women students rise and fall in line with total enrollments, female enrollments declined well below historical averages during the expansion of the early 1950s, falling from 10.6 percent in 1948–1949 to 3.3 percent in 1951–1952 and to just 2.2 percent in 1954–1955. After the transition of the early 1950s, both total enrollments and female enrollments held essentially steady into the 1960s.

Table 4.4 College of Medicine Enrollments, 1945–1965

	Male	Female	Total
1944–45	380	23	403
1949–50	313	24	337
1954–55	436	10	446
1959–60	421	14	435
1964–65	394	30	424

Source: Board of Education/Regents Biennial Reports.

A major increase in the number of faculty in the basic science departments—anatomy, biochemistry, microbiology, pharmacology, and physiology—began well before the increase in student enrollments, reflecting, as did the parallel increase in the clinical departments, the deficiencies in the college of medicine faculty at the end of World War II (Table 4.3). Overall, basic science faculty numbers rose more than 60 percent from 1945 to 1950 and more than 70 percent in the decade between 1946 and 1955. Expansion in the basic science departments, however, as in the clinical departments and in the medical student body, did not mean significant new opportunities for women. In 1945, women made up 10.7 percent of basic science faculty; in 1950, the number grew to 15.6 percent; but women held just 12.7 percent of basic science faculty positions in 1955.

A major postwar expansion in graduate medical education, particularly at the residency level, also preceded the growth in undergraduate student numbers, bringing a substantial increase in the costs of graduate medical education at the University Hospitals. In 1945, reflecting the attenuation of graduate training during the war years, the University Hospitals reported a total of 17 interns and 46 residents. In 1947, numbers rose to 20 interns and 112 residents, reflecting in turn the flood of young physicians returning from wartime service. The total continued to grow in later years, standing at 23 interns and 150 residents in 1955, and peaking at 22 interns and 229 residents a decade later. In the late 1940s, as noted earlier, both the added costs and the larger issue of control over graduate medical education heightened frictions between the hospitals and the college of medicine. At the same time, national oversight of graduate medical education became more formalized, reflecting increased collaboration between specialty boards and the AMA's Council on Medical Education and Hospitals, and the period of residency training lengthened in some specialties. In part to relieve fiscal pressures on the University Hospitals, the board of education in 1947 approved a proposal from Dean MacEwen and Gerhard Hartman establishing preceptorship programs for residency training in several Iowa hospitals, with participating institutions paying the residents' salaries and other expenses.[132]

By the early 1950s, after pent-up wartime demand had moved through the system, America's enormously expanded hospital internship and residency programs outstripped the supply of medical graduates, making the placement process increasingly competitive. In 1951, medical schools and hospitals sought to rationalize placement by establishing the National Internship and Residency Matching Program. The "Match," however, did not change the basic demographic imbalance in graduate medical education, and the University of Iowa College of Medicine and the University Hospitals, in part for fiscal reasons, found themselves at a competitive disadvantage in attracting the best candidates, including their own graduates. In the first two postwar decades, for example, the hospitals never recruited more than three University of Iowa graduates as interns at any one time,[133] although the success rate was somewhat better with regard to residency programs. As administrators sought to cope with that recruitment problem and also to keep pace with national standards set by specialty boards, salary costs associated with graduate medical education represented an increasing burden on the hospitals' finances. In 1955, interns at University Hospitals earned $1,500 for a year's service; residents, depending on experience, earned from $1,680 to $2,100; in 1965, interns' salaries had risen to $3,100, while residents' salaries ranged from $2,500 to $5,000. The total cost of interns' and residents' salaries rose from $150,000 in 1950 to $851,000 in 1965.[134]

For the University Hospitals, the growth in students and staff meant added pressures on facilities. The first class of 120 entered the college of medicine in the fall of 1950, destined to begin the clinical phase of their training in the fall of 1952. Gerhard Hartman's brief report on the hospitals' needs submitted to the legislature in June 1949—a report that set the cost of improvements at $200,000—was largely rhetorical in nature and offered no specific recommendations. In February 1950, President Hancher appointed a committee including representation from the university business office, the college of medicine executive committee, and the hospitals administration, in addition to the dean of nursing, the executive dean, and the university provost, to determine the "minimal and absolutely necessary changes" needed in the hospitals to accommodate the soon-to-be enlarged clinical classes. The committee suggested two priorities: first, expansion and renovation of the Children's Hospital, much of that already in process with the help of a Public Health Service grant and, second, construction of a 42,750-square-foot addition south of the existing General Hospital to house offices, teaching facilities, and laboratories—a plan that was largely the work of Glen Clasen, Gerhard Hartman's assistant superintendent. The board of education approved a more limited project for the General Hospital involving renovation of the hospital tower, work that was completed in 1952.[135]

Rapid growth in medical education also exacerbated existing problems in supplying adequate patient volume for clinical instruction. By the early 1950s, in part because of Hill-Burton hospital construction, the University Hospitals were fast becoming a regional medical center, a transition endorsed by both Robert Neff and Gerhard Hartman but one that carried profound and not altogether welcome implications for medical education. Most important, the indigent patient population included a larger proportion of elderly patients suffering from chronic illnesses of dubious value in clinical instruction, an especially difficult problem at a time when the college of medicine was under increasing political pressure to train primary caregivers. Increasingly, it seemed, the hospitals' service and educational roles made an uncomfortable fit, an issue that defied resolution in the short term and one that grew more insistent with the passage of time. In its 1960 review of the college, the Liaison Committee on Medical Education, for example, took note of the dilemma, finding the number of patients "barely adequate," yet noting also that the heavy demands of patient service interfered with both teaching and research.[136]

Growth in Patient Service, 1956–1965

Total patient admissions rose 45.3 percent from 1956 to 1965 (Table 4.5), a figure in keeping with pre-World War II historical patterns and one that reflected substantial growth in all patient categories. Indigent patient admissions rose 44.3 percent; private patient admissions rose 27.3 percent. However, the total of indigent patient-days rose just 2.7 percent over the decade, compared to 28.9 percent for total private patient-days. The total of patient-days for patients of all classes rose just 14.9 percent, two-thirds of that increase accompanying the surge of indigent admissions in 1964–65. The average length of stay for indigent patients fell dramatically to 11.0 days, a 29 percent fall between 1954–1955 and 1964–1965. In large part, that decline reflected the impact of the Hill-Burton program in upgrading community hospitals and significant advances in therapies for chronic diseases such as high blood pressure. Meanwhile, the average length of stay for private patients stood at 8.5 days in 1965, a slight increase from 1956.

Direct patient admissions from three clinical departments accounted for more than 40 percent of the overall increase in patient admissions in the decade from 1955 to 1965. Obstetrics-gynecology saw an increase of 64.6 percent, from 2,548 to 4,195; pediatrics rose 48.5 percent, from 2,997 to

Table 4.5   University Hospitals Admissions and Patient-Days, 1956–1965

Fiscal Year	Indigent Admissions	Indigent Patient-Days	Private Admissions	Private Patient-Days	Other Admissions*	Other Patient-Days*	Total Admissions	Total Patient-Days
1955–56	12,943	200,874	5,565	46,945	3,953	35,252	22,461	283,071
1956–57	12,594	200,903	5,997	49,556	4,633	36,317	23,224	286,776
1957–58	13,070	199,830	5,979	50,233	5,062	38,138	24,111	288,201
1958–59	13,347	195,774	6,218	51,190	5,103	38,288	24,668	285,252
1959–60	13,642	189,408	6,023	49,682	5,212	40,137	24,877	279,227
1960–61	14,759	195,956	6,181	51,892	5,349	40,198	26,289	288,046
1961–62	15,690	191,910	6,024	50,103	4,599	37,955	26,313	279,968
1962–63	15,654	191,025	6,388	52,487	5,104	43,546	27,146	287,058
1963–64	15,757	188,277	6,770	56,586	5,912	50,352	28,439	295,215
1964–65	18,675	206,210	7,082	60,532	6,869	58,405	32,626	325,147

Note: All categories include acute, newborn, and housed clinic patients.

*Includes clinical pay, county clinical pay, cost, student, staff, research, and State Services for Crippled Children patients.

Source: University of Iowa Hospitals and Clinics Annual Statistical Reports.

4,452; and internal medicine climbed 35.7 percent, from 3,049 to 4,139. At the same time, ophthalmology saw an increase of 32.0 percent, from 1,474 to 1,946; otolaryngology 16.0 percent, from 2,291 to 2,658; and surgery 13.1 percent, from 3,282 to 3,713. Orthopædics, neurology, and dermatology saw small increases, while urology saw a 26.0 percent decline in patient admissions, from 1,938 to 1,434.

The hospitals' total revenues continued to climb, rising 104 percent between 1955 and 1965 (Table 4.6). State appropriations for indigent care rose 79 percent, and, unlike the case in the previous ten years, private patient revenues rose at an even faster rate, 128 percent. The ratio of state revenues to indigent patient admissions rose a relatively modest 23 percent from $323.68 to $396.98, but the ratio of private patient revenues to private patient admissions rose 80 percent from $193.95 to $349.48.

Like patient population figures and total revenues, the number of clinical faculty—tenure track and non-tenure track—climbed 39.5 percent from 1955 to 1965, well below the rate in the previous decade (see Table 4.3 and Table 4.7). The 64.8 percent increase in tenure track appointments far outpaced the increase in total faculty, and tenure track positions made up 62.2 percent of total faculty positions in 1965, compared to 52.7 percent in 1955 and 37.4 percent in 1945. Increases of 100 percent and more in tenure track faculty were commonplace across the departments. Neurology

Table 4.6 University Hospitals Gross Patient Charges and Net Revenues, 1956–1965

Fiscal Year	Indigent Charges ($000)	Private Patient Charges ($000)	Net Revenues ($000)
1955–56	4,082	1,083	6,227
1956–57	4,152	1,155	6,426
1957–58	4,839	1,352	7,468
1958–59	5,221	1,457	8,121
1959–60	5,760	1,653	9,049
1960–61	5,889	1,731	9,425
1961–62	6,402	1,889	10,184
1962–63	6,401	2,036	10,684
1963–64	6,868	2,446	12,091
1964–65	7,312	2,475	12,728

Note: Net Revenues column includes income from sources not shown in table, such as ward charges from clinical, county clinical, student, staff, and State Services for Crippled Children patients, as well as laboratory fees, visitor cafeteria receipts, and the like.

Source: University of Iowa Hospitals and Clinics; University of Iowa Financial Reports.

at 250 percent and pathology at 140 percent led the list. Psychiatry, radiology, otolaryngology, and obstetrics-gynecology followed at 100 percent. Ophthalmology, too, showed a 100 percent increase in tenure track faculty but with no change in total faculty numbers. Internal medicine remained the largest of the clinical departments; indeed, its margin increased substantially, both in terms of tenure track positions and total faculty. Not depicted in the table, but important nonetheless, 78.8 percent of the growth in faculty numbers came in the years between 1960 and 1965. Meanwhile, the proportion of women faculty in all clinical departments dropped over the span of a decade, from 10.2 percent in 1955 to 6.9 percent in 1965.

The overall picture in the college of medicine's basic science and other departments was much the same. Total faculty numbers increased 76.2 percent from 1955 to 1965 with 95.8 percent of that growth coming in the years from 1960 to 1965, a growth spurt reflecting the influx of research funding and the more aggressive policies of a new dean from 1962. Likewise, the proportion of women faculty declined, from 12.7 percent in 1955 to 12.3 percent in 1960 and to 9.0 percent in 1965. Hidden in the figures, it should be noted, were substantial and ongoing changes in all basic science departments. As the knowledge base in basic science areas expanded exponentially, basic science departments on the whole became much more like other scientific disciplines, each with its independent research agenda and approaches to teaching. The latter change, in particular, posed significant problems for medical education; as classroom presentations in the basic sciences shed their specifically medical orientation, students were left to construct for themselves an integrated view of an increasingly fragmented and specialized knowledge base.

From 1955 to 1965, despite the expansion in the medical staff, physicians declined as a proportion of total hospitals staff, falling from 12.6 percent in 1954–1955 to 8.7 percent in 1960–1961 before rebounding to 11.3 percent in 1964–1965. At the same time, the proportion of nurses continued to increase, reaching 44.3 percent of total hospitals staff in 1964–1965, up from 26.1 percent in 1946. However, the occupational mix among nurses shifted substantially. The number of graduate nurses rose just 7.9 percent, from 279 to 301, whereas the number of licensed practical nurses and nurses' aides—hired in large part to replace the student nurses who disappeared entirely from the hospitals' service in the early 1960s—rose just over 100 percent, from 234 in 1954–1955 to 470 in 1964–1965, with more than 70 percent of that increase coming after 1960. Overall, the costs of professional care, a category including nurses' salaries, increased 135 percent over the decade from 1955 to 1965.

The rapid postwar spread of private health insurance accompanied by increased hospital utilization rates from the early 1950s had significant

Table 4.7   College of Medicine Faculty By Department and Gender, 1960 and 1965

	1960					1965				
	Tenure Track	*Other*	*Total*	*Male*	*Female*	*Tenure Track*	*Other*	*Total*	*Male*	*Female*
Anatomy*	10	0	10	8	2	15	0	15	12	3
Anesthesiology	—	—	—	—	—	7	1	8	8	0
Biochemistry*	10	0	10	10	0	21	0	21	19	2
Dermatology	3	0	3	3	0	3	0	3	3	0
Internal Medicine	24	12	36	29	7	34	21	55	49	6
Microbiology*	8	0	8	6	2	10	0	10	10	0
Neurology	4	3	7	7	0	8	5	12	12	0
Obstetrics-Gynecology	5	1	6	6	0	9	2	11	10	1
Ophthalmology	8	3	11	11	0	9	0	9	9	0
Orthopædics	5	3	8	7	1	7	3	10	7	3
Otolaryngology	14	5	19	14	5	14	5	19	17	2
Pathology	13	1	14	14	0	19	1	20	20	0
Pediatrics	18	2	20	16	4	17	5	22	20	2
Pharmacology*	5	0	5	5	0	13	0	13	12	1
Physical Therapy-Rehabilitation*	8	2	10	6	4	7	3	10	7	3
Physiology*	10	0	10	9	1	22	0	22	21	1
Preventive Medicine*	22	0	22	19	3	30	0	30	27	3
Program in Hospital Administration*	5	0	5	5	0	4	0	4	4	0
Psychiatry	16	4	20	17	3	22	6	28	26	2
Radiology-Radiation Research	11	6	17	14	3	16	4	20	19	1
Surgery	20	4	24	24	0	20	7	27	27	0
Urology	3	0	3	3	0	4	1	5	5	0
Total Clinical	144	44	188	165	23	188	61	249	232	17
Basic Science/Other	78	2	80	68	12	122	3	125	112	13
Grand Total	**222**	**46**	**268**	**233**	**35**	**310**	**64**	**374**	**344**	**30**

*Basic science and other departments.

Source: University of Iowa College of Medicine annual staffing lists.

effects on the University Hospitals. Across America, hospital utilization, calculated on a per capita basis, rose almost 40 percent from 1945 to 1965,[137] reflecting greater consumer confidence in the efficacy of hospital care and the greater number of healthcare consumers covered by health insurance. In Iowa, the increase in utilization rates was most striking in the ten years from 1955 to 1965, as annual admissions per 1,000 population jumped from 115.6 to 153.0, a 32.4 percent increase almost identical—perhaps not surprisingly—to the 34.1 percent increase in acute care hospital beds.[138] Hospital utilization increased despite the fact that per diem hospital costs roughly doubled during that period, rising from twenty dollars to nearly forty dollars. Nationally, the proportion of the population with health insurance coverage reached 50 percent for the first time in 1950, and the figure rose to 70 percent in 1965,[139] fueled especially by the negotiating strategies of organized labor, by the entry of commercial insurance companies into the field, by the efforts of physicians and hospitals to promote private insurance, and by an emerging perception that "every person has an inalienable right to hospital and medical care."[140] Iowa matched the national trend toward health insurance coverage, equaling the national average through 1955 and reaching 84 percent in 1965.[141]

The University Hospitals derived considerable benefit from the spread of health insurance despite the continued dedication of the university facilities to indigent care. Both private patient admissions and revenues continued to grow dramatically in the 1950s and early 1960s. Facilitating that growth, a 1952 attorney general's ruling effectively ended the long-established and long-contested limits on private practice in the University Hospitals, making the availability of beds the only real restriction on private patient admissions.[142] In addition, a 1954 patient survey showing 81 percent of private patients and 66 percent of clinical pay patients with insurance coverage demonstrated the importance of health insurance to University Hospitals.[143] In the same year, notwithstanding the addition of more private beds, officials reported that demand exceeded "all expectations."[144]

The issue of medical benefits in clinical pay cases highlighted the University Hospitals' adaptation to fundamental changes in the healthcare marketplace. Traditionally, clinical pay patients paid for hospital care but not for physicians' services, and in 1951, the Medical Service Plan Compensation Committee ruled that physicians' remuneration in clinical pay cases should be returned to insurance companies.[145] A year later, however, the medical faculty sought permission to retain such fees. President Hancher quashed the proposal.[146] There the matter rested for more than three years, until assistant superintendent Glen Clasen estimated in April 1956 that clinical pay patients with Blue Shield coverage represented potential income of $50,000. Some six weeks later, another estimate raised that amount to $115,000.[147] At that point, the medical council of department heads asserted that the hospitals were "legally entitled and morally obligated" to collect those fees and to remit the proceeds to the Medical Service Plan.[148] This time President Hancher passed the matter to the board of education, whose members ruled that the prerogative of assessing and collecting fees for physicians' services rested with the medical staff.[149] After much debate, the hospitals' administration and the compensation committee agreed to apply this new income to the support of residency training.

Spurred by improved and expanded community hospitals and the increasing availability of private health insurance, the new competition for patients forced the University Hospitals to give some attention to the marketing of healthcare services. As the state's largest teaching hospital, the University Hospitals afforded an array of diagnostic and therapeutic options unavailable elsewhere, through a combination of specialized technologies and specially trained staff, and university authorities made a greater effort to publicize the hospitals' unique services. In the mid-1950s, Dean Norman Nelson, in response to a query from Virgil Hancher, compiled a list of more than 100 such specialized services. Nelson's list included diagnostic breakthroughs in pneumo-encephalography; myelography; cardiac catheterization; cancer cytology; pulmonary, hepatic, and renal function tests; intracardiac EKGs; vitamin deficiency tests; peritonoscopy; and the diagnostic applications of radioactive isotopes. Nelson also highlighted specialized therapeutic options, including surgical correction of detached retinas, corneal transplantation, and the reconstruction of fallopian tubes; the use of radioactive isotopes in the treatment of cancers; and a near monopoly in neurological procedures.[150]

Postwar Capital Expansion

By the mid-1950s, the University Hospitals had seen substantial growth in all areas except in its physical facilities, which had changed little since 1928. At the same time, stiff competition from the university's other colleges and departments for the small capital appropriations from the legislature gave little hope of major improvements; so, for the most part, officials coped with overcrowding through installing temporary buildings in the nooks and crannies of the hospital grounds.[151] The remodeling of the General Hospital tower, completed in 1952, had accommodated some changing space needs and allowed for upgraded surgical, outpatient, and business office facilities, but it did not add to the hospitals' overall physical plant. Only the Children's Hospital had seen significant expansion. Then, in 1953, the worrisome incidence of poliomyelitis and the lure of matching federal funding spurred state legislators to appropriate nearly $1.2 million for a polio-pediatrics wing and a new medical research building, marking the first phase of a piecemeal expansion program that accelerated from the late 1960s and has continued to the present. Through the 1960s, federal funding sustained much of that expansion, and the availability of federal money for buildings in turn influenced local priorities for research and service.

An unusually severe poliomyelitis epidemic in the fall of 1952 had sent 674 polio cases to the University Hospitals over the span of just four months, straining both staff and facilities. With that experience fresh in mind, Iowa's 55th General Assembly in early 1953 allocated $296,000 for a construction and remodeling project to bolster the hospitals' ability to handle such outbreaks in the future. The project, which university officials described as "rapidly conceived but carefully and intricately drawn," included a new three-story wing of 12,000 square feet to accommodate the pediatric isolation unit and the pediatric outpatient clinic, allowing polio isolation and respirator units to expand in space vacated in the Children's Hospital.[152] Connecting the north tower and the projecting west wing of the General Hospital, with two stories above ground and one below, the addition would also house a new medical records room, the Perkins School for hospitalized children, and a behavior and speech therapy clinic.

University officials ordered remodeling portions of the work to begin as soon as state funds became available on July 1, 1953, "to expand the facilities for the reception of polio patients in the event of an epidemic in the summer and autumn of 1953."[153] President Hancher characterized the work not as capital improvement but as "repairs, replacements, and alterations." However, when university authorities requested the transfer of $130,000 to replenish the capital improvement account and to serve as matching funds for the federal contribution, the state comptroller objected that such a transfer would be illegal under state law since the funds were intended for capital improvements, not "repairs, replacements, and alterations." Despite a state attorney general's opinion that resolved the issue in favor of the university administration (at least in Hancher's estimation), the comptroller refused to accede to the transfer, an issue that was part of a growing dispute with state agencies over the university's fiscal practices. Facing the loss of federal funds for the overall project, the board of education took funds from the university's general contingency fund in order to move the project forward.[154] Parts of the new pediatrics wing opened as early as October 1955, while work at the Children's Hospital continued until 1958.

In all, the combined construction and remodeling cost $661,000, of which $185,000 came from Hill-Burton funds.[155] While the introduction of the Salk vaccine undermined the original rationale for the hospital addition, the new and renovated areas of the General Hospital and Children's Hospital were readily—and no doubt happily—converted to other uses, and the project had the additional virtue of integrating pediatrics into the General Hospital, a goal articulated at least as early as 1950–1951.[156] Moreover, planning and funding of the project helped the university form relationships with state and federal officials involved in Hill-Burton and other federal programs.

The second major project funded by the state legislature in 1953, the Medical Research Center, grew out of the same general discussion of capital needs, but in this instance it focused specifically on the need for research space. Indeed, growth in staff and resources devoted to research in the late 1940s and early 1950s far outstripped the modest growth in the hospitals' patient service and, according to university officials, displaced clinical functions within the hospital. This, along with the reciprocal relationship between research and patient service, formed the official justification for the research center, which was important both in winning support from the Iowa legislature and in obtaining Hill-Burton funds.[157]

In 1954, Congress broadened the scope of the Hill-Burton program to include diagnostic and treatment centers as well as hospitals, but the program's goals remained closely linked to patient care. Only by tying laboratory work in the proposed building to medical service could the university justify its application for federal money. To do that, Dean Norman Nelson compiled his list of more than 100 surgical and laboratory procedures "available to the people of Iowa *only* at the University Hospitals and College of Medicine," and many of those procedures, he added, still in the investigational stage. "In most instances," Nelson maintained, "patient service and clinical research are so closely inter-related that they cannot be separated."[158] When Hancher and Nelson met in Des Moines with the governor's Advisory Committee on Hospitalization in November 1953, several months before the anticipated extension of the Hill-Burton program, some doubts remained.[159] However, F. W. Pickworth, head of the State Department of Health's Hospital Services Division and a key figure in designating Iowa hospital projects for Hill-Burton funding, was a staunch ally of the university in the application process. In February 1954, at Pickworth's urging, the university sent a delegation to Washington, DC, to speak with federal officials about the project; later that year, Pickworth accompanied Gerhard Hartman and Norman Nelson to Kansas City to meet with Public Health Service officials. Pickworth also helped Hartman and Nelson to calculate the percentage of the new building's cost eligible for federal matching funds, and he was on hand when Public Health Service representatives from the Kansas City office visited Iowa City in September 1954.[160]

Meanwhile, university officials received approval from the state legislature's Interim Committee to finalize building plans, hire an architect, and advertise for construction bids. A faculty building committee led by internal medicine chief William Bean also surveyed departmental research needs to determine the apportionment of space within the new facility and began planning as well for utilization of space to be vacated in the General Hospital.[161] The division of space between clinical functions and basic science and teaching functions determined the portion of the building's cost eligible for matching federal funds, and the application in its final form eliminated just 8,940 of 49,300 square feet from the matching formula. In December 1954, Hancher received word that the Public Health Service had given its preliminary approval to the project, and the final funding package included $454,000 in Hill–Burton funds, $900,000 from the state legislature, $152,000 derived from moneys originating with the Rockefeller grants of the 1920s, $34,000 from the National Fund for Medical Education, and $13,000 in university capital funds, for a total of $1.56 million.[162]

Design of the Medical Research Center incorporated movable partitions and flexible plumbing and mechanical systems to facilitate later renovation, an idea that arose from a visit by university officials to the clinical research facilities of the National Institutes of Health in Bethesda, Maryland. At the outset, the building housed several basic science and clinical laboratories, a metabolic unit, a tumor registry, and the dean's offices. In addition, the American Cancer Society donated cobalt therapy equipment to the radiology department, and that, too, found a home in the center's lower level. Also, the department of biochemistry, which had, since its origins in 1924, remained in the Chemistry Building east of the Iowa River, occupied one wing of three floors, fully integrating the department into the college of medicine for the first time, and two-thirds of the space allotted to biochemistry was designated for clinically related activities.

Completion of the Medical Research Center, coupled with relocation of the Student Health Service to the erstwhile Children's Hospital isolation unit, triggered a chain reaction of spatial reorganization within the General Hospital. For example, an electrocardiogram unit and cardiovascular research laboratories moved into quarters vacated by the clinical biochemistry laboratory and metabolism unit. In turn, space vacated by the first two of those services became offices and waiting rooms. Similarly, the allergy clinic moved to the area formerly occupied by student health, and the internal medicine outpatient clinic took over what had been the allergy clinic space. Overall, outpatient clinics in internal medicine, neurology, obstetrics and gynecology, and urology gained additional space; obstetrics and gynecology also added three labor rooms; and many staff and residents occupied new quarters.[163] It is worth noting, too, that two of the biggest winners in the reallocation of space—internal medicine and obstetrics-gynecology—were among the fastest-growing departments in terms of staff and service.

A third major project, the south wing to the General Hospital, had been in gestation in one form or another since at least 1950, when Gerhard Hartman had estimated the cost at some three million dollars.[164] The suggestion resurfaced in 1956, this time as an outpatient facility to replace the badly deteriorated "Hotel Annex" of war surplus quonset huts. The proposed south wing would comprise 50,000 square feet, housing 250 beds.[165] When finally approved in 1961, the project—known then as the Minimal Care Unit—was much like that 1956 proposal. Although not strictly an outpatient facility, it was meant to serve ambulatory patients undergoing diagnosis, convalescence, and rehabilitation, minimizing construction and operating costs and complementing the University Hospitals' "intensive and intermediate care and the full complex of diagnostic and treatment facilities and out-patient clinics."[166] The project topped the university's list of capital projects in 1961 and received approval from both the legislature—at a cost of $1.1 million in state funds—and the state Hospital Advisory Council. The board of regents—a body that superseded the board of education in 1956— awarded the construction contract in June 1962. When completed, the south wing encompassed six floors, rather than the seven initially planned, with 240 patient beds arranged in sixteen three-bed rooms on each of five floors, and kitchen, dining, and other service functions on the two lower levels.

A fourth capital project, the Medical Research Facility, which would house a new Clinical Research Center, surfaced unexpectedly in November 1960 in the form of a request for $400,000 from the regents' general contingency fund in order to obtain matching funds from two National Institutes of Health programs. Needing approval from the legislature's interim Budget and Financial Control Committee, President Hancher exhorted committee members to act quickly. "The federal programs are limited in time, [and] limited in the funds available, and the competition for funds under these programs is intense," Hancher warned. But prompt action on the $400,000 request, Hancher assured the committee, "can be expected to bring five times that amount in federal funds for needed medical research facilities and operational funds to Iowa"[167]; his an estimate was based on the likelihood of receiving renewable NIH operational grants for a period of five years.[168] Both the budget committee and the board of regents approved the plan and in June 1961 added a further $88,000 to the original $400,000 commitment.[169] The NIH provided a $462,000 matching grant, and the National Cancer Institute awarded $206,000 to build and equip a floor dedicated to cancer research. In its final design, the 26,000-square-foot Medical Research Facility consisted of six levels, with the option of an additional three floors. The basement level was designed to house research areas in medical electronics and dermatology; the first and second floors contained facilities for hospital-based clinical research, including offices, laboratories, and patient testing areas; the third and fourth floors were home to pediatric, metabolic, and endocrine research; the fifth floor accommodated the cancer research facility.

By the early 1960s, the limited improvements in actual patient care facilities—coupled with the fact that some 50 percent of Iowa's community hospital beds had come into service in the preceding fifteen years—had placed the University Hospitals at a competitive disadvantage in terms of appearance and amenities and, to an increasing extent, in terms of the hospitals' ability to meet rising licensing standards for patient accommodations. Between 1957 and 1960, according to the standards of the Iowa State Division of Hospitals, the University Hospitals' beds had slipped from "acceptable" to "replaceable." In 1963, under new criteria adopted by the division of hospitals in 1961, the University Hospitals' beds failed even to meet the standard for "correctable beds"—that is, beds falling below acceptable standards but housed in facilities less than thirty years old and deemed worthy of improvement. A 1963 report charged, in short, that the university's aging facilities were "rather intolerable in light of present day design and usage." Most damning, the report stated that the hospitals "can hardly be considered appropriate as a model training environment for Iowa's only medical school." "There can be very little progress made in the future," the report concluded, "unless there is a reconstruction program."[170] In the last half of the 1960s, as described in the next chapter, that report and other similar evaluations buttressed arguments for a dramatically accelerated capital improvement program.

Growth in Scientific Research

Although poorly funded and overshadowed by teaching and patient service through the first half of the twentieth century, the university teaching hospital's research mission was virtually as old as the hospital itself. In the first two decades after World War II, the research mission truly came of age, driven by an extended period of economic expansion and the political uncertainties attendant to the Cold War.[171] With the rapid expansion of federal programs in medical research and training, the extent and quality of research played an increasingly important part in the evaluation of both medical schools and individual faculty. Moreover, the developing research emphasis profoundly changed the nature and politics of medical education. Not only did modern research require "access to larger scale, complex resources, diverse technical skills, and collaborative relationships";[172] it also promoted a publish-or-perish ethos in academic medicine and injected an element of individual entrepreneurship into the collegial structure of medical education.

The growth of medical scientific research at the University of Iowa makes a complicated story, involving Congress and agencies of the federal government—especially the National Institutes of Health (NIH)—as well as an evolving cast of local actors, several of whom changed over time in their thinking with regard to the issue of research. The college of medicine was the chief beneficiary of federal largess, using these funds to expand and to enhance its competitive stance among American medical schools. Yet not all saw federal funding as a boon; indeed, some perceived it, and not without reason, as a threat to traditional structures and practices, including the traditional distribution of authority within the college. For the University Hospitals, meanwhile, the blossoming of scientific research posed a dilemma. The new learning and technologies were essential to the hospitals' image and to the maintenance of their tertiary care mission; however, the growth of the research enterprise also placed major additional demands on the hospitals' facilities and budgets.

Overall expenditures—public and private—for medical research in America increased by a factor of 21 from 1947 to 1965, with federal expenditures rising by a factor of 42, most of that reflected in NIH budgets (Table 4.8). During that period, the share of gross national product invested in medical research increased 5.7 times, and, by 1965, medical research commanded 9 percent of all research and development spending in the United States. Importantly, as NIH spending increased 100-fold, the federal share of total research funding increased from 31 percent in 1947 to 64 percent in 1965. In the meantime, the NIH continually broadened the scope of its research support apparatus, with additional categorical institutes serving as clearinghouses for project and training grants and the Health Research Facilities and Construction Act of 1956 providing funds for capital grants.

The new partnership between federal agencies and academic medical centers did not develop without misgivings on both sides. In particular, academic medical centers at times feared for their autonomy. For example,

Table 4.8   U.S. Medical Research Expenditures, 1940–1965

	GNP ($billions)	Medical Research ($millions)	Federal Medical Research F($millions)	NIH Funding ($millions)
1940	99.7	45	3	na
1947	231.3	87	27	8.3
1950	284.8	161	73	52
1955	398.0	261	139	81
1960	503.7	845	448	300
1965	684.9	1,837	1,174	800

Sources: *Historical Statistics of the United States,* p. 228; Robert Berliner and Thomas J. Kennedy, "National Expenditures for Biomedical Research," *Journal of Medical Education* 45 (1970), p. 667; Strickland, *Politics, Science, and Dread Disease*; Shannon, "Advance of Medical Research," p. 97.

Morris Fishbein warned in a 1945 editorial in the *Journal of the American Medical Association* that the federal government "must avoid bureaucratic domination of research and restrictions on research scientists."[173] Local officials, encouraged in the 1950s to expand their faculties and facilities, also worried about the burdens they would have to assume in the event that federal aid was withdrawn. As late as 1961, one member of the University of Iowa College of Medicine executive committee complained, "Doctors do not want to become dependent on federal funds." Another charged that "some doctors feel that we would sell our souls for money from the federal government."[174] Over time, the rising tide of federal spending on medical research and training muted such concerns, particularly as new grant programs took on an appearance of permanence. Nonetheless, academic medical centers sought to maintain their autonomy and flexibility, even as they pushed for ever higher levels of federal funding.

Thanks chiefly to federal research programs, the modern American biomedical research enterprise that emerged in the first two postwar decades was built around the academic medical center. The University of Iowa's medical center benefited as did most others (Table 4.9), and much of the university's expansion in faculty, facilities, and administration during that era reflected the growth in the research sector. In the two decades from 1946 through 1965, external funds grew at a rate eight times that of other sources of income in the college of medicine, with federal grants eclipsing all other funding sources by the late 1950s. Federal grants made up nearly 40 percent of the college's total budget by 1965, putting the college in line with national trends after some initial hesitation and repeated disappointments in seeking state funding for research.[175] In the early years of NIH programs, the bulk of the federal funding received at the University of Iowa was for training grants in graduate medical education, while private funding—from the American Cancer Society, for example—still constituted the majority of funding aimed strictly at research. It was only with the continued growth of federal programs through the 1950s that the balance shifted decidedly toward federal research funding, even as federal training programs grew apace. Initially, too, the bulk of NIH funding supported training and research in the most established areas, such as cancer, heart disease, and psychiatry, areas which, not by coincidence, were also among the best established at the University of Iowa.

Incrementally, the university developed an institutional relationship with the NIH, a relationship grounded to some extent in personal connections. By the mid-1950s, the college of medicine employed an assistant dean whose duties included coordinating research grants and assisting faculty in preparing grant applications. In 1961, the college added a staff member specifically to advise faculty on grant applications—where to apply and

Table 4.9   **University of Iowa College of Medicine Funding Sources, 1940–1965**

	Total Budget ($000)	State Funding ($000)	Medical Fees ($000)	Gifts and Grants ($000)
1940	418	342	47	29
1945	557	378	148	31
1950	1,767	865	660	242
1955	2,962	1,268	1,021	673
1960	5,425	2,229	1,423	1,773
1965	10,613	3,520	2,015	5,078

Source: University of Iowa Annual Financial Reports.

what funds were available.[176] Federal funding for the Medical Research Facility was one of the fruits of the college's new orientation toward federal programs; that project had begun with a November 1960 memorandum from the assistant dean in charge of grants apprising President Hancher of the availability of federal funds to support clinical research.[177]

Through the 1950s and into the 1960s, Dean Norman Nelson had critics on both sides of the research issue. On the one hand, traditionalists worried about the loss of autonomy, although such arguments may have been little more than a cover for their general aversion to research. On the other hand, younger, more research-oriented faculty faulted Nelson for his lack of leadership in making room for research in the college. Beset by health problems and lacking the confidence of many faculty, Nelson resigned the deanship in May 1962, to be replaced by Robert Hardin, a native Iowan who had received his undergraduate and graduate training at the University of Iowa and who had first been appointed to the faculty just before World War II.[178] Hardin maintained that the divisions among teaching, research, and service were largely artificial; in his view, medical research and training, including patient service, were "mutually dependent." Hardin also observed that research opportunities were essential to faculty recruitment and that attracting federal funding was essential in supporting the research mission, views conditioned by Hardin's frequent contacts with NIH officials and his service on the AAMC Committee on Medical Research.[179] In response to the bleak 1960 assessment of the college of medicine's basic science programs by the Liaison Committee on Medical Education, Hardin instituted planning for a new basic science building. Later, when the NIH announced its interest in categorical research centers for heart disease, stroke, and cancer, Hardin saw to it that grant applications in each area were prepared in time for the earliest possible consideration.[180]

Hardin's favorable position on research paralleled the views of new university President Howard Bowen, who came to office in the fall of 1964 at the end of Virgil Hancher's 24-year tenure. Bowen came to the University of Iowa from Grinnell College and brought with him ambitious plans for expansion at the university, including the capture of federal dollars to accommodate the flood of baby boomers into the university's classrooms. Hardin and Bowen both anticipated continued growth in federal programs related to medical education and research. Both agreed also that the University of Iowa should position itself to attract a fair share of those dollars. In the late 1960s, as detailed in the next chapter, the partnership between Hardin and Bowen, while a troubled one in some important particulars, helped to lay the foundations for an extraordinary expansion of the entire health sciences campus.

Administration: Straddling Divergent Missions

To many observers, the new academic medical centers, like the University of Iowa's, that emerged from the fusion of federal funding, national standards, and significant advances in the medical sciences seemed larger than the sum of their parts. By the late 1950s, more and more observers noted the "increasing complexity of the modern medical school."[181] By the early 1960s, such sentiments were commonplace, as both public and private institutions added faculty, facilities, and equipment at a dizzying rate and experienced rapid rises in cash flows, much of them flowing from the growing array of federal programs. In 1965, one observer noted that "medical school and hospital operations are growing in both scope and depth," a trend associated with "stronger external forces affecting the development of policies" and "increasing specialization at all levels."[182]

The academic medical center's rapid development also entailed significant changes in existing relationships among its missions and component parts. For example, the teaching-service-research relationship became increasingly strained, as money and resources lavished on research raised questions about the implications for teaching and service. One official of the Department of Health, Education and Welfare wondered openly, "Are some of our modern medical schools becoming vast research institutes instead of teaching centers?" He also noted that research grants by his agency did not cover overhead costs, a fact with obvious implications for teaching hospitals.[183] Just as troubling, leaders of the medical school and the teaching hospital had, by the nature of the institutions, different perspectives on the proper balance among their shared missions. Certainly, the medical school needed the hospital's patients for clinical teaching and increasingly for research as well, while the hospital needed the medical school faculty and students in order to provide patient care, which was—directly and indirectly—the source of the hospitals' revenues. Thus, it was true, as one writer observed, that "the ends of each serve as a program means for the other," but it was not true that the coordination of ends and means was a simple matter. Perhaps most obviously, standards for medical schools emphasized excellence in teaching and research, while standards for hospitals emphasized quality of patient care and overall efficiency in operations. Similarly, in part because the system of research grants was centered on individual researchers and their specialized interests, medical schools permitted a high degree of independence to faculty members; however, hospitals, viewing those same faculty members as medical staff, expected a greater degree of uniformity.[184]

The great complexity of the modern academic medical center as it emerged in the postwar years, the simultaneous interdependence of and tension among its three major missions, and the differing outlooks and approaches of the medical school and the teaching hospital combined to produce administrative complications on a new and unprecedented scale. For the University of Iowa College of Medicine, the forces of change bore most heavily upon the dean; it was the dean who stood, on the one hand, between an increasingly distant university president and board of regents and an increasingly restive and independent medical faculty and, on the other hand, between that same faculty and the University Hospitals administration. For the hospitals, meanwhile, the forces of change meant an administrative expansion and differentiation and a programmatic development that necessarily heightened an already existing emphasis on patient service above both teaching and research. Just as important, the hospitals remained more or less firmly under the control of the college of medicine through the 1950s and 1960s, the hospitals' independence yet limited by a number of factors, including the continued importance of state-funded indigent care in hospitals operations.

One crude measure of the growing complexity of the University of Iowa's academic medical center was the addition of administrative staff at both the college of medicine and the University Hospitals. In the college, postwar growth had begun with the appointment of a full-time staff member in December 1949 to manage the Medical Service Plan and, in July 1950, with the appointment of Robert Hardin as assistant dean for Veterans Administration affairs, a position involving the coordination of medical services at the soon-to-be-completed Veterans Administration Hospital and the integration of teaching programs at the VA and University Hospitals. As noted earlier, the prospectus on the deanship, drafted and redrafted by the Executive Committee in the late 1940s and early 1950s, contained a significant emphasis on administrative organization, including appointment of an associate dean who would "have as his chief duty the direction of professional medical services of the University Hospitals" and an assistant dean for student affairs.[185] Neither position survived the 1953 installation of Norman Nelson as dean, in part because Nelson himself assumed the role of hospitals medical director. Nelson did appoint an assistant dean in 1954 to oversee grants and public relations for the college, a part-time position held by Robert C. Hickey of surgery.

Growth in the scope and complexity of hospitals services had accelerated the process of administrative differentiation in the University Hospitals, and, despite the fiasco in the financial office in the late 1940s, Gerhard Hartman had compiled an admirable record in the area of personnel recruitment. In the late 1940s, Glen Clasen became an assistant superintendent, and Clasen's responsibilities expanded rapidly thereafter. By 1953, university accounts showed two more assistant superintendents, and Clasen had become associate superintendent. Overall, the hospitals' financial accounts showed a 71.4 percent increase in administrative staff between 1945–46 and 1954–55 and a total increase of 84 percent in the first two postwar decades.[186] In 1957, nearly a decade after the uproar over the hospitals' accounting procedures, the university business office surrendered management of hospital accounts to a reconstituted hospitals business office, a move reflecting in part the increasing complexity of hospitals billing procedures caused by the growth in private health insurance and the changing patient mix. Initially, the university business manager assigned one of his assistants to the new office, but in 1958, Gerhard Hartman hired John W. Colloton, a recent graduate of his own master's program in hospital administration, to take over the duties. In 1962, Colloton became an assistant superintendent in charge of the Medical Assistance to the Aged program under the Kerr-Mills Act, a program that provided $300,000 in federal and state money annually to University Hospitals for the care of medically indigent elderly patients. In all, the hospitals had become, by the early 1960s, a $10 million enterprise with 275,000 customers and a labor force exceeding 1,500.

Following an Iowa–Ohio State football game in November 1956, Virgil Hancher suffered a heart attack, and from that time on Hancher began to distance himself from the day-to-day details of affairs on the health sciences campus. Hancher later remarked that he had spent a third of his time on medical affairs in his early years as president, but that in later years he had abandoned "the detailed study of internal problems which I once regarded as a regular part of my assignment."[187] In late 1961 and early 1962, during the final planning phase for the General Hospital's south wing, Norman Nelson and the university's vice-president for business affairs decided unilaterally on the reduction from six floors to five, apprising Hancher of the change only moments before a board of regents meeting at which the project was to be discussed. In explaining his action, Nelson pointed to the university's emerging central administratrive structure with substantial areas of responsibility effectively delegated to the several vice-presidents. "There is nothing I would like better than direct access to the President," Nelson wrote Hancher, but, he added, "in my interpretation of the current set-up . . . it appears as though the only areas of direct access to the President are areas that do not clearly fall under any single member of your staff."[188]

While an increasingly complex central administrative structure, coupled with Hancher's advancing age and his health concerns, insulated the president more and more from medical affairs, the board of regents, by contrast, was mired in the routine details of administration within each of the three major institutions—the University of Iowa, Iowa State University, and Iowa State Teachers College—under its authority. In Hancher's estimate, perhaps exaggerated, the board spent three-fourths of its time approving faculty appointments, ordinary business transactions, building maintenance decisions, and other relatively minor operational details. Hancher considered the board's focus not only time-consuming but redundant, since such matters had "already been threshed out in great detail inside the institutions" and "cannot be and usually are not revised when they come to the Board."[189]

Even larger issues, such as the statutory requirement that the regents approve all increases in institutional budgets, entailed much the same redundancy. As the University Hospitals' revenues from patient charges and other sources grew steadily, its expenditures grew apace, and at a rate normally in excess of that contemplated by the state legislature in formulating its biennial appropriations. Twice in 1960 and once each year through 1964, events forced university officials to document needed increases in the hospitals' budget ceiling, increases that the regents then considered and approved before reporting the changes to the state comptroller.[190] The board secretary's intimate involvement in compiling federal construction grants for the General Hospital's south wing and the Medical Research Facility further illustrated Virgil Hancher's point. Whether or not the regents' attention to detail diminished their interest in broad policy and planning questions is difficult to document, but Hancher believed it to be so. Should the board continue on its present course, Hancher thought, it would "work itself to death with no compensating advantage to the institutions under its jurisdiction."[191]

Within the University Hospitals in the 1950s and 1960s, Gerhard Hartman relied to an ever greater extent on his top deputy, assistant then associate

superintendent Glen Clasen, to oversee operations, while the superintendent maintained his highly visible role as University Hospitals spokesman in
dealing with the public, the press, the board of regents, and the Iowa General
Assembly. Clasen evidenced the administrative toughness that Hartman
admired, and Clasen's administrative jurisdiction grew progressively wider.
In 1953, at Norman Nelson's suggestion, Clasen became de facto hospitals
representative on the Medical Service Plan compensation committee.[192]
Also at Nelson's suggestion, he served on a committee appointed in 1954
by the college of medicine's executive committee to study improvements in
patient care.[193] Likewise, when the hospital advisory committee, disbanded
in 1955, was reconstituted in 1961, it was Clasen who represented the
hospital administration on the committee, joining Dean Norman Nelson,
associate Dean Robert Hardin, and the clinical department heads.[194] Just
how the superintendent and his deputy arrived at their pattern of shared
responsibilities is unclear, but by 1959 Clasen was reporting directly to the
university's central administration on budgetary and other matters, his signa-
ture appearing on virtually all communications regarding the hospitals' internal operations. Meanwhile, Hartman handled external matters, such as the
pursuit of grant funds for construction and relations with the state legislature.

Much as was the case in earlier years, Gerhard Hartman was also
a lightning rod, a man whose outspokenness—a habit often seemingly
calculated to produce a desired effect—could at times raise the ire of his
superiors. For example, in a talk to the local Rotary Club in 1959, Hartman
reportedly referred to the outpatient barracks as "slums" and "tin cans."
Local newspaper accounts did not repeat that inflammatory language but
did focus on the obvious inadequacies in the barracks and the General
Hospital kitchen, essentially stating Hartman's case for a new minimal care
unit and noting that the university had requested funds for such an addition
from the state legislature then in session in Des Moines. The newspaper
report attributed "many serious fractures and other injuries" to conditions
at the barracks and to the fact that patients had to walk next door to the
hospital for meals and treatment. As for the 30-year-old hospital kitchen,
the article claimed that "accidents due to the crowded conditions, defective
and worn equipment, and leaky plumbing are frequent." Some forty injuries
to kitchen staff were traceable, according to the report, "to the age of the
kitchen and its crowded condition."[195]

Within days, the university president posted a blunt letter to Hartman,
Dean Norman Nelson, and assistant superintendent Glen Clasen, charging that Hartman's "denigration of the barracks" would likely necessitate
allocating "more than the usual attention and probably more money to
maintenance of these barracks, in order to satisfy everyone that we are
not deliberately allowing them to deteriorate."[196] Hancher alleged also

that this latest incident was part of a larger pattern of insubordination on Hartman's part regarding the barracks issue. In Hancher's view, Hartman had clearly overstepped his authority in his public advocacy of the proposed new minimal care unit, pressing his case before legislative committees, individual lawmakers, and, in this instance, the Iowa City Rotary Club. In a blistering memorandum intended as the text of a conference with the superintendent, Hancher contended that Hartman had threatened legislators with the need to reduce patient admissions if the minimal care unit were not approved, a threat Hancher had specifically forbidden. "By whose authority did you refuse to follow my instructions?" Hancher fumed. Hancher expressed similar displeasure about "an impassioned presentation for a minimal care unit" the superintendent had made before a senate subcommittee, and he disparaged Hartman also for having approached two lawmakers regarding funds to retain an architect for the facility. "On whose authorization did you act?" Hancher demanded, noting that Hartman's intemperate actions "flouted" the authority of Dean Nelson and provost Harvey Davis as well as the president, "angered" the board of regents finance committee and board members, and "lessened" Hartman's own stature in the eyes of "very influential members of the [senate] subcommittee." Finally, if the barracks were indeed "slums" and "tin cans," who, Hancher wanted to know, was at fault and why had Hartman not corrected the situation? In an apparent change of heart at the end of the memo, Hancher crossed out a statement demanding Hartman's resignation and substituted the question, "How can I rely on you in the future?"[197]

That incident may have played a role in Glen Clasen's increasing prominence in the hospitals' administration; in any event, Clasen's assumption of greater administrative responsibility allowed Gerhard Hartman to concentrate more of his energy on his graduate program in hospital administration. By the late 1950s, the extraordinary expansion in American hospitals at large and the increasing complexity of emerging academic medical centers spurred interest in graduate education in hospital administration. The first twelve such programs claimed 842 alumni in 1953, a number that swelled to 3,360 in 1962. The hospital administrator's job also changed significantly in the postwar years; a 1961 survey found that business and financial management issues had moved to the top of the list of administrators' concerns, while problems in working with medical staff had fallen to seventh place.[198] In that changing environment, the University of Iowa program, until 1960 the only U.S. program offering the Ph.D., earned a solid national reputation built in part on Hartman's ability to marshall local resources—facilities and personnel—for educational purposes and to recruit graduate students of unusual promise. "I was like a football recruiter looking for people all over the nation," he later recalled.[199]

Meanwhile, Norman Nelson's star faded significantly following his initial successes as college of medicine dean, although Nelson appears never to have lost Hancher's confidence. Indeed, at the time of Nelson's resignation in 1962, Hancher expressed admiration for the "quiet effectiveness" of Nelson's leadership.[200] Even the college of medicine executive committee sought a raise for the dean without his knowledge in 1957, noting that the college had "moved ahead" during Nelson's tenure.[201] By 1961, however, Nelson faced a strong challenge to his leadership from a young and vocal core of faculty who questioned the drift of policy regarding scholarship and research in the college. Led by Raymond Sheets of internal medicine, this challenge erupted in a March 1961 faculty meeting in which Sheets launched a broad attack on Nelson's administration for failing to achieve a "proper balance" among service, teaching, and research. Moreover, Sheets faulted the college's administrative structure for not providing an avenue for faculty input on important policy questions. Sheets asserted that patient care consumed too much faculty time at the expense of both teaching and research; he questioned whether the dean's office had any long-range plan for the college; and he criticized Nelson for the undue influence of smaller clinical departments on the allocation of college resources.[202]

In short, Sheets called for a complete reorganization of the college of medicine, and shortly thereafter, the medical faculty moved to appoint a committee to study such a reorganization.[203] The September 1961 appointment of an administrative assistant to oversee the college's grant application procedures and to advise faculty on application requirements was one outcome of Sheets' charges. On the whole, however, Norman Nelson, who had suffered a debilitating stroke in February 1960 and had taken two extended leaves of absence as a result, seemed at a loss in dealing with calls for sweeping change at a time when the flow of federal research money to individual investigators and the rapid expansion in faculty numbers undermined his authority. The best that Nelson could do in response to the attack from Sheets was to read from the minutes of his first faculty meeting in 1953, when he had pledged "a definite and important place for the faculty in the conduct of medical affairs."[204]

Citing health problems, Norman Nelson tendered his resignation in April 1962, to take effect June 26, and Robert C. Hardin was the candidate favored to succeed him. Hardin was then an associate dean, had served as acting dean during Nelson's recent absences, and enjoyed the esteem of Hancher. The selection committee, which was also the faculty committee charged with devising a new administrative structure for the college, interviewed more than three-fourths of faculty members, finding most in favor of elevating one of their own number to the deanship and more than one-third suggesting Hardin for the job.[205] President Hancher urged quick action from the selection committee, worrying that "distasteful outside pressures" would come to bear on the search process and likely also hoping to promote Hardin's candidacy.[206] Despite the president's urgings, the committee was deliberate in its actions, inviting three candidates to campus for interviews before recommending Hardin for the position in July. In August, the board of regents approved the formal appointment, making Hardin dean of medicine and coordinator of medical sciences and services, including the University Hospitals, the Psychopathic Hospital, the Hospital School, and the State Bacteriological Laboratory. Hardin's salary of $30,000 exceeded even Hancher's $26,000.[207]

As an internist with a long association with the college of medicine and a decade's experience in administration, Hardin was well known for his abilities and outlook. In many respects, his views were not revolutionary, particularly on the issue of college of medicine governance, but his philosophy of medical education stressed the interdependence of teaching and research and the need to achieve a "proper balance between the two."[208] Hardin also brought a new energy and forcefulness to the dean's office, and he held an expansive view of the growth potential of the health sciences campus. In the middle and late 1960s, as described in the next chapter, the new dean helped to energize an ambitious program of planned growth in enrollments, faculty numbers, and facilities, even as faculty unrest, swept briefly aside with the change in the deanship, mounted once again.

Conclusion

In several important respects, the first two postwar decades were pivotal in the making of the modern University of Iowa Hospitals and Clinics. The University Hospitals, like most other such institutions, had suffered greatly during the Depression and World War II, and administrators and university officials had been only partially successful in offsetting the effects of tight budgets on hospitals operations. Stagnant funding levels had seriously eroded staffing levels, from professional staff to housekeeping. With the hospitals operating well below full capacity, patient service and medical education diminished in quality. In addition, after a decade and a half of scant maintenance, and in the face of rapidly evolving national standards, the hospitals' physical facilities seemed well on the way to obsolescence at war's end. Making matters worse, faculty unrest in the college of medicine over the private practice issue posed a serious crisis as well, one that—in the estimation of Virgil Hancher and many other principals and outside observers—threatened at the very least to drive away some of the most capable faculty members and to degrade further the hospitals' patient service and educational missions.

At the same time that hospitals administrators and university officials coped with serious internal problems at the University Hospitals, external factors were radically altering the environment in which the hospitals operated, a shift that raised new issues regarding the hospitals' administrative structure and objectives. An unexpected economic boom, coupled with the rapid spread of private health insurance, sharply increased the demand for healthcare goods and services in postwar America. Just as important, the postwar combination of economic prosperity, Cold War politics, and a determined congressional lobby produced a series of unprecedented measures to initiate and subsequently to expand federal investment in hospital construction, medical scientific research, and medical education and training. The first of those measures, the Hill–Burton Hospital Survey and Construction Act of 1946, reinforced by related statutes approved by the Iowa legislature, led to a substantial reconstruction and reorganization of Iowa's hospital system and increased competition in the healthcare marketplace. Meanwhile, from the late 1940s, the remarkable expansion of the National Institutes of Health and exponential increases in its research and training programs unleashed a comparative flood of federal funds on American medical schools and teaching hospitals. This funding stream, while generally welcome, posed new problems and changed the terms for evaluating the performance of teaching hospitals, colleges of medicine, and academic physicians.

Inevitably, the much enlarged and much strengthened University of Iowa Hospitals of 1965 owed a great deal to those external factors. The Hill–Burton Act, for example, played a central part in the slow but inescapable reorientation of the University Hospitals toward specialized care and a role as Iowa's "tertiary care" institution. Likewise, federal research and training grants, which constituted an increasingly important element in local funding, most obviously in the college of medicine, fueled a second reorientation of the hospitals toward scientific research—a reorientation more halting, uneven, and divisive than the embrace of specialized care, but just as important over the long term. At the same time, however, local developments in the first two postwar decades also bore the identifiable imprint of local actors who responded to external pressures and opportunities in ways that reflected their personal values and goals and that, in turn, gave the University of Iowa Hospitals—for better and for worse—its own distinctive flavor.

University of Iowa President Virgil Hancher was chief among those local actors. Although faulted by many for his essentially conservative administration, Hancher nonetheless shepherded the University Hospitals and the larger academic medical center through a host of postwar challenges, occasionally, as in the case of the Medical Service Plan, imposing much needed reforms by presidential fiat. University Hospitals Superintendent Gerhard Hartman, too, was a central actor in local events. Although, like

Hancher, subject to criticism on several counts, Hartman brought to the University Hospitals a dynamic vision that many rejected as overly ambitious but one that nonetheless led to the introduction of a new level of administrative expertise and to the implementation of necessary improvements in facilities and services, changes that strengthened the foundations of the entire academic medical center. A long list of other actors, some of greater importance than others, appeared in this chapter, all of them participating in the institutional give-and-take through which national developments took form in the University of Iowa Hospitals.

Notes

1. "Report of the College of Medicine, 1940–41 through 1954–55," Table I, "College of Medicine Income, All Sources," Presidents Folder, Norman Nelson Papers, College of Medicine Archives.

2. For statewide statistics, see Iowa Hospital Association, *Fifty Years of Community Service to Iowans, 1929–79,* April 1979, "Patient Days: Private, State, Other" and "Admissions: Private, State, Other."

3. Iowa State Board of Education Minutes, 1944–46, p. 16. Also, A. W. Dakin to V. M. Hancher, October 1945, File 58, 1945–46, V. M. Hancher Papers, University of Iowa Archives.

4. Rosemary Stevens, *In Sickness and in Wealth,* p. 203.

5. For the story of penicillin, see W. H. Helfand, H. B. Woodruff, K. M. H. Coleman, and D. L. Cowen, "Wartime Industrial Development of Penicillin in the United States," in John Parascandola, ed., *The History of Antibiotics* (Madison, WI: American Institute of the History of Pharmacy, 1980), pp. 31–56.

6. *Historical Statistics of the United States, Colonial Times to 1970* (Washington, DC: Department of Commerce, 1975), p. 1140.

7. G. Clasen to V. M. Hancher, February 6, 1953, File 56, 1952–53, V. M. Hancher Papers, University of Iowa Archives.

8. Report of the Ad Hoc Hospital Committee of the Medical Council, Medical Council Minutes, January 26, 1951, College of Medicine Archives.

9. Continually discussed in the journal *Hospitals* in 1945 and 1946, new standards called for close to 700 square feet of hospital space per bed. The University Hospitals' wards, many of which had twenty to thirty beds, could accommodate only four to six beds under these newer standards. The Report of the Ad Hoc Hospital Committee of the Medical Council, January 21, 1951, described overcrowded conditions in the Hospitals. See Medical Council Minutes, January 21, 1951, College of Medicine Archives.

10. On color, see *The Daily Iowan,* May 27, 1947. On new color standards, see, for example, "Color in Balance," *Hospitals* (June 1945), pp. 52–55.

11. On temperature, see Board of Education Minutes, January–May 1945, University of Iowa Archives, regarding bids for installing thermostatic controls in surgical and some ward areas. On surgical dressing, see Report of the Ad Hoc Hospital Committee of the Medical Council, Medical Council Minutes, January 21, 1951, College of Medicine Archives. On emergency care, see Robert Tidrick, Department of Surgery Annual Report, 1952–53, p. 58, File 114, 1953–54, V. M. Hancher Papers, University of Iowa Archives.

12. Report of the Ad Hoc Hospital Committee of the Medical Council, Medical Council Minutes, January 21, 1951, College of Medicine Archives.

13. Comment on the declining recovery period is from Gerhard Hartman lecture notes, Hospital Administration course, delivered February 8 and 9, 1951, Gerhard Hartman Papers, Offsight

Storage, Oakdale Campus. On the dangers of cyclopropane, see oral interview with John Tinker, May 1993; oral interview with Jack Moyers, former head of Anesthesia, University of Iowa Hospitals and Clinics, February 1994.

14. See Walter Bierring's monthly (1940s to early 1950s) *Journal of the Iowa State Medical Society* updates on diseases in Iowa, especially 41 (May 1951): 175–181.

15. Rosemary Stevens, *In Sickness and In Wealth,* p. 203.

16. College of Medicine Annual Report, 1937–38, College of Medicine Archives. For discussion of the cancer clinics, see V. M. Hancher to Harry L. Johnson, Extension Division of State Department of Health, February 26, 1941, a letter not sent but converted into a memo for Hancher's files, File 107 (College of Medicine "Special File"), 1940–41, V. M. Hancher Papers, University of Iowa Archives.

17. The five-month selection process is described in Hancher's notes taken during an interview with Hartman on April 19, 1946, File 58, 1945–46; V. M. Hancher to H. C. Shull, April 22, 1946, File 58, 1945–46; and V. M. Hancher, N. G. Alcock, January and February 1946, File 58 1945–46, V. M. Hancher Papers, University of Iowa Archives. Hancher notified MacEwen and Neff of SUI Faculty Committee approval of the hospital administration on April 21, 1945, File 58, 1944–45, V. M. Hancher Papers, University of Iowa Archives.

18. On selection of Hartman, see N. G. Alcock to E. M. MacEwen during February 1946, and V. M. Hancher to H. C. Shull, April 22, 1946, File 58, 1945–46, V. M. Hancher Papers, University of Iowa Archives.

19. V. M. Hancher to H. C. Shull, April 22, 1946.

20. This information appeared in curriculum vita found in File 58, 1945–46, V. M. Hancher Papers, University of Iowa Archives. See also Gerhard Hartman, "Graduate Education in Hospital Administration, 1934–37," *Journal of Business* 11 (October 1938): 1–13.

21. Gerhard Hartman, "In First Person: An Oral History," interview by Lewis A. Weeks, Hospital Administration Oral History Collection, AHA Library, Chicago.

22. Ira A. Kipnis, *A Venture Forward: A History of the American College of Hospital Administrators* (Chicago: ACHA, 1955), pp. 36–37.

23. Ibid.

24. Rosemary Stevens, *In Sickness and in Wealth,* pp. 156–157.

25. See, for example, "Raising Standards of Administrators" *Hospitals* 20 (April 1946): 57.

26. See Charles E. Prall, *The College Curriculum in Hospital Administration* (Chicago: Physicians' Record Company, 1948); *Problems of Hospital Administrators* (Chicago: Physicians' Record Company, 1948). See also George R. Wren, "An Historical View of Health Administration Education," *Hospital and Health Services Administration* 25 (Summer 1980): 31–42.

27. Weeks interview, p. 22.

28. Samuel Levey telephone interview with Gerhard Hartman, May 1995.

29. Gerhard Hartman Lecture Notes, "Organization of Hospital Care and Medical Service," February 8–9, 1951, "Organization Data" Binder, Gerhard Hartman Papers, Offsight Storage, Oakdale Campus.

30. Ibid.

31. V. M. Hancher to G. Hartman, April 2, 1946, Gerhard Hartman Papers, University Hospitals Offsite Storage, Oakdale Campus.

32. V. M. Hancher to J. T. McClintock, May 16, 1950, File, 1949–50, V. M. Hancher Papers, University of Iowa Archives.

33. V. M. Hancher to E. M. MacEwen, December 8, 1945, Presidents Folder, E. M. MacEwen Papers, College of Medicine Archives.

34. E. M. MacEwen to N. G. Alcock, November 26, 1945, Presidents Folder, E. M. MacEwen Papers, College of Medicine Archives.

35. E. M. MacEwen to V. M. Hancher, April 30, 1946, File 58, 1945–46, V. M. Hancher Papers, University of Iowa Archives.

36. E. M. MacEwen to V. M. Hancher, November 26, 1945, File 58, 1945–46; J. T. McClintock to Hancher, May 24, 1950, File 115A, 1949–50, V. M. Hancher Papers, Univeristy of Iowa Archives.

37. E. M. MacEwen to E. Gilmore, July 20, 1939 and September 12, 1939, Presidents Folder, Ewen MacEwen Papers, College of Medicine Archives.

38. See retrospective view from N. B. Nelson, "Report to the Faculty 1961," Dean's Office Folder, Norman Nelson Papers, College of Medicine Archives.

39. J. T. McClintock to V. M. Hancher, April 28, 1950, File 115A, 1949–50, V. M. Hancher Papers, University of Iowa Archives.

40. V. M. Hancher to College of Medicine department heads, June 29, 1946, File 58, 1945–46, V. M. Hancher Papers, University of Iowa Archives.

41. V. M. Hancher to G. Hartman, February 27, 1947, File 58, 1946–47, V. M. Hancher Papers, University of Iowa Archives.

42. See C. F. Jacobsen to G. Hartman, September 30, 1947, File 57, 1947–48, V. M. Hancher Papers, University of Iowa Archives.

43. E. M. MacEwen to G. Hartman, May 14, 1947, University Hospitals Folder, MacEwen Papers, College of Medicine Archives.

44. *Daily Iowan*, May 27, 1947.

45. V. M. Hancher to J. C. Reid, September 6, 1947, File 112, 1947–48, V. M. Hancher Papers, University of Iowa Archives.

46. Medical Council Minutes, September 23, 1947, College of Medicine Archives.

47. C. F. Jacobsen to G. Hartman, September 30, 1947, File 57, 1947–48, V. M. Hancher Papers, University of Iowa Archives.

48. C. F. Jacobsen to V. M. Hancher, December 28, 1948, File 60, 1948–49, V. M. Hancher Papers, University of Iowa Archives.

49. C. F. Jacobsen to M. H. Soley, February 19, 1948, File 112, 1947–48, V. M. Hancher Papers, University of Iowa Archives.

50. College of Medicine Faculty to V. M. Hancher, June 23, 1949, File 115, 1948–49, V. M. Hancher Papers, University of Iowa Archives.

51. Address to Medical Faculty, June 27, 1949, File 115, 1949–50, V. M. Hancher Papers, University of Iowa Archives.

52. E. D. Plass to V. M. Hancher, June 29, 1949, File 115, 1949–50, V. M. Hancher Papers, University of Iowa Archives.

53. Faculty Survey, June 28, 1949, File 115, 1949–50, V. M. Hancher Papers, University of Iowa Archives.

54. H. S. Houghton to V. M. Hancher, September 17, 1949, File 115, 1949–50, V. M. Hancher Papers, University of Iowa Archives.

55. C. F. Jacobsen to G. Hartman, September 30, 1947, File 57, 1947–48; V. M. Hancher to G. Hartman, April 12, 1947, File 58, 1946–47, V. M. Hancher Papers, University of Iowa Archives.

56. A. W. Dakin to C. Jacobsen, October 31, 1947, File 57, 1947–48, V. M. Hancher Papers, University of Iowa Archives.

57. V. M. Hancher to C. F. Jacobsen, April 10, 1949, File 60, 1948–49, V. M. Hancher Papers, University of Iowa Archives.

58. See Executive Committee Minutes, November 1949, and Medical Council Minutes, December 7, 1949, College of Medicine Archives.

59. F. W. Ambrose to C. F. Jacobsen, September 15, 1949, File 57, 1949–50, V. M. Hancher Papers, University of Iowa Archives.

60. Medical Council Minutes, November 30, 1949, College of Medicine Archives; C. F. Jacobsen to G. Hartman, November 30, 1949, University Hospitals Folder, Norman Nelson Papers, College of Medicine Archives; and Russell Myers to V. M. Hancher, April 27, 1950, E. DeGowin to V. M. Hancher, April 29, 1950; R. M. Featherstone to V. M. Hancher, April 27, 1950, File 115, 1949–50, V. M. Hancher Papers, University of Iowa Archives.

61. Medical Council Minutes, January 12, 1945, College of Medicine Archives.

62. C. F. Jacobsen to G. Hartman, November 30, 1949, University Hospitals Folder, Norman Nelson Papers, College of Medicine Archives.

63. R. E. Tidrick to V. M. Hancher, February 28, 1950, File 115, 1949–1950, V. M. Hancher Papers, University of Iowa Archives. Original and revised versions of the "Prospectus" discussed in V. M. Hancher to P. E. Huston, June 22, 1951, Presidents Folder, Norman Nelson Papers, College of Medicine Archives.

64. V. M. Hancher to Medical Faculty, April 24, 1950, File 115, 1949–50, V. M. Hancher Papers, University of Iowa Archives.

65. R. Meyers to V. M. Hancher, April 27, 1950, File 115, 1949–50, V. M. Hancher Papers, University of Iowa Archives.

66. R. M. Featherstone to V. M. Hancher, April 27, 1950, File 115, 1949–50, V. M. Hancher Papers, University of Iowa Archives.

67. E. DeGowin to V. M. Hancher, April 29, 1950, File 115, 1949–50, V. M. Hancher Papers, University of Iowa Archives.

68. M. E. Barnes to V. M. Hancher, May 2, 1950, File 115, 1949–50, V. M. Hancher Papers, University of Iowa Archives.

69. R. Myers to V. M. Hancher, April 27, 1950, File 115, 1949–50, V. M. Hancher Papers, University of Iowa Archives.

70. Hancher speech to medical faculty, July 9, 1950, Presidents Folder, Norman Nelson Papers, College of Medicine Archives.

71. Discussed in V. M. Hancher to P. E. Huston, June 22, 1951, Presidents Folder, Norman Nelson Papers, College of Medicine Archives.

72. W. M. Fowler to G. Hartman, June 30, 1952, File 57, 1951–52, V. M. Hancher Papers, University of Iowa Archives.

73. V. M. Hancher to G. Hartman, June 30, 1952, File 53, 1951–52, V. M. Hancher Papers, University of Iowa Archives.

74. N. B. Nelson address to the faculty, 1961, Presidents Folder, Norman Nelson Papers, College of Medicine Archives.

75. This description comes from N. B. Nelson, "Report to the Faculty, 1961," Dean's Office Folder, Norman Nelson Papers, College of Medicine Archives.

76. V. M. Hancher to G. Hartman, December 15, 1953, File 56, 1953–54, V. M. Hancher Papers, University of Iowa Archives.

77. "SUI Hospital Today," *University of Iowa School of Nursing Alumnæ Journal* (1948).

78. Board of Education Minutes, May 12, 1947, University of Iowa Archives.

79. Report of the Ad Hoc Hospital Committee, January 26, 1951, Medical Council Minutes, College of Medicine Archives.

80. "SUI Hospitals Offer Top Service at Bargain Prices." *Mason City Globe-Gazette,* January 4, 1949. See also, Gerhard Hartman, "The State University of Iowa Hospitals—A Continuing Contribution to the Health of the People," *Journal of the Iowa State Medical Society* 38 (April 1948): 155.

81. Rosemary Stevens, *In Sickness and In Wealth,* pp. 218–219.

82. Iowa Hospital Association, *Seventy-Five Years of Community Service to Iowans,* p. 7. The tally of beds excluded osteopathic hospitals but include homeopathic hospitals not registered with the AMA.

83. The 52nd General Assembly passed legislation authorizing the Department of Health to conduct the statewide survey, to staff the administration of the program, and to license hospitals and nursing homes. See *Code of Iowa, 1946,* chapter 90.

84. The preliminary count of 500 hospitals from Christine Newark, "Doctors and Hospitals in Iowa," *Iowa Farm Economist* 11 (September 1945). Sea also, Iowa Hospital Survey Committee, "Proposed Iowa Hospital Plan," December 10, 1947. The committee's plan was approved by the public health service the following February. All in File 57, 1947–48, V. M. Hancher Papers, University of Iowa Archives.

85. "39 Iowa Communities Raise $6,700,000 for New Hospitals," *Hospital Management* 62 (December 1946): 37–38.

86. "Problems in Medical Service in Iowa," *Journal of the Iowa State Medical Society* 37 (November 1947): 510–511.

87. Ibid., p. 510.

88. Iowa Hospital Survey Committee, "Proposed Iowa Hospital Plan," December 10, 1947, File 57, 1947–48, V. M. Hancher Papers, University of Iowa Archives.

89. Twelve percent of Iowans enjoyed some degree of Blue Cross coverage in 1946; a figure that increased to 25 percent by 1952, when the insured population accounted for 37 percent of all hospital admissions, excluding admissions to the University Hospitals. At the same time, 1,900 of Iowa's 2,500 physicians were Blue Shield participants by 1952. Blue Cross family coverage cost $2.65 per month in 1952; combined Blue Cross and Blue Shield enrollment cost $5.40. See *Journal of the Iowa State Medical Society* 40 (February 1950): 93; "Record Payments by Blue Cross/Blue Shield," *Journal of the Iowa State Medical Society* 43 (May 1953): 242; Iowa Hospital Association, *Seventy-Five Years of Community Service to Iowans,* p. 8.

90. For discussion, see Board of Education Minutes, December 29, 1947, University of Iowa Archives.

91. Gerhard Hartman, "The State University of Iowa Hospitals—A continuing contribution to the health of the people," *Journal of the Iowa State Medical Society* 38 (April 1948): 156–157.

92. Board of Education Minutes, December 15, 1948, University of Iowa Archives.

93. Board of Education Minutes, January 13, 1949; C. F. Jacobsen to V. M. Hancher, December 7, 1948, File 60, 1948–49, V. M. Hancher Papers, University of Iowa Archives.

94. A. Leff to A. W. Dakin, October 11, 1950, File 51, 1950–51, V. M. Hancher Papers, University of Iowa Archives.

95. James Roberts, Jack Conle, and Robert Redmen, "History of the Joint Commission on the Accreditation of Hospitals," *Journal of the American Medical Association* 258 (1987): 936–940.

96. JCAH reviews of University Hospital for the years 1955, 1958, 1961, and 1964 are held in the University of Iowa Hospitals and Clinics off-site storage at the Oakdale campus.

97. A draft of a "statement of policy," V. M. Hancher to D. Kerr, January 3, 1946, in Hancher to E. M. MacEwen of the same date, Presidents Folder, E. M. MacEwen Papers, College of Medicine Archives.

98. V. M. Hancher to George Scanlon, April 2, 1948, File 112, 1947–48, V. M. Hancher Papers, University of Iowa Archives.

99. R. Beye to V. M. Hancher, August 25, 1945, File 111, 1945–46, V. M. Hancher Papers, University of Iowa Archives.

100. From Hancher's interview with R. A. Flocks on or about September 13, 1945, File 111, 1945–46, V. M. Hancher Papers, University of Iowa Archives.

101. See Hancher notes June 26, 1943, File 109, 1943–44, V. M. Hancher Papers, University of Iowa Archives.

102. V. M. Hancher to E. M. MacEwen, September 6, 1945, File 111, 1945–46, V. M. Hancher Papers, University of Iowa Archives.

103. V. M. Hancher to A. W. Dakin, October 25, 1945, File 111, 1945–46, V. M. Hancher Papers, University of Iowa Archives.

104. A. C. Furstenberg, "Address of the President: A Consideration of Full-Time and Part-Time Faculty Services in the Medical Schools of North America in Relation to Medical Education and the Care of the Sick." Delivered in Pittsburgh at the 56th Annual Meeting of the AAMC, October 29–31, 1945. In File 111, 1945–46, V. M. Hancher Papers, University of Iowa Archives. Also published in *Journal of the Association of American Medical Colleges* 20 (November 1945): 339–348.

105. See V. M. Hancher to John C. Reid, July 19, 1943, File 109, 1943–44, V. M. Hancher Papers, University of Iowa Archives.

106. Hancher later recapped the alternatives: V. M. Hancher to G. H. Scanlon, April 2, 1948, File 112, 1947–48, V. M. Hancher Papers, University of Iowa Archives.

107. V. M. Hancher notes, apparently from interviews held with Plass, F. M. Smith, Van Epps, Gregg, and Percival Bailey, dated June 26, 1943, File 109, 1943–44, V. M. Hancher Papers, University of Iowa Archives.

108. V. M. Hancher, "Statement of Policy," including cover letter to Dabney Kerr, January 3, 1946, Presidents Folder, Ewen MacEwen Papers, College of Medicine Archives. For McClintock language, see E. M. MacEwen to V. M. Hancher, December 18, 1945, Presidents Folder, Ewen MacEwen Papers, College of Medicine Archives.

109. See Nathaniel Alcock's minority report, appended to the Medical Service Plan submitted to the Board of Education, June 3, 1946.

110. V. M. Hancher to Abraham Flexner, June 18, 1950, File 115, 1949–50, V. M. Hancher Papers, University of Iowa Archives.

111. "The Medical Service Plan," *Journal of the Iowa State Medical Society* 37 (July 1947).

112. Ibid.

113. *Journal of the Iowa State Medical Society,* 37 (July 1947): 303.

114. Board of Education Minutes, January 15, 1947, University of Iowa Archives.

115. Executive Committee chairman Willis M. Fowler said in 1952 that medical service fees were "going a long way toward financing an ever-expanding program of valuable and vital research at Iowa." By that year $60,000 to $70,000 was going into the scientific fund each year. "SUI Medical Wage System Aids Research," *Des Moines Register,* February 10, 1952.

116. V. M. Hancher to G. H. Scanlon, April 2, 1948, File 112, 1947–48, V. Hancher Papers, University of Iowa Archives.

117. Alcock's observations are contained in Hancher to Scanlon, Ibid.

118. C. F. Jacobsen to V. M. Hancher, December 8, 1948, File 57, 1948–49, V. M. Hancher Papers, University of Iowa Archives. Quite rightly, Jacobsen told the board of education in a memo that a surge in the number and quality of applicants was a temporary result of the war's end: December 13, 1948, File 57, 1948–49, V. M. Hancher Papers, University of Iowa Archives.

119. "Problems in Medical Service in Iowa," *Journal of the Iowa State Medical Society* 37 (November 1947), p. 510.

120. M. E. Barnes to V. M. Hancher, May 2, 1950, File 115, 1949–50, V. M. Hancher Papers, University of Iowa Archives.

121. Board of Education Minutes, January 1, 1949, University of Iowa Archives.

122. Press Release, State University of Iowa Information Service, April 23, 1949, File 117, 1948–49, V. M. Hancher Papers, University of Iowa Archives.

123. Board of Education Minutes, May 9, 1949, University of Iowa Archives.

124. See V. M. Hancher to H. C. Shull, June 9, 1949, Hancher to C. F. Jacobsen, May 24, 1949, Jacobsen to Hancher, May 5, 1949, File 117, 1948–49, V. M. Hancher Papers, University of Iowa Archives.

125. See Gerhard Hartman comments in Hospital Advisory Committee Minutes, July 20, 1950, College of Medicine Archives.

126. A. W. Dakin to M. H. Soley, October 31, 1948, and December 14, 1948; Soley to medical department heads, November 23, 1948, File 117, 1948–49, V. M. Hancher Papers, University of Iowa Archives.

127. Medical Council Minutes, June 7, 1949, College of Medicine Archives.

128. M. E. Barnes to M. H. Soley, "Report on Replacement of Iowa Physicians," June 8, 1949, File 117, 1948–49, V. M. Hancher Papers, University of Iowa Archives.

129. V. M. Hancher to board of education President Henry Shull, June 9, 1949, File 117R, 1948–49, V. M. Hancher Papers, University of Iowa Archives.

130. V. M. Hancher to the 53rd General Assembly Interim Committee on Retrenchment and Reform, August 4, 1949, and Hancher to Board of Education, August 12, 1949, File 115, 1949–50, V. M. Hancher Papers, University of Iowa Archives.

131. R. E. Tidrick to V. M. Hancher, August 26, 1949, File 115, 1949–50, V. M. Hancher Papers, University of Iowa Archives. See also, V. M. Hancher report in Board of Education Minutes, October 14, 1949, University of Iowa Archives.

132. See Board of Education Minutes, May 12, 1947, University of Iowa Archives. An undated memo from A. W. Dakin to G. Hartman, E. M. MacEwen and University Business Office outlined the policies governing the program: MacEwen Files, College of Medicine Archives.

133. Office of the Dean, "Placement of College of Medicine Graduates as Interns, 1915–1965," College of Medicine Archives.

134. University of Iowa, *Internal Allocations*, 1955 and 1965, University of Iowa Archives; University of Iowa Hospitals, "Annual Statistical Reports, 1950–1965," University of Iowa Hospitals and Clinics Office of Financial Management and Control.

135. "Provisional Report of the Subcommittee on the Health Science Area," Campus Planning Committee, March 1950, File 57, 1949–1950, V. M. Hancher Papers, University of Iowa Archives; Board of Education Minutes, October 14, 1950, September 13, 1951, November 29, 1951, May 22, 1952, and June 30, 1952, University of Iowa Archives.

136. Report of the Liaison Committee on Medical Education, April 14, 1960, File 65, 1960–61, V. M. Hancher Papers, University of Iowa Archives.

137. Health Insurance Association of America, *Source Book of Health Insurance Data* (New York: HIAA, 1965), p. 66.

138. Iowa Hospital Association, *Fifty Years of Service to Iowa*, Tables 2–4.

139. HIAA, *Source Book of Health Insurance Data*, p. 12.

140. Frank Groner, "Can Blue Cross Be Saved?" *Hospitals* 34 (1960): 46.

141. Health Insurance Council Annual Reports, 1951–59, *Extent of Voluntary Health Insurance in the United States*; HIAA, *Source Book of Health Insurance Data*.

142. Board of Education Minutes, September 10, 1952, University of Iowa Archives.

143. K. Lange to G. Hartman, September 21, 1954, Gerhard Hartman Papers, 1955–1957, Legislative Askings Binder, University of Iowa Hospitals and Clinics Off-Site Storage. Lange's survey covered the months of June through August 1954; among his findings, Lange noted that 11 percent of indigent patients had insurance coverage.

144. G. Clasen and N. B. Nelson to V. M. Hancher, November 16, 1954, File 60, 1954–55, V. M. Hancher Papers, University of Iowa Archives.

145. Compensation Committee Minutes, November 5, 1951, College of Medicine Archives.

146. Compensation Committee Minutes, November 4, 1952, and January 6, 1953, College of Medicine Archives.

147. Compensation Committee Minutes, April 17, 1956, and June 5, 1956, College of Medicine Archives.

148. Medical Council Minutes, July 31, 1956, College of Medicine Archives.

149. See Compensation Committee Minutes, December 11, 1956, and November 5, 1957, College of Medicine Archives.

150. N. B. Nelson to V. M. Hancher, September 1, 1954, File 118, 1954–55, V. M. Hancher Papers, University of Iowa Archives.

151. An informational packet prepared for a visit of the legislative Budget and Financial Control Committee in October 1955 claimed that temporary buildings in use across the university—which included war surplus barracks housing married students—totaled over 500,000 square feet of floor space: "Capital Appropriations and Projects," October 14, 1955, Gerhard Hartman Papers, College of Medicine Off-Site Storage, Oakdale Campus.

152. "Capital Appropriations and Projects," October 14, 1955; see also V. M. Hancher memorandum, March 5, 1953, File 56, 1952–53, V. M. Hancher Papers, University of Iowa Archives.

153. V. M. Hancher memorandum, June 25, 1954, File 60, 1954–55, V. M. Hancher Papers, University of Iowa Archives.

154. Board of Education Minutes, July 8, 1954, University of Iowa Archives.

155. Board of Education Minutes, March 13 and June 19, 1958, University of Iowa Archives.

156. "Womack Report," Medical Council Minutes, January 26, 1951, College of Medicine Archives. Prepared by a faculty committee headed by surgery professor Nathan Womack, the report was a detailed study of hospital space and overall facilities needs.

157. "Explanation of Research Wing," addendum to N. B. Nelson to V. M. Hancher, November 3, 1954, File 118, 1954–55, V. M. Hancher Papers, University of Iowa Archives.

158. "Capital appropriations and projects," October 14, 1955.

159. N. B. Nelson to V. M. Hancher, November 3, 1954, File 118, 1954–55, V. M. Hancher Papers, University of Iowa Archives.

160. Ibid.; see also G. Hartman to V. M. Hancher, July 15, 1954, File 60, 1954–55, V. M. Hancher Papers, University of Iowa Archives.

161. Board of Education Minutes, January 14 and February 11, 1954, University of Iowa Archives.

162. Board of Education Minutes, October 23, 1957, University of Iowa Archives.

163. "Remodeling, Space Conversion Under Way in General Hospital," *Medical Bulletin* (Winter–Spring 1959): 4–10.

164. G. Hartman to V. M. Hancher, July 14, 1950; Hospital Advisory Committee Minutes, July 20, 1950, both in Hospital Advisory Committee, Vol. 1, May 1950–December 1963, Gerhard Hartman Papers, College of Medicine off-site storage.

165. G. Clasen to N. B. Nelson, July 19, 1956, File 79, 1956–57, V. M. Hancher Papers, University of Iowa Archives.

166. "Supplemental Information to Form PHS-62–1: Project Construction Application, Part I. Minimal Care Unit, State University of Iowa Hospitals, Iowa City, Iowa," April 24, 1961, File 41A, V. M. Hancher Papers, University of Iowa Archives.

167. V. M. Hancher to Budget and Financial Control Committee, November 1960; V. M. Hancher personal memorandum, November 1, 1960, File 65, subfolder "Medical Research Facilities," 1960–61, V. M. Hancher Papers, University of Iowa Archives.

168. Board of Regents Minutes, November 10, 1960, University of Iowa Archives.

169. Board of Regents Minutes, November 10, 1960 and June 22, 1961, University of Iowa Archives.

170. Iowa State Division of Hospitals, *Iowa Hospital and Related Services Facilities Plan, 1963* (Des Moines, IA: ISDH, 1963), p. 2.

171. James A. Shannon, "Advance of Medical Research: A Twenty Year View on the Role of the NIH," *Journal of Medical Education* 42 (1967): 97–108; Stephen Strickland, *Politics, Science, and Dread Disease: Short History of the United States Medical Research Policy* (Cambridge: Harvard University Press, 1972).

172. Shannon, "Advance of Medical Research," p. 105.

173. Quoted in Strickland, *Politics, Science, and Dread Disease*, p. 121.

174. Executive Committee Minutes, July 3, 1961, College of Medicine Archives.

175. "Regular Operating and Sponsored Program Medical School Spending," *Journal of Medical Education* 45 (1968): 861–862.

176. Medical Council Minutes, September 26, 1961, College of Medicine Archives.

177. R. Hickey to V. M. Hancher, November 1, 1960, File 65, 1960–61, V. M. Hancher Papers, University of Iowa Archives.

178. Hardin was absent from the university from 1942 to 1945 for wartime service and again for a two-year stint with the Red Cross beginning in the late 1940s.

179. President Hancher reported Hardin's position in a letter to Robert Prentiss, February 6, 1961, File 65, 1960–61, V. M. Hancher Papers, University of Iowa Archives.

180. See Executive Committee Minutes, November 12, 1962, February 8, 1965, and February 15, 1965, College of Medicine Archives.

181. Aims C. McGuinness, "Government and the Medical School," *Journal of Medical Education* 33 (July 1958): 523–527.

182. H. Lawrence Wilsey, "The Importance of Long-Range Planning for Medical Schools and Teaching Hospitals," *Journal of Medical Education* 40 (November 1965): 94–115.

183. McGuinness, "Government and the Medical School," 524–525.

184. Ray E. Brown, "Dollars and Sense in Medical School–Teaching Hospital Relationships," *Journal of Medical Education* 40 (November 1965): 126–136.

185. "Redraft of Prospectus—Organization of the Deanship," pp. 2–3, Medical Council Minutes, July 16, 1953, College of Medicine Archives.

186. University of Iowa Hospitals and Clinics Financial Office.

187. V. M. Hancher to R. J. Prentiss, February 6, 1961, File 65, 1960–61, V. M. Hancher Papers, University of Iowa Archives.

188. N. B. Nelson to V. M. Hancher, January 11, 1962, File 65, 1961–62, V. M. Hancher Papers, University of Iowa Archives.

189. V. M. Hancher to Board of Regents, March 1, 1964, File 6, 1964–65, Howard R. Bowen Papers, University of Iowa Archives.

190. Board of Regents Minutes, February 25 and September 8, 1960, April 13, 1961, September 12, 1962, February 15, 1963, and June 17, 1964, University of Iowa Archives.

191. Hancher to Board of Regents, March 1, 1964, op. cit.

192. On the suggestion of Nelson, the committee invited Clasen to its meetings. See Compensation Committee Minutes, October 13, 1953, College of Medicine Archives.

193. Executive Committee Minutes, February 15, 1954, College of Medicine Archives.

194. For the reorganization of the committee, see Hospital Advisory Committee Minutes, February 2 and February 8, 1961, College of Medicine Archives.

195. "Seek Funds to Construct New U-Hospital Facilities," *Iowa City Press Citizen*, March 14, 1959.

196. V. M. Hancher to G. Hartman, N. B. Nelson, and G. Clasen, March 19, 1959, File 41 (University Hospital), 1958–59, V. M. Hancher Papers, University of Iowa Archives.

197. V. M. Hancher Memorandum, c. April 1, 1959, File 41, 1958–59, V. M. Hancher Papers, University of Iowa Archives.

198. Samuel Levey and Thomas McCarthy, "What Administrators Worry About: Money," *Modern Hospital* (February 1962): 91.

199. Lewis Weeks oral history interview with Gerhard Hartman for American Hospital Association, p. 197.

200. V. M. Hancher to N. B. Nelson, May 9, 1962, File 65, 1962–63, V. M. Hancher Papers, University of Iowa Archives.

201. Executive Committee to H. H. Davis, February 26, 1957, and March 15, 1957, File 65, 1956–57, V. M. Hancher Papers, University of Iowa Archives.

202. Medical Faculty Minutes, March 28, 1961, College of Medicine Archives.

203. Medical Faculty Minutes, April 12, 1961, College of Medicine Archives.

204. Medical Faculty Minutes, June 4, 1961, College of Medicine Archives.

205. Ad Hoc Committee Minutes, May 21, 1962, File 65, 1961–62, V. M. Hancher Papers, University of Iowa Archives.

206. Ad Hoc Committee Minutes, May 24, 1962, File 65, 1961–62, V. M. Hancher Papers, University of Iowa Archives.

207. Board of Regents Minutes, August 9, 1962, University of Iowa Archives.

208. R. C. Hardin to V. M. Hancher, January 23, 1961, File 65, 1960–61, V. M. Hancher Papers, University of Iowa Archives.

29. Walter Jessup, president from 1916 to 1934. (Kent Collection, University of Iowa Archives.)

30. Eugene A. Gilmore, president from 1934 to 1940. (Kent Collection, University of Iowa Archives.)

31. Virgil M. Hancher, president from 1940 to 1964. (Kent Collection, University of Iowa Archives.)

32. Howard R. Bowen, president from 1964 to 1969.

33. Willard L. Boyd, president from 1969 to 1981. (Kent Collection, University of Iowa Archives.)

34. James O. Freedman, president from 1982 to 1987.

35. Hunter R. Rawlings III, president from 1988 to 1995.

36. Mary Sue Coleman, appointed president in 1995.

37. Robert E. Neff, hospitals superintendent from 1928 to 1945. (Kent Collection, University of Iowa Archives.)

38. Gerhard Hartman, hospitals superintendent from 1946 to 1971.

39. John W. Colloton, director of University of Iowa Hospitals and Clinics from 1971 to 1993.

40. R. Edward Howell, appointed director of University of Iowa Hospitals and Clinics, 1994.

41. Glen Clasen, associate hospital superintendent from about 1953 to 1969. (Kent Collection, University of Iowa Archives.)

42. Myrtle Aydellotte, dean of nursing from 1949 to 1957 and director of nursing from 1968 to 1976.

284

43. Henry S. Houghton, dean of medicine
from 1928 to 1933. (Kent Collection,
University of Iowa Archives.)

44. Ewen M. MacEwen, dean of medicine
from 1935 to 1947. (Kent Collection,
University of Iowa Archives.)

45. Norman B. Nelson, dean of medicine
from 1953 to 1962. (Kent Collection,
University of Iowa Archives.)

285

46. Robert C. Hardin, dean of medicine from 1962 to 1969. (Kent Collection, University of Iowa Archives.)

47. John W. Eckstein, dean of medicine from 1970 to 1991.

48. Robert P. Kelch, appointed dean of medicine in 1994.

5

The Transformation of the Teaching Hospital, 1966–1982

In the late 1960s, the University of Iowa Hospitals embarked on a major expansion program that has continued without visible interruption to the present. The debate over growth and modernization at the University Hospitals had of course begun in the 1950s, with both the administration and clinical staff voicing concern about overcrowding and other shortcomings. Likewise, the Hospital Division of the Iowa Department of Health, reinforced by rising accreditation standards for teaching hospitals, had repeatedly called for the replacement of the University Hospitals' obsolete facilities in the late 1950s and early 1960s. Some limited capital improvements had followed; however, the real thrust toward a thoroughgoing modernization did not occur until the late 1960s, energized by medical scientific advances, substantial new federal programs, the enactment of innovative bonding legislation for the hospitals and clinics by the Iowa legislature, and the interplay of local issues and personalities.

By the early 1960s, the wonders of postwar medical science had become staples of American popular culture, fostering an unprecedented faith in the health sciences in general and medicine in particular. From the mid-1960s, reflecting both public sentiment and solid Democratic majorities in both houses after the 1964 elections, Congress approved several major federal initiatives in medical education, medical research, and the organization and delivery of healthcare services, and those initiatives, filtered through various federal and state agencies and adapted by local officials to serve local needs, profoundly affected the University of Iowa, the health science campus, and, most important, University Hospitals. University presidents Howard Bowen (1964–1969) and Willard Boyd (1969–1981), hospital director John Colloton (1971–1993), college of medicine dean (1962–1969) and university vice president (1964–1975) Robert Hardin, and executive associate medical dean Paul Seebohm guided much of the strategic planning, drawn together by a shared vision of what the medical center could become in this new era of healthcare spending.

Tied closely to Medicare and Medicaid revenues, expanded federal funding of medical research and graduate medical education, and the rapid growth of private health insurance, that vision entailed major changes in direction for University Hospitals. Perhaps most important, University Hospitals jettisoned its image as an indigent care institution in the 1970s and 1980s, and by expanding existing strengths in state-of-the-art specialty care and the patient referral system won formal recognition as Iowa's tertiary care facility, simultaneously ending the hospitals' longstanding two-class system of care that accommodated indigent and private patients separately. Circumstances also brought the university hospitals a new fiscal autonomy that in turn, profoundly altered traditional relationships between the hospitals and the college of medicine, the university, and the state government.

By 1982, although much planning and construction remained, a nationally recognized teaching hospital complex had taken form on the University of Iowa campus. The hospitals' transformation was more than just physical. Unlike the modestly appointed public hospital, with its indigent patient base, that had stood in one or another form since 1898, the reconstructed University of Iowa Hospitals and Clinics—the name adopted in 1972—attracted an overwhelmingly private patient clientele and enjoyed operating revenues of more than $80 million, a figure more than four times that of 1965. Impressive though it was, the ambitious reconstruction of the university hospitals was not a simple rags-to-riches story. Indeed, in some respects and to many inside observers, the hospitals' outlook remained troubled. Behind the remarkable growth in facilities, staff, and programs in the 1970s lay an uncertainty born of the soaring inflation in healthcare costs, ever widening federal budget deficits, and a worrisome shift in public attitudes toward healthcare in general and toward "big medicine" in particular. In short, the university hospitals, while in some ways more prosperous and secure than ever before, had grown increasingly complicated and presented a different set of challenges in planning and management.

The Growth of Federal Programs

Various federal programs, some dating to the immediate postwar years but most enacted only in the 1960s, constituted the basic building blocks for the new academic health science center at the University of Iowa and the new University of Iowa Hospitals and Clinics. Indeed, by 1970, the federal alliance with the University of Iowa—cemented by federal funding for research, education, facilities, and patient care, and by the increasing weight of federal regulation—dramatically changed the University Hospitals' long-standing relationship with the state, and in some respects overshadowed it.

Federal funding of medical research was the least controversial as well as one of the oldest of federal programs in the health sciences, although its history, too, scarcely predated World War II. By 1960, the research programs of the National Institutes of Health, including intramural research and extramural grants, had become a $448 million annual commitment. By 1965, federal support for biomedical research, most of it dispersed through the NIH and other agencies of the Department of Health, Education and Welfare, more than doubled, reaching nearly $1.2 billion, with extramural grants making up an ever increasing share. By 1970, the total federal investment in such research stood just short of $1.7 billion.[1] A substantial part of that money—$106 million in 1960, nearly $300 million in 1965, and nearly $400 million in 1970[2]—flowed to academic medical centers like the University of Iowa, much of it supporting nonspecific "basic research" into fundamental cellular processes rather than "applied research" aimed at specific health problems and issues.

For political reasons, the history of direct federal support for medical education, particularly undergraduate medical education, was more problematic. From the late 1940s, federal programs funded graduate research training in medical schools, and funding levels rose rapidly from just $4 million in 1950 to $41.5 million in 1960, $107.2 million in 1965, and $161.8 million in 1970.[3] In contrast, it was not until 1963 that the Health Professions Education Act provided the first direct federal funding of undergraduate medical education. However, once fears of a looming "physician shortage" and concerns over declining applications to medical schools had overridden long-standing opposition (especially from the American Medical Association), the program grew rapidly. Initially, the act provided student loans and construction grants, the latter in return for promises of expanded enrollments. In 1965, disbursements totaled $6.6 million for student loans and $59.1 million nationally for construction of new facilities. Congress amended the act in 1965 to provide more generous incentives for higher enrollments and also instituted a scholarship program for low-income students.

In 1966, the Bureau of Health Manpower of the U.S. Public Health Service projected a need of one million more healthcare workers by 1975, a projection that called for a doubling of the output of health professionals— physicians, nurses, dentists, pharmacists, and others.[4] In response to that report and to calls for expansion of medical education from the American Medical Association and the Association of American Medical Colleges, Congress broadened the terms of federal educational assistance programs in 1968 through the Health Manpower Act.[5] In 1970, national expenditures included nearly $100 million for construction of teaching facilities, $8.4 million for student loans, $7.2 million for scholarships, $21.2 million for capitation grants, and nearly $35 million for special projects grants.[6] In all, from 1965 to 1971, medical schools received more than $5 billion in federal funds, 18 percent of that for educational purposes, and 82 percent for research.[7] Meanwhile, expenditures for medical school construction in the United States rose from $56 million in 1965–66 to a peak of nearly $400 million in 1973–1974.[8]

The mid-1960s also saw the emergence of the first federal programs targeted at both specific health problems and the organization, financing, and delivery of healthcare. In 1964, a Presidential Commission on Heart Disease, Cancer, and Stroke, headed by heart surgeon Michael DeBakey and known more popularly as the "DeBakey Commission," suggested a "frontal assault," in the words of the commission report, on those major health problems through an integrated program of research, education, and patient care organized around regional medical centers.[9] What emerged from Congress (P.L. 89-239), after negotiations with the AMA and other interested parties, was a less ambitious program than the DeBakey Commission had envisioned, particularly in its effect on healthcare delivery systems.[10] Moreover, the commission's conclusions were subject, then and later, to criticism on several counts, including their categorical focus, their failure to consider prevention measures, and their implicit—if misplaced— confidence that medical science offered relatively quick and certain solutions to such complex disease problems.[11] Whatever its weaknesses, the federal heart disease, cancer, and stroke legislation enacted in 1965 was significant, both nationally and at the University of Iowa, both in the regional medical programs that it spawned and in its foreshadowing of a change toward a more categorical policy of research funding.

Federal aid for healthcare, whether for universal health insurance or for programs addressing the health needs of specific groups, was by far the most controversial of all federal programs affecting academic medical centers in the 1960s. It also proved to be the most dramatic in its direct effect on teaching hospitals. By the 1960s, the debate over access to healthcare in America, especially private and public health insurance, had experienced a long and complicated history dominated by opposition from the American Medical Association and by a degree of public ambivalence as well. For example, while restrictions on wage increases during World War II led to acceptance of private health insurance as a non-wage fringe benefit, just 33 percent of respondents in a 1949 Gallup Poll approved of the Truman administration's plan for national health insurance. Forty-seven percent of respondents favored an AMA program of expanded private insurance, and in a separate poll, 43 percent feared that the quality of care would suffer under any federal healthcare plan.[12]

By the early 1960s, however, the situation had changed substantially, particularly with regard to the issue of healthcare for the elderly, an area on which a broad spectrum of interests—from the insurance industry to the hospital industry—concurred on the need for action.[13] Reading again from Gallup Poll results, a solid majority of respondents in all age groups expressed approval in May 1961 for a healthcare plan for the aged financed from social security deductions. Moreover, respondents in March 1962 favored public over private insurance for the elderly by a margin of 55 to 34 percent.[14] Clearly, to all segments of the public, the elderly were among the "deserving poor," and the Kerr-Mills Act of 1960, a forerunner of later Medicare and Medicaid legislation, provided federal matching grants to existing state old-age assistance plans, including medical assistance for the aged.[15]

The combination of inadequacies in the Kerr-Mills program, the Democratic electoral landslide of 1964, and President Lyndon Johnson's expansive Great Society programs, led to the enactment of Medicare and Medicaid legislation in 1965, despite last-ditch opposition from the AMA. On July 30, 1965, President Johnson signed a three-part legislative package (P.L. 89-97) providing, first, in Title XVIII (Medicare), hospital insurance for the elderly financed through social security (Part A), a companion voluntary program of subsidized insurance covering physicians' fees (Part B), and, third, in Title XIX (Medicaid), expansion of the federal-state partnership begun under Kerr-Mills to provide coverage for hospitalization, physician services, and drugs to the medically indigent.

Medicare and Medicaid were landmark programs designed to achieve a major redistribution of healthcare resources and, as such, the two new programs enfranchised America's medically indigent population. Heretofore a burden on healthcare providers and a more or less captive population base for teaching facilities like the University of Iowa Hospitals, the medically indigent, under Medicare and Medicaid, became valued full-fledged "customers" of health goods and services. In 1967, Medicare spending totaled $4.5 billion; in 1970, it rose to $7.1 billion, some 70 percent of that total earmarked for hospital care. Meanwhile, in 1967, state and federal Medicaid spending totaled $2.9 billion and rose to $5.2 billion in 1970, some 42 percent of that amount for hospital care.[16] Fueled largely by Medicare and Medicaid spending, per capita expenditures for hospital care in the United States rose from $70 to $133 between 1965 and 1970, with public financing rising from 38.7 to 52.4 percent of that total and private financing falling from 61.3 to 47.6 percent.[17]

Overall, then, the role of the federal government in healthcare expanded enormously in the 1960s and affected medical education, research, and patient care—and a broad range of health problems found a place in the domestic agenda. In some key respects, the idea of a national mobilization against disease proved more illusory than real; still, in subsequent years, the variety of new and expanded federal programs were to become the most important factors in shaping the American healthcare system, including America's teaching hospitals. At the University of Iowa Hospitals, their impact was readily apparent in all areas, from patient service and staff numbers to undergraduate and postgraduate medical education, the conduct of scientific research, and the expansion of the health science campus itself.

Transitions in Patient Service

Medicare and, to a lesser extent, Medicaid programs introduced a new element of competition to patient service at the University of Iowa Hospitals between 1966 and 1970. The advent of Medicare sparked concerns among some clinical faculty that the University Hospitals would lose a substantial portion of its patients, and early results appeared in part at least to justify those fears. In the first full fiscal year of Medicare, the hospitals' average daily patient census dropped by 24, and it fell an additional 54 the following year.[18] From 1966 to 1970, private patient admissions rose just 2.3 percent (Table 5.1), well below the average five-year increase of nearly 30 percent during the previous two decades. At the same time, indigent (state) patient admissions slipped nearly 12 percent, falling from 55.6 percent to 51.6 percent of total admissions.

Meanwhile, the 5.8 percent decline in total patient-days between 1966 and 1970 paralleled the 5.0 percent decline in overall patient admissions. However, indigent patient-days dropped 21.6 percent, while private patient-days rose 17.4 percent, largely owing to the shift of some elderly patients with long-term illnesses from indigent to private status under Medicare. In contrast to the downward trend in patient admissions, the number of outpatient visits climbed 12.7 percent, from 225,368 to 253,970, with indigent visits falling from 28.9 to 23.2 percent of the total.

The effect of shifting patient demographics was not consistent across the clinical departments (Table 5.2). In general, departments that most

Table 5.1   University Hospitals Admissions and Patient-Days, 1966–1970

Fiscal Year	Indigent Admissions	Indigent Patient-Days	Private Admissions	Private Patient-Days	Other Admissions*	Other Patient-Days*	Total Admissions	Total Patient-Days
1965–66	19,716	213,113	8,342	71,977	7,409	55,555	35,467	340,645
1966–67	17,345	184,727	8,498	82,898	7,860	67,540	33,703	335,165
1967–68	16,114	158,243	8,388	82,064	7,758	72,593	32,260	312,900
1968–69	16,250	160,789	8,404	87,149	8,037	69,800	32,691	317,738
1969–70	17,368	167,008	8,537	84,490	7,773	69,448	33,678	320,946

Note: All categories include acute, newborn, and housed clinic patients.
*Includes clinical pay, county clinical pay, cost, student, staff, research, and State Services for Crippled Children patients.
Source: University of Iowa Hospitals and Clinics *Annual Statistical Reports.*

clearly focused on highly specialized, or "tertiary," services were least apt to be affected by competition from other providers; the same was true of departments, especially smaller departments, with recognized expertise in selected areas. For example, with its broad array of services, some of them highly specialized and some less so, internal medicine saw a decline of 11.7 percent in patient admissions. Similarly, surgery admissions fell 15.6 percent. In contrast, neurology admissions rose 13.0 percent, while pediatrics and urology held essentially steady.

Paradoxically, the University Hospitals' gross revenues increased by 71.9 percent from 1965 to 1970, rising from $15 million to $25.8 million.[19] State appropriations increased 41.6 percent, from $8.2 million to $11.7 million, but declined from 54.9 to 45.2 percent of total revenues. By 1970, Medicare and Medicaid billings together contributed 20.2 percent of gross revenues, $4.6 million and $651,000 respectively. Symptomatic of the increase in private insurance and the already worrisome escalation in healthcare costs, private patient revenues—apart from Medicare and Medicaid—rose 134 percent between 1965 and 1970, swelling from $3.1 million to more than $7.3 million, the latter constituting 28.5 percent of total revenues. Overall, hospital expenditures rose somewhat more slowly than revenues, increasing 68 percent from $12.8 million in fiscal 1965 to $21.5 million in 1970.

The University Hospitals had long existed, in theory at least, at the apex of a statewide hospital system. However, sharply expanded public funding of healthcare in combination with federal guidelines for the regional

Table 5.2   Admissions by Clinical Department, 1966–1970

	1965–66	*1966–67*	*1967–68*	*1968–69*	*1969–70*
Dermatology	425	420	427	433	438
Internal Medicine	6,233	5,847	5,690	5,552	5,581
Neurology	1,538	1,649	1,595	1,663	1,738
Obstetrics-Gynecology	4,973	4,914	4,527	4,472	5,105
Ophthalmology	2,493	2,364	2,225	2,191	2,221
Orthopædics	2,773	2,549	2,298	2,535	2,578
Otolaryngology	3,786	3,545	3,821	3,782	3,534
Pediatrics	4,999	4,785	4,423	4,853	5,065
Surgery	5,694	5,279	4,898	4,824	4,806
Urology	2,341	2,170	2,102	2,182	2,329
Other	212	181	254	204	283
Totals	**35,467**	**33,703**	**32,260**	**32,691**	**33,678**

Source: University of Iowa Hospitals and Clinics *Annual Statistical Reports.*

organization of healthcare services accelerated the move toward a formal tertiary care mission in the late 1960s and early 1970s, a mission premised on the application of science, technology, and specialized expertise to the production and marketing of new patient services. The intensive care concept, kidney dialysis, and organ transplants were dramatic examples of that synthesis. The department of internal medicine opened a three-bed pilot intensive care unit in September 1964; in addition to its patient service function, the unit also was a training area for residents and nursing staff. An eight-bed unit to accommodate both medical and surgical patients opened in 1967, and the following year internal medicine also opened coronary care units in both University Hospitals and Veterans Administration Hospital.

Also in 1964, the Veterans Administration Hospital, which shared faculty and programs with University Hospitals, established a chronic hemodialysis program, following on work in hemodialysis begun there in the late 1950s. The University Hospitals opened its hemodialysis unit early in 1969, a unit tied to a statewide network of affiliated centers. In 1969–1970, staff at University Hospitals and Veterans Administration Hospital performed more than 2,300 hemodialysis and peritoneal dialysis procedures. Meanwhile, an interdepartmental committee began to establish guidelines for major organ transplant programs in 1969, beginning with kidney transplants. The first human kidney transplant in Iowa took place at the Veterans Administration Hospital in November 1969 and a second followed at University Hospitals two weeks later.[20] Buoyed by those successes, the transplant committee envisioned routine transplantation of a full range of organs, from liver and lungs to heart and bone marrow.[21]

The inception of Medicare and the continued rise of private insurance coverage increased the competition for patients and lent new urgency to the issue of public relations by University Hospitals. In the 1960–1961 fiscal year, according to statistics from the university's annual reports and from the American Hospital Association, the University Hospitals accounted for 9.9 percent of all patient-days in Iowa hospitals and 10.2 percent of all hospital expenditures in the state. By 1965–1966, the figures had slipped to 9.6 and 9.7 percent respectively, and in 1970, the University Hospitals claimed just 8.0 percent of patient-days in the state and 8.4 percent of hospital expenditures. Given its largely captive patient base, the hospitals had traditionally invested little energy in courting prospective patients; however, in the Medicare era, appearances, amenities, and customer service assumed an unaccustomed importance in hospitals planning and in daily routines. "Call it 'merchandising,' or what you will," Dean Robert Hardin wrote in 1968, "the cold fact is that we no longer have an assured, captive clientele."[22]

In combination with market pressures, the new emphasis on tertiary care heightened the importance of professional relations between the clinical staff of the University Hospitals and practicing physicians both in Iowa and in surrounding states. Responding to a 1968 consultant's report, officials sought to shore up the hospitals' far-flung referral network by maintaining lists of medical alumni and of physicians in Iowa and nearby states, by direct contact with all new Iowa physicians, and by installation of WATS lines to encourage telephone consultation with referring physicians.[23] The Iowa Regional Medical Program, a product of the federal heart disease, cancer, and stroke legislation of 1965, was also meant to foster closer cooperation between academic and practicing physicians and other health professionals. Despite early fears in the Iowa Medical Society that it would bring about a "complete revolution in the practice of medicine,"[24] and despite funding levels that fell far short of initial hopes, the program's continuing education and training programs provided an additional avenue for interaction between the academic medical center and community health professionals and institutions.[25]

Growth in Clinical and Basic Science Departments

Notwithstanding the modest dip in patient volume in the late 1960s, clinical staffing levels increased substantially. From 1965 to 1970 the number of tenure track faculty in the major clinical departments rose 50 percent, from 165 to 248 (Table 5.3). Several factors accounted for the increase, including President Howard Bowen's expansive vision of the university and its medical center, a vision shared by Dean Robert Hardin; the undeniable importance of practice revenues in clinical department budgets; the growing emphasis on specialized care; the expanding focus on scientific research; and Medicare requirements regarding direct faculty participation in patient care. It was significant, too, that between 1965 and 1970 the number of clinical faculty nationwide rose 49.6 percent, from 11,489 to 17,184.[26]

Some departments clearly had greater growth potential than others, with the differences having to do, among other things, with the vagaries of departmental leadership. In absolute numbers, by far the largest growth occurred in internal medicine, historically the largest of the clinical departments, where the number of tenure track positions grew more than 70 percent, from 35 to 60. In pediatrics, the second-largest of the clinical departments, tenure track faculty numbers nearly doubled from 17 to 32. It was significant, too, that the percentage increases in internal medicine and pediatrics were among the highest in the clinical departments. Moreover, internal medicine, like many other departments on a smaller scale, effectively converted significant numbers of non-tenure track positions to tenure track, as the number of clinical faculty, associates, assistants, and the like declined from 20 percent to just 4.8 percent of department faculty.

Table 5.3   College of Medicine Faculty by Department and Gender, 1965 and 1970

	1965					1970				
	Tenure Track	Other	Total	Male	Female	Tenure Track	Other	Total	Male	Female
Anatomy*	12	1	13	11	2	15	2	17	17	0
Anesthesiology	7	1	8	7	1	9	1	10	9	1
Biochemistry*	13	0	13	13	0	18	0	18	18	0
Dermatology	3	0	3	3	0	5	0	5	5	0
Internal Medicine	35	9	44	41	3	60	3	63	59	4
Microbiology*	10	0	10	10	0	12	0	12	12	0
Neurology	6	0	6	6	0	9	1	10	10	0
Obstetrics-Gynecology	9	0	9	9	0	13	0	13	12	1
Ophthalmology	8	1	9	9	0	11	7	18	17	1
Orthopædics	9	0	9	9	0	11	0	11	11	0
Otolaryngology-Oral Surgery	9	1	10	10	0	15	1	16	15	1
Pathology	11	5	16	16	0	13	1	14	13	1
Pediatrics	17	0	17	16	1	32	2	34	31	3
Pharmacology*	9	0	9	9	0	10	2	12	12	0
Program in Hospital Administration*	2	2	4	4	0	2	3	5	5	0
Physiology*	11	3	14	13	1	19	2	21	20	1
Preventive Medicine*	19	2	21	20	1	20	5	25	21	4
Psychiatry	15	6	21	19	2	23	7	30	22	8
Radiology-Radiation Research	16	0	16	16	0	19	4	23	23	0
Rehabilitation-Physical Therapy*	0	0	0	0	0	4	1	5	5	0
Surgery	16	4	20	20	0	21	8	29	28	1
Urology	4	0	4	4	0	7	0	7	7	0
Clinical Totals	165	27	192	185	7	248	35	283	262	21
Basic Science/Other	76	8	84	80	4	100	15	115	110	5
Grand Totals	**241**	**35**	**276**	**265**	**11**	**348**	**50**	**398**	**372**	**26**

*Basic Science and other departments.
Source: University of Iowa College of Medicine annual staffing lists and "Filled Positions" binders.

In keeping with the growth in clinical faculty in the college of medicine, other professional staff in the hospitals, such as nurses and dietitians, increased in number as well, albeit at slower rates. For example, the number of graduate nurses increased 13.4 percent from 1965 to 1970, from 306 to 347, while the nursing administration staff increased from eleven to sixteen, and the number of licensed practical nurses and nurse assistants rose 5.9 percent, from 439 to 465. Meanwhile, the net gain in faculty numbers in the basic science and other departments lagged somewhat behind the rate of increase in clinical areas. Indeed, the aggregate increase in basic science and other non-clinical faculty (including preventive medicine, hospital administration, and in 1970, physical therapy) from 84 to 115 amounted to 36.9 percent, compared with the 47.4 percent increase in clinical faculty, from 192 to 283.

One striking consistency in all departments was the near absence of female faculty in 1965 and the dearth of women among the new faculty recruits prior to 1970, a legacy of women's historic underrepresentation in the medical profession at large and of continued reluctance to include women in academic medicine. Of the total of 192 clinical faculty in 1965, just seven—3.6 percent—were women, a number that rose to twenty one out of 283 clinical faculty—7.4 percent—in 1970. Even fewer women held tenure track positions. Outside the clinical departments, both the numbers and percentage of women stayed essentially the same, from four (4.7 percent) in 1965 to five (4.3 percent) in 1970.

Behind the increase in clinical faculty numbers—and perhaps the contrast in clinical and non-clinical faculty growth patterns—lay a sharp rise in Medical Service Plan income across all clinical departments, despite limited gains in patient admissions and outpatient services (Table 5.4). In 1965–1966, all clinical departments garnered $2.2 million dollars from patient service; in 1969–1970, the total rose to $4.6 million. Surgery and internal medicine topped all departments in service income, notwithstanding the significant decline in patient volume in both areas, and both showed strong percentage gains as well, 112 and 121 percent respectively. Orthopædics and radiology enjoyed the largest percentage increases in income, at 161 percent. In most departments, the rapid rise in medical service income was an important recruiting tool for the college of medicine, augmenting salaries of existing faculty and also underwriting new faculty positions. Differences in the rates of faculty expansion in the various departments, however, suggest substantial interdepartmental policy differences over the balance between expansion and income augmentation.

Research funding also rose substantially in the late 1960s. Although uneven and subject to significant fluctuations from year to year, total external research funding in the college of medicine rose from an average of $3.1 million annually for 1960–1965 to $6.7 million annually for 1966–1971. Available figures for the clinical departments (Table 5.5) reflected, among other things, disparities in department size and the strength of the research culture within each department, as well as the impact of national politics in the allocation of federal research funds. Internal medicine, the largest of

Table 5.4   Medical Service Plan Income by Department, 1966 and 1970

	1965–66 ($000)	1969–70 ($000)	Increase ($000)	Percentage Increase
Anesthesiology	116	286	170	147
Dermatology	69	108	39	56
Internal Medicine	268	593	325	121
Neurology	78	182	104	133
Obstetrics-Gynecology	107	264	157	147
Ophthalmology	257	494	237	92
Oral Surgery	42	50	8	19
Orthopædics	116	303	187	161
Otolaryngology	257	445	188	73
Pathology	56	94	38	68
Pediatrics	94	175	81	86
Radiology	199	519	320	161
Surgery	359	760	401	112
Urology	185	339	154	83
Totals	**$2,215**	**$4,633**	**$2,418**	**109%**

Source: University of Iowa College of Medicine Administrative Offices.

the clinical departments, attracted more than two and one-half times the external support for research in 1960–1965 as did the next highest ranking department, neurology. Medicine widened that margin in 1966–1971, with neurology, otolaryngology, and ophthalmology in close competition for second place. Taking into account disparities in size, all four departments enjoyed roughly the same level of success in procuring research funding, and all four appear to have led other departments in developing a research culture. At the same time, internal medicine in particular was also well positioned to tap the resources of some of the oldest and best-funded NIH units, including the National Cancer Institute and National Heart Institute.

Undergraduate and Graduate Medical Education

In the mid-1960s, "health manpower" needs became a major concern at a national level. In 1966, as noted earlier, the Bureau of Health Manpower of the U.S. Public Health Service projected that one million more health-care workers—physicians, nurses, dentists, pharmacists, and allied health workers—would be needed by 1975, up from the then current total of 2.8 million.[27] The American Medical Association and the Association of

Table 5.5 College of Medicine Research Funding by Department—Five-Year Averages, 1960–1965 and 1966–1971

	1960–65 ($000)	1966–71 ($000)	Change (%)
Anatomy	101	201	+98
Anesthesiology	na	na	—
Biochemistry	273	620	+127
Dermatology	na	na	—
Internal Medicine	904	1,688	+87
Microbiology	180	160	−11
Neurology	359	570	+59
Obstetrics-Gynecology	42	119	+183
Ophthalmology	183	539	+195
Orthopædics	74	206	+178
Otolaryngology	160	556	+247
Pathology	90	70	−22
Pediatrics	223	471	+111
Pharmacology	370	115	−69
Physiology	237	622	+163
Preventive Medicine	168	616	+266
Psychiatry	86	241	+180
Radiology	252	143	−43
Surgery	195	75	−62
Urology	47	40	−15

Source: University of Iowa Division of Sponsored Programs.

American Medical Colleges joined in calling for larger enrollments in health professions schools. Eventually, medical education at the University of Iowa, both undergraduate and graduate, benefited from the federal health manpower legislation that accompanied those projections and exhortations.

President Howard Bowen, an economist with an intense interest in social policy, acknowledged in 1965 that the college of medicine carried "a heavy responsibility to respond to the clear social need for more physicians." He outlined an ambitious plan to increase enrollments through the next decade calling for a 50 percent rise in undergraduate enrollments and similar increases in the numbers of interns, residents, and fellows.[28] Responding to Bowen's message and to calls from outside the university, administrators applied for a variety of grants to finance educational programs and the construction of new facilities in medicine and in the other health science colleges as well. In 1966, the college of medicine accepted 122 applicants for the entering class, and total enrollment stood at 472. In the fall of 1970, the college greeted 145 new students, and total enrollment increased to 554. Nationally, total enrollments in four-year medical schools rose 12.4 percent, from 32,521 to 36,536, between the fall of 1966 and the fall of 1970.[29]

The expansion of undergraduate medical education at the University of Iowa and elsewhere coincided with a new wave of interest from prospective students, reversing the downward spiral in medical school applications during the 1950s. Between 1961 and 1965, the number of applicants to American medical schools rose from 14,000 to 19,000, the latter matching the record set in the early postwar period.[30] More than 24,000 would-be medical students filed nearly 134,000 applications for entry into fall 1969 classes.[31] The trend was much the same at the University of Iowa. In 1961, there were just 172 applications for the 116 positions in the entering class; in 1968, the college of medicine received 383 applications for the 127 available positions. The motives behind the renewed student interest in medical careers ranged from the sublime to the mundane, from the challenge and excitement of the new high-technology medicine to the availability of educational loans and the pressures of the military draft.

A sharp rise in applications from women added a new element to undergraduate medical education in the late 1960s and the 1970s. In 1961, only 8.4 percent of American medical students were women.[32] As late as 1965, there were just 30 women among the 424 medical students at the University of Iowa (7.1 percent), and women comprised just 6 percent of all medical students, interns, residents, and fellows in training at the college of medicine and the University Hospitals. In his 1965 president's report, Howard Bowen noted that the aggregate enrollment of women in all of the university's colleges and programs lagged well behind levels obtaining in the mid-1920s, and he suggested "a review of the admissions and recruitment policy with respect to women, not only in the Liberal Arts but also in the professional colleges."[33] A decade later, women made up 21 percent of the entering class at the University of Iowa College of Medicine, compared to 22 percent nationwide. At the same time, thanks in part to a new Educational Opportunities Program, African Americans made up 3 percent of total undergraduate enrollments.[34]

The medical student of the late 1960s was the most studied and tested of the twentieth century, as medical educators considered yet again what should be included in the curriculum and, for the first time since Abraham Flexner, how it should be taught. In its report on a 1960 inspection visit to the University of Iowa, the Council on Medical Education and Hospitals/Association of American Medical Colleges Liaison Committee had charged that the curriculum was "a ponderous one . . . developed over the years by accretion." In its recommendations, the committee called for more elective courses and less lecture time in clinical areas.[35] Conceding the validity of the committee's charge, administrators and faculty committees spent much of the following decade deciding how to address the problems.

A protracted series of committee meetings and reports led to several major changes in the undergraduate curriculum, most of them having immediate impact on teaching carried out in the University Hospitals. In its finished form, the reorganized curriculum sought once again to define an essential core of medical knowledge while, at a more practical level, it emphasized independent study, small-group instruction, and elective course work. The basic sciences curriculum shrank from four semesters to three, with the second semester of the sophomore year devoted to a revamped introductory course in clinical medicine. Junior clinical clerkships were expanded and all lectures were abolished, shifting the focus from the classroom to the patient. Senior students, meanwhile, enjoyed the option of choosing from a menu of specialized electives.

Graduate medical education at the University of Iowa also changed significantly in the late 1960s, having grown in fits and starts from the opening of the first University Hospital in 1898. In the post–World War II era, the accelerated trend toward specialization in medical practice, together with the rapid growth in federal funding of graduate training programs, provided new impetus to graduate education, an impetus that carried through the 1960s and beyond. Also, the 1965 Coggeshall Report to the Association of American Medical Colleges, buttressed by the AMA's Millis Commission Report of 1966 and recommendations from a 1968 AAMC Council of Academic Societies conference on graduate medical education, led to the gradual consolidation of graduate medical training in academic medical centers. For example, in 1974–1975, university-affiliated teaching hospitals accommodated 93 percent of all residents, compared to just 54 percent in 1960–1961.[36]

Across America, internship programs were increasingly troubled in the 1960s,[37] under attack for the often marginal experience they offered and for their duplication of much of the senior clerkship. Nationally, the number of internship positions increased from 12,954 in 1965–1966 to 15,003 in the fall of 1970. However, in 1965–1966, just 75 percent (9,670) of positions were filled; in 1970, only 72 percent (10,808) were filled. In Iowa in 1965, fifteen hospitals offered a total of 102 internships, only 62 percent (63 of 102) of them filled; in 1970, ten Iowa hospitals offered a total of 135 positions, just 56 percent (75 of 135) of which were filled, 20 percent of those by foreign-trained graduates. By the mid-1960s, the traditional rotating internship had rapidly lost favor to straight (specialty) and mixed internships, the latter a rotating internship with a substantial specialty emphasis. In the fall of 1965, 45 percent of U.S. internships were of the rotating kind, 37 percent were straight internships, and 17 percent were mixed. In 1970, rotating internships made up just 17 percent of the total, while straight internships had fallen to 25 percent, and mixed internships had risen to 57 percent.[38] In line with that trend, the University of Iowa Department of Internal Medicine, for example, instituted a straight internship program in 1965, and enrolled 15 interns in 1969–1970.[39]

Residency positions showed some similar patterns at a national level, rising from 38,558 in 1965–1966 to 46,005 in the fall of 1970. In 1965–1966, 82 percent (31,687) of positions were filled, 29 percent (9,113) of those by foreign-trained physicians; in 1970, 85 percent (39,220) of the positions offered were filled, 33 percent (12,943) of those by foreign-trained physicians. In addition, women held 3,929 residencies in 1970, 10 percent of the total positions filled. In Iowa in the fall of 1965, twelve hospitals offered 342 residency positions, 88 percent (301) of which were filled; in 1970, thirteen hospitals offered 360 positions, 89 percent (321) of them filled. In 1965–1966, the University of Iowa Hospitals numbered 242 residents and interns among its house staff. In 1969–1970, residents alone numbered 248, and the total of interns and residents stood at 294, an increase of 21.5 percent in five years, with fourteen clinical services offering resident training programs.[40] Gerhard Hartman reported in 1968 that residency evaluations placed the University Hospitals in the top ten among eighty teaching hospitals.[41]

The emergence of the fellowship was another striking change in graduate medical education in the 1960s, a change that effectively lengthened graduate medical training to six years or more and placed significant additional burdens on teaching hospitals. In the 1960s and even more so in the 1970s, fellowship training rapidly became a prerequisite to a research career and, increasingly, to specialized private practice as well. At the University of Iowa, the rapid growth of fellowship programs paralleled the rise of the research culture in the college of medicine and the emergence of the University Hospitals' tertiary care mission. Prior to 1967–1968, University Hospitals service records did not include fellows in the count of house staff, but limited fellowship programs were in operation in some departments at least from the late 1950s. Supported by training grants from the NIH and the Veterans Administration, the number of fellowship programs rose steadily through the 1960s, and, by 1969–1970, the hospitals' staff census listed 48 fellows.[42] Like most other innovations, fellowship programs were not spread uniformly among the clinical departments; the subspecialty areas of internal medicine claimed more than half the 48 fellows in 1969–1970.

Overall, the shift in focus of undergraduate medical education toward an intensified—and increasingly specialized—clinical experience and the expansion of specialized graduate medical education matched the shift toward specialized care in the University Hospitals. Elimination of the distinction between private and indigent patients broadened the variety of clinical experience, as did the rapidly expanding outpatient clinics and the first affiliations of the University Hospitals' clinical departments with satellite centers. Increasingly, however, both students and faculty noted that more complicated and unusual cases—many of them older patients suffering from the panoply of debilitating conditions associated with aging—comprised much of the patient base for clinical instruction, a problem virtually as old as the original University Hospital but one that grew more and more acute and seemed more and more to defy resolution.

The tendency toward specialization in undergraduate education and in graduate training also accompanied a continued decline, or at least the perception of a decline, in Iowa's rural healthcare services. To be sure, Iowa's healthcare services, like much of its population and economy, shifted from small towns to regional centers in the 1960s, and the political response was neither surprising nor new, with charges that the University of Iowa College of Medicine and the University Hospitals were to blame for the disappearance of small-town general practitioners. Why, one correspondent asked President Bowen, should Iowans "continue to support a medical college that has no interest in them?"[43] The issue of specialty care versus general practice was of course not peculiar to Iowa; the 1966 report of the AMA's Citizens Commission on Graduate Medical Education (Millis Report) had raised the issue at a national level.[44]

In 1968, Dean Robert Hardin answered critics—many of them supporting establishment of a competing medical school in Des Moines in addition to the existing school of osteopathic medicine—with the promise that the college of medicine would become more active in helping to improve healthcare delivery throughout the state and, further, that the college would attempt to direct more of its graduates into primary care and place them in physician-poor communities.[45] Meanwhile, the board of regents expressed "unqualified opposition to establishment of an additional medical school in Iowa for the foreseeable future."[46] As noted earlier, the college of medicine was already committed to expanding enrollments, but the dean offered little assurance that the results would satisfy critics, since expanded enrollments had not in the past had any discernible effect on the long downtrend in the rural physician population.[47]

While young men and women from rural states like Iowa enrolled in medical schools in higher proportions than did their counterparts in other states, the problem was that few of the students recruited from rural areas went on to general practice, and fewer still wanted to practice in small towns. To address the need for more family practitioners in the small towns of Iowa, the regents and the dean of the college of medicine endorsed the establishment of a family practice residency at the university in 1970, with satellite programs around the state.[48] Greeted with skepticism by many in the existing clinical departments, the family practice program ran counter to the trend toward specialization in medical education and practice. It was, however, no more than a partial solution to the problem of rural healthcare delivery, and the real test of the new program lay in its ability to stop the out-migration of Iowa-trained physicians.

Administrative Reorganizations

Early in his tenure as university president, Howard Bowen noted that "one area of the University in which administrative problems have multiplied, without commensurate additions to staff or reorganization, is the health sciences, including the four health colleges, the hospitals, and various ancillary organizations."[49] Citing the "turbulent change and uncertainty" on the health sciences campus, Bowen proposed a fundamental reorganization of a complex that accounted for half of the university's budget,[50] hoping also to further "communication and interchange between the health science campus and the rest of the university . . . to the end that we may be one, not two, universities."[51]

At the heart of Bowen's reorganization plan, implemented in July 1967 over the objections of the medical council, was a new vice-president for medical affairs who would oversee both the college of medicine and the University Hospitals, in some respects a reprise of President Hancher's ill-fated attempt to achieve administrative consolidation in 1947. To fill the new post, Bowen named the dean of the college of medicine, Robert Hardin, who had been vice-president of medical services since 1964, a position similar in name but not in authority. Under the new organizational plan, the head of the University Hospitals, now designated director rather than superintendent, and the heads of other hospital units on campus would report to the vice-president. Meanwhile, with the broadening of Hardin's jurisdiction, a newly appointed executive associate dean, Daniel Stone, inherited authority over day-to-day operations in the college of medicine, including faculty recruitment and budget matters.

Among other things, Bowen intended his reorganization to ease frictions between the college of medicine and the University Hospitals. Those frictions, of course, were virtually as old as the hospitals. Most recently, as noted in the two previous chapters, the differences between the hospital administration and the medical faculty over the proper balance among service, teaching, and research had become increasingly vexing. In 1950, Virgil Hancher had conceded the inherent conflict in the hospital's ambiguous position as a "laboratory" of the college and a "service institution" of the state,[52] but defining the problem did not resolve it. By the 1960s, that ambiguity and the conflict it engendered had grown worse. For his part, Howard Bowen came down firmly on the "laboratory" side of the debate; in keeping with his university-wide emphasis on research, he argued that the "primary purpose" of the hospitals was as "laboratory facilities for instruction and research,"[53] a position clearly opposed to the administrative independence for the hospitals that Gerhard Hartman championed and one that justified the subordination of the hospitals director to the vice-president–dean. Aiming to ease frictions, Bowen also created a new Hospital Policy Board to serve in an advisory capacity to the director and the vice-president.

On paper at least, the new organizational plan (Figure 5.1) addressed several long-standing and increasingly troublesome administrative issues. However, it also failed to address some existing problems, and it created new problems as well. For example, it did not resolve continued internal conflict over hospital operations. Late in 1968, in a meeting with President Bowen, the college of medicine executive committee voiced dissatisfaction over the "overlapping administrative jurisdictions in the University Hospitals" and the conflicts engendered by this situation. Bowen expressed hope that his recently created policy board for the University Hospitals would "alleviate this problem in the near future," but committee members Robert Hardin, Daniel Stone, and James Clifton argued that the conflict manifested itself at operational levels below that of concern to the policy board. Bowen, perhaps reflecting some of the exasperation shared by university presidents before and since, suggested that the resolution of such conflicts was up to Hardin, Stone, and hospital administrators.[54]

One weakness of the new organizational scheme was that, while the health science deans were to report to the vice-president for academic affairs, the dean of the college of medicine was himself a vice-president. More important, the reorganization plan did not have Robert Hardin's whole-hearted support.[55] The reasons for Hardin's dislike of the plan were many, including personal differences with the president and clashing administrative styles. Bowen preferred to delegate administrative responsibility, a tendency exemplified in his installation of an associate executive dean to assume the bulk of the dean's day-to-day duties. In contrast, Hardin, who was a protegé of Virgil Hancher, was less inclined to delegate his authority to subordinates, perhaps particularly so in response to presidential decree.

Like Hardin, the new executive associate dean, Daniel Stone, was an internist, and his professional interests, also like Hardin's, lay in diabetes treatment and research. Perhaps Bowen expected that association to foster a smooth working relationship between the two men, but the outcome was far from that, as Hardin continually chafed at having been pushed into

Figure 5.1   Health Sciences Administration, 1967

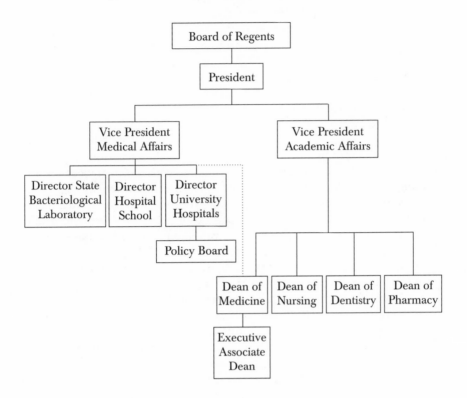

a more remote administrative role. Hardin's enforced separation from his duties as dean was not just operational but physical as well, since Stone's occupation of the dean's office exiled Hardin to Westlawn, the old nurses' dormitory. At the same time, and especially in light of Hardin's recalcitrance, the reorganization muddled the lines of communication and jurisdictional boundaries within the college of medicine and between the college and the university administration. All the while, despite repeated attempts to reach a mutually agreeable modus vivendi, the relationship between Hardin and Stone grew increasingly sour.

The medical school's manual of procedure issue—first broached in the early 1960s but dormant during the first years of Robert Hardin's tenure as dean—was a second major irritant to the vice-president. Despite Hardin's determination to maintain a strong, centralized administrative structure in the college of medicine, Bowen's concerted effort to broaden faculty participation in university affairs ultimately tipped the balance of power toward administrative reform within the college of medicine, much as it did elsewhere in the university. By the mid-1960s, faculty resentment toward the autocratic administrative structure of the college, the main outlines of which dated to the regime of Lee Wallace Dean, was once again near the crisis point, and in the summer of 1967, Robert Hardin faced not only physical isolation from the dean's office but also revival of the faculty movement to secure a manual of procedure to formalize and democratize relations and procedures within the college.

Backed by Howard Bowen and chaired by Raymond Sheets of internal medicine, a Committee on Faculty Participation, created in July 1967, submitted a draft of the manual to the university administration in October, a document based in large part on the work of its early 1960s predecessor, the Committee on Administrative Structure. Hardin did not welcome the committee's recommendations; in a November meeting with committee members, Hardin argued that few faculty were well enough informed to handle the duties and responsibilities that the proposed manual would entrust to them. At the same time, many department chairmen, resenting the implied diminution of their authority within the college, were also vehemently opposed. However, on November 30, the faculty overwhelmingly approved the manual, with 219 of 295 eligible voters returning ballots and 81 percent approving. In January 1968, President Bowen gave his final approval as well.[56]

The manual of procedure codified the faculty's right to make policy recommendations to the dean through an elected executive committee. In turn, the committee, vested with the power to elect its own officers, included representation from basic science and clinical departments and also guaranteed the participation of assistant and associate professors. Over the long term, perhaps the most important provisions in the manual were those requiring periodic reviews of departmental performance in teaching, research, and service. Those reviews commenced immediately, beginning with a scathing report on the department of surgery, compiled with the chief of surgery at the University of Florida as an outside consultant. Citing a "medical Appalachia" in the department, that report led to the resignation of the department head and amply demonstrated the power of departmental reviews as a tool of reform.

Meanwhile, the forced reorganization and reform of 1967 and 1968 made Robert Hardin's position precarious, beset on one side by a rebellious faculty seeking a formal voice in college affairs and on the other side by conservative department heads incensed that he had caved in to faculty demands. In part as a result of that, when Howard Bowen resigned as university president in 1969, and the board of regents selected his chief lieutenant and vice-president for academic affairs Willard L. ("Sandy") Boyd to succeed him, Hardin resigned as dean of the college of medicine. He became Boyd's vice-president for health affairs, an office more vaguely defined than his previous vice-presidency, with responsibility for the "coordination and administration of University Hospital and its affiliation with professional societies, government boards, colleges and universities, and other hospital facilities."

One of the many ironies of Hardin's story was that he had brought to the deanship many of the qualities that Norman Nelson had lacked. Indeed, Hardin's tenure was strikingly successful in many respects, particularly in his role in the modernization of the medical curriculum, the planning of several major construction projects on the health sciences campus, the aggressive expansion in faculty numbers and salaries, and the modernization of facilities and programs at the Veterans Administration Hospital. In addition, Hardin was elected president of the American Diabetes Association in 1969 and played an important part in the remaking of the ADA from a professional association into a voluntary health organization.

Within the University Hospitals, meanwhile, Gerhard Hartman continued as superintendent/director through the sometimes tumultuous 1960s. After more than twenty years in office, Hartman had worked with two university presidents and four medical deans. His achievements during his long tenure as head of University Hospitals reflected both his personal talents and a historical shift of executive power in American hospitals, including teaching hospitals, away from physicians and toward professional, non-physician administrators. As noted in the previous chapter, Hartman had sought from the outset of his tenure to solidify and broaden the powers of the professional hospital administrator; however, as also noted, such efforts on many occasions triggered jurisdictional disputes between the hospital administration and the college of medicine—the latest chapters in a story stretching back to the conflicts between the Sisters of Mercy and the medical faculty in the 1870s.

From the first, Hartman had sought to use the power of his personality and his direct access to President Virgil Hancher, the regents, and the state legislature to widen the superintendent's authority. In legislative hearings, his credentials as an academician in the field of hospital management and his great personal charm—that of a "showman," according to colleagues—served him well. However, perhaps worn down by the resistance he encountered, Hartman had increasingly relied on his deputy Glen Clasen, in today's parlance his chief operating officer, to assume responsibility for hospital operations and eventually for many larger issues as well. In 1969, John Colloton, assistant director of the hospitals, assumed Clasen's position as associate director, and Clasen, ailing from lung cancer and unable to work at full capacity, became consultant director.[57] In important respects,

Colloton became the de facto director of the hospitals, as Clasen had before him, presiding over a rapidly expanding healthcare enterprise. Between the 1960–1961 fiscal year and 1969–1970, the roster of full-time hospitals staff—from physicians and nurses to clerks and housekeepers—rose 50 percent, from 1,625 to 2,439. At the same time, expenditures for professional care rose 175 percent, from $5.1 million to $14 million, while expenditures for administration rose 207 percent, from $672,000 to $2.061 million.

Colloton also headed the hospital advisory committee made up of representatives from the hospitals' administration, the clinical departments, and the dean of medicine's office. Overcoming protests that it duplicated the functions of the medical council, the committee became a provisional "board of directors," an internal policymaking body for the University Hospitals and an important communications link between the hospitals and the clinical faculty, its importance increasing in direct proportion to the growing complexity of hospitals operations and also in response to the administrative reorganizations of 1967–1968. Through its various subcommittees, the hospital advisory committee also shared in planning the initial stages of the hospitals' expansion described in the next section. The committee's deliberations and reports dealt with several key policy issues as well, including upgrading and expanding services in line with the tertiary care ideal, consolidating clinics and inpatient accommodations, reorganizing medical services to create a single class of care, making the medical center a regional anchor under the federal Regional Medical Program, and supporting the establishment of a kidney transplant program.[58]

Howard Bowen's initial appointment of Robert Hardin as vice-president of medical services and, in 1967, as vice-president for medical affairs further diminished Hartman's administrative role, ending Hartman's direct formal access to the president and giving Hardin responsibility for representing the medical center before the board of regents. To be sure, Hartman continued in some respects to operate as before, in particular traveling to Des Moines to appear at legislative hearings, including hearings regarding hospital appropriations,[59] but it was Hardin, alone and in the company of President Bowen, who reported to the regents on fiscal and planning matters. For their part, the regents generally approved what Hardin asked of them. Indeed, the board of regents dissolved its once powerful finance committee in 1966 and turned over most of the committee's functions to the university presidents—functions, in the case of the University of Iowa Hospitals, that devolved upon Hardin.

While that administrative arrangement appeared to eliminate many of the ambiguities in the relationship between the college of medicine dean and the hospitals administration, it did not, of course, survive Howard Bowen's presidency. In fact, it lasted no longer than had Virgil Hancher's administrative experiment in the late 1940s. The inauguration of a new university administration in 1969, followed by Hardin's resignation as dean and the elimination of the vice-presidency he had held—and followed, in turn, by Hartman's resignation in 1971—left to Hardin's and Hartman's successors the problem of forging a new working relationship between the college and the hospitals.

Planning an Expanded Medical Center

In the mid-1960s, the University Hospitals' physical plant was, apart from minor cosmetics, not much changed since the late 1920s. In its July 1963 report, the Division of Hospital Service of the Iowa State Department of Health cited the hospitals' shortcomings in recommending creation of "a long-range master plan . . . for guiding future planned adjustment and expansion."[60] That assessment came as no surprise to faculty and administrators, most of whom knew that the clinical departments were in a condition of "accelerated physical deterioration" that made modernization "a matter of the direst urgency."[61] In a 1966 study, Superintendent Gerhard Hartman argued that the hospitals' facilities were, in large part, outdated, a problem made worse by the accelerated pace of obsolescence in postwar healthcare. "According to current standards of construction, technology, fire safety, mechanical and electrical equipment and functional lay-out," Hartman wrote in his report, few beds were "considered to be of acceptable conforming quality for modern hospital operations."[62] Even so, University Hospitals continued to operate under the sanction of the Department of Health and the Joint Commission on Accreditation of Hospitals. In view of that, the degree of obsolescence may well have been overstated; the label "nonconforming" was a potent weapon wielded by University Hospitals supporters, as by their counterparts all across America, in strengthening their case for capital replacement.

Advocates of modernization at the University Hospitals also raised the specter of competition. In April 1967, associate superintendent Glen Clasen warned President Bowen that "if we are to stay competitive with the Midwest medical centers and large teaching hospitals, we must make an early start on the replacement of our outmoded patient facilities."[63] In the absence of improvements, medical centers in neighboring states—such as the Mayo Clinic and the University of Minnesota to the north or Clarkson and Methodist Hospitals in Omaha to the west—would cut into the University Hospitals' regional patient bases. Gerhard Hartman had expressed much the same sentiment in his 1966 study, noting that "the evolution of Medicare and its accompanying 'free choice' and semi-private accommodation provisions" forced the University Hospitals "to provide private patient facilities and modern supporting services for patients who are referred here because of the superior specialty level care available within the medical center." "If such accommodations are not available," Hartman continued, "there will be decreasing ability to attract that patient load necessary to meet the institution's objectives."[64]

Noting also the new hospital standards specified under Medicare legislation, Hartman argued in favor of a new hospital rather than a piecemeal expansion like that of the original University Hospital in the early twentieth century. The existing open wards, clinical areas, and operating rooms, he maintained, were not readily adaptable to modern standards. Instead, Hartman counseled "an entirely new teaching hospital to meet the University Hospitals' specialty service role to the State of Iowa."[65] For a building site, Hartman proposed the university's campus at Oakdale, on the grounds of the recently phased-out state tuberculosis sanitarium, four miles from the current University Hospitals.[66] The college of medicine's medical center building committee and the college's executive committee had already rejected the Oakdale move as too expensive and too damaging to the working relationship with the Veterans Administration Hospital.[67] Nonetheless, in a newspaper interview in May 1966, Hartman mentioned the Oakdale site and estimated the cost of a new medical center at $63 million, a story that drew the ire of Howard Bowen, a not unfamiliar situation for the sometimes outspoken hospitals superintendent. Bowen was just then preparing ten-year capital requests for the regents and moved quickly to mend the damage, explaining that the article was "based on the totally unauthorized release of a document." Moreover, he said, "we have no intention of starting from scratch with our medical center, and we have no institutional position whatever on future needs for hospitals." In conclusion, Bowen expressed his regret over "the unwarranted release of what was a mere study document expressing the views of one person."[68]

The episode was an awkward one for Howard Bowen because, despite his contrary claim, the president was formulating a plan for a coordinated development of the entire health science campus as part of a larger plan of university-wide expansion. Bowen saw the arrival of the baby boom generation on the nation's college campuses and the rapid expansion of federal programs in support of higher education as an opportunity for major growth and development at the university as a whole, and in two May 1966 memos, he notified the regents of the need to increase the estimates contained in an existing ten-year capital improvement plan. Bowen identified $115 million in capital needs, with the hospital accounting for $48 million of that total, some of it occasioned by "immense new requirements" mandated under Medicare.[69]

In the meantime, the question of relocating the medical campus seems to have been settled, at least in Howard Bowen's mind, as early as 1965, based in part on an unpromising September 1964 survey of the Oakdale facility.[70] In response to questions posed by the Iowa City mayor in December 1965, Bowen stated that the university wished to have a large area along Newton Road between Riverside Drive and Woolf Avenue vacated for the expected "enormous expansion of the Medical Center" fueled by federal funds for medical education and biomedical research. Bowen noted also that the university expected to develop south of Melrose Avenue, and thus did not wish to see that road become an arterial route.[71] In 1966, in conjunction with planning for a new basic sciences building, an architectural consulting firm—Sasaki, Walker, and Associates—endorsed the plan to continue development of the health sciences campus on the west bank of the Iowa River,[72] and Bowen concurred.

The arguments against relocating the medical campus, as Bowen listed them, centered on issues of cost, geographic unity with the rest of the university and the Veterans Administration Hospital, and general aesthetic considerations. Bowen also approved the Sasaki firm's "land-use scheme" as the "general basis for planning of the Medical Center,"[73] a scheme that had the University Hospitals expanding to the south with the other health science buildings—including the basic science building and new facilities to house the college of nursing, the college of dentistry, and the health sciences library—fanning out to the north, east, and west. By the time Bowen left office in 1969, several projects were either completed, under construction, or already funded, including the Wendall Johnson Speech and Hearing Center, the College of Nursing, the Basic Medical Science Building (later named for Bowen), the Dental Science Building, and the Health Sciences Library (later named for Robert Hardin).

Expansion of the University of Iowa Hospitals, particularly on the scale envisioned by Bowen and others, posed special problems. Most important, such expansion would be an ongoing process requiring repeated capital infusions, and it would be enormously expensive. In addition, a sharp reduction in federal grants and state appropriations for hospital construction in the late 1960s and the 1970s compounded financing problems. Across America in 1969, federal grants covered 13 percent of teaching hospitals' construction costs, while support from state and local governments covered an additional 24 percent, but those numbers fell to 1 percent and 7 percent respectively in 1977. During that period, the proportion of teaching hospitals' construction costs covered by debt rose from 20 percent to 67 percent.[74]

Many University of Iowa officials recognized early on the attractions of debt financing as an alternative in facilitating long-range planning. In his 1966 biennial report to the regents, Howard Bowen criticized the customary manner of university capital development, pointing out that "the gestation period for a large building program is lengthy because vast amounts of time are needed for planning, for seeking federal and other funds, and for construction." He went on to point out that another source of delay had been a long-standing legislative policy that planning for buildings should not be started until appropriations had been made.[75] This traditional approach of appropriate-and-build, he noted, was a dilatory process and detrimental to long-term planning. Freed from such uncertainties, university planners could move forward more quickly with modernization of the hospitals.[76]

At its May 1966 meeting, the board of regents instructed the presidents of the three state universities to investigate the limits of borrowing for long-range construction.[77] That suggestion led to plans, developed by Robert Hardin, Howard Bowen, and John Colloton, that would, in effect, provide independent bonding authority for the University Hospitals, for which the growing stream of revenue from private insurance and Medicare could generate enough income to finance borrowings and to build up reserves. A year later the hospital administration reported that the University Hospitals' income was sufficient to finance borrowings of $10 to $12 million. Such a sum, combined with state appropriations and federal grants, "would provide a new outpatient clinic, new operating rooms, a new x-ray department, and the replacement of up to 300 beds," for a total estimated cost of $17 million.[78]

In the spring of 1967, Hardin, Hartman, Colloton, and Max Hawkins, the university's legislative representative, met with members from both houses of the Iowa General Assembly to answer questions regarding a proposed bonding bill.[79] On the whole, the concept appealed to most legislators since it cost the legislature nothing at all, and the 62nd General Assembly adopted Senate File 532 in June authorizing the State Board of Regents to borrow money for capital expansion and development at the University Hospitals. Signed into law by Governor Harold Hughes, the act empowered the regents, with the legislature's approval in each instance, to borrow against future hospitals revenues. One board of regents member objected at a June 1968 meeting that the General Assembly ought to "participate biennially as a check" on debt financing, but President Bowen deflected his criticism with the observation that the legislature had trouble thinking long-term. Besides, Bowen explained, if bonding authority had been in place fifteen years earlier, the present needs would not be so great.[80] In the end, the sustained rise in patient revenues at the University of Iowa Hospitals and Clinics, revenues chiefly derived from third-party sources, provided the key to long-term financing and planning for hospitals expansion. Rosemary Stevens describes a similar phenomenon at the national level, as Medicare reimbursements powered a trend "toward borrowing funds for hospital capital projects" as government and philanthropic support diminished.[81]

There remained the problem of achieving a working consensus among the many interested parties—including the university administration, the hospitals administration, the dean of the college of medicine, and the medical staff—on planning issues. Already in 1966, Robert Hardin had appointed a planning council, with Gerhard Hartman as chairman; however, the council's work was crippled by its ill-defined mission and by Hardin's insistence on retaining "overall responsibility for planning of the hospital."[82] Within a year, Hardin disbanded the council.[83] Whether by choice or by default, associate superintendent Glen Clasen then assumed, along with Hardin, a major planning role. By December 1967, university officials had signed contracts with two architectural firms, Skidmore, Owings and Merrill of Chicago, and Hansen, Lind, Meyer of Iowa City. Shortly thereafter, the hospital administrative staff, led by Clasen, and four faculty planning subcommittees of what was then called the Executive Planning Committee presented the architects with a comprehensive list of needs for new clinical facilities.[84] The 424-page document, *A Perspective for Planning the University of Iowa Hospitals and Clinics*, was designed as a working document for "architects, engineers, systems consultants, faculty, university officials, state board of regents, members of the Iowa General Assembly, governmental officials, capital financiers, and others concerned with planning."[85]

Exhaustive though it was, the *Perspective for Planning* nettled a substantial segment of the medical faculty who felt that their voices had not been represented in its compilation. Despite the appointment of planning committees, they complained, the "faculty has had little official authoritative information about hospital planning, and decisions have been made without opportunity for careful evaluation by the faculty."[86] Part of the larger movement for a greater faculty voice in college of medicine affairs, that protest was defused, after a meeting between the dissenters and Robert Hardin, with the appointment of Paul Seebohm of internal medicine as a liaison to Clasen. Nonetheless, Hardin, as vice-president for medical affairs as well as dean, retained for himself the place of first importance. "Although the faculty will have a major role in planning the building together with the university and hospital administration," Hardin advised, "neither the faculty nor the hospital administrator has an executive role in this matter."[87] Consequently, it fell to Seebohm and Clasen, who were in daily contact, to relay the desires of fourteen specialized committees offering input to Hardin and the architects.[88] Although cumbersome, the device—in conjunction with the internal reorganization of the college itself—seems to have quieted criticism, and the college of medicine's executive committee, in its 1968 annual report, noted that "planning appears to be proceeding rather well." In particular, the committee commended the "heavy involvement of the faculty" for having "generated a high interest in the planning program" and helping "to smooth out many of the irritative foci that were present a few months ago."[89]

Between 1968 and 1969, architects prepared plans for a twin-tower hospital addition that eventually would replace all of the functions of the General Hospital and the Children's Hospital and would bring the University Hospitals up to standards. The plan projected expansion to the south of the General Hospital in two phases, the first to be completed in 1972 and the second in 1980. When completed, the hospital would encompass 1.5 million square feet and accommodate 1,000 beds, reaching the desired teaching hospital ratio of 1,500 square feet per bed. The first phase of expansion, encompassing 466,000 square feet in all, was an eight-floor tower with "a large, coordinated outclinic, a large, integrated operating suite, an emergency clinic, a radiology suite, and 400 inpatient beds."[90] The second phase was a similar eight-floor tower. Together the "twin towers" carried a $17.5 million price tag, $11 million projected from revenue bonds, $1.55 million from the hospital building usage fund, and $5 million from federal funds, with no contribution from the state.[91]

By early 1969, plans for the proposed hospital addition had grown by a third and the total cost had nearly doubled to $34.2 million, in part because of a projected 40 percent rise in construction costs.[92] Planners forged ahead nonetheless, and Robert Hardin cultivated his contacts in Washington, DC, to firm up federal support. In 1970, cost projections increased further to $40 million, and university officials applied for a federal construction grant of $25.1 million under the Health Professions Facility Support Program,[93] with the balance of construction funds to come through borrowing ($12.9 million) and from the hospital's cash reserves ($2 million). In a cover letter accompanying the 580-page federal grant application, Hardin emphasized the University of Iowa's compliance with the federal health manpower build-up. "The application," he wrote, "is based upon a major expansion of the College of Medicine from an entering class of 122 to one of 175." Hardin also promised "an augmentation of our programs in intern and residency training, post-doctoral advanced education and continuing education."[94]

The application won approval without reductions or deletions. Yet Hardin—and no doubt many others as well—had misread the intentions of the Nixon administration, whose budget reduction program specifically excluded teaching hospitals from federal construction grants, apparently on the assumption, in Hardin's estimation, "that we had too many hospital beds in this country now."[95] With that realization, years of organizing and planning for hospital expansion collapsed virtually overnight, even as two new health sciences colleges—nursing and dentistry—were under construction and as medical school enrollments increased, with both developments promising greater demands on hospital facilities. For the time being, only a coordinating committee remained in place to examine smaller projects to be funded primarily with bond revenues.

Growth in the College of Medicine

Howard Bowen's resignation as university president in 1969 inaugurated a remarkable transition at the University of Iowa medical center. Along with a new university president, Willard Boyd, came, in rapid succession, John W. Eckstein's selection in 1970 as dean of the college of medicine and the elevation of John W. Colloton to the office of hospitals director. All three men were appointed from within, Boyd having been Bowen's vice-president for academic affairs, Eckstein a professor of internal medicine, and Colloton the hospitals associate superintendent. Each had also gained substantial experience within his administrative milieu; each came to his new position with a clear agenda; and both Eckstein and Colloton sought additional autonomy, in contrast to the "one university" concept that President Bowen had attempted to institute.

In important respects, John Eckstein's appointment as dean of the college of medicine in 1970 marked the triumph of a new research-oriented agenda over an older service-oriented tradition. Author of many scientific papers, recipient of an American Heart Association Established Investigator Award and a U.S. Public Health Service Research Career Award, and with long experience in regional and national professional groups, Eckstein himself had compiled an impressive research record during the period from the late 1950s to the late 1960s when the college's commitment to research was less than wholehearted. In part as a result of that experience, Eckstein had sought and received Willard Boyd's assurance on a number of important points during negotiations over the deanship, including the provision of additional space and funds "to staff the administrative offices of the College at an appropriate level," enunciation of a "clear understanding of the responsibilities of the Dean and the relationships among the College, the Hospitals, and the Central Administrative Offices of the University," and appointment of a full-time associate dean. Eckstein also asked for President Boyd's "complete backing" in dealing with troublesome department heads, some of whom had opposed his selection as dean and would likely resist his administrative agenda, and a "moral commitment" to fund all of the college's programs and operations, filling "the voids which exist in a number of major teaching departments."[96]

Eckstein's reference to a "clear understanding" regarding administrative relationships was, in part at least, aimed at securing assurance that the vice-president for health affairs would have no direct oversight over the college's internal operations. In the new administrative structure, the dean was to have authority over faculty appointments and educational and research programs, student admissions, budgeting and fiscal management, space assignments within the college, and internal planning and resource allocation, including "establishing the sizes of various departments." In all of the above areas, the dean was to report to the university provost, as was the case with all other health science colleges; however, in matters relating to internal planning he was expected to "inform" the vice-president for health affairs.[97]

Similarly, Eckstein's stipulation that Boyd give him "complete backing" in confronting problems "which concern attitudes of some of the department heads" marked the beginning of a concerted effort to strengthen the dean's hand in dealing with the long-standing problem of independent-minded department chiefs. In that vein, Eckstein served notice to the medical council in 1971 that traditional, informal administrative practices were "no longer acceptable" in light of the college's growth and increased responsibilities. Moreover, he insisted that all decisions, particularly those relating to external funding, go through the dean's office.[98] In 1974, he chided department heads about departures from university policy, specifically their reluctance to implement merit system policies and procedures recently approved by the board of regents for clerical and service workers. "Direct opposition to established policy is inappropriate," he told the medical council, and he threatened that his general preference to leave "as much power as possible at the department level" was subject to change should department heads fail to comply with university policy on such matters."[99]

Eckstein's apparently contentious relations with at least some department heads were accompanied by unusually high turnover rates among their ranks. In December 1973, the dean reported the loss of 11 of 21 department heads.[100] Included in the total were the heads of six clinical departments who had left the college between 1970 and 1973. Some of those were simply cases of older men stepping down after long service; William B. Bean of internal medicine, for example, retired in 1970 after 22 years as department chair. In surgery, on the other hand, turmoil had begun with Robert Tidrick's ouster in 1969 as a result of the devastating internal review mentioned earlier. Tidrick's successor, Robert E. Condon, left after just fourteen months, and the situation stabilized only with the appointment of Sidney E. Ziffren in 1972.

Finally, Eckstein's insistence that President Boyd seek higher state appropriations for the college stemmed from fears that it would not be able to carry out its commitments under existing arrangements. First, the college faced a legislated mandate to establish a department of family practice, meant to address the loss of general practitioners across the state. Second, prodded by the central administration and by conditions attached to federal undergraduate training grants, the college was committed to increasing enrollments, while at the same time working to implement curriculum changes requiring both expansion of the basic sciences and the appointment of additional clinical faculty. Last, Eckstein foresaw rising demand for patient service in the University Hospitals, a condition likewise demanding additional clinical faculty.[101]

Fiscal issues proved among the most challenging during John Eckstein's early years in the deanship. As recently as the mid-1960s, it had appeared to most observers at the University of Iowa and elsewhere that federal support for medical education and research might well continue to grow indefinitely, but by the early 1970s, that was clearly not to be the case. By and large, the quality of research supported by federal funds was undisputed; moreover, advances in understanding, diagnosing, and ameliorating conditions such as arthritis, kidney disease, juvenile diabetes, cancer, heart disease, and mental illness seemed, at least to most observers, to justify the cost of research and training programs alike. Already in 1967, Thomas Turner, dean of the Johns Hopkins University medical faculty, could claim—with some justification— that it was "virtually impossible to put a dollar figure" on the fruits of medical scientific research since the inception of NIH extramural programs.[102] Still, by the end of the 1960s, not all were convinced of the balance of costs and benefits in the vastly expanded research and training effort, and some who accepted the virtues of federally funded research questioned the distribution of benefits. The result, in the early 1970s, was a substantial slowing of the rate of growth in federal expenditures in support of medical scientific research and training.

In 1973, Eckstein warned the college of medicine's executive committee of "seriously reduced" federal funding in the near future, and in November of that year an official of the Department of Health, Education and Welfare announced that the federal government would cut medical education grants in response to a doctor surplus projected for the 1980s.[103] The years from 1973 to 1975 saw significant cutbacks in college of medicine grants both for education and for research. From 1973 to 1974, research grants fell from $15.5 million to $12.77 million; from 1974 to 1975, training grants fell from $3.57 million to $2 million.[104] Thus, by the mid-1970s, external funding, particularly NIH funding, had come to seem a shaky foundation for long-term growth, forcing the college of medicine to turn to the state for supplementary funding. In late 1973, the college received a special appropriation to hire the new faculty needed to meet the demands imposed by increased enrollments and curricular revision, testament to the strong support of the college on the part of President Boyd and the university administration.[105]

Despite the sometimes grim outlook early in the 1970s, the aggressive expansion of the college of medicine that began in the late 1960s carried through the next decade. Total clinical faculty numbers increased 23.4 percent, from 329 in 1975 to 406 in 1980, while faculty in basic science and other departments increased 9.7 percent, from 123 to 135 (Table 5.6). One important change in clinical areas was the addition of fifteen family practice faculty, ten of whom were tenure track; the department also recruited more than 100 community physicians throughout the state to instruct and supervise resident doctors in family practice. Some older departments turned in impressive growth rates, including pediatrics, which increased from 40 to 60 members; internal medicine, which increased from 73 to 94 faculty; and anesthesiology, which tripled in size from 10 to 30 faculty. The remaining clinical departments showed much smaller growth, and some in fact declined slightly in size. Meanwhile, anatomy, physiology, preventive medicine, and hospital and health administration accounted for nearly all of the growth in basic science departments and allied programs.

Overall, external funding for research and training, more than 80 percent of which came from federal agencies, outpaced the growth in faculty numbers, as it rose from $11.1 million in fiscal 1970 to $17.5 million in 1975 and $32.8 million in 1980—a total gain of almost 194 percent over the ten-year period. Research funding increased substantially in nearly all departments, clinical and non–clinical alike (Table 5.7), although with some striking disparities among departments. The increasing frequency of larger grants was also striking, as the number of faculty members receiving grants of $100,000 or more increased from just 8 to 95 between 1962–1963 and 1980–1981. In 1982, college of medicine gifts and grants for all purposes— research, teaching, and capital development—accounted for 56 percent of all external support at the University of Iowa. Overall, the rapid growth in research funding attests to the maturation of the research enterprise, with allowance for significant variations among departments.

In its increasing specialization, medical scientific research at the University of Iowa paralleled the University Hospitals' new tertiary care mission. By and large, the policies of federal granting agencies encouraged the trend toward specialized research and, at the same time, the trend toward research into the fine details of molecular structure and function. Moreover, research potential, defined in part as the ability to attract grant money, became a critical factor in the recruitment of new faculty, weakening the traditional relationships between faculty numbers and patient service and teaching responsibilities. Simultaneously, the emphasis on grantsmanship as a measure of faculty worth fostered an entrepreneurial ethos that, to some

Table 5.6   College of Medicine Faculty by Department, 1975 and 1980

Department	1975			1980		
	Tenure	Other	Total	Tenure	Other	Total
Anesthesia	10.00		10.00	24.00	6.00	30.00
Dermatology	5.00	2.00	7.00	7.00		7.00
Family Practice	10.50	5.00	15.50	11.00	7.00	18.00
Internal Medicine	68.00	5.00	73.00	76.50	18.00	94.50
Neurology	11.70	1.00	12.70	15.10		15.10
Obstetrics-Gynecology	12.00		12.00	14.80	2.80	17.60
Ophthalmology	13.70	4.00	17.70	14.00	4.00	18.00
Orthopædics	9.00	3.00	12.00	13.40		13.40
Otolaryngology	14.10		14.10	12.70		12.70
Pathology	17.70	6.00	23.70	18.60	9.00	27.60
Pediatrics	38.00	1.80	39.80	54.50	5.60	60.10
Psychiatry	24.00		24.00	25.00	2.00	27.00
Radiology	20.00	6.40	26.40	22.00	2.00	24.00
Surgery	26.00	8.00	34.00	30.10	3.00	33.10
Urology	6.00	1.00	7.00	8.00		8.00
Subtotal Clinical	285.70	43.20	328.90	346.70	59.40	406.10
Anatomy	18.00	5.50	23.50	24.30	3.50	27.80
Biochemistry	18.00	1.00	19.00	18.00		18.00
Microbiology	17.00	5.00	22.00	18.00		18.00
Pharmacology	15.00		15.00	14.00		14.00
Physiology	16.70	3.00	19.70	22.60	1.00	23.60
Preventive Medicine	15.00	1.00	16.00	20.10		20.10
Subtotal Basic Science	99.70	15.50	115.20	117.00	4.50	121.50
Hospital and Health Administration	2.00		2.00	5.00	1.00	6.00
Physical Therapy	4.00	2.00	6.00	5.00	2.00	7.00
Physician Assistant Program				1.00		1.00
Subtotal Allied Programs	6.00	2.00	8.00	11.00	3.00	14.00
Grand Total	**391.40**	**60.70**	**452.10**	**474.70**	**66.90**	**541.60**

Note: "Tenure" includes the ranks of professor, associate professor, and assistant professor; "Other" includes the ranks of instructor, lecturer, associate, and fellow associate.
Source: Filled Positions binder, University of Iowa College of Medicine.

extent, undermined collegiality and, from the 1950s, played a significant part in weakening the central authority of the dean of the college of medicine.

Table 5.7   College of Medicine Gift, Grant, and Contract Funding by Department, 1970–1980

Department	Funding in Dollars for Fiscal Year		
	1970	1975	1980
Anatomy	249,590	239,381	845,371
Anesthesia	5,090	1,098	500
Biochemistry	557,759	944,251	2,059,541
Cardiovascular Center			2,204,629
Clinical Research Center			45,078
Dermatology	6,200		290,076
Family Practice		1,800	640,078
Hospital and Health Administration	11,647		311,810
Hospital School	35,485	74,195	158,931
Internal Medicine	1,575,381	3,888,394	7,683,571
Medical College Administration	2,004,990	4,056,560	3,182,941
Microbiology	115,258	379,960	1,188,389
Neurology	522,769	725,573	115,732
Obstetrics-Gynecology	98,046	447,222	558,435
Ophthalmology	677,409	475,099	158,493
Orthopaedic Surgery	176,249	377,760	872,789
Otolaryngology	519,921	760,399	441,729
Pathology	28,394	39,044	158,667
Pediatrics	450,141	1,167,312	3,880,937
Pharmacology	1,341,798	1,429,073	1,889,330
Physical Therapy		200,717	114,155
Physiology	428,803	752,042	1,134,050
Preventive Medicine	976,993	420,467	2,306,466
Psychiatry	277,104	647,075	1,612,866
Radiation Research Laboratory		132,441	252,853
Radiology	112,157	6,000	219,062
Surgery	49,154	22,560	107,267
Urology	25,724	77,275	291,722
College of Medicine Total	**11,135,727**	**17,545,078**	**32,728,868**

Source: Approved and funded gift, grant, and contract reports, University of Iowa College of Medicine.

Notwithstanding the tendency toward increased specialization, the new research culture provided an environment in which new communities of interest crystallized around specific research problems. Indeed, beginning in the late 1960s, federal research policy explicitly, if only in limited degree, endorsed such interdisciplinary collaboration. At the University of Iowa, one result was a sharp increase in the number of joint appointments among medical faculty, from 11 in 1960 to 25 already in 1970, including growing cross-fertilization between basic science and the clinical areas. The earliest formal interdisciplinary site at the University of Iowa was the Clinical Research Center, established with NIH funding in 1961 in response to concerns over the depreciation of clinical research and the need to encourage collaborative research. Initially a cramped eight-bed unit, the center added facilities and personnel in the mid-1960s, and by the end of the decade, the center's research projects involved some sixty researchers from eight departments. The Clinical Research Center proved to be the first and largest of several new organizational structures that, like the Cardiovascular Research Center established in 1974, cut across older boundaries separating departments and disciplines in the 1970s and later. By the early 1980s, a major part of the external funding flowing into the college of medicine in fact supported a growing range of such interdisciplinary projects.

Throughout the 1970s and into the 1980s, U.S. Public Health Service tabulations of research awards by the National Institutes of Health placed the University of Iowa College of Medicine significantly below the largest Big Ten research universities and, predictably enough, further still behind institutions such as Harvard and Johns Hopkins. The former, in particular, was testimony to the university's late start in the research race. In 1970, the University of Iowa's $4.2 million in NIH research funding represented just 42.9 percent of the $9.8 million in awards at the University of Wisconsin, 48.3 percent of the $8.7 million at the University of Minnesota, 53.2 percent of the $7.9 million at the University of Michigan, 32.1 percent of the $13.1 million at Harvard, and 40.0 percent of the $10.5 million at Johns Hopkins. By 1980, the University of Iowa was, in most cases, closing the gap in percentage terms, if not in dollars. The university's $19 million in awards in 1980 equaled 56.9 percent of Wisconsin's total, 52.9 percent of Minnesota's, 62.5 percent of Michigan's, 48.6 percent of Harvard's, and 36.8 percent of total research awards at Johns Hopkins.[106]

Medical Service Plan income was a second major engine of growth for clinical departments in the 1970s (Table 5.8). Moreover, with increases of 300–400 percent commonplace among the departments, patient income was even more important to departmental vitality than in the previous decade. As college of medicine expenditures rose from $5.9 million in 1970–1971 to $71.6 million in 1979–1980, Medical Service Plan income accounted for some 30 percent of total college expenditures by the end of the decade, compared to 45 percent from gifts and grants and 25 percent from the university's general fund. Although welcome, the strong growth in Medical Service Plan income also had its negative side, for it meant increasing dependence on the part of individual departments and the college as a whole on patient fees. Many faculty, both clinical and non-clinical, were less than

Table 5.8   Medical Service Plan Income by Department, 1971–1981

	1970–71 ($000)	1975–76 ($000)	1980–81 ($000)	Increase, 1971–1981 ($000)	Increase, 1971–1981 (%)
Anesthesiology	471	1,219	2,763	2,292	487
Dermatology	129	205	555	426	330
Family Practice	na	213	439	439	na
Internal Medicine	588	1,442	3,847	3,259	554
Neurology	190	575	1,100	910	479
Obstetrics-Gynecology	284	671	1,339	1,055	371
Ophthalmology	510	1,342	2,982	2,472	485
Oral Surgery	59	277	332	273	463
Orthopædics	389	708	1,251	862	222
Otolaryngology	493	819	2,214	1,721	349
Pathology	326	619	1,275	949	291
Pediatrics	176	594	1,813	1,637	930
Radiology	566	986	1,955	1,389	245
Surgery	1,025	2,560	4,979	3,954	386
Urology	434	679	853	419	97
Totals	**$5,663,000**	**$12,909,000**	**$28,265,000**	**$22,602,000**	**399**

Source: University of Iowa College of Medicine administrative offices.

enthusiastic over that trend, observing that it represented a throwback to the service-oriented 1950s, detracted from the college's hard-won research mission, and cast a pall over the future by complicating the recruitment of new faculty put off by the demands of patient care.

The Hospitals Move toward Independence

Upon succeeding Gerhard Hartman as director of the University Hospitals, John Colloton, like John Eckstein, took great care in establishing the precise boundaries of his authority within the administrative hierarchy of the health sciences campus and the university at large. From a historical perspective, Colloton had good reason to do so, perhaps more than Eckstein. With his appointment as hospitals director, Colloton also became assistant vice-president for health affairs, reporting to the university president through the vice-president for health affairs, not through the dean of the college of medicine. Colloton's position was a notable departure from past practice, and his salary, which he considered an important symbol of his status, made him the fourth-highest paid administrator on the campus.

President Boyd did retain one important element of the previous administrative structure, albeit in a watered-down form, naming Robert Hardin his vice-president for health affairs. With formal responsibility for the University Hospitals, Psychopathic Hospital, the Hospital School, the Oakdale alcoholism unit, and the state hygienic laboratory, Hardin's role, in theory at least, was that of central coordinator and supervisor, with specific authority over space allocation within the hospitals complex. Hardin also held primary responsibility for the hospitals' relations with the board of regents and the state legislature, and he took considerable initiative, too, with regard to planning. Meanwhile, his role with regard to the college of medicine, as noted earlier, was more circumscribed, embracing planning and external relations.[107]

Over the long term, Boyd appears to have valued Hardin's services, praising him in 1974—on the occasion of Hardin's resignation—for helping to hold in check the centrifugal forces tending toward decentralization and fragmentation within what Boyd called the modern "multiversity."[108] Other observers were less certain of the virtues of the complicated organizational structure on the health sciences campus. After reviewing the college of medicine in the spring of 1971, the Liaison Committee on Medical Education noted its concern regarding the "diverse, and potentially divisive" administrative relationships among the dean of the college of medicine, the university provost, the vice-president for health affairs, and the hospitals director. The committee specifically cited the practice by the clinical department heads of negotiating directly with the hospitals administration, rather than the vice-president, over issues of space allocation. Overall, however, the committee concluded that the positive working relationship between the dean of the college of medicine and the hospitals director mitigated the awkwardness inherent in the structure.[109] By 1975, Boyd himself was convinced of the redundancy and eliminated the vice-presidency in the wake of Robert Hardin's resignation.[110]

Meanwhile, John Colloton endured five months of protracted and difficult negotiations before gaining his appointment as hospitals director. On June 11, 1971, Gerhard Hartman announced his resignation as hospitals director effective August 1, although retaining his position as head of the graduate program in hospital and health administration. Hartman assumed that Colloton would succeed him, noting that his associate superintendent would bring to the position "a high level continuum in effective managerial performance and social commitment."[111] Since his arrival at the hospitals in 1958, Colloton had performed ably in a variety of roles, such as overseeing the integration of the Kerr-Mills and Medicare and Medicaid programs at University Hospitals and co-authoring with Glen Clasen the major planning document that served as the basis for the hospitals' capital program. He had served on the Hospital Advisory Committee and on a number of other committees pertaining to clinical facilities planning, inpatient facilities planning, department head searches, and interinstitutional affiliations. He was also active in state and national organizations, including the American College of Hospital Administrators, the American Hospital Association, the Iowa Hospital Association, and the AAMC's Council on Teaching Hospitals.

Based on Colloton's experience and performance and his close involvement in key issues surrounding planning and operations, provost Ray Heffner—acting for Willard Boyd during the president's absence—considered asking the board of regents to appoint Colloton at its meeting scarcely two weeks after Hartman's resignation. Robert Hardin, however, dissuaded the provost, citing university rules requiring a formal search before filling such an important post.[112] What followed was a five-month struggle over process, lines of authority, pay, and status that, although disquieting for Colloton, resulted in a significant rearrangement of the bonds of governance over the hospitals.

In accordance with university policy, Hardin convened a search committee, chaired by Rubin H. Flocks of urology, and urged the committee to "consider persons already on campus as well as others." However, the committee seriously considered only one candidate, John Colloton. Committee members consulted with two teaching hospital directors, the associate director of the Council on Teaching Hospitals, and President Nixon's health affairs adviser James Cavanaugh, all of whom, the committee reported, "praised Mr. Colloton and did not suggest other names." (Cavanaugh, incidentally, earned his doctorate in hospital administration at the University of Iowa under Gerhard Hartman.) Moreover, all sources testified to the effect that "you have the best man in the field in Iowa City."[113] Clinical chiefs and department heads within University Hospitals likewise heaped superlatives on Colloton. "John Colloton is the best administrator I have ever known," wrote one supporter. "I would give my right arm to have just a small fraction of his ability," he continued. "It is inconceivable to me that we could find anyone as competent, or effective as [Colloton] has been in this position," another added.[114] Without exception, the health science deans also spoke of Colloton in glowing terms. John Eckstein, who had been ready to support the provost in appointing Colloton without a wider search, wrote, "I believe that my job will be much less difficult with Mr. Colloton as Hospital Director." Nursing dean Laura Dustan, who may well have welcomed the prospect of weakening the college of medicine's hold on the hospitals, wrote that Colloton was "impressively knowledgeable" about nursing education issues, and that she was "encouraged by his statements that he views University Hospitals as a teaching resource for all the Health Science Colleges."[115]

Such an embarrassment of praise from outsiders and from colleagues did not assure quick action on Colloton's appointment. Neither did it reflect the unequivocal support of those higher in the administrative hierarchy. As vice-president for health affairs, Robert Hardin appeared tentative in his endorsement of Colloton, and his actions were ambiguous. Hardin did not impanel the search committee until six weeks after Hartman announced his resignation, and after receiving the committee's unanimous recommendation in September, waited almost two weeks before transmitting the result to President Boyd. Between the time that Hartman announced his resignation and its effective date, the board of regents met on three occasions, and at no time did university officials broach the naming of a new director or acting director. For his part, Willard Boyd appeared hesitant to name Colloton to the directorship. Indeed, according to Colloton's personal notes, Boyd once suggested that Hardin assume the responsibilities of the post because he believed it required academic credentials. Even when the president finally settled on Colloton as his choice, and initially informed him at a social gathering, the two men were far from agreement on the jurisdiction of the director-to-be.

From the beginning, President Boyd insisted that the director would report through Vice-President Hardin, who would represent University Hospitals to the president, the board of regents, and the state legislature. However, he also wanted to improve communications between the hospitals and the health science colleges and between the hospitals and the university's central administration. The president suggested that Colloton be included in meetings of the health sciences deans owing to "the magnitude of the responsibilities he will carry and their significance for the Health Colleges," responsibilities that would be heightened by the planned integration of the Psychopathic Hospital and Oakdale Hospital into the existing University Hospitals administration. Likewise, he considered it essential that the director communicate effectively with the university's vice-president for financial affairs, who shared responsibility "for compliance with all University and Regential business regulations," and that the hospitals' administration coordinate with the central administration in matters of personnel, planning, and budgeting.[116]

In line with those objectives, President Boyd offered Colloton the position of director of University Hospitals and assistant vice-president for health affairs, an offer including a salary comparable to that of the vice-president for financial affairs. In turn, Colloton conveyed his "enthusiastic acceptance" and recapped the job description as he understood it. In Colloton's rendering, he would, as hospitals director, be the hospitals' chief executive officer; as assistant vice-president, he would advise Hardin on budgeting, operations, personnel, and coordination among the other health service units; he would also work with Hardin to consolidate those units into a "single, coordinated University Hospitals System with the eventual aim of having for them a single director"; he would consult with the health science deans "concerning their needs for instruction and research in the hospitals"; and he would maintain liaison with the Iowa Hospital Association and hospital administrators throughout the state, while serving as the university's official representative to the AAMC's Council of Teaching Hospitals.[117]

Privately, John Colloton was unhappy with the small raise from his salary as associate superintendent. Believing the director's job to be the number two position on the health sciences campus, he felt it important that his salary be pegged to comparable executive positions at other academic medical centers, not to the University of Iowa's general administrative scale. In his mind, the University Hospitals could be either "the best" or "second rate," depending on whether or not the university rewarded "true managerial talent" appropriately.[118] In formal communication with the university president, Colloton made the same point in more diplomatic fashion, arguing that "an optimum achievement of goals by the health science colleges is impossible without quality, top-level management within the prime clinical teaching laboratory." Failure on that score, he noted, had "contributed to the breeding of many second-class academic health science centers." Moreover, Colloton maintained, salaries should emphasize the status of "top-level management." "How much of a credibility gap will exist in the minds of the medical faculty, my staff and hospital department heads regarding the level of support and regard that exists in the University administration when a job description encompassing number two level medical center administrative responsibility is made coordinate with a number six or seven level salary remuneration?" he asked. Colloton backed his argument with documentation drawn from the work of organizational theorists and medical sociologists as well as a breakdown of directors' salaries at peer institutions. Finally, he asked, what salary would have been offered to an outside candidate appointed to the same position?[119]

President Boyd finally agreed to a salary of $35,000, and Colloton conceded to wait until the following July for that raise to take effect. Robert Hardin, too, gave his support to the compromise, although the subtext of Hardin's line of reasoning could hardly have escaped John Colloton. "I am of the opinion that the correct salary is $35,000," Hardin counseled the president. "If we go outside," he observed matter-of-factly, "we will have to go to $40,000 to get a man of [Colloton's] capability."[120] In light of such obvious ambivalence, Colloton was understandably shaken. Indeed, fearing that the delay damaged his credibility with the hospitals staff, at one point he drafted a letter—never sent—withdrawing his name from consideration.[121] In the end, however, Colloton weathered the long delay, in part because of the consistent support of Gerhard Hartman, John Eckstein, and Rubin Flocks, and the board of regents approved his appointment on November 12, 1971.

The University Hospitals had in John Colloton a director of remarkable ability, energy, and ambition, a man with a command of institutional politics and a natural bent for the role of chief executive officer. In Colloton's self-assessment, an assessment shared by a good many others, he possessed both an "analytical mind" and an "unusual capacity for hard physical [and] mental activity on a continuing basis." He recognized in himself not only the requisite organizational abilities but also the capacity to motivate others in ways "aimed at *institutional* objectives." Just as important, he thought that medical faculty and hospital staff saw his administrative style as collaborative, and he professed a "respect for [and] understanding of the teaching process" and a grasp of the hospitals' "obligation to contribute to it."[122] In short, the force of John Colloton's personality and drive, as much as any other single factor, would shape the hospitals' development over the next two decades, including the evolution of governance structures that led to what Colloton called a more independent "corporate identity" for the hospitals.

Colloton initially reported to the university's central administration and the state board of regents through the vice-president for health affairs, Robert Hardin, who also reserved to himself the principal role in hospital planning and capital development. It was Hardin, for example, who compiled in 1973 a comprehensive response to a twenty-item questionnaire from a consulting firm retained by the university addressing issues such as the hospitals' optimal size and organizational structure, its priorities for resources and planning, and its projected growth and general direction.[123] Hardin also took a direct hand in arranging funding for specific capital projects, making applications for federal grants a personal specialty. Before long, however, Colloton assumed a more important role in such matters. In August 1973, President Boyd asked him to apprise the board of regents of the hospitals' capital replacement program, which Colloton did in a detailed written report that he later presented directly to the regents.[124] Further extending his planning role, Colloton corresponded with the governor's office in 1974 regarding efforts to secure federal funds for a new hospital pavilion, and along with internal medicine head James Clifton he participated in negotiations with Muscatine, Iowa, businessman Roy Carver for a large private donation to the project.[125] President Boyd acknowledged the director's part in lining up funding for the new hospital addition, congratulating him specifically on the "marvelous" Hill-Burton grant of $1 million.[126]

When Robert Hardin resigned as vice-president for health affairs effective January 1, 1975, President Boyd discontinued the position, and the health service units previously reporting to Hardin came under Colloton's

administrative purview. For the time being, Colloton reported to an executive vice-president, a position created in a university-wide administrative
restructuring approved in 1973. However, that arrangement, too, ended in
January 1977 (Figure 5.2), and Colloton became assistant to the university
president for statewide health services, joining a small number of university
teaching hospital directors who reported directly to their presidents rather
than to a vice-president or medical dean.[127]

In the meantime, the board of regents became the University Hospitals
board of trustees in 1976, primarily in response to the Joint Commission on
Accreditation of Hospitals' (JCAH) requirement that hospitals have written
bylaws and clearly established governing structures. In the 1960s, Gerhard
Hartman had deflected the Joint Commission's demands by citing sections
of the Iowa Code designating the place of the University Hospitals in the
state system of higher education under the general authority of the board
of regents. In 1970, however, Joint Commission reviewers noted the lack of
formal bylaws governing hospitals operations and procedures. In September
1973, just a month before the next Joint Commission visit, the Hospital
Advisory Committee—chaired by John Colloton—approved a set of bylaws
delineating the functions of the committee itself, the clinical departments,
other operating departments, and the hospitals administration.[128] Those
bylaws did not conform to the Joint Commission's newer and more rigorous
standards, and the 1973 review team commented that the bylaws needed
periodic review. Team members also noted that the hospitals' "ultimate
authority" must receive reports from and respond to the medical staff and
that the Hospital Advisory Committee must document that it had received
and acted upon the reports of its subcommittees."[129]

The Hospital Advisory Committee again revised the bylaws just before
the next Joint Commission visit in October 1975; however, the commission site team objected that the board of regents still did not fulfill its
putative role as the hospitals' governing board, finding it "still to be in
noncompliance in oversight of medical staff." Joint Commission reviewers
recommended changing the hospital bylaws to "show evidence of approval
by the governing body" in such areas as medical care evaluation reports, staff
appointments, and utilization review reports, in short, specifying a formal
administrative relationship between the board of regents and the Hospital
Advisory Committee.[130]

Subsequent revision of hospitals bylaws, approved by the board of
regents in December 1976, defined board of regents members as the trustees
of the hospitals and designated the advisory committee as the hospitals'
internal governing authority under the chairmanship of the hospitals' director. Thereafter, the regents met quarterly in their capacity as trustees, a
change that John Colloton labeled a "major advance." Following the 1977

Figure 5.2   University of Iowa Hospitals and Clinics Organization Chart, October 1977

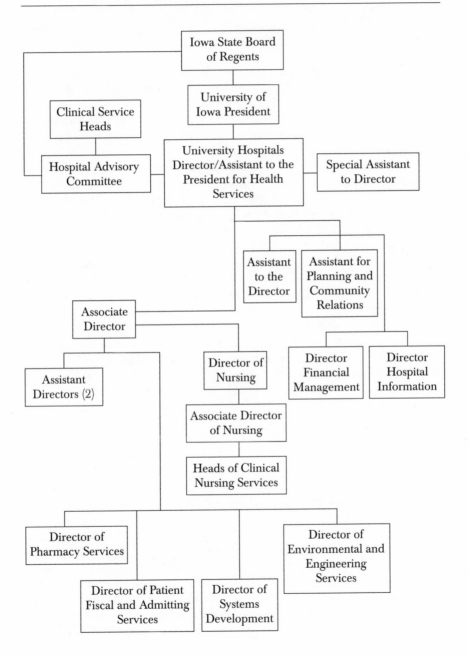

Joint Commission review, Colloton reported to department heads that the review team had found the new governance structure "fully consistent with their standards."[131] That new structure gave Colloton a direct reporting relationship to the board of regents as chair of the advisory committee, paralleling his direct link to the university president, a rare situation in university teaching hospitals.

The consolidation of the university's other health service units under the University of Iowa Hospitals and Clinics, the name adopted in 1971, occurred in stages during the 1970s. The first consolidation, in 1974, involved the Psychopathic Hospital. Next, in 1975, came the Oakdale Hospital, a tuberculosis sanitarium transferred to the authority of the board of regents in 1964 and housing only a chemical dependency treatment unit by the mid-1970s. In 1978, the Hospital School, providing for the special educational needs of physically and developmentally disabled children, joined the hospitals and clinics. Finally, in 1979, the Student Health Service, the State Hygienic Laboratory, and the State Services for Crippled Children came into the administrative fold, the hygienic laboratory having been a division of the Department of Preventive Medicine since the 1930s.

At the same time, then, that John Colloton expanded his administrative jurisdiction over the University Hospitals, forging direct links to both the university president and the board of regents, he also took responsibility for a variety of service areas long outside the purview of the hospitals. Importantly, as noted in the next section, all of this occurred at a time when Colloton was also directing a near-total replacement of the hospitals' capital facilities. Thanks to a combination of circumstances, Colloton had achieved the authority and the degree of autonomy that consultants had recommended when the University Hospital hired its first full-time superintendent in 1916 and that Gerhard Hartman had sought when he first came to the hospitals in 1946.

In part, John Colloton's performance was no surprise. In the 1960s, he had shown himself to be an able administrator and had made significant contributions in planning councils as well, but, as assistant and later associate hospitals director, Colloton was cast in a supportive role. As hospitals director, however, Colloton had had the opportunity to put his considerable talents on open display and had done so in a variety of ways and to diverse audiences. By the early 1980s, he had put his mark on the hospitals and clinics and the entire medical center through his role in the building campaigns, through his administrative style, and through service on innumerable committees. Just as important, he had invested a sizable effort in promoting the hospitals and clinics across the state of Iowa, winning the Iowa Medical Society's John Sanford Award in 1979 for "leadership in developing innovative programs" at the hospitals and clinics and for "strengthening relations between the University of Iowa Hospitals and Clinics and the physicians of Iowa." Testifying to his growing national reputation, Colloton had also been elected chairman of the AAMC's Council of Teaching Hospitals in 1979.

By the late 1970s, John Colloton's accomplishments and his national reputation had earned attention from a variety of public and private organizations in the healthcare field, attention that, in turn, prompted President Willard Boyd to propose a $25,050 salary increase for the director in the summer of 1980. To be sure, Colloton's salary had doubled to nearly $72,000 between 1972 and 1979; however, the latter figure fell well below the fiftieth percentile among chief executives in charge of Council of Teaching Hospitals member institutions of 695 beds or more. In the view of University of Iowa officials, then, there was strong evidence that the hospitals and clinics director was, in relative terms, underpaid; moreover, the proposed raise also fulfilled President Boyd's 1972 promise to bring Colloton's pay to a level commensurate with that of his peers at other institutions.

Although the bulk of the money would come from Medical Service Plan revenues, not from state appropriations, Colloton's 35 percent salary increase sparked a minor furor, coming, as it did, at a time of intense and persistent inflation in the economy, stringent state budgets, and minimal wage hikes for state employees. One local newspaper, for example, labeled it a "whopping" raise,[132] another questioned its propriety and pointed to the adverse psychological impact on other employees.[133] Similarly, the Iowa House Democratic party leaders argued against it on the grounds that it set a poor example for state employees in general, who faced a 7 percent cap on pay increases.[134] Nonetheless, the university administration, spearheaded by President Boyd and the vice-president for finance, Randall Bezanson, were steadfast in highlighting Colloton's contributions to the University of Iowa medical center, including the relative harmony prevailing between the college of medicine and the hospitals and clinics.[135] For his part, Boyd maintained that Colloton should have received larger salary increases in previous years. "I was," the president confessed, "too conservative in approaching his salary in the beginning."[136] There was also a general closing of ranks within the medical center in support of the director and similar support from the greater Iowa healthcare community. In the end, this episode, as one of John Colloton's supporters assured him at the time, was soon forgotten, submerged in an extraordinary expansion of physical facilities and patient service.

The Capital Development Program

The Medicare-Medicaid legislation of 1965 denied reimbursement for services provided in hospital wards of more than four beds, a statutory death knell for the open wards that had characterized the modern hospital since its birth in the late nineteenth century. The law also deemed institutions accredited by the Joint Commission on Accreditation of Hospitals to be in compliance with published Medicare standards.[137] Revisions to the Medicare-Medicaid legislation, enacted in 1972, drew the Joint Commission more tightly into the web of federal standards by empowering the Department of Health, Education and Welfare to review the commission's work. As University of Iowa Hospitals Director John Colloton noted after the commission's particularly stringent review of 1975, "It is incumbent on JCAH surveyors to conduct such wide ranging and precise surveys as the Social Security Administration is randomly resurveying hospitals to validate the work of the Commission."[138]

Its responsibility and credibility bolstered, the Joint Commission had begun to toughen its standards almost immediately after initial passage of the Medicare-Medicaid legislation. In 1966, the commission had shifted its aim from "minimal essential levels of care" to the "optimal achievable."[139] Among other things, the commission's new target meant additional attention to physical plant, a fact of importance to the University of Iowa Hospitals, which had easily gained the maximum three-year accreditation under the previous standards. The 1970 review brought harsh criticism of the hospital's physical facilities, especially the Children's Hospital—labeled "an antiquated building"—and the General Hospital's sixth-floor operating rooms—dismissed as "decompensated anachronisms." For the first time, reviewers noted the need to upgrade "buildings of ordinary construction" used for patient care and called for efforts to minimize fire and infection hazards in storage areas.[140]

In 1970, the Joint Commission awarded the hospitals only a two-year accreditation, which, in practice, became three years since the next review team arrived in 1973. By that time, the commission's survey questionnaire had grown to 150-plus pages, containing more than 4,000 questions and reflecting the greater emphasis on physical plant. After the site team review, the commission awarded just one year's accreditation, a pattern that held for the rest of the decade even though there were no site team visits in 1974 and 1976. Reviews repeatedly cited fire and safety violations at Children's Hospital, Psychopathic Hospital, and Westlawn. By 1977, even the most hopeful of observers had to agree with John Colloton that "recently amended and considerably more expansive environmental standards, including very rigid standards now being applied to all in-patient nursing units," precluded the possibility of ever bringing the hospitals' 1920s-era facilities into compliance.[141]

There were piecemeal improvements to the hospitals' physical plant early in the decade, aimed in part to address Joint Commission complaints.

Also, the hospitals' administration took a much more aggressive approach to preparing for Joint Commission accreditation reviews, investigating reviewers' backgrounds, contacting other hospitals to determine points of emphasis in site team reviews, briefing department heads and staff regarding upcoming reviews, setting out a rigorous schedule for site team members, and thoroughly documenting reviewers' comments during summation conferences. Finally, administrative staff were charged with follow-up on commission recommendations and with documenting efforts to address specific problems.

Despite that, Joint Commission reviews confirmed again and again the shortcomings of the hospitals' older buildings, shortcomings that had been subjects of no little debate since at least the early 1960s. In the end, the commission's findings reinforced the view that only an ambitious program of new construction could bring the hospitals' clinical facilities up to modern standards, helping John Colloton and other officials to maintain pressure on the university administration, the board of regents, and the state legislature to approve each succeeding phase of an ambitious capital replacement program. As a result, the 1970s and 1980s were years of constant planning and construction in the hospitals and clinics, with major additions springing up in overlapping phases. Meanwhile, renovations in existing facilities allowed their conversion to new uses and facilitated the enlargement and consolidation of services. By 1983, the hospitals and clinics had sold $60 million in revenue bonds to finance the greater part of the $109.6 million in construction costs, with an additional $7.4 million coming from gifts and grants and the remainder taken from the hospitals' accumulated capital reserves. Not only did the explosion of new construction and nearly constant renovation dramatically change the face of this midwestern teaching hospital; the combination of bonding and capital reserves—both predicated on the remarkable pattern of growth in patient revenues—freed the hospitals and clinics from its traditional reliance on state appropriations.

University of Iowa hospital officials rebounded quickly from the crushing collapse of hospital construction plans in the fall of 1970, but the experience had sensitized local officials to the risks in relying on federal construction funds, and it did have lasting impact. By January 1972, John Colloton, only recently installed as hospitals director and convinced of the need to meet Medicare standards and to compete for private patients in an evolving healthcare market, presented to the Hospital Advisory Committee a plan for two smaller capital projects dubbed the North and South Towers, a plan that, by parceling construction into discrete phases, represented a significant departure from the previous "all or nothing" plan for a massive 2 million-square-foot project. Colloton's phased approach did not win immediate acceptance. As late as March 1972, for example, the board of regents still harbored hopes of reviving the original plan.[142] Meanwhile, several members of the Hospital Advisory Committee questioned the wisdom of attempting any "strenuous capital development," wary of the Nixon administration's wage and price controls and an apparent decline in the hospitals' occupancy rate.[143] The university president expressed reservations, too, about the ad hoc nature of phased capital development, fearing that the result might well be shoddy, unsightly additions that would only complicate future building plans.[144]

Brushing aside such concerns, Colloton pushed for approval of the first component of his proposal, the North Tower, a seven-story structure joining the General Hospital's existing east and west wings and partially obscuring the much-celebrated Gothic tower. The diminished probability of federal funding for hospital construction was perhaps Colloton's strongest argument for his proposal, an argument strengthened by an $800 million nationwide backlog of unfunded construction projects. Spiraling construction costs since the late 1960s had also pushed cost estimates to the range of $70 million to $80 million for the original project, further reinforcing the director's position in favor of a radically different approach to capital development. The time had come, Colloton argued, to build what could be built with the resources available, a sum estimated at $4.4 million in hospital building funds and $9.5 million in bonding capacity.[145] An ad hoc coordinating committee on university hospital capital planning—including Colloton, Robert Hardin, John Eckstein, and others—gave strong support to Colloton's position.[146]

To those who objected to "strenuous capital development" in the present political and economic climate, Colloton answered that the hospitals had little choice. Current standards for teaching hospitals called for 1,500 square feet per inpatient bed to accommodate modern patient care needs and the ancillary needs of teaching and research; the current University Hospitals had less than half that. In all, the hospitals needed some 750,000 square feet of additional space to support the 925 beds in the General Hospital and Children's Hospital, and, in Colloton's mind, the 168,000 square feet in his proposed North Tower addition represented an economical first step toward "bringing immediate correction to a broad scope of functionally interrelated teaching and service problems."[147] Moreover, the North Tower would satisfy immediate needs without blocking long-proposed expansion to the south, thus addressing President Boyd's concerns regarding the risks of piecemeal expansion. The North Tower, Colloton assured Boyd, would fit in with long-range plans for the medical center.[148]

The prospect of declining occupancy rates was the most persuasive argument against new construction. An issue first raised early in 1972, it resurfaced in the spring of 1973 as the Iowa legislature considered whether to grant the hospitals the authority to sell almost $10 million in bonds for the North Tower. Opponents of the bonding proposal pointed to an average occupancy of 75 percent for fiscal 1972 and asked how the hospitals could justify more space. On that basis, the bonding proposal stalled in the House of Representatives. Colloton at first downplayed the extent of the decline in occupancy, telling the Hospital Advisory Committee that the decline was more apparent than real.[149] But by early 1973 he was searching for a more effective argument grounded in the "tertiary" nature of much of the care provided in University Hospitals. For example, he noted, no other hospital in the state had a heart-lung machine, and university surgeons performed ten to twelve procedures each week using this advanced technology. Just then undergoing clearer articulation, the hospitals' tertiary care mission became a central argument for capital development.

One last obstacle to the North Tower project was administrative in nature. Shortly after Colloton first presented his plan, the University of Iowa, at Willard Boyd's behest, enlisted a new campus planning consultant, Hodne/Stageberg Partners of Minneapolis–St. Paul.[150] Boyd wanted a "fresh approach" in what appeared to be a "critical period in campus planning," and the president wanted Hodne/Stageberg to review the North Tower proposal. "The proposal needs to be studied in depth," Boyd wrote the consultants in April 1972, "with the objective of determining if it is the best functional alternative for hospital expansion."[151] In turn, the consultants advised that they needed several weeks of basic orientation to the university before offering counsel on specific issues,[152] an approach that, while reasonable on its face, ran afoul of a June 15 deadline for applications for federal funding of improvements associated with the project. "Unfortunately," Robert Hardin notified the president, "we cannot proceed in a truly orderly fashion which would entail stopping all planning at this point for the time necessary for the Hodne/Stageberg Partners to become thoroughly familiar with our problems and with the hospital operation."[153] Hastily staged meetings in early May between university officials and Hodne/Stageberg representatives established some basic understandings about medical center priorities but did not afford the consultants enough time to master the details of the North Tower proposal. Nonetheless, they recommended sending the federal grant applications with preliminary drawings developed by the Iowa City architectural firm of Hansen, Lind, Meyer, with the proviso that the plans would not be final until the consulting firm reviewed them in more detail.[154]

True to his original position, President Boyd withheld final approval of the North Tower proposal until receiving the consultant's endorsement in late summer 1972. His doubts assuaged, Boyd then became an enthusiastic supporter of the project and agreed to present the plan to the board of regents in the fall of 1972. Despite lingering concerns over the esthetic effects on the original Gothic tower, the project gained approval from the board in March 1973 and shortly thereafter from the state legislature. Excavation began in June, and some $10 million in twenty-year revenue bonds were sold in July, which, with $4 million in building funds, financed construction.[155] No federal money directly supported construction, although a $557,000 federal grant paid most of the cost of a pediatric cardiovascular clinic that was among the renovations included in the overall project. At its completion in 1976, the North Tower integrated outpatient clinics and inpatient facilities, replacing eighty non-complying beds. Radiology added 12,000 square feet to its facilities; surgery finally obtained eight new operating theatres with related facilities; internal medicine gained new clinic space, forty replacement beds, and a blood donor center; obstetrics and gycecology consolidated its clinic operations; and the tower also added space for physical therapy, a centralized sterilizing service, and urology and neurology departments.

In many respects, the North Tower—renamed the Boyd Tower in 1981—set the pattern for the hospitals' further capital expansion. First, that initial development phase forced officials to define and articulate the rationale for phased capital replacement and to consider each project within the context of a long-term development plan, emphasizing not only the replacement of outdated facilities but also capitalizing on the hospitals' statewide tertiary care mission. Second, the North Tower forced officials— especially the dean of the college of medicine, the hospitals director, and the university vice-president for health affairs—to achieve an informal working agreement with regard to their respective roles in the planning process itself, an agreement that allowed President Willard Boyd to avoid close involvement in planning details. Just as important, the North Tower established the pattern of bonded financing for future additions, and it also cemented the relationship between the hospitals and the Hansen, Lind, Meyer architectural firm that designed all future phases of the capital development program.

Even before the July 1973 sale of revenue bonds to finance the North Tower, university officials began planning the subsequent phases of the hospitals' expansion, phases that would begin the southward expansion envisioned since the 1960s. The initial phase, dubbed South Pavilion, was designed to address the hospitals' most pressing needs, namely, eliminating inpatient beds at Children's Hospital and providing a new multispecialty trauma and emergency treatment center. The projected cost of this addition was $11.3 million, including a hoped-for $7.8 million in federal matching funds. However, HEW guidelines denying funding for inpatient beds meant that federal money would not cover replacement of the 96 beds from Children's Hospital, reducing potential federal funding to just $4.4 million. To make up the difference, the university obtained $1 million from the state's

Hill-Burton funds, and Roy J. Carver, a Muscatine, Iowa, industrialist and founder of the Bandag Corporation, made a $2 million gift. Combined with $3.9 million from the hospitals' capital reserve fund, those sources made up the final financing package approved in September 1974.[156]

That project, however, was only the first phase—Phase A—of what was to become the Roy J. Carver Pavilion, which, in its finished configuration, also comprised 139 replacement beds as well as offices, laboratories, clinics, and other facilities for orthopædics. Phases B and C took shape on the drawing boards even as site preparation for Phase A began, adding an additional $30 million to the total cost of the project. With completion of construction in 1984, the Carver Pavilion meant a net increase of more than 235,000 square feet of floor space at a cost of nearly $46 million, $12 million of that total coming from 25-year revenue bonds sold in 1978.[157]

In the meantime, plans for yet another pavilion—also known initially as the south pavilion—were also underway by the late 1970s; however, the further expansion of the hospitals complex raised some concerns among members of the board of regents. One critic questioned whether director John Colloton and other officials had kept the board properly informed about capital development plans and complained that the board seemed to be locked into decisions made many years previously. Colloton responded by citing the various occasions at which plans had been presented and approved, including review by the state Department of Health. More pointedly, Colloton remarked that the south pavilion then under discussion would be financed entirely from hospital resources.[158] Despite that exchange, the planned south pavilion went forward with board of regents approval, the initial phase of construction beginning in September 1980. An $18 million dollar bond issue financed much of the $24.5 million cost of the first phase, with the balance taken from the hospitals' capital reserve fund. A second phase, begun in May 1983, likewise carried a $24.5 million price tag, $20 million derived from the sale of revenue bonds and the remainder from the capital reserve fund. In a noteworthy turn of events, the board of regents gave John Colloton's name to this latest pavilion, a tribute that recognized Colloton's persistence in pursuing long dormant capital development plans and that symbolized, too, his extraordinary professional ascent.

Along with the phased expansion to the south, several smaller additions and remodeling projects reshaped the General Hospital during the 1970s and 1980s. The six-story southeast addition of 1972–1973, for example, added materially to the hospital's floor space, while a host of other improvements accommodated new equipment and allowed for the consolidation of a variety of services. In September 1977, John Colloton presented to the board of regents a list of 56 projects completed in the previous three years at a combined cost of $5.6 million, and he described sixteen additional projects totaling $3 million scheduled for the coming year.[159] Ten years later, the total for such projects reached $74 million, comprising 113,700 square feet and including a new entrance created in the space between the south wing and the Carver Pavilion.

The New Era of Patient Service

Vigorous growth in patient service revenues supported the construction and reconstruction of the University of Iowa Hospitals and Clinics through the 1970s and into the 1980s (Table 5.9). Although patient admissions fell for a brief period in the early 1970s, they recovered by 1974–1975 and ended the decade with a gain of 14.4 percent. Outpatient visits increased at a faster rate, rising 24.5 percent. Through 1975–1976, total patient-days followed much the same pattern as patient admissions, falling early on and rising to new highs at mid-decade. However, total patient-days declined in the late 1970s, consistent with the slow fall in the average length of stay.

Throughout the period, Medicare and Medicaid programs, as well as private health insurance, had a striking impact on the hospitals' patient mix. Indeed, the shifting of Medicare patients in particular from clinical pay to private status in 1973—a change discussed in the next section—was a major factor in the rapid increase in the private patient census from 1970–1971 to 1981–1982, the total rising from 23.9 percent to 62.8 percent of total

Table 5.9 University of Iowa Hospitals and Clinics Patient Service, 1971–1982

Fiscal Year	Private Admissions	Clinical Pay Admissions	Indigent Admissions	Total Admissions	Total Patient-Days	Outpatient Visits
1970–71	8,406	7,593	19,133	35,132	323,250	262,901
1971–72	8,608	9,436	13,269	31,313	296,822	260,229
1972–73	10,379	9,324	11,754	31,457	287,112	261,133
1973–74	15,910	6,760	10,531	33,201	290,896	269,824
1974–75	17,855	6,642	11,404	35,901	315,416	288,178
1975–76	20,204	6,020	12,448	38,672	329,931	299,592
1976–77	21,815	6,023	11,403	39,241	323,417	309,693
1977–78	21,679	5,063	12,650	39,392	305,214	314,071
1978–79	24,381	3,880	12,308	40,569	317,298	313,928
1979–80	25,440	3,229	11,535	40,204	313,009	318,056
1980–81	25,394	2,215	11,943	39,552	309,812	333,163
1981–82	25,095	2,366	12,500	39,961	309,059	327,304

Source: University of Iowa Hospitals and Clinics *Annual Statistical Reports.*

patient admissions. Meanwhile, following a precipitous decline in the late 1960s and early 1970s, tracking the impact of both Medicaid and Medicare on the medically indigent population, the number of state (indigent) patients reached a plateau by 1972.

Despite the reduced and nearly steady number of state indigent patients, the state's indigent care appropriation almost tripled from $8.5 million in 1970–1971 to more than $22.2 million in 1981–1982 (Table 5.10). Even so, the hospitals and clinics administration said the appropriation did not cover the full cost of indigent care, calculating in 1981 that the medical faculty provided some $11 million annually in free service to indigent patients.[160] Moreover, the indigent care appropriation sank as a proportion of total patient revenue from 35.4 percent in 1971—having fallen below 50 percent for the first time only in 1969—to barely 20 percent in 1982. The rise in paying-patient income, which now included Medicare and Medicaid reimbursements, made up the difference in total revenues. Income from paying patients increased from less than $15.8 million in 1971 to almost $88.3 million in 1982, while the hospitals' total operating expenditures rose from $24.4 million to $110.5 million.

Table 5.10   Hospitals and Clinics Revenues and Expenditures, 1971–1982

Fiscal Year	State Appropriation (Dollars)	Percent of Total	Patient Income (Dollars)	Percent of Total	Total Expenditures (Dollars)
1970–71	8,550,000	35.10	15,795,481	64.90	24,345,481
1971–72	8,738,000	31.60	18,940,729	68.40	27,678,729
1972–73	8,738,000	29.80	20,609,182	70.20	29,347,182
1973–74	10,876,100	32.40	22,740,618	67.60	33,616,718
1974–75	11,904,000	30.60	26,944,755	69.40	38,848,755
1975–76	13,331,884	27.80	34,616,840	72.20	47,948,724
1976–77	15,502,600	26.90	42,146,428	73.10	57,649,028
1977–78	17,143,317	26.50	47,633,604	73.50	64,776,921
1978–79	18,590,085	25.20	55,256,496	74.80	73,846,581
1979–80	20,115,663	24.00	63,706,427	76.00	83,822,090
1980–81	20,782,083	21.80	74,445,226	78.20	95,227,309
1981–82	22,276,702	20.10	88,279,450	79.90	110,556,152

Note: Figures do not include expenses of or appropriations for Psychiatric Hospital or University Hospital School.

Source: "Proportionality of Support of Total Operating Expense—Appropriation Versus Paying Patient Income, 1927–28 to Date," dated January 28, 1995; University of Iowa Hospitals and Clinics Office of Financial Management and Control.

According to American Hospital Association figures, the University of Iowa Hospitals and Clinics in the early 1970s treated more patients with fewer staff and at lower cost than the average of six other major teaching hospitals at Big Ten universities (Michigan, Ohio State, Minnesota, Wisconsin, Indiana, and Illinois), a situation that had changed little since the 1930s. In 1970, those peer institutions averaged 17,700 patient admissions, scarcely half the total at the University of Iowa, but employed an average of 2,367 hospital staff, compared to 2,011 at the University of Iowa, with an average operating budget of $27.2 million, compared to $23.1 million at Iowa. By 1980, that differential had narrowed, with average admissions at other Big Ten institutions standing at 20,200, again roughly half the number at Iowa, but with the University of Iowa Hospitals' budget and staff exceeding the mean figures, $102.2 million to $90.8 million and 3,518 to 3,161 respectively. Nonetheless, the University of Michigan, for example, still maintained a sizable lead in staffing ratio and budget, with 24,580 admissions, 4,880 staff, and a budget in excess of $130 million.[161]

In the 1970s and early 1980s, the various clinical departments at the University of Iowa Hospitals and Clinics developed a bewildering array of highly specialized diagnostic techniques and therapeutic procedures, ranging from corneal transplants, kidney dialysis, and hip and knee replacements to cardiac imaging, open heart surgery, and organ transplants—the last symbolic of a new era for the long-troubled surgery department. The largest increases in patient admissions from 1970–1971 to 1981–1982 occurred in obstetrics and gynecology at 87 percent, internal medicine at 28 percent, otolaryngology and surgery at 27 percent each, and ophthalmology at 24 percent. In 1982, obstetrics and gynecology—with 93 beds at the department's disposal—also counted the largest number of admissions at 7,302, followed by internal medicine, with its 197 beds, at 6,429; surgery, with 191 beds, at 6,095; pediatrics, with 133 beds, at 5,334; and otolaryngology, with 61 beds, at 3,579. Meanwhile, internal medicine led all departments in initial outpatient registrations with 32,245 in 1982, followed by ophthalmology with 26,085, surgery with 20,861, otolaryngology with 20,600, and orthopædics with a total of 17,955 outpatients.

The increasing patient load, both inpatient and outpatient, in combination with increasing technological sophistication in the hospitals and clinics' patient services meant significant expansion in virtually all areas of operations. Total hospital staff rose from 2,200 in 1970 to more than 4,300 in 1980, the result both of increases in existing areas and of the establishment of new operating departments. For example, in response to the rising concern for patients' rights, the hospitals added a corps of patient representatives—six full-time positions in 1980—whose job it was to reassure anxious patients and families and to provide basic information about hospital services and procedures. Likewise, the advent of computerization brought a rapidly expanding hospital information system, with seven full-time positions by 1980 and a budget of $157,000. Full-time laboratory staff increased from 154 in 1970–1971 to 246 in 1980–1981, and the number of laboratory examinations rose from some 915,600 to more than 3.2 million. With the expansion of the physical plant, housekeeping staff grew from 162 in 1970–1971 to 269 in 1980–1981, and operations and maintenance personnel grew from 47 to 87.

The pharmacy department was one long-established service area that experienced a major transformation in the 1970s. In the mid-1960s, administration of the department moved from the college of pharmacy to the hospitals. With support from a U.S. Public Health Service grant, the department introduced on a pilot basis a decentralized unit-dose drug distribution system in 1964, an innovation that also boosted the clinical pharmacy concept that brought the hospital pharmacists out of the basement—literally so in the case of the University of Iowa Hospitals—to take a more active role in consultation with other health care professionals and with patients as well. The department also established a computerized drug formulary; it began the Iowa Drug Information System, an operation that later became a global drug literature indexing service; and it also operated a regional poison control center. In the 1970s, the department expanded the unit-dose system to additional clinical areas, particularly to completed portions of the Carver and Colloton pavilions, and also expanded clinical pharmacy services to outpatient clinics, beginning with the hematology-oncology clinic in 1975. By the early 1980s, the pharmacy department processed some 1.5 million drug orders annually, and did so with a total staff, including large numbers of pharmacy technicians, scarcely larger than that of 1970.

The social service department was a second example of a service area that saw significant growth and differentiation in the 1970s. Responsible for creating an environment conducive to therapeutic success, for helping patients to negotiate the labyrinths of hospital procedures, and for the education of primary care physicians regarding the importance of cultural factors in health and healing, the social service department had, much like the hospitals themselves, grown slowly from its modest beginning in the 1920s. In 1970, the department numbered eighteen full-time-equivalent staff, most of them graduate-trained medical social workers. The expansion and increasing specialization of the hospitals and clinics' patient services and the increasing cultural diversity of the patient population during the 1970s placed significantly greater demands on social service workers, leading to the addition of a vocational rehabilitation counselor, interpreters, and a benefits assistance staff. In addition, 1974 brought the department's merger with the social service staff of the Psychiatric Hospital. In 1980–1981, the social service department comprised 35 full-time-equivalent staff who processed some 16,000 patient referrals.

Nursing was a third area to undergo substantial change during the decade, chiefly a consequence of the increasing technological demands implicit in the hospitals' tertiary care focus; the determination of the hospitals' administration to boost the staff-to-patient ratio, particularly in nursing; and the increasing sophistication of nursing education itself. Citing the central position of nursing staff in patient care, medical center and university officials repeatedly emphasized to the board of regents in the 1970s the importance of increased staffing levels and pointed to national nurse-to-bed averages to buttress their case. In an October 1975 regents meeting, as one example, University President Willard Boyd, hospitals and clinics director John Colloton, internal medicine head James Clifton, and nursing service chief Myrtle Kitchell Aydelotte collectively pressed their argument for higher staffing levels.[162] Colloton pointed to rising patient volume, a shift to tertiary care functions, and an increasing proportion of private patients as justifications for more nursing staff. An increase in patient charges, the director assured the regents, would cover the costs of additional nursing personnel, while maintaining the hospitals' comparatively low per diem rates. Clifton and Aydelotte supported Colloton, emphasizing the increasing proportion of complex cases requiring highly specialized care. During the 1970s, total nursing staff at the University of Iowa Hospitals and Clinics rose from 912 to 1,643, roughly 60 percent of whom were registered nurses; expenditures for professional care—of which nursing made up a major share—rose from $16.3 million in 1970–1971 to nearly $86 million in 1982.

More important than aggregate numbers, however, was the changing complexion of the nursing service in those years. Myrtle Kitchell Aydelotte, nursing service director from 1968 to 1976, instituted significant changes and her successors, Mary Fuller and Sally Mathis, continued them. The University of Iowa College of Nursing's first dean from 1949 to 1957, Aydelotte was recruited by Glen Clasen, associate director of the hospitals, to the post of director of nursing services in 1968. Aydelotte and Clasen, while good friends, had long been at odds over key issues regarding the status and makeup of the nursing service, but on this occasion Clasen made several key concessions, giving Aydelotte control over the nursing budget, agreeing to the introduction of a system of clinical nursing specialization, and allowing her free communication with other hospitals staff. With an eye to the creation of "a self-governed . . . professional department," the new director of nursing worked with the hospitals' administration, with the medical staff, and with the nurses themselves to create a nursing service that reflected the impress of modern technology, recognized and rewarded nurses' skills, and provided an outlet for their professional aspirations.[163] She also established a nurses' library and encouraged clinical research within her department.

Aydelotte instituted a thorough reorganization of the nursing service administrative structure (Figure 5.3). In 1974, the nursing service administration included two associate directors and one special assistant, three divisions, and thirteen clinical nursing areas. In addition, much as she had done as dean of the college of nursing some twenty years earlier, Aydelotte created a remarkably open and democratic infrastructure of councils and committees in the nursing service—including an Administrative Council, a Professional Nursing Council, a Nurse Clinician Council, and a Staff Nurse Council—to facilitate communication, to foster collegial relations, and to aid in the implementation of department objectives.

A major shift in the educational background of the hospitals' nursing staff accompanied the increased specialization of nursing services and the increased levels of skills and training. The growth in administrative staff and the development of the clinical nurse specialist areas emphasized the recruitment of master's degree nurses, although suitable clinical experience was accepted in lieu of formal academic training in clinical specialist positions. Also, in line with Aydelotte's endorsement of the baccalaureate degree as the appropriate entry-level credential in nursing, the nursing service as a whole saw an increase in the proportion of nurses holding bachelor's degrees and a corresponding decrease in the proportion holding associate degrees and hospital diplomas. In 1971–1972, for example, the service appointed 62 nurses with baccalaureate degrees, 83 with hospital diplomas, and 6 with associate degrees; in 1974–1975, the numbers changed to 138 baccalaureate, 84 diploma, and 31 associate—the growth in the last category partially reflecting the expansion of the statewide community college system. By 1977, some 55 percent of registered nurses on staff at the University of Iowa Hospitals and Clinics held baccalaureate degrees, more than 70 percent of them graduates of the University of Iowa College of Nursing.

The restructuring and expansion of the nursing service took place against a national backdrop of declining nursing enrollments by the late 1970s, increasing competition among hospitals for available nursing personnel, and very high turnover rates within the nursing staff. Director Sally Mathis noted in 1981 that nearly 90 percent of hospitals nationwide reported unfilled full-time nursing positions and that turnover rates hovered between 30 and 40 percent. At the time, 10 percent of budgeted nursing positions were vacant in Mathis' own service.[164] Overall, the University of Iowa Hospitals and Clinics reported nursing turnover of some 70 percent in 1973–1974, a figure that fell to less than 50 percent in 1976–1977 as a result both of concerted efforts to increase job satisfaction and of the inherently greater rewards of specialized nursing duties. In the late 1970s

Figure 5.3   Nursing Service Organization Chart, University of Iowa Hospitals and Clinics, 1974

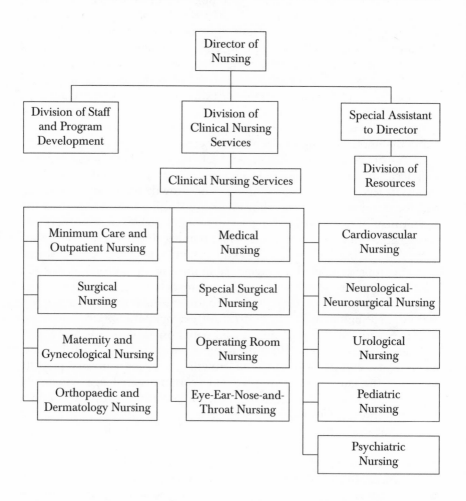

and early 1980s, further efforts to increase job satisfaction and retention included improved salaries, enlarged programs of staff development, and more flexible scheduling.

The New Regulatory Environment

The 1970s and early 1980s saw extraordinary inflation in healthcare costs, a spiral tied to the rise in the general rate of inflation and also to specific characteristics of the healthcare marketplace. Total health expenditures in the United States rose from $75 billion in 1970 to $322 billion in 1982, increasing from 7.6 to 10.5 percent of the gross national product. From 1966 to 1978, healthcare costs in the United States increased at an annual rate of 11.6 percent; in Iowa the figure was 11.5 percent. Consistent with that overall increase, Medicare expenditures rose from $7.1 billion in 1970 to $51.1 billion in 1982—71.9 percent of the latter total for hospital care—while combined federal and state Medicaid expenditures rose from $5.2 billion in 1970 to $31.3 billion in 1982.[165]

For the short term, "runaway inflation" in healthcare costs, abetted by a rising tide of skepticism toward the promise of scientific medicine, fostered a new emphasis on cost containment and regulation at federal and state levels, leading to legislative mandates that became ever more "specific," more "complex," and more "regulatory" in nature.[166] In a 1977 address as incoming chairman of the Iowa Hospital Association board of directors, John Colloton recognized the current shift in decision making from providers to consumers and their elected representatives; providers, he noted, were commonly "blamed for the deficiencies of the current system."[167] While he professed to welcome "long overdue efforts toward a more structured health system," Colloton worried about the concomitant increase in bureaucratic "red tape." As he saw it, the public was of two minds, increasingly convinced that healthcare was a basic right and strongly supportive, according to public opinion polls, of healthcare in general and hospitals and physicians in particular but also concerned over the benefits of "massive expenditures in health." Iowa hospitals, Colloton pointed out, had gone to considerable lengths to respond to public criticisms, negotiating shared service arrangements, outright mergers of facilities, and group purchase agreements, but would have to focus more effort on consumer education to guide debate on the most difficult questions in healthcare.

In general, cost-containment efforts led in three major directions. First, they stimulated interest in alternative healthcare delivery systems, perhaps best exemplified in the health maintenance organization. Second, cost concerns slowed the trend toward wider access to federally financed healthcare services, as illustrated by the slow strangulation of national health insurance proposals endorsed and rejected in turn by three presidents, Richard Nixon, Gerald Ford, and Jimmy Carter. Third, cost-containment efforts led to the imposition of restrictions, albeit less serious than first supposed, on the freedom of physicians and other providers to organize the healthcare delivery system.

The health maintenance organization, a variant of the venerable pre-paid group practice concept, was not a new idea in the 1970s, but as a key element in a 1971 Nixon administration "national health strategy," HMOs were one of the earliest proposed solutions to overutilization of healthcare services and the rapid inflation in healthcare costs.[168] To political and economic conservatives, the HMO's virtue was that it introduced market competition along with negative incentives to overutilization, and it promised to do so without direct federal regulation of the healthcare marketplace. With Richard Nixon setting an ambitious goal of some 40 million consumers enrolled by 1976, the HMO concept also afforded an additional avenue of investment for corporate healthcare providers, a fact greeted with enthusiasm by conservatives and with varying degrees of uneasiness by liberals.[169] Although the Nixon administration initially requested funds for planning grants and loan guarantees to support the establishment of HMOs, it was not until December 1973 that Congress took positive action by requiring—in the Health Maintenance Organization Act (P.L. 93-222)—large employers to offer HMO coverage to their employees. At the same time, the 1973 act set detailed standards for HMO coverage and charges, standards which, in the view of many critics, stifled the struggling HMOs. Congressional action in 1976 and again in 1978 eased restrictions and provided limited federal aid to HMOs, and, partly as a result, total enrollment in HMOs reached nearly 8 million by the end of the decade. Enrolling scarcely 4 percent of the American population, HMOs were yet limited factors in the healthcare marketplace; however, the 1980s and early 1990s saw the HMOs move to center stage.

In contrast, the impact of the 1972 amendments to the Social Security Act (P.L. 92-603) was more immediate. Symbolic of the shifting attitudes and growing ambivalence toward the healthcare system, the 1972 amendments were of two minds. On the one hand, they significantly extended the Medicare umbrella by providing benefits to the disabled and to victims of end-stage renal disease, regardless of age, the latter change transforming kidney dialysis into a major, federally subsidized industry. On the other hand, the principal impetus behind P.L. 92-603 was cost containment, specifically reforming the largely ineffective utilization review mechanisms established under the original Medicare and Medicaid legislation of 1965. Inspired by increases in the unit costs of services—attributed by many to the existing "usual, reasonable, and customary" fee structure—and the broadening array of services available to beneficiaries, the Senate Finance Committee pointed to studies by the Social Security Administration and to the committee's own investigations to suggest that the activities of local utilization review committees, like the one set up at the University of Iowa Hospitals in 1966, "have, generally speaking, been of a token nature and ineffective as a curb to unnecessary use of institutional care and services." That was particularly so, the committee concluded, in hospitals where occupancy rates were low.[170]

P.L. 92-603 dealt with the utilization review dilemma by establishing, in Part B of Title XI, regional Professional Standards Review Organizations (PSROs) organized, administered, and directed by physicians—a plan that surfaced as an alternative to a more radical proposal to have the Department of Health, Education and Welfare directly appoint review agencies and perhaps also to include non-physicians in their membership. The newly defined regional PSROs were to scrutinize the treatment of Medicare and Medicaid cases—at the time of hospitalization rather than after the fact—and to build databases for the long-term comparative assessment of procedures and charges. DHEW recognized the Iowa Foundation for Medical Care, an agency created by Iowa physicians in 1971, as the state's PSRO in 1975. However, the bulk of responsibility for utilization review remained, as before, in the hands of the medical staff at local institutions who devised and operated individual PSRO programs, a situation that many disappointed critics called a case of "the fox guarding the henhouse."[171]

As early as October 1971, John Colloton and the Hospital Advisory Committee had anticipated the trend toward more formal and more substantive utilization review structures and, in preparation for that change, began a reorganization of the hospitals' review function, placing it under the advisory committee's professional practice/utilization review subcommittee and setting up a prototype review program in urology.[172] By the time of the designation of the Iowa PSRO in late 1975, the hospitals' reorganized utilization review mechanism was in place and functioning, with the hope at least that the utilization review process would encourage physicians to become more aware of cost and quality issues. Yet at the University of Iowa Hospitals, as elsewhere, costs continued to climb during the 1970s. In July 1979, Colloton explained several contributing factors to the board of regents, including the rapid advance in the general inflation rate, adverse changes in the hospitals and clinics patient mix, an increased staff-to-patient ratio, and increasing technological sophistication in diagnostic and therapeutic procedures. Despite a marked reduction in both average length of stay and number of beds since 1965 and an occupancy rate of more than 83 percent, the University of Iowa Hospitals and Clinics' per diem costs had risen 61.2 percent since 1972, to $347 per patient. Still, Colloton noted, the recent rate of increase and the current per diem cost at University Hospitals compared favorably with national figures of 82.9 percent and $500 respectively.[173]

In addition to its PSRO requirements, P.L. 92-603, in section 227, mandated that the patient base of teaching hospitals must include at least 50 percent private patients in order to qualify for reimbursement of physicians' services on the basis of "usual and customary" charges. Hospitals failing to meet that standard—presumed, then, to be indigent care institutions—

would receive reimbursement on a cost basis. At the University of Iowa, the difference in the two reimbursement formulas posed a dire threat to Medical Service Plan revenues, and the 1972–73 patient census of 31,357 included just 10,379 private patients, or barely more than 33 percent. In large part, at least in the view of the hospitals and clinics administration, the problem was a conceptual one having to do with the assignment of patients into the three traditional classifications, private, indigent, and clinical pay, and the imperfect decision—based on patient resources—to place some two-thirds of Medicare patients in the clinical pay category. By the simple act of shifting roughly 4,000 Medicare patients from clinical pay to private status along with other clinical patients with some insurance coverage, the University Hospitals could achieve the 50 percent private patient goal.[174] For the longer term, however, the hospitals and clinics administration initiated changes aimed at creating a single class of care for all patients.

As it happened, implementation of section 227 was at first stayed and ultimately canceled, but it nonetheless had a lasting effect, graphically displayed in Table 5.9, page 340. From 1973 into the early 1980s, the number of clinical pay patients declined steeply, falling 27.5 percent from 1973 to 1974 and a total of 74.5 percent from 1970 to 1982. The clinical pay category comprised 29.6 percent of all patient admissions in 1972–1973, but only 5.9 percent in 1981–1982, approaching fulfillment of the medical faculty's 1973 plea to achieve "the total elimination of the clinical pay category with all possible speed."[175] In the same period, the private patient classification showed an increase from 33.0 to 62.8 percent of total patient admissions. Section 227, then, was a catalyst in the conversion to a single patient classification in the University of Iowa Hospitals and Clinics, which the administration considered one of the greatest achievements of the era.

A fourth major provision of P.L. 92-603, meant to impose limits on claims for "usual and customary" charges, set ceilings on Medicare reimbursement for the cost of routine hospital services based on each hospital's size, its location, and the per capita income of the surrounding community. Initially, this provision posed no threat to the University of Iowa Hospitals and Clinics because of their comparatively low per diem charges. However, the Health Care Finance Administration (HCFA), responsible for administering the Medicare and Medicaid programs, made important changes in reimbursement formulas in 1979, the most important of which would classify the University Hospitals as a rural hospital and drastically diminish allowable reimbursement rates. Under the proposed new guidelines, HCFA would lower the University Hospitals' per diem reimbursement 40 percent, at a cost of some $3.8 million dollars in annual revenues. John Colloton and University of Iowa President Willard Boyd—joining with officials at the University of Virginia who faced the same plight—successfully lobbied

HCFA to exempt the hospitals and clinics based on the institution's similarity to large urban hospitals in terms of specialized services and patient mix.[176]

A fifth element of P.L. 92-603 was its mandate for statewide healthcare planning, a concept first embodied in a 1966 federal law that required states to undertake state and areawide comprehensive planning to assure access to quality healthcare. The emphasis on health planning helped to solidify the University of Iowa Hospitals and Clinics' position as Iowa's tertiary care facility; however, it also for the first time formally recognized that Iowa could support at least one competing tertiary center. In 1972, the Health Manpower Committee of the Iowa Comprehensive Health Planning Council, headed by college of medicine assistant dean John C. MacQueen, proposed a regional, stratified healthcare system for Iowa and defined the cardinal points of tertiary care as "specialized medical, diagnostic, and therapeutic services for unusual and complicated cases that require specialized care," "specialized surgical care for unusual and complicated cases (neurosurgery, organ transplants, etc.)," "emergency care," and "specialized surgical dental services." Under the committee's proposal, a tertiary health center would serve a population of "at least 1,500,000 people" and would marshall "a full complement of medical and surgical specialists (as well as dentists and allied health care personnel) so that all types of medical and surgical procedures [could] be provided, e.g., open heart surgery, neurosurgery, radiation therapy, endocrine and metabolic studies, rehabilitation services, and emergency care." Moreover, a tertiary care center would be "affiliated with a large modern hospital or hospitals capable of providing all special service units, e.g., intensive care units, pediatric high-risk units, rehabilitation units," and would also "be a center for training all types of health personnel, but [with] a particular emphasis . . . placed on training physicians in subspecialty training." In the committee's estimation, Iowa's only two sites fulfilling the criteria for tertiary care centers were the University of Iowa Hospitals and Clinics and the Des Moines area hospitals.[177]

P.L. 92-603 charged such state health planning bodies with developing regional planning guidelines with respect to the three levels of care, a task completed by the Iowa Office for Comprehensive Health Planning in 1974.[178] In an attempt to rationalize investment in costly facilities and technology under the hierarchical scheme, the next Congress enacted the National Health Planning and Resource Development Act, P.L. 93-641, creating a new system of Health Systems Agencies to replace the previous generation of comprehensive health planning agencies. Financed by the federal government, the HSAs—governed by consumer majorities on their boards—were to review plans for new facilities and to make recommendations regarding need. As part of that process, the act also required states to create statewide planning and development agencies and to enact certificate-of-need legislation, which would make hospitals accountable for large investments in new services. Together, as Paul Starr has noted, the 1972 social security amendments and the 1974 planning laws were important milestones, not only expected to effect substantial reforms in the healthcare system but also constituting "a decisive rejection of the view that the market could correct itself and that the doctors and hospitals had the last word on how medical care ought to be organized."[179]

The Iowa legislature passed a certificate-of-need law in 1977, creating the Health Facilities Council. In part at least because John Colloton and Max Hawkins, the university's lobbyist in Des Moines, helped draft the bill along with Robert Rush, a state legislator from Cedar Rapids, the 1977 law also explicitly recognized the statewide tertiary care role of the University of Iowa Hospitals and Clinics, stipulating that in evaluating certificate-of-need applications "the unique capacity of university hospitals for the evaluation of technologically innovative equipment and other new health services shall be utilized."[180] By that time, the hospitals and clinics had already invested considerable effort in promoting its tertiary care image. A February 1973 conference, for example, entitled "Strengthening the Health Care System in Iowa," highlighted the comprehensive nature of the university's facilities, services, and personnel. At the time of that conference, the Hospital Advisory Committee reiterated the importance of the hospitals and clinics' 600 physicians in 15 specialty and 47 subspecialty areas and the highly specialized services they afforded, including cardiac catheterization, a burn center, a neonatal intensive care unit, end-stage kidney dialysis and transplantation, a high-risk obstetrical clinic, and laser and cryosurgery services in ophthalmology.

In the decade after the institutionalization of the tertiary care center concept, utilization of the tertiary services available at the University of Iowa Hospitals and Clinics expanded steadily. By 1983, for example, some 1,500 patients underwent cardiac catheterization annually, compared to 800 just ten years before, while the high-risk obstetrical service treated 1,200 patients, compared to 750 in 1973. The menu of services also continually expanded. Among the newest were cochlear implants, orthopædic microvascular surgery, and microsurgery in the treatment of melanoma, a procedure then available at only twenty hospitals nationwide. Surely the most dramatic new services were the organ transplant programs, which, in the public mind at least, virtually defined the tertiary care center. In addition to growth in the kidney and corneal transplants begun in 1973, the hospitals and clinics had, by 1983, inaugurated pancreas and bone marrow transplantation programs. Underlying those more public services were a host of less publicized technological innovations. Overall, the hospitals and clinics invested a total of $7 million in advanced diagnostic and therapeutic equipment from 1970 to 1976 and an additional $35 million from 1976 to 1982. Among the acquisitions were IBM mainframe computers and upgrades, imaging scanners for head and whole-body images, pulmonary function computer systems, and whole-body computerized axial tomography (CAT) scanners.

By the end of the 1970s, such massive investments in healthcare technology were multiplied many times over at hospitals and private offices and laboratories across the nation and were often cited as factors in the alarming increase in healthcare costs, an increase that outstripped even the unprecedented general rate of inflation. In turn, a broad national consensus concluded that PSROs and other cost-containment measures had failed. By 1982, national healthcare expenditures reached $1,365 per capita, with hospital care accounting for 42 percent of that total. The federal government shouldered 29.2 percent of the total healthcare bill and some 53 percent of hospital charges.[181] In the eyes of critics, the reasons for that failure were manifold, ranging from the burdensome investment in technology to the unshakable opposition of many, if not most, physicians to the concept of utilization review in particular and cost containment in general. Moreover, critics agreed, too, that utilization review and other cost-containment measures, as currently constituted, were seriously flawed by inherent statutory and administrative weaknesses.

In an address to the North Central Medical Conference in November 1977, John Colloton acknowledged that the explosion in medical scientific knowledge and technologies was responsible for major cost increases in healthcare, but he also pointed to other factors, such as the extension of collective bargaining to hospitals, as significant contributions to the cost spiral.[182] Once again, Colloton charged hospitals with failing to educate the public on the causes and benefits of increasing hospital costs. Commonly cited life expectancy and infant mortality figures, in which the United States fared poorly compared to other industrialized nations, Colloton claimed, were not valid barometers of the efficacy of the health system; nor were comparisons of healthcare costs as a percentage of GNP. Moreover, he noted that, according to American Hospital Association calculations, the hospital service charge component of the consumer price index tended to overstate increases in real costs. Iowa hospitals, Colloton pointed out, had performed far better than national averages in terms of costs per admission (26 percent below the national average), costs per patient day (25 percent below the national average), and hospital costs per capita (13 percent below the national average). In closing, Colloton turned the discussion from supply to demand and to the responsibilities of consumers in controlling healthcare costs, a theme of increasing importance in the following decade.

Conclusion

The period from 1965 to 1982 brought fundamental change in many of the basic premises underlying America's university teaching hospitals and the academic medical centers of which they were a part. Before 1965, most such hospitals were chiefly devoted, first, to the training of physicians—and, to a lesser extent, allied health professionals—and, second, to the care of the medically indigent. Such was the case at the University of Iowa Hospitals. Prospects for growth at most university teaching hospitals were severely limited, since operating and capital budgets were normally dependent on appropriations by state and local governments or, in rare moments, on philanthropic contributions. In that environment, growth was episodic and unpredictable, and the concept of strategic planning had little place. This, too, was the case at the University of Iowa Hospitals.

In many ways as outgrowths of trends traceable to the early postwar years, events from the late 1960s to the early 1980s challenged the quiet certainties of America's university teaching hospitals. Most important was the way in which federal programs and money fundamentally transformed the larger healthcare system, often in unforeseen ways. The Medicare and Medicaid programs that converted a great part of the medically indigent population into market actors, free to choose among available providers, were key elements in that transformation. Medicare and Medicaid substantially enhanced revenues for teaching hospitals, bringing an unprecedented degree of fiscal autonomy, bolstering cash reserves, and providing surety for the revenue bonds that, as at the University of Iowa Hospitals and Clinics, helped finance massive construction projects. However, the Medicare and Medicaid programs presented two faces. Just as they bolstered cash-strapped teaching hospitals, Medicare and Medicaid—in league with the billions of dollars in Hill-Burton hospital construction funds that had been disbursed since 1946—also enhanced competition for teaching hospitals' traditional patient base. Moreover, Medicare and Medicaid balanced financial benefits on the one hand with increasingly insistent regulatory demands on the other.

A second major result of the expanded federal role in healthcare, also with significant ramifications for university teaching hospitals, was the conversion of colleges of medicine into research institutions. Federal programs to support medical scientific research and to train future generations of researchers fueled that conversion directly, while income from patient fees—driven by a combination of public and private health insurance—contributed indirectly by helping to finance an aggressive expansion in the ranks of clinical faculty. The exponential growth in faculty numbers and in research and associated training programs was especially important for university-owned teaching hospitals like the University of Iowa Hospitals and Clinics, where the demands of medical scientific research and the constant growth in faculty numbers loomed large in the expansion of hospital facilities and mandated a coordinated approach to strategic planning for the college of medicine and the hospitals.

Overall, the exuberant growth at the University of Iowa medical center in the 1970s reinforced the mutual interdependence of the college of medicine and the hospitals and clinics. Paradoxically, however, the extraordinarily rapid pace of growth and internal differentiation, in the context of constantly shifting external economic and political environments, also increased the potential for friction between the college and the hospitals, each of which had historically struggled to maintain its own identity and freedom of action. Indeed, in light of their long history of ambivalence marked by occasional episodes of intense conflict, the degree of good will and cooperation between the two institutions was one of the more remarkable features of the 1970s and early 1980s. Three principal players, augmented by an extensive supporting cast, were essential to that outcome: first, John Colloton, the savvy and gifted protegé of Gerhard Hartman and Glen Clasen, whose forceful personality and vision took the hospitals and clinics in new directions, often, it seemed, with the state board of regents in tow; second, John Eckstein, the scientist-turned-dean whose confidence in his abilities, his place, and his mission guided the college of medicine into the research era; and third, Willard Boyd, the university president who appreciated the significance of changes underway in the academic medical center and served as facilitator to both the director and the dean.

Importantly, however, despite the enormous strides of the 1970s and early 1980s, the transformation of the University of Iowa medical center was not yet finished in 1982. The years from 1982 to the mid-1990s were to bring continued capital development and renovation, continued growth in patient service and in revenues, and continued expansion in faculty and staff numbers. Meanwhile, at a national level, the perceived failures of the 1970s, particularly in the area of cost control, led, first, to more rigorous federal cost-control efforts; second, to reforms meant to achieve cost savings through greater market competition, including the reinvigoration of the HMO concept; and, third, to demands from health insurance companies and large employers for a greater voice in the organization and delivery of healthcare services. The University of Iowa Hospitals and Clinics was to emerge as a significantly larger institution, better appointed and staffed than in 1982 and reoriented toward a competitive environment. Yet the long period of sustained growth—accompanied by increasing regulatory and market pressures—intensified some old challenges and gave birth to new ones, the combination of which, among their other effects, strained the working relationship between the hospitals and clinics and the college of medicine.

Notes

1. William G. Rothstein, *American Medical Schools and the Practice of Medicine*, p. 238.

2. John A. D. Cooper, "Undergraduate Medical Education," in John Z. Bowers and Elizabeth F. Purcell, eds., *Advances in American Medicine: Essays at the Bicentennial*, vol. 1 (New York: Josiah Macy, Jr. Foundation, 1976), p. 277.

3. Ibid.

4. *Health Manpower: Perspective 1967*, Public Health Service Publication Number 1667 (Washington, DC: Government Printing Office, 1967).

5. William Rothstein, *American Medical Schools and the Practice of Medicine*, pp. 283–287.

6. John A. D. Cooper, "Undergraduate Medical Education," p. 277.

7. William Rothstein, *American Medical Schools and the Practice of Medicine*, p. 285.

8. *Journal of the American Medical Association* 234 (December 29, 1975): 1334–1335.

9. See President's Commission on Heart Disease, Cancer, and Stroke, *Report to the President: A National Program to Conquer Heart Disease, Cancer, and Stroke*, 2 vols. (Washington, DC: Government Printing Office, 1964, 1965).

10. Rosemary Stevens, *American Medicine and the Public Interest*, pp. 513–514.

11. See, for example, Paul Starr, *The Social Transformation of American Medicine*, p. 370.

12. *The Gallup Poll: Public Opinion, 1935–1971*, vol. 2 (New York: Random House, 1972), pp. 802–803.

13. For a well-considered perspective on events leading up to passage of Medicare and Medicaid legislation, see Sheri David, *With Dignity: The Search for Medicare and Medicaid* (Westport, CT: Greenwood Press, 1985).

14. *The Gallup Poll*, vol. 3, pp. 1721, 1759–1760.

15. Rosemary Stevens, *American Medicine and the Public Interest*, pp. 436–437.

16. U.S. Department of Health and Human Services, *Health: United States, 1982* (Washington, DC: Government Printing Office), pp. 153–154.

17. Ibid., p. 151.

18. Hospital Advisory Committee Minutes, September 20, 1967, University of Iowa Hospitals and Clinics Administrative Offices.

19. University of Iowa Hospitals and Clinics Finance Director, Annual Statistical Reports, 1965–1970.

20. "U of I/VA Team Performs First Kidney Transplants," *Iowa Alumni Review* (December 1969/January 1970): 15.

21. Transplantation Committee Minutes, October 23, 1969, Box 15, College of Medicine Archives.

22. R. C. Hardin to M. Ludwig, February 2, 1968, File 65, 1967–68, H. R. Bowen Papers, University of Iowa Archives.

23. See Max Elder, "A Public Relations Program for the University of Iowa Health Center," Minutes of the University of Iowa Hospitals and Clinics Hospital Advisory Committee, July 1968–July 1969, University of Iowa Hospitals and Clinics Administrative Offices.

24. F. G. Ober, "President's Address," *Journal of the Iowa Medical Society* 56 (July 1966): 647.

25. For an overview of the Regional Medical Program concept, see Ralph W. Yarborough, "Alleviating Fragmented Systems of Health Care: The Regional Medical Programs," *Journal of Medical Education* 45 (June 1970): 411–414. For specifics concerning the background and operation of the Iowa program, see Iowa Regional Medical Program, *Annual Report, 1970*.

26. John A. D. Cooper, "Undergraduate Medical Education," p. 289.

27. *Health Manpower: Perspective 1967*, Public Health Service Publication Number 1667 (Washington, DC: Government Printing Office, 1967).

28. Howard Bowen, *The University of Iowa: The President's Report*, September 1, 1965, pp. 8–9.

29. "Medical Education in the United States," *Journal of the American Medical Association* 198 (November 21, 1966): 847–938; "Medical Education in the United States," *Journal of the American Medical Association* 218 (November 22, 1971): 1199–1278.

30. Davis G. Johnson, "The Study of Applicants, 1964–65," *Journal of Medical Education* 40 (November 1965): 1017–1030.

31. *Journal of the American Medical Association* 214 (November 23, 1970): 1512.

32. Edwin Hutchins and Helen Hofer Gee, "The Study of Applicants, 1960–61," *Journal of Medical Education* 36 (April 1961): 289–304.

33. Howard Bowen, *The President's Report, 1965*, p. 17.

34. *Journal of the American Medical Association* 234 (December 29, 1975): 1336, 1338, 1410.

35. Liaison Committee Report, File 65G, 1960–61, Virgil M. Hancher Papers, University of Iowa Archives.

36. William Rothstein, *American Medical Schools and the Practice of Medicine*, pp. 318–319; Rosemary Stevens, *American Medicine and the Public Interest*, p. 393.

37. See "The Dilemma of the Internship," *Journal of Medical Education* 39 (May 1964): 437–443; William Rothstein, *American Medical Schools and the Practice of Medicine*, pp. 302–303.

38. Statistics taken from "Medical Education in the United States," *Journal of the American Medical Association* 198 (November 21, 1966): 847–938; "Medical Education in the United States," *Journal of the American Medical Association* 218 (November 22, 1971): 1199–1278.

39. Department of Internal Medicine, *Annual Report, 1969–70*, p. 7.

40. Again, statistics taken from "Medical Education in the United States," *Journal of the American Medical Association* 198 (November 21, 1966): 847–938; "Medical Education in the United States," *Journal of the American Medical Association* 218 (November 22, 1971): 1199–1278.

41. Medical Council Minutes, August 20, 1968, University of Iowa College of Medicine Archives.

42. University Hospitals Service Records, University of Iowa Hospitals and Clinics Office of Public Information.

43. L. R. Garlock to H. R. Bowen, October 22, 1968, File 64, 1968–69, H. R. Bowen Papers, University of Iowa Archives.

44. The Citizens Commission on Graduate Medical Education, *The Graduate Education of Physicians* (Chicago: The American Medical Association, 1966).

45. Medical Council Minutes, May 14, 1968, College of Medicine Archives.

46. Board of Regents Minutes, September 12, 1968, University of Iowa Archives.

47. R. C. Hardin, "Does Iowa Need Another Medical School?" File 64, 1968–69, H. R. Bowen Papers, University of Iowa Archives.

48. See Board of Regents Minutes, December 11, 1969, January 15, 1970, and September 10, 1970, University of Iowa Archives.

49. H. R. Bowen, "Notes on Administrative Reorganization of the University of Iowa," File 65, 1966–67, H. R. Bowen Papers, University of Iowa Archives.

50. See H. R. Bowen to R. C. Hardin, "Some Notes on the Future of Medical Service at the University of Iowa," n.d., File 65, 1968–69, H. R. Bowen Papers, University of Iowa Archives.

51. See "Notes on Administrative Reorganization of the University of Iowa," op. cit.

52. V. M. Hancher to Medical Faculty, April 24, 1950, File 115, 1949–50, V. M. Hancher Papers, University of Iowa Archives.

53. H. R. Bowen to Medical Faculty, July 6, 1966, University of Iowa Department of Internal Medicine Archives.

54. Agenda of the Meeting of Executive Committee with President Bowen, December 17, 1968, Executive Committee Minutes, December 19, 1968, College of Medicine Archives.

55. Much of this discussion is adapted from Lee Anderson, *Internal Medicine and the Structures of Modern Medical Science* (Ames: Iowa State University Press, 1996), pp. 204–207.

56. Raymond Sheets Papers, Minutes and Other Documents Related to the Ad Hoc Committee on Faculty Participation in the College of Medicine Affairs, 1967–68, University of Iowa Archives; see also Stow Persons, *The University of Iowa in the Twentieth Century,* pp, 236–241.

57. Executive Committee Minutes, February 17, 1969, College of Medicine Archives.

58. Hospital Advisory Committee Minutes, September 9, 1967, November 15, 1967, and February 21, 1968, University of Iowa Hospitals and Clinics Administrative Offices.

59. See, for example, the report on the 1969–70 budget hearings in the March 19, 1969 minutes of the Hospital Advisory Committee, September 1967–June 1969 volume, University of Iowa Hospitals and Clinics Administrative Offices.

60. Iowa State Department of Health, "Iowa Plan for Hospitals and Related Health Facilities," July 1, 1963, University of Iowa Hospitals and Clinics Administrative Offices.

61. Department of Internal Medicine, *Annual Report, 1965–66,* p. 2.

62. Gerhard Hartman, "Study Document Regarding University of Iowa Hospitals and the Era of Increasing Federal Involvement in Health," Gerhard Hartman Papers, Off-Site Storage, Oakdale Campus.

63. G. Clasen to H. R. Bowen, April 18, 1967, "Testimony Relating to Senate File 532, Submitted to House of Representatives Sixty-Second Iowa General Assembly," University of Iowa Hospitals and Clinics Administrative Offices.

64. G. Hartman, "Study Document Regarding University of Iowa Hospitals and the Era of Increasing Federal Involvement in Health," op. cit. After reviewing the impact of increased federal involvement on the University Hospitals, Hartman concluded: "The nation's medical centers are faced with the choice of expanding their facilities, services, and teaching and research programs within the framework laid down by the health programs of the 'Great Society' or being relegated to lesser positions within the nation's health network."

65. G. Hartman, "Study Document Regarding University of Iowa Hospitals and the Era of Increasing Federal Involvement in Health," op. cit.

66. With more effective treatment for tuberculosis and better hygiene and sanitation, the number of patients at Oakdale at any given time fell far below the sanitarium's capacity of 380 beds, and by the early 1960s most officials connected to the hospital knew that it was underutilized. In 1964 the Iowa legislature transferred administration of the sanitarium to the University Hospitals, clearing the way for Oakdale's facilities to be put to use for other services and research activities.

67. Executive Committee Minutes, October 14, 1963, College of Medicine Archives.

68. H. R. Bowen to Board of Regents, May 4, 1966, File 41, 1965–66, H. R. Bowen Papers, University of Iowa Archives.

69. File 6, 1965–66, H. R. Bowen Papers, University of Iowa Archives.

70. Executive Committee Minutes, September 21, 1964, College of Medicine Archives.

71. H. R. Bowen to R. Burger, December 20, 1965, File 46, 1965–66, H. R. Bowen Papers, University of Iowa Archives.

72. H. R. Bowen to Board of Regents, June 18, 1965, File 6, 1964–65, H. R. Bowen Papers, University of Iowa Archives. Sasaki's review took place in early May and concluded that the Iowa River should be the geographic center, uniting the campus. They also emphasized the importance of keeping the campus pedestrian oriented, aiming to keep all academic buildings within a five-minute walk of the Old Capitol and all medical center buildings within easy walking distance of the hospital. See also H. R. Bowen to P. Seebohm, May 10, 1965, File 65F, 1964–65, H. R. Bowen Papers, University of Iowa Archives.

73. See H. R. Bowen to R. C. Hardin, July 5, 1966, File 65, 1966–67, H. R. Bowen Papers, University of Iowa Archives. Interestingly, it appears that the medical center was the last planning done by

the Sasaki firm; soon after, the architectural firm of Skidmore, Owings, and Merrill took on planning tasks.

74. "Sources of Construction Funds for Teaching Hospitals, 1977," *Journal of Medical Education* 54 (August 1979): 669–671.

75. "Report of the President," in *Report of the State Board of Regents, 1966*, p. 57.

76. As early as 1927, the Iowa General Assembly had in fact authorized the regents to issue bonds in order to construct buildings at the University of Iowa. See Board of Regents Minutes, March 10, 1927, University of Iowa Archives.

77. Board of Regents Minutes, July 14, 1966, University of Iowa Archives.

78. Board of Regents Minutes, May 11, 1967, University of Iowa Archives.

79. Robert Hardin, "Oral History Interview," 1976/77, by James Beilman, University of Iowa Archives.

80. Board of Regents Minutes, June 12, 1968, University of Iowa Archives.

81. Rosemary Stevens, *In Sickness and in Wealth*, pp. 293–294.

82. Executive Committee Minutes, July 11, 1968, College of Medicine Archives.

83. Medical Council Minutes, July 21, 1966; Executive Committee Minutes, June 26, 1967, College of Medicine Archives.

84. The four subcommittees were "Emergency Clinic," chaired by S. E. Ziffren, "Operating Suite," chaired by D. A. Culp, "Outpatient Clinic," chaired by A. L. Sahs, and the "Diagnostic Roentgenographic Suite," chaired by H. B. Latourette.

85. Glen Clasen and associates, *Perspective for Planning the University of Iowa Hospitals and Clinics*, University of Iowa Hospitals and Clinics Administrative Offices.

86. Executive Committee Minutes, July 11, 1968, College of Medicine Archives.

87. R. C. Hardin to Executive Committee, Medical Faculty, and Medical Council, July 13, 1968, College of Medicine Archives.

88. Medical Faculty Minutes, July 30, 1968, College of Medicine Archives.

89. December 17, 1968 Agenda of the Meeting of Executive Committee with President Bowen, Executive Committee Minutes, December 19, 1969, College of Medicine Archives.

90. Board of Regents Minutes, May 9, 1968, University of Iowa Archives.

91. The building usage fund was composed of earnings from a capital replacement fraction included in payments from Medicare and private insurance carriers.

92. Board of Regents Minutes, March 13, 1969.

93. "Application for Federal Assistance for Construction of Health and Educational Facilities: Phase I, Capital Development for the University Hospital," University of Iowa Hospitals and Clinics Administrative Offices.

94. Ibid., p. 1.

95. Robert Hardin, "Oral History Interview," pp. 32, 33.

96. J. W. Eckstein to W. L. Boyd, April 1, 1970, File 64, 1969–70, W. L. Boyd Papers, University of Iowa Archives.

97. J. W. Eckstein to W. L. Boyd, April 1, 1970, File 64, 1969–70, W. L. Boyd Papers, University of Iowa Archives.

98. Medical Council Minutes, August 5, 1971, College of Medicine Archives.

99. Medical Council Minutes, October 3, 1974, College of Medicine Archives.

100. Board of Regents Minutes, December 13, 1973, University of Iowa Archives.

101. J. W. Eckstein to W. L. Boyd, April 1, 1970, File 64, 1969–70, W. L. Boyd Papers, University of Iowa Archives.

102. Thomas Turner, "Medical Schools Twenty Years Afterward: Impact of Extramural Support Programs of NIH," *Journal of Medical Education* 42 (1967): 109.

103. Executive Committee Minutes, February 5 and November 12, 1973, College of Medicine Archives.

104. Figures from the UI Office of the Vice President for Research, Division of Sponsored Programs.

105. Board of Regents Minutes, December 13, 1973, University of Iowa Archives. See also Executive Committee Annual Report, June 18, 1976, for special needs appropriations, 1973–75.

106. U. S. Public Health Service, National Institutes of Health Grants and Awards, Serial Publication 20.3013, p. 970.

107. W. L. Boyd to R. C. Hardin, April 8, 1970, File 64, 1969–70, W. L. Boyd Papers, University of Iowa Archives.

108. W. L. Boyd to R. C. Hardin, September 10, 1974, File 34, 1974–75, W. L. Boyd Papers, University of Iowa Archives.

109. The Liaison Committee Report, based upon March 27–April 1, 1971, File 64A, 1971–72, W. L. Boyd Papers, University of Iowa Archives.

110. W. L. Boyd to J. W. Eckstein, August 16, 1975, File 44, 1975–76, W. L. Boyd Papers, University of Iowa Archives.

111. G. Hartman to R. C. Hardin, June 11, 1971, "Search Committee Report, University of Iowa Hospitals Director," John Colloton personal files, referred to below as Office of the Vice President for Statewide Health Services. Those files contain a chronology of documents and comment compiled by Colloton and serve as the basis for much of this narrative.

112. Search Committee Report, Office of the Vice President for Statewide Health Services.

113. Search Committee to R. C. Hardin, August 4, 1971, Search Committee Report, "Committee Recommendation," Office of the Vice President for Statewide Health Services.

114. J. Moyers to R. H. Flocks, August 2, 1971; D. Dunphy to Flocks, August 3, 1971, Search Committee Report, "Clinical and Hospital Department Heads Supporting Letters," Office of the Vice President for Statewide Health Services.

115. J. W. Eckstein to R. C. Hardin, August 10, 1971; L. Dustan to Hardin, August 5, 1971, Search Committee Report, "Health Science Deans Supporting Letters," Office of the Vice President for Statewide Health Services.

116. W. L. Boyd to R. C. Hardin, September 2, 1971, File 41, 1971–72, W. L. Boyd Papers, University of Iowa Archives.

117. J. W. Colloton memorandum, September 22, 1971, included with Colloton to W. L. Boyd, September 28, 1971, File 41, 1971–72, W. L. Boyd Papers, University of Iowa Archives.

118. J. W. Colloton, "Salary Talk" notes, Search Committee Report, "Interviews," Office of the Vice President for Statewide Health Services.

119. J. W. Colloton to W. L. Boyd, September 28, 1971, File 41, 1971–72, W. L. Boyd Papers, University of Iowa Archives.

120. R. C. Hardin to W. L. Boyd, attached to Colloton to Boyd, September 28, 1971, Ibid.

121. J. W. Colloton to W. L. Boyd, October 1, 1971 [two drafts], Search Committee Report, "Meetings and Corres. with Pres. Boyd," Office of the Vice President for Statewide Health Services.

122. J. W. Colloton, notes in Search Committee Report, "Interviews."

123. Robert Hardin's document is attached to a September 11, 1973, memorandum from Willard Boyd to various university officials, File 41, 1973–74, W. L. Boyd Papers, University of Iowa Archives.

124. Hospital Advisory Committee Minutes, August 20, 1973, University of Iowa Hospitals and Clinics Administrative Files, Board of Regents minutes, September 13, 1973, University of Iowa Archives.

125. J. W. Colloton to D. Nagel, July 28, 1974; Colloton to W. L. Boyd, September 12, 1974, File 34G, 1974–75, W. L. Boyd Papers, University of Iowa Archives.

126. W. L. Boyd to J. W. Colloton, January 18, 1975, File 34G, 1974–75, W. L. Boyd Papers, University of Iowa Archives.

127. See Irving J. Lewis and Cecil G. Sheps, *The Sick Citadel: The American Academic Medical Center and the Public Interest* (Cambridge, MA: Oelgeschlager, Gunn & Hain, Publishers, Inc., 1983), pp. 203–204.

128. "Bylaws, Rules and Regulations of the University of Iowa Hospitals and Clinics and its Clinical Staff," University of Iowa Hospitals and Clinics Administrative Offices.

129. D. R. Williamson notes, September 20, 1973, on summation conference with JCAH reviewers, appended to JCAH review, University of Iowa Hospitals and Clinics Off-Site Storage.

130. Notes on summation conference with JCAH reviewers, October 23, 1975, appended to 1975 review, University of Iowa Hospitals and Clinics Off-Site Storage.

131. J. W. Colloton memorandum, June 10, 1977, appended to the JCAH 1977 review, University of Iowa Hospitals and Clinics Off-Site Storage.

132. *Iowa City Press-Citizen*, August 2, 1980.

133. *Cedar Rapids Gazette*, August 8, 1980.

134. The University of Iowa *Daily Iowan*, August 1, 1980.

135. Ibid. See also, for example, the *Des Moines Register*, August 2, 1980; the *Cedar Rapids Gazette*, August 1, 1980.

136. *Daily Iowan*, op. cit.

137. James Roberts, Jack Coate, and Robert Redmen, "History of the Joint Commission on Accreditation of Hospitals," *Journal of the American Medical Association* 258 (August 21, 1987): 938.

138. J. W. Colloton to Department Heads and Hospital Advisory Committee, October 31, 1975, appended to 1975 JCAH survey, University of Iowa Hospitals and Clinics Off-Site Storage, office of Ted Yanks.

139. James Roberts, Jack Coate, and Robert Redmen, "History of the Joint Commission on Accreditation of Hospitals," p. 938.

140. Joint Commission on Accreditation of Hospitals, Review and notes on summation conference, October 15, 1970, University of Iowa Hospitals and Clinics Off-Site Storage.

141. J. W. Colloton memorandum to department heads, June 10, 1977; see JCAH review for 1977.

142. Hospital Advisory Committee Minutes, March 29, 1972, University of Iowa Hospitals and Clinics Administrative Offices.

143. Hospital Advisory Committee Minutes, January 5, 1972, University of Iowa Hospitals and Clinics Administrative Offices.

144. Executive Committee Minutes, April 17, 1972, College of Medicine Archives; Hospital Advisory Committee Minutes, April 19, 1972, University of Iowa Hospitals and Clinics Administrative Offices.

145. J. W. Colloton to W. L. Boyd, May 15, 1972, File 41, 1971–72, W. L. Boyd Papers, University of Iowa Archives.

146. "Re: Background statement for all currently involved in planning University Hospital capital expansion and redevelopment," Executive Committee Minutes, October 5, 1972, College of Medicine Archives.

147. J. W. Colloton to W. L. Boyd, May 31, 1972, File 42A, 1971–72, W. L. Boyd Papers, University of Iowa Archives.

148. J. W. Colloton to W. L. Boyd, May 31, 1972, File 42A, 1971–72, W. L. Boyd Papers, University of Iowa Archives.

149. Hospital Advisory Committee Minutes, January 5, 1972, University of Iowa Hospitals and Clinics Administrative Offices.

150. For approval, see Board of Regents Minutes, April 13, 1972, University of Iowa Archives.

151. W. L. Boyd to Thomas Hodne, April 11, 1972, File 33, 1971–72, W. L. Boyd Papers, University of Iowa Archives.

152. R. E. Gibson to W. L. Boyd, April 25, 1972, File 33, 1971–72, W. L. Boyd Papers, University of Iowa Archives.

153. R. C. Hardin to W. L. Boyd, May 17, 1972, File 41, 1971–72, W. L. Boyd Papers, University of Iowa Archives.

154. T. Hodne to W. L. Boyd, May 14, 1972, File 33, 1971–72, W. L. Boyd Papers, University of Iowa Archives.

155. Board of Regents Minutes, October 19, 1972; March 8, 1973; June 18, 1973; July 26, 1973, University of Iowa Archives.

156. Board of Regents Minutes, September 19, 1974, and November 13, 1974, University of Iowa Archives.

157. See University of Iowa Hospitals and Clinics, "Statewide Service and Educational Roles and Capital Replacement Plan with Associated Financing," September 1987, University of Iowa Hospitals and Clinics Administrative Offices.

158. Board of Regents Minutes, January 19, 1979, University of Iowa Archives.

159. Board of Regents Minutes, September 15, 1977, University of Iowa Archives.

160. Medical Council Minutes, October 15, 1981, College of Medicine Archives.

161. American Hospital Association, *Hospitals Guides.*

162. Board of Regents Minutes, October 16, 1975, University of Iowa Archives.

163. Tali Neumann, "The Administrations of Marie E. Tener, Hellen F. Watters, Myrtle Kitchell Aydelotte, and Mary E. Fuller: Four Directors of Nursing Service, the University of Iowa Hospitals and Clinics, 1949–1979" (Master's Thesis, University of Iowa, 1987), p. 166.

164. Sally Mathis to Mary Fuller, February 23, 1981, University of Iowa Hospitals and Clinics Department of Nursing.

165. *Health, United States, 1984* (Washington, DC: Department of Health and Human Services, 1984), pp. 137, 158, 139.

166. John J. Moscato, "Federal Health Legislation: Overview and Assessment." In Samuel Levey and Thomas McCarthy, eds., *Health Management for Tomorrow* (Philadelphia: JB Lippincott Company, 1980), pp. 20–35.

167. John Colloton, "A New Beginning," Address to the Iowa Hospital Association, 1977, File 32.7, "University Hospitals," 1976–77, W. L. Boyd Papers, University of Iowa Archives.

168. For discussion, see Paul Starr, *The Social Transformation of American Medicine,* pp. 396–398.

169. For a biting commentary, see J. Warren Salmon, "The Health Maintenance Organization Strategy: A Corporate Takeover of Health Services Delivery," *International Journal of Health Services* 5 (1975): 609–624.

170. "Report of the Committee on Finance, United States Senate," *Legislative History of Professional Standards Review Organizations* (Washington, DC: Department of Health, Education and Welfare, 1977), pp. 2–3.

171. Paul Starr attributes the reference to Ralph Nader, *The Social Transformation of American Medicine,* p. 400.

172. Hospital Advisory Committee Minutes, October 27, 1971, and December 4, 1974, University of Iowa Hospitals and Clinics Administrative Offices; Executive Committee Minutes, June 4, 1973, College of Medicine Archives.

173. Board of Regents Minutes, July 18, 1979, University of Iowa Archives.

174. Hospital Advisory Committee Minutes, February 20, 1973, and September 12, 1973, University of Iowa Hospitals and Clinics Administrative Offices.

175. Medical Faculty Minutes, October 3, 1973, College of Medicine Archives.

176. Board of Regents Minutes, May 17, 1979, University of Iowa Archives.

177. John C. MacQueen and Eber Eldridge, *A Proposed Organizational Structure for Providing Health Services and Medical Care in the State of Iowa*, Iowa Comprehensive Health Planning Council, August 1972.

178. Iowa Office for Comprehensive Health Planning, "State and Planning Area Patterns of Patient Origin and Hospital Utilization," June 1974.

179. Paul Starr, *The Social Transformation of American Medicine*, p. 402.

180. *Acts of the Sixty-Seventh General Assembly, 1977*, Chapter 75.

181. William Rothstein, *American Medical Schools and the Practice of Medicine*, pp. 184–185, 209.

182. John Colloton, Address to the North Central Medical Conference, November 1977, File 30.7, 1977–78, W. L. Boyd Papers, University of Iowa Archives.

6

The University Teaching Hospital's Changing Covenant, 1983–1995

In his chairman's address to the Association of American Medical Colleges' annual meeting in November 1988, University of Iowa Hospitals and Clinics director John Colloton spoke of a covenant between academic medicine and society.[1] This traditional covenant, he asserted, was "based on the mutual understanding of both parties" and "had its origin in trust." In return for academic medicine's "broad societal contributions," society granted academic medical centers "substantial autonomy in the conduct of our programs" and "generous financial support for our educational, research, and patient care missions."

With regard to patient care, Colloton noted that teaching hospitals accounted for more than one-fifth of all hospital admissions in the United States and treated 28 percent of all hospital ambulatory patients. They also provided high proportions of specialized care services such as organ transplantation, open-heart surgery, burn treatment, and trauma centers. "In effect," Colloton observed, "the major teaching hospitals of our nation serve as the 'court of last appeal' for members of our society in need of highly specialized medical services." Moreover, he noted, teaching hospitals provided more than $4.6 billion in free care to medically indigent Americans in 1986.

This patient care service, combined with their teaching and research missions, earned academic medical centers not only substantial autonomy, but considerations as well for the added costs to teaching hospitals of the educational programs, research, advanced technology development, and charity care. Reimbursement under contracts with Medicare, Medicaid, and even private insurers included "cost-plus" and "pass-through" charges that compensated teaching hospitals for their higher costs, allowing them "to operate, until very recent years, without significant financial concern."

But, Colloton warned, "this long-standing and mutually supportive covenant is now encountering substantial stress." Not only had Congress reduced support for graduate medical education through both direct payments and indirect subsidies; some states had implemented payment policies across the board "without appropriate adjustments to reflect the multiple missions and complex patient case mix of teaching hospitals." Thus, Colloton said, various forces had together reduced compensation for teaching hospitals' educational and research missions, traditionally financed through patient care charges. The fault for these problems, Colloton charged, lay in "the changing values and erosion of trust emanating, in large part, from the competition model of delivering and financing medical services." Overall, the injection of "bottom-line values" into healthcare, Colloton said, represented a "massive and perilous experiment."

Critics might quarrel over elements of that covenant thesis; nonetheless, the first four post-World War II decades without doubt constituted an unprecedented—indeed, unimagined—period of prosperity for university teaching hospitals, an era of nearly continuous growth in staff and facilities as well as in programs and services. Moreover, as John Colloton suggested, the university teaching hospital was, throughout much of the period, largely insulated from public scrutiny, its accountability vouchsafed in a well-tended image crafted around good works, chiefly the provision of indigent care, and objective scientific authority. The University of Iowa Hospitals and Clinics symbolized that development, transformed as it was—with remarkably little interference from the state legislature and the board of regents—from an indigent care facility of modest size and reputation to a multifaceted healthcare enterprise with claims to national and, in some specialty areas, international stature.

In retrospect, the cries of alarm so loudly sounded in the 1970s may well have been overblown; certainly, the continued strong growth of the academic medical center and teaching hospital suggested as much. However, more serious concerns surfaced in the 1980s with the advent of prospective payment systems and the embrace by third party payers of market competition as a means of cost control. It was those concerns that formed the basis for John Colloton's remarks before the AAMC, and by the late 1980s, a growing body of literature in medical education and hospital administration focused in one way or another on the impact of an increasingly competitive health-care market on the academic medical center and the teaching hospital.[2] Overall, those critiques centered on two major concerns: first, the ability of the academic health center and teaching hospital to compete in an emerging low-cost, managed care environment, and, second, the financing of graduate medical education in the face of diminished support from third party payers, including the federal government.[3] As an American College of Healthcare Executives report noted in 1987, medical educators and teaching hospital administrators were "extremely uneasy about the prospects of a system in which issues are addressed on the basis of cost, rather than quality or need."[4] Nonetheless, the same report noted, healthcare leaders overwhelmingly expected to see the healthcare system dominated by market incentives within the next decade.

Dire warnings notwithstanding, the University of Iowa Hospitals and Clinics in the 1980s showed little sign of an institution under siege, its ambitious capital replacement program continuing unabated into the 1990s and its staff numbers and patient services continuing to expand. Yet the hospitals and clinics' leaders, acutely aware of the changing environment, worked behind the scenes to anticipate the meaning and extent of that shift and to adapt the hospitals and clinics to an increasingly uncertain future. Further complicating matters, relations between administrations of the hospitals and clinics and the college of medicine showed worrisome signs of deterioration by the late 1980s. The remarkable harmony between the hospitals and clinics and the college of medicine during the 1970s—an uncommon occurrence in the long history of that relationship—was instrumental in the medical center's climb to national prominence; conversely, at least in the view of some insiders, increasing dissonance in that relationship impaired the medical center's ability to respond to the rapid changes in the healthcare marketplace in the late 1980s and early 1990s. In like manner, the warm working relationship between John Colloton and presidents Willard L. Boyd and James O. Freedman (1982–1988) turned cooler under Hunter R. Rawlings III (1988–1995).

The 1980s and early 1990s brought dramatic changes to the University of Iowa Hospitals and Clinics, not only in physical appearance but also in orientation, in operations, and in leadership. While the ongoing capital replacement program—totaling over a half-billion dollars from the early 1970s to the mid-1990s—added further to the physical plant from 1983 to 1995 and accommodated major advances in tertiary care, the imposition of prospective payment systems by public and private insurers and the growth of health maintenance organizations, healthcare alliances, and managed care concepts heightened efforts to expand and solidify the hospitals and clinics' referral networks and also fostered a significant reorientation toward the provision of primary care services.

Competition and Cost Containment

In his 1988 "covenant" speech to the AAMC, John Colloton also identified six major problems that the competitive model of healthcare—grounded in the drive for lowest-cost services and strict limitations on access—had either caused or failed to resolve. First, uninsured and underinsured Americans had lost access to the healthcare system, subsidies for their care wrung out of paying patient charges even as their number—then estimated at some 37 million—continued to rise. Second, "long-standing cooperation" between academic medical centers and community hospitals and physicians, wherein the role of each in the stratified health system was understood, had given way to that competitive atmosphere in which "each group sees the other as a rival rather than a colleague," leading to the proliferation and duplication of costly equipment and technology. Third, teaching hospitals had damaged the public trust and undermined their covenant with society by adopting that competitive stance. Fourth, provision for teaching hospitals' education-related costs through patient charges had eroded "with no reliable funding alternative yet in sight." Fifth, heightened commercialization, lowered esteem for the medical profession, and "deceptive" advertising were all "direct consequences of the competition model." Finally, competition in the healthcare marketplace had failed to reduce or even slow the growth of healthcare expenditures as its proponents had promised.

In sum, Colloton warned his colleagues in the AAMC, the emerging competition model in healthcare posed a grave threat to academic medical centers and especially to teaching hospitals, which—thanks to their societal obligations to train physicians and allied health professionals, to help support clinical research, to provide expensive new technologies, and to treat those who could not pay for their care—carried distinct disadvantages onto the field of competition. At the same time, their traditional advantages—superior staff, equipment, and facilities, and associated expertise in treating the most complicated cases with the latest and costliest machinery and procedures—were fast disappearing, increasingly duplicated by other hospitals in search of expanded market shares. In short, teaching hospitals' place at the apex of stratified healthcare systems appeared less secure with each new development in the country's experiment with market-based healthcare reform.

Rising Medicare expenditures were a powerful catalyst behind cost control efforts. As an entitlement program, Medicare Part A, hospital insurance, provided benefits to all who qualified, without regard to cost, and total expenditures rose from $6.3 billion in 1972 to $33.3 billion in 1982, a 428 percent increase. Meanwhile, 8 million more Americans received Medicare hospital benefits in 1982 than in 1972, the total rising from 21.1 million to 29.1 million, a 38 percent increase. Overall, then, per capita benefits rose from $300 in 1972 to $1,145 in 1982, a 282 percent increase influenced by the 130 percent rise in the consumer price index, the introduction of a host of new technological procedures, and the costs of capital investment in new facilities.[5] By 1994, Medicare Part A expenditures reached $104.5 billion, while Part B, supplemental medical insurance, added an additional $60.3 billion to the total, for an average cost of $4,449 per enrollee. In the same year, Medicaid added another $79 billion to the federal healthcare bill, augmenting the $58 billion contributed to Medicaid by the individual states.

Two years into the Reagan administration, spiraling Medicare costs led to enactment of the prospective payment system, which set standard payments in 23 major diagnostic categories differentiated by body system and subdivided into 489 diagnostic-related groups (DRGs), reimbursing hospitals at those pre-established rates rather than on the traditional basis of cost-plus charges. Further refinements of the payment system took into account the complexity of the case, with major surgery, for example, weighing more heavily than minor procedures. Geography, too, became a factor in reimbursement formulas, with urban hospitals accorded higher rates than rural hospitals.[6] One important effect of prospective payment was to push hospitals to increase their market shares in order to spread their fixed costs over greater numbers of patients, thus spurring competition.

At the University of Iowa Hospitals and Clinics, preparations for prospective payment began well in advance of the July 1, 1984, effective date. In June 1983, John Colloton reported to the Hospital Advisory Committee on his attendance at a Houston meeting, one of several regional meetings sponsored by the Association of American Medical Colleges devoted to the implications of prospective payment for academic medical centers.[7] His own administrative staff, Colloton reported, had for several months been compiling a database that would provide information for DRG-based costs and would also help in monitoring clinical patterns of resource utilization. Colloton emphasized that institution of the prospective payment system demanded a coordinated response from several operating departments, including medical records, finance, and information systems. He warned that much of the burden would fall on the clinical departments, particularly with regard to controlling the use of expensive diagnostic technologies, and on the department heads, each of them responsible for the education and cooperation of departmental staff. Overall, Colloton assured his listeners that prospective payment need not pose a serious threat to the hospitals and clinics, given their comparatively low operating costs and strong financial position. By late 1983, a hospitals and clinics administrative team had begun orientation sessions with clinical staff, and a steering committee, reporting to the Hospital Advisory Committee, had assumed responsibility for implementation of the new system.[8]

The effects of the trend toward prospective payments were evident soon enough, both at the University of Iowa Hospitals and Clinics and beyond. Nationally, according to figures from the Department of Health and Human Services Council on Graduate Medical Education, operating margins in prospective payment care cases plummeted from an average for all hospitals of 14.7 percent and 21.2 percent for teaching hospitals in 1984 to 2.1 percent for all hospitals and 12.5 percent for the largest teaching hospitals in 1988.[9] The relative strength of major teaching hospitals, based on their reputations for high-quality care, came as a surprise to many observers; moreover, a 1993 survey of Health Care Financing Administration data showed that these institutions had maintained their vitality into the early 1990s.[10] Nonetheless, at the University of Iowa Hospitals and Clinics, contractual adjustments with Medicare alone totaled $3.6 million in fiscal 1986, $7.8 million in fiscal 1988, and $12.7 million in fiscal 1990, a worrisome trend that, while not pushing operating margins into the red, heightened concern for the future. As a 1990 report to the board of regents noted, "third party payers have and are continuing to develop increasingly restrictive reimbursement payment systems, limiting hospital reimbursement for each inpatient to predetermined levels regardless of cost incurred in treating the patient."[11] This report echoed the discussion taking place nationally, as noted earlier, over the issue of financing graduate medical education and capital expenses.[12]

Across Iowa in the early 1980s, some 600,000 residents were eligible for Medicare or Medicaid, and Medicare accounted for more than 40 percent of hospital revenues in the state in 1985.[13] At the University of Iowa Hospitals and Clinics, Medicare patients accounted for more than a quarter of all patient-days in the fiscal year ending in 1981.[14] In addition, the financial impact of prospective payment and DRGs, as yet unknown, was not limited to Medicare; other insurers, notably Blue Cross, followed closely in adopting DRG guidelines.[15] From the mid-1980s, according to Iowa Hospital Association figures, contractual adjustments negotiated by Medicare, Medicaid, Blue Cross and other third party payers grew as a percentage of hospital charges. Medicare, for example, negotiated discounts amounting to 10.1 percent of charges with all Iowa hospitals in 1986; by 1990, the aggregate discount had risen to 31.9 percent or some $385.75 million, an amount counted as losses by the state's hospitals but as savings by Medicare.[16] Medicaid likewise negotiated discounts valued at $71.3 million with Iowa hospitals in 1990, up from $43.2 million in 1988. Meanwhile, also according to the Iowa Hospital Association, the statewide total of contractual adjustments hospitals ceded to Blue Cross, commercial insurers, health maintenance organizations, and self-funded employer plans reached $81.4 million in 1990, up from $41.5 million in 1988.[17]

Prospective payment also carried implications for graduate medical education, which constituted a major part of the so-called "societal costs" that, John Colloton maintained in 1984, made up some 30 percent of teaching hospitals' budgets.[18] Historically, Medicare had made generous provisions for the costs of graduate medical education by reimbursing teaching hospitals a "pass-through" based on reasonable costs as assessed by a formal audit. As recently as 1980, in a comprehensive study of issues surrounding the organization, standards, and financing of graduate medical education, an AAMC task force had strongly endorsed the existing system in which some 75 percent of the costs of graduate medical education came from hospitals' general operating revenues in the form of such subsidies from third party payers.[19] Initially under the prospective payment system, Medicare reimbursement for graduate medical education costs was little changed, with separate provisions for direct costs (DGME) and indirect costs (IME), the latter a percentage add-on to basic DRG charges. The Consolidated Omnibus Budget Reconciliation Act (P.L. 99-72) of 1986 put the funding of direct costs of graduate medical education on a prospective payment rather than a cost basis, allowing a fixed amount for each resident while also limiting the number of years residencies could qualify for full reimbursement. In 1990, with the resident staff at the University of Iowa Hospitals and Clinics having grown to more than 670, the hospitals and clinics administration apprised the board of regents that Medicare and other payers' "ever more restrictive payment practices for graduate medical education" and for capital replacement were cause for increasing concern.[20] Nonetheless, it should be noted that Medicare continued to distribute large sums—$1.9 billion for direct costs and $4.2 billion for indirect costs—as late as 1995, an average of some $70,000 per resident per year.[21]

The issue of support for graduate medical education involved more than just an equitable distribution of costs. It also involved important, but generally unspoken, issues of overall physician supply and geographic and specialty distribution. As early as 1979, the Graduate Medical Education National Advisory Committee forecast a possible excess of physicians by 1990, a surplus perhaps as high as 70,000.[22] The following year, the congressional Office of Technology Assessment suggested a potential surplus as high as 185,000 by 1990, the precise figure depending on growth rates in the utilization of healthcare services.[23] While understandably reluctant to endorse such projections, the Association of American Medical Colleges, in its 1980 report on graduate medical education, did concede that the question of physician supply, and particularly the mix of primary care and specialist physicians, was too important to leave solely to chance but should be settled by negotiations between public and private agencies and groups.[24] For many critics in the 1980s, however, Medicare provisions for the reimbursement of direct and indirect costs of graduate medical education were important elements in the perceived oversupply of specialist practitioners.[25]

Meanwhile, prospective payment systems may also have contributed to the movement already underway toward outpatient rather than inpatient care, since outpatient care was not affected by the new reimbursement formula. American Hospital Association data for Iowa showed a precipitous fall in hospital admissions from nearly 550,000 in 1981 to fewer than 410,000 in 1986, and a further decline to fewer than 385,000 by 1990. The data also showed a similar drop in the number of hospital admissions per 1,000 population for Iowa, the midwest, and for the United States as a whole for the same period. Iowa hospital inpatient days fell from more than 4.2 million in 1981 to just over 3.1 million in 1985 before rising slightly to 3.2 million in 1990. Inpatient days per 1,000 population for Iowa reflected the same pattern, while for the midwest and the United States as a whole they continued to fall from 1985 to 1990.[26] Meanwhile, outpatient visits to Iowa hospitals showed a marked increase from 2.46 million in 1981, to just under 3 million in 1985, to more than 4 million in 1990. The number of surgical procedures performed on an outpatient basis in Iowa overtook the number performed on an inpatient basis in 1988, and outpatient procedures accounted for 58.8 percent of all surgeries by 1990.[27]

University of Iowa Hospitals and Clinics figures show that both ad-missions and patient-days peaked in fiscal year 1979 at 40,569 and 317,298 respectively (see chapter 5, Table 5.9). From those levels, admissions fell to 38,261 in fiscal 1985 and to 34,525 in fiscal 1990, a drop of more than 14 percent for the decade; patient-days fell to 269,220 in fiscal 1985 and to 259,885 in fiscal 1990, a drop of 17 percent (Table 6.1). After bottoming in 1991–92, admissions figures began to rise once more, climbing 9.3 percent from fiscal 1992 to 1995. In contrast, outpatient visits rose from 333,163 in fiscal 1980 to 358,510 in fiscal 1985, to 451,636 in fiscal 1990, an increase of 26 percent during that ten-year period; by fiscal year 1995, outpatient visits had increased a further 23.7 percent. The increasing emphasis on ambulatory care had a significant impact on physician training, providing a different case mix than inpatients, presenting diseases at different stages of development, and in many cases calling for alternative therapeutic approaches.[28] The slump in patient admissions and patient-days eventually led to a 13.4 percent contraction in the number of beds, as the hospitals and clinics' occupancy rate slid from 80 percent in 1985 to 74 percent in 1994, and average length of stay dropped from 7.04 days to 6.81 days in the same period. Driven largely

Table 6.1 Hospitals and Clinics Operations, 1983–1995

	Admissions*	Patient Days*	Outpatient Visits	Staff Physicians/ Dentists	Residents/ Fellows	Registered Nurses	Total Staff [FTE]	Beds	Total Expenditures† ($000)
1982–83	38,530	299,484	337,457	425	562	1,209	6,584	1,029	132,401
1983–84	37,557	283,505	352,743	441	581	1,283	6,660	953	133,796
1984–85	38,261	269,220	358,510	449	592	1,301	6,793	913	148,078
1985–86	37,081	262,966	368,032	455	602	1,335	6,832	922	157,404
1986–87	34,480	259,595	382,211	478	607	1,403	6,799	902	173,098
1987–88	33,090	251,583	402,933	493	624	1,481	6,968	902	192,208
1988–89	33,669	254,086	425,508	515	645	1,511	7,187	902	213,793
1989–90	34,525	259,885	451,636	535	678	1,520	7,260	902	256,902
1990–91	34,136	250,402	461,465	560	684	1,543	7,400	891	293,027
1991–92	33,932	250,767	465,610	583	657	1,540	7,459	891	318,748
1992–93	34,060	236,961	466,429	597	681	1,562	7,588	891	349,330
1993–94	35,147	239,263	483,306	625	671	1,558	7,569	881	366,267
1994–95	37,073	234,529	529,786‡	634	686	1,560	7,624	845	384,318

*In addition to acute patients, figures include newborns and housed clinic patients.

†The authors report operating expenditures rather than revenues because of the many complications introduced by negotiated reductions in charges and other factors. Source: UIHC Annual Statistical Reports, Departmental Analysis of Expenditures of University Hospitals and Psychiatric Hospital.

‡Includes 27,208 outreach visits.

Source: University of Iowa Hospitals and Clinics Annual Statistical Reports and Service Records.

by expanding outpatient services, total staff numbers nonetheless continued to climb, rising 22.7 percent from 1982 to 1993.

Although perhaps not obvious, the variation in reimbursement formulas for urban and rural hospitals under the prospective payment system were important to the University of Iowa Hospitals and Clinics. The formula used at the federal level to calculate reimbursement rates assumed lower labor and non-labor costs for rural hospitals, leading to lower reimbursements per Medicare patient. With Medicare being the largest single source of patient revenues for Iowa hospitals—by 1989, just over half of gross income for Iowa's rural hospitals and 41.8 percent for urban hospitals[29]—this differential had a higher proportionate impact on rural hospitals' revenues and operating margins. American Hospital Association statistics published by the Iowa Hospital Association consistently showed rural Iowa hospitals taking a loss on patient revenues of about 5 percent through the late 1980s.[30] Iowa's Medicaid program likewise implemented a prospective payment system in 1987, but minimized the difference in reimbursement rates for rural and urban hospitals by using state-specific data in its calculations.[31]

In 1987, John Colloton called Medicare reimbursement for rural Iowa hospitals "disproportionately low," compounding the problems caused by the shift to ambulatory care and increased competition for primary care patients from secondary level health providers. Together, Colloton observed, such trends had pushed the average occupancy rate for small rural hospitals down to just 41 percent, leaving many rural hospitals "struggling for survival" and seeking HMO affiliations, satellite clinical service arrangements, management contracts with larger hospitals, and affiliations offering access to patient networks.[32] In the long run, such developments posed a threat to the integrity of the referral network built by the University of Iowa Hospitals and Clinics over many decades. If rural hospitals formed closer ties with other hospitals and with large provider organizations, the chances increased that their more difficult cases would end up somewhere other than the University of Iowa Hospitals and Clinics. Hospitals in Des Moines, Waterloo, Cedar Rapids, and Sioux City, after all, offered an ever increasing number of tertiary level services.

The map (Figure 6.1), showing University of Iowa Hospitals and Clinics admissions and clinic visits in 1993–94 from each of Iowa's 99 counties, illustrates the importance of such referrals from across the state. It also highlights the fact that the hospitals and clinics remained chiefly a state rather than a regional resource, with admissions and ambulatory patients from within the state making up nearly 90 percent of the patient population. Overall, too, the pattern of patient distribution mirrored the impact of geography and of market competition on hospitals and clinics operations. Johnson County, the home of the University of Iowa, provided

Figure 6.1   University of Iowa Hospitals and Clinics Patient Service by County, 1993–94

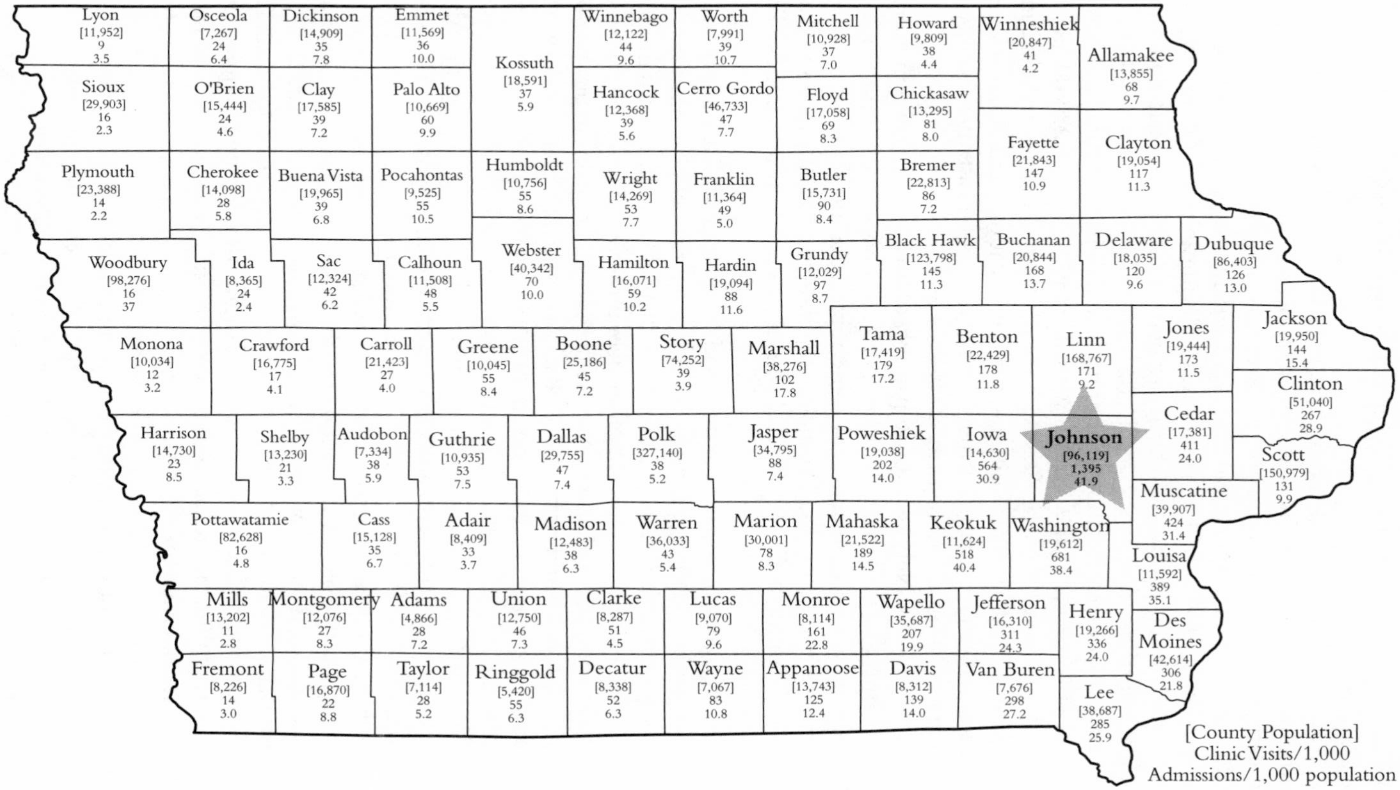

[County Population]
Clinic Visits/1,000
Admissions/1,000 population

Lyon [11,952] 9 3.5
Osceola [7,267] 24 6.4
Dickinson [14,909] 35 7.8
Emmet [11,569] 36 10.0
Winnebago [12,122] 44 9.6
Worth [7,991] 39 10.7
Mitchell [10,928] 37 7.0
Howard [9,809] 38 4.4
Winneshiek [20,847] 41 4.2
Allamakee [13,855] 68 9.7

Sioux [29,903] 16 2.3
O'Brien [15,444] 24 4.6
Clay [17,585] 39 7.2
Palo Alto [10,669] 60 9.9
Kossuth [18,591] 37 5.9
Hancock [12,368] 39 5.6
Cerro Gordo [46,733] 47 7.7
Floyd [17,058] 69 8.3
Chickasaw [13,295] 81 8.0
Clayton [19,054] 117 11.3

Plymouth [23,388] 14 2.2
Cherokee [14,098] 28 5.8
Buena Vista [19,965] 39 6.8
Pocahontas [9,525] 55 10.5
Humboldt [10,756] 55 8.6
Wright [14,269] 53 7.7
Franklin [11,364] 49 5.0
Butler [15,731] 90 8.4
Bremer [22,813] 86 7.2
Fayette [21,843] 147 10.9
Winneshiek [20,847] 41 4.2

Woodbury [98,276] 16 37
Ida [8,365] 24 2.4
Sac [12,324] 42 6.2
Calhoun [11,508] 48 5.5
Webster [40,342] 70 10.0
Hamilton [16,071] 59 10.2
Hardin [19,094] 88 11.6
Grundy [12,029] 97 8.7
Black Hawk [123,798] 145 11.3
Buchanan [20,844] 168 13.7
Delaware [18,035] 120 9.6
Dubuque [86,403] 126 13.0

Monona [10,034] 12 3.2
Crawford [16,775] 17 4.1
Carroll [21,423] 27 4.0
Greene [10,045] 55 8.4
Boone [25,186] 45 7.2
Story [74,252] 38 3.9
Marshall [38,276] 102 17.8
Tama [17,419] 179 17.2
Benton [22,429] 178 11.8
Linn [168,767] 171 9.2
Jones [19,444] 173 11.5
Jackson [19,950] 144 15.4

Harrison [14,730] 23 8.5
Shelby [13,230] 21 3.3
Audobon [7,334] 38 5.9
Guthrie [10,935] 53 7.5
Dallas [29,755] 47 7.4
Polk [327,140] 38 5.2
Jasper [34,795] 88 7.4
Poweshiek [19,038] 202 14.0
Iowa [14,630] 564 30.9
Johnson [96,119] 1,395 41.9
Cedar [17,381] 411 24.0
Clinton [51,040] 267 28.9

Pottawatamie [82,628] 16 4.8
Cass [15,128] 35 6.7
Adair [8,409] 33 3.7
Madison [12,483] 38 6.3
Warren [36,033] 43 5.4
Marion [30,001] 78 8.3
Mahaska [21,522] 189 14.5
Keokuk [11,624] 518 40.4
Washington [19,612] 681 38.4
Muscatine [39,907] 424 31.4
Scott [150,979] 131 9.9

Mills [13,202] 11 2.8
Montgomery [12,076] 27 8.3
Adams [4,866] 28 7.2
Union [12,750] 46 7.3
Clarke [8,287] 51 4.5
Lucas [9,070] 79 9.6
Monroe [8,114] 161 22.8
Wapello [35,687] 207 19.9
Jefferson [16,310] 311 24.3
Louisa [11,592] 389 35.1
Muscatine [39,907] 424 31.4

Fremont [8,226] 14 3.0
Page [16,870] 22 8.8
Taylor [7,114] 28 5.2
Ringgold [5,420] 55 6.3
Decatur [8,338] 52 6.3
Wayne [7,067] 83 10.8
Appanoose [13,743] 125 12.4
Davis [8,312] 139 14.0
Van Buren [7,676] 298 27.2
Henry [19,266] 336 24.0
Des Moines [42,614] 306 21.8
Lee [38,687] 285 25.9

Source: University of Iowa Hospitals and Clinics.

41.9 patient admissions and 1,395 clinic visits per 1,000 residents, and most contiguous counties were likewise generally over-represented in the patient population. All told, Johnson and its seven contiguous counties accounted for 26.0 percent of hospitals and clinics patient admissions and 44.9 percent of clinic visits. However, Linn County, bordering Johnson County on the north and claiming a population nearly 75 percent larger than that of Johnson County, contributed only 9.2 admissions and 171 clinic visits per 1,000, a consequence of market competition from hospitals in Cedar Rapids. Much the same was true of Polk County; with its population of 327,000 and its market dominated by major Des Moines hospitals, Polk contributed just 5.2 admissions and 38 clinic visits per 1,000 population to the University of Iowa Hospitals and Clinics. Further to the west, Pottawattamie County—with its population of more than 80,000 located just across the Missouri River from Omaha, Nebraska and its panoply of hospital services—mustered just 4.8 admissions and 16 clinic visits per 1,000 population. Nonetheless, the indigent care program ensured some representation from all counties, regardless of distance and local competition; indigent patients accounted for 80 percent or more of all hospitals and clinics patient admissions from several distant counties.

The prospective payment system had a much greater impact on hospitals than earlier Medicare reforms such as peer review organizations and professional standards review organizations that had sought to contain hospital costs by tightening oversight of services provided. One could argue, of course, that contractual adjustments were not unheard of prior to prospective payments.[33] One could argue, too, that the Iowa Hospital Association's calculations regarding revenues lost in the 1980s to contractual adjustments were to some extent suspect, calculated on the basis of charges assessed self-paying patients, a small and fast-diminishing patient category. Also, competition for patients was hardly new to the University of Iowa Hospitals and Clinics in the 1980s; Robert Hardin, as noted in the previous chapter, had observed the phenomenon in 1968.[34] What was important, however, was that prospective payments symbolized the power of third party payers to set the rates they would pay, overturning hospitals' ability to charge "usual and customary" rates and their ability—especially important for teaching hospitals—to shift the costs of charity care, capital development, equipment purchases, teaching, and research to paying patients. The era of cost competition, then, imperiled the cross-subsidization of services that was, for better or worse, built into the structure of modern teaching hospitals.

Moreover, cost competition became an explicit object of state policy in Iowa beginning in 1983 with the adoption of recommendations by the Governor's Commission on Health Care Costs. The commission, which Governor Robert D. Ray appointed in 1981, issued recommendations in late 1982 in the areas of regulation and competition, provider payments, hospital data and information, utilization controls, long-term care services, substance abuse and mental health services, and preventive health and primary care services. With respect to competition, the governor's commission wrote that healthcare costs were "increasing at an extreme rate because the system has no controls to discipline performance." Commission members recommended introducing "the discipline of market forces . . . [to] create incentives for efficiency in the health care system," including changes in state regulations to facilitate movement toward a competitive healthcare market. The commission also contended that coverage and service were "a matter of negotiation between purchasers and provider[s]" and that state legislation "should facilitate provider efforts to create vertically and horizontally integrated organizations and arrangements for the delivery of health services." Finally, the commission urged providers and purchasers alike to experiment with alternative healthcare delivery systems such as health maintenance organizations, independent practice associations, and preferred provider organizations.[35]

The commission's endorsement of the principle of competition and market-based healthcare reform led to incorporation of the Health Policy Corporation of Iowa. A private, nonprofit organization dominated by business and insurance interests, the Health Policy Corporation set about implementing the commission's goals by networking with the state's health providers and purchasers and with large businesses, seeking legislation to implement its goals, and cultivating ongoing contacts within state government. Whether by design of the Health Policy Corporation or as the result of larger economic forces, the 1980s brought an increasingly competitive healthcare market to Iowa. The number of health maintenance organizations expanded from one in 1980, to six in 1985, to ten in 1990, covering all of the state's larger population centers; HMO enrollments swelled to 139,062 in 1985 and to 323,376 in 1990. Already in 1982, a University of Iowa Hospitals and Clinics report estimated that HMOs had, by reducing patient referrals, cost $2.2 million in hospitals and clinics revenues and had diminished Medical Service Plan revenues by $770,000.[36] By 1985, the largest HMO, Quad City Health Plan of Davenport, had 55,300 clients enrolled and 753 participating physicians; the largest HMO in 1990, Heritage National Health Plan, also of Davenport, had 141,656 clients enrolled and 2,453 participating physicians.[37]

John Colloton noted in 1987 that Iowa's HMOs, like others throughout the country, applied disincentives for participating physicians to refer patients outside their home communities by making the physicians financially liable for the cost of referral care. This and "a host of other managed care features," Colloton said, "impinge upon the free clinical decisionmaking process that has characterized traditional medical practice."[38] Such changes in the healthcare delivery system also did their part to chip away at the hospitals and clinics' referral network, which in turn sparked efforts to strengthen outreach programs, some of which dated back to the 1930s. By the mid-1980s, the hospitals and clinics operated or participated in at least fifteen outreach programs ranging in purpose from the direct delivery of healthcare services to targeted populations to the training of physicians and allied health personnel.[39]

The University of Iowa Hospitals and Clinics also faced increased competition in the provision of a variety of highly specialized services. Mercy Medical Center in Des Moines, for example, initiated a heart transplantation program in 1985, the same year the University of Iowa Hospitals and Clinics' first heart transplant was performed. Mercy also began a kidney transplant program in 1986, while Iowa Methodist Medical Center, also in Des Moines, initiated a smaller kidney transplant program in 1987.[40] The Des Moines hospitals also competed with the University of Iowa Hospitals and Clinics to acquire the state's first kidney lithotripter in 1984, submitting a joint certificate-of-need application to the state at the same time the hospitals and clinics' application was pending.[41] John Colloton attacked the "mounting aggressiveness" of these "secondary level hospitals," asserting that Iowa did not have a big enough patient base to support duplicate organ transplantation programs. "The traditional orientation of secondary level hospitals toward a role of community service focused on those clinical services appropriate to their respective level in the system is rapidly being compromised by the economic values and attitudes intrinsic to the competition model," Colloton charged. "Some hospitals and their governing boards are now inclined to enter into any clinical venture which is deemed economically attractive, and even some which are not." John Colloton may not have been an unbiased observer; nonetheless, the director had put his finger on a serious flaw in the promotion of the competition model of healthcare as a mechanism of cost control. In fact, the encouragement of investment in highly specialized and expensive technologies and personnel appeared to drive inflation in healthcare costs while undermining the certificate-of-need program originally meant to ensure the rational distribution of healthcare services.

As the University of Iowa Hospitals and Clinics faced mounting competitive pressures in the 1980s, it also faced significant political concerns. Just as had occurred in the late 1920s and early 1930s, the indigent patient care program became a lightning rod for opposition to the hospitals and clinics in the Iowa legislature. On this occasion, the opposition brought together a diverse coalition including maternal and child health advocates and small rural hospitals pushing for indigent care decentralization. Beginning in 1978, proponents of decentralized indigent patient care floated proposals during each legislative session, proposals that lobbyists for the regents and university had little trouble deflecting. By 1983, however, advocates of decentralization were sufficiently united to force serious consideration of their proposals.[42]

Obstetrical and newborn care were a special focus of decentralization efforts largely because those services were exempt from the fifty-year-old county quota system, and virtually all the state's indigent obstetrical patients came to the University of Iowa Hospitals and Clinics for delivery. Some maternal and infant health advocates argued that this system was not in the best interests of pregnant women living far from Iowa City, for whom traveling to the hospitals and clinics could be, as one University of Iowa law professor noted, "a particular burden . . . in view of the general inability to predict with precision the onset of labor." Some patients might arrive two weeks or more prior to delivery, meaning additional hardship for patients and their families. Critics of the system believed the costs of transportation and lengthy hospital stays were significant issues as well.[43]

Changes in federal law in the early 1980s allowing states to extend Medicaid coverage to medically needy individuals not qualifying for Aid to Families with Dependent Children furthered the cause of decentralization advocates in Iowa, since the new category of Medicaid recipients, unlike candidates for the state indigent care program, would be free to choose their providers. Legislation to implement such a program in Iowa failed during the 1983 session of the General Assembly; it prevailed in 1984, however, setting up a limited program applying to pregnant women and to children under the age of 21. The new program for obstetric care did not specifically replace any part of the indigent patient care program at the University of Iowa Hospitals and Clinics, and the legislature continued indigent care funding at the same level as in the past. But because pregnant women and newborns constituted more than a third of the indigent patients at the hospitals and clinics, officials predicted that the extension of Medicaid coverage to this segment of the indigent patient population would eventually mean a significant drop in indigent patient service with no corresponding gain in Medicaid patients. They also feared that a substantial drop in the number of births at the hospitals and clinics—then running between 2,500 and 3,000 annually—could threaten the obstetrics and gynecology department's educational programs, accreditation, and academic standing.[44]

Administrative problems hampered implementation of Iowa's medically needy program, however, and in its first year the program used just a fraction of the funding earmarked for it. Births at the hospitals and clinics numbered 2,901 in fiscal 1985, a figure little changed from the three previous years.[45] Interest in altering the indigent care program continued to build, however, fueled by a growing political alliance of advocates for maternal and child health, rural medical services, and market-based health reform; by pressure from rural hospital administrators; and by 1986 election-year politics, which obliged rural legislators to seek any kind of benefit for their constituents, still suffering from the agricultural recession of the 1980s. Increased activity among interim legislative committees and other bodies reflected this heightened interest in the indigent care program, and five different studies were undertaken after the 1985 legislative session concluded.[46]

With passage of some form of decentralization bill a virtual certainty in early 1986, John Colloton informed the Hospital Advisory Committee that university officials were collaborating in two initiatives. The first of those involved facilitating implementation of the medically needy program; the second involved a bill to provide indigent obstetrical and newborn care locally to patients in western Iowa, an option that Colloton characterized as "the next reasonable step in decentralization," albeit one that likely would draw its funding from the state's indigent care appropriation to the University of Iowa Hospitals and Clinics.[47] More radical legislation to decentralize the entire indigent care program appeared as well, introduced in both the House and the Senate. That bill, House File 2392, would repeal the existing indigent care law and substitute a nearly identical version preserving the basic tenets of the existing program, including the county quota system, but allowing the state to reimburse local doctors and hospitals for such care.[48]

Hospitals and clinics officials warned that losing most of its indigent patients would hurt the hospitals and clinics' education programs and reduce its revenues by more than 15 percent. John Colloton anticipated that the departments of pediatrics and obstetrics would be hardest hit if the bill became law. And while hospitals and clinics administrators estimated that state funds covered only 61 percent of the cost of indigent care, those funds were so thoroughly embedded in the hospitals and clinics' revenue structure that their loss would, according to Colloton, compromise educational programs and cause the hospital to "regress." Administrators also claimed that the new proposal for a thoroughgoing decentralization would cost the state significantly more than the present program, not only because the hospitals and clinics provided care over and above the state appropriation but also because it would require the state to pay doctors' fees, which were not part of the existing system.[49] To be sure, university officials did not expect the radical decentralization plan to win legislative approval; it survived subcommittee consideration without a fiscal analysis and without the opportunity for testimony from the university or its lobbyist. Influential legislators branded the bill irresponsible, and the Iowa Hospital Association opposed it. Whatever its chances for passage—indeed, it died later in the session—the bill did underscore the uncertainty of the University of Iowa Hospitals and Clinics' indigent care appropriation, and university officials began searching for alternative funding, especially to cover education costs, should the indigent care program dissolve.

In the meantime, provisions for partial decentralization of indigent care made their way into a large appropriations bill, stating the General Assembly's intent to decentralize indigent obstetric and newborn care by July 1, 1988, "so as to allow reimbursement for care locally as well as at the University of Iowa Hospitals and Clinics." Under this plan, funding would come from the state indigent patient care program, "equal to the amount that would otherwise have been appropriated for obstetrical and newborn patients under the indigent care program."[50] The following year, the legislature established the Obstetrical and Newborn Indigent Patient Care Program under the state department of health "to provide obstetrical and newborn care to medically indigent individuals in this state, at the appropriate and necessary level, at a licensed hospital or healthcare facility closest and most available to the residence of the eligible individual." The new program did, however, reserve to the University of Iowa Hospitals and Clinics patients drawn from nine eastern Iowa counties—Cedar, Clinton, Iowa, Johnson, Keokuk, Louisa, Muscatine, Scott, and Washington.[51] Also, the legislature maintained the hospitals and clinics' annual appropriation for indigent care at the previous level; in fact, the appropriation remained essentially unchanged in real terms into the 1990s, although it diminished substantially as a percentage of hospitals and clinics' operating revenues. Into the 1990s, then, the University of Iowa Hospitals and Clinics ceded some ground to those favoring the decentralization of indigent care but managed to hold decentralization to obstetrical and newborn care only and even then to maintain an exclusive franchise on several nearby counties.

As the legislature considered the future of the indigent care program, a Governor's Blue Ribbon Commission on Future Financing of Educationally Related Costs of the University of Iowa Hospitals and Clinics studied the financing issues surrounding education-related costs at the hospitals and clinics. In the early 1970s, John Colloton had pondered the prospects of converting the annual state appropriation for indigent care to a more general fund to cover other expenses. Taking for granted the eventual passage of universal national health insurance, which would eliminate the problem of indigent healthcare, Colloton had suggested shifting state funds allotted to indigent care to the University of Iowa Hospitals and Clinics' capital replacement program. By the late 1970s, however, it was clear that universal health insurance was a dead issue; moreover, the capital replacement program was well along, financed with patient earnings. As a result, the conversion idea fell into dormancy until revived in the 1980s by proposals to decentralize indigent care—thus threatening the hospitals and clinics' state funding—and by limitations that Colloton and others anticipated in reimbursements for education and research-related costs allowed under prospective payment programs.

In July 1984, the board of regents approved a resolution urging "that the integrity of the annual appropriation to the University Hospitals be maintained at the level necessary to . . . provide needed indigent patient care and to support uncompensated costs related to clinical education programs; new technology development; clinical research support; and other unique societal contributions of the University Hospitals."[52] By the following year, the board had begun discussion of a blue ribbon commission, working also to assure that commission members would reach conclusions favorable to the hospitals and clinics. Governor Terry Branstad formally impaneled the eleven-member commission in August 1986, its membership including one current and one former member of the board of regents. Branstad's charge to the commission was to identify those education-related costs over and above basic patient care that were historically folded into paying patient charges; evaluate how changing payment systems would affect the hospitals and clinics' ability to maintain educational programs traditionally funded by cost shifting; identify state policy options for financing those programs; identify the role the state appropriation should play in such financing; identify specific steps the state should take to maintain the hospitals and clinics' financial integrity; and address the impact of total decentralization of indigent obstetrical and newborn care on health education programs at the University of Iowa.[53]

The commission met four times in the autumn of 1986, receiving written and oral comments, reviewing the hospitals and clinics' statewide programs, and debating policy issues relating to the governor's charge. The commission also retained a Chicago consulting firm to gather and analyze additional information. In its final report submitted on January 7, 1987, the commission defined the University of Iowa Hospitals and Clinics' education, research, and charity care costs as "societal contributions" and calculated that such costs accounted for 22 percent—then $42.6 million—of the hospitals and clinics' total annual operating budget. Of that amount, the hospitals and clinics needed $14.9 million for graduate medical education and other teaching programs, $19.3 million for technology development and research support, $5.5 million for uncompensated care, and $2.9 million for what it called the "ambulatory care teaching deficit," this latter referring to extra costs—for example, additional time spent with patients and additional diagnostic procedures—incurred by resident doctors because of their relative inexperience.

The commission foresaw a transition in the hospitals and clinics' financial structure from the late 1980s to the early 1990s, with a gradual phasing out of the indigent care function as the state's new medically needy and obstetrical care programs distributed much of that burden across the state. In the commission's view, that transition would allow the hospitals and clinics to redirect some $20 million in state funds appropriated for indigent care to other purposes. But the commission also envisioned further reductions in education-related reimbursements from third party payers, which the hospitals and clinics then valued at $22 million. The commission's principal recommendation, then, was to maintain the state appropriation at its current level, with adjustments for inflation, and to permit the hospitals and clinics greater flexibility in the use of those funds, affording reimbursement for costs no longer covered in the traditional manner by patient charges. The commission further recommended that the board of regents determine the allocation of state funds among hospitals and clinics programs requiring support, including "residual indigent patient care," and that the board be accountable to the state legislature for its decisions.

The blue ribbon commission's report was an important document for several reasons. Most important, it made clear that the hospitals and clinics' administration did not oppose the concept of decentralized indigent care; instead the crucial issue was continuing the state funding traditionally tied to indigent care and condoning its use for other purposes, especially to cover those education-related expenses that private insurers were increasingly unwilling to pay. Still, the phasing out of indigent care at the hospitals and clinics would involve a delicate balance between the need to divert indigent care resources to new uses and the need to maintain sufficient patient volume for educational programs, as well, of course, as the need to assure access to medical care for those who needed it. In the end, contrary to expectations, the medically needy program did not significantly reduce the burden of the indigent care program; by the mid-1990s the University of Iowa Hospitals and Clinics still carried a significant indigent patient care caseload—12.9 percent of direct patient admissions, 11.2 percent of patient-days, and 7.6 percent of clinic visits in fiscal 1995, compared, for example, to 28.7 percent of admissions and 28.5 percent of patient-days in fiscal 1980.

The Final Phases of Capital Development

Market-driven changes that worked their way through the healthcare system in the 1980s and 1990s restructured not only the way insurers reimbursed hospitals for their services but also the manner in which patients gained access to care. With more consumers enrolled in health maintenance organizations, and with HMOs restricting access to the kind of high-end, expensive services available at university teaching hospitals, the new external environment posed deep and far-reaching challenges to the University of

Iowa Hospitals and Clinics' tertiary care orientation. However, while hospitals and clinics officials studied the possibility of incorporating more primary care services into the teaching hospital's programs as early as the mid-1980s, it was not until 1991 that they signaled a clear shift in that direction. That signal came in the form of plans for a new $71 million pavilion—the Pomerantz Family Pavilion—to house family medicine, a women's health clinic, and other services aimed at providing basic medical care to the local community. Before that, the hospitals and clinics' building program had continued to emphasize tertiary medical services such as cardiac care, burn treatment, integrated cancer care, organ transplant surgery, and radiology and nuclear medicine, all aimed at its statewide constituency. It bears noting, however, that those earlier building projects did also include at least 20,000 square feet of space for ambulatory care clinics.

By late 1982, all phases of three major additions—the Boyd Tower and the Roy J. Carver and John Colloton Pavilions—were completed, under construction, or already approved, and total program costs had reached $120 million. Most of the total—some $110 million—paid for major building additions and the remainder went to smaller projects such as the Southeast and Southwest additions as well as numerous remodeling and modernization projects within the General Hospital.[54]

Approved in September 1982, the so-called Colloton Pavilion-Phase B, projected at $24.5 million, would add five floors to the three-story inpatient tower already built, providing space for 140 replacement beds and housing a new consolidated cardiac care unit, inpatient beds for the department of surgery, and a relocated burn treatment center. The existing burn unit, housed in a modified open ward area of General Hospital, had no private rooms or baths; patient rooms were small, storage and equipment space inadequate, and the heating, ventilation, and air-conditioning services outdated. Construction of Phase B went forward on a "fast track," meaning work on the building's exterior was under way even as design of the interior continued. This, combined with unexpectedly low bids for the construction contract, permitted the hospital to add 4,800 square feet of space for a digestive diseases center that ultimately was named for James Clifton, professor and former head of the department of internal medicine.[55]

With this project, the hospitals and clinics reduced the complement of non-conforming beds to 145, nearly half of those—72—located in Psychiatric Hospital, another 60 in General Hospital, and 13 in Westlawn, the former nurses' dormitory that now housed, among other operations, an indigent antepartum unit.[56] In a major milestone, Phase B boosted the hospitals and clinics past the magic number of 1,500 gross square feet per bed, which had been the long-sought goal of the capital replacement program.[57] Phase B of the Colloton Pavilion was also noteworthy as the last project to derive any funding from hospital revenue bonds. The sale in April 1983 of $20 million in twenty-year bonds provided the bulk of financing, the remainder coming from the hospital's building depreciation reserves built up from patient revenues. This brought the total value of hospital revenue bonds to $60 million, and pushed debt service per bed to $49.[58]

With approval of Colloton-Phase B in September 1982, the capital development program was scarcely one-quarter complete. Indeed, a part of the new addition remained unfinished in anticipation of construction of a Phase C, the latter to include new operating rooms served by ancillary facilities in the unfinished fifth floor of Phase B.[59] Construction of that third phase began in January 1986. Smaller than either of the earlier phases in terms of physical space, Phase C nonetheless cost more, at $30.7 million. Adding two floors to the Colloton Pavilion's clinical wing and including 11,500 square feet of space for new operating suites, 20,000 square feet for radiology and nuclear medicine, and 20,000 square feet for ambulatory care clinics, as well as additional space for offices, conference facilities, and support services, the original schedule for Phase C called for completion by 1988, but ongoing revisions delayed finishing work into 1992.[60] By that time, a Phase D was under construction adding floors five and six to the clinic wing at an additional cost of $19.3 million.[61]

The early stages of the capital development program left untouched the 72 non-conforming beds in the Psychiatric Hospital. The 1920-vintage building—even older than the consistently cited General Hospital—failed each succeeding inspection on the grounds of fire and safety code violations, a situation that prompted planning for a new psychiatric pavilion to replace the outdated psychiatric facility. Hospital and university officials, including department of psychiatry head George Winokur, secured board of regents approval for the project in September 1987. Designed to accommodate adult and child psychiatry as well as to provide additional space for internal medicine, radiology, surgery, and sports medicine, construction of the first phase of the new pavilion was projected to cost $17.5 million.[62]

Construction of the psychiatric pavilion entailed razing the student armory, which served as home to the Reserve Officer Training Corps and also included an indoor track and other recreational facilities. Concern over a shortage of recreational opportunities on campus meant that the new pavilion could go forward only if the hospitals and clinics helped to provide alternative facilities, in the end contributing $2.3 million in building depreciation reserves and unrestricted gifts toward a $5.6 million project to remodel, refurbish, and expand the adjoining Iowa Field House, which the men's and women's intercollegiate basketball programs had vacated in recent years to move to a new sports arena.[63] Construction of the new pavilion was again put on a fast track, commencing in January 1988, just weeks after design work began.[64] The first phase of the project, finished at a cost of $22.7 million, created facilities for a positron emission tomography (PET) scanner, psychiatric clinic space, pediatric clinic space, and offices for the departments of pediatrics and psychiatry.[65]

As the project began, hospitals and clinics officials envisioned three distinct construction phases because of financial constraints; the board of regents, however, expressed concern that phased construction of the pavilion would increase building costs, both because of inflation and because of the need for a temporary roof on the first section.[66] A timely $3 million gift by Des Moines venture capitalist John Pappajohn, which University of Iowa President Hunter R. Rawlings announced on August 14, 1989, helped alter the construction schedule so that the psychiatric pavilion could be built to its full height with no intermediate steps. Pappajohn, a longtime friend of hospitals and clinics director John Colloton, was, like Colloton, a native of Mason City and had earned a graduate degree from the University of Iowa in the 1950s. Pappajohn's $3 million, joined with about $30 million in building depreciation reserves, financed what were originally planned as two distinct phases of the project, and the board of regents duly named the new building the John Pappajohn Pavilion.

Pappajohn and his wife, Mary Pappajohn, also established two endowment funds at the university, one of which was to help support the multidisciplinary cancer center planned for the pavilion, and the board of regents then named the cancer center the John and Mary Pappajohn Clinical Cancer Center.[67] Occupying most of the third and fourth floors of Pappajohn Pavilion's clinic and inpatient wings, the clinical cancer center brought together multiple cancer services—inpatient units, ambulatory clinics, diagnostic and therapeutic facilities, and educational and clinical research supporting units—that had previously been distributed throughout the hospital complex.[68] In addition to the cancer center, the hospitals and clinics developed a new 34-bed surgical intensive care unit for the fifth floor of the pavilion to replace an overburdened 24-bed unit in Carver Pavilion. The Carver unit, in service only since 1980, was running at more than 90 percent occupancy owing to the greater than expected numbers of patients undergoing complex procedures such as organ transplants and neurosurgery. The space vacated in Carver Pavilion became a medical intensive care unit to replace even older facilities in General Hospital.[69] By 1990, with the removal from service of the old Psychiatric Hospital's 72 beds, just 73 non-conforming beds remained in the hospitals and clinics, and, by late 1992, with completion of the Pappajohn Pavilion just months away, the survey team of the Joint Commission on Accreditation of Healthcare Organizations—formerly the Joint Commission on Accreditation of Hospitals—found no important defects in the hospitals and clinics physical plant.[70]

At the time university officials announced the $3 million Pappajohn gift, in August 1989, they asserted that the Pappajohn Pavilion was "the final phase of the 20-year capital replacement plan at The University of Iowa Hospitals and Clinics."[71] But hospitals and clinics director John Colloton noted in September 1989 that plans for the Pappajohn Pavilion left the departments of obstetrics and gynecology, ophthalmology, and otolaryngology with substandard facilities in the old General Hospital. Colloton told the board of regents that "sometime in the future these very large departments will have to be relocated in the south complex, but they will not be moved into this pavilion."[72] That conclusion, coupled with concerns to expand the hospitals and clinics' primary care presence, led in 1991 to development of another pavilion with space for an eye institute, a women's health clinic, a family care center, a geriatric clinic, and otolaryngology and dental clinics. Designed in two phases and approved by the board of regents in December 1991, total costs of the project ran to more than $71 million,[73] nearly all financed from the hospitals and clinics building depreciation reserves. When former board of regents president Marvin Pomerantz, a close political ally of Iowa Governor Terry Branstad, teamed with his wife Rose Lee, brother Harry, and sister-in-law Dorothy Pomerantz to give $3 million to support the new facility, the building became the Pomerantz Family Pavilion.

With this project, the University of Iowa Hospitals and Clinics came at last to occupy the field that extended several hundred feet south of the original General Hospital to Iowa City's Melrose Avenue, an area that had, as late as 1970, contained three intramural football fields and the University of Iowa baseball field. More important, the Pomerantz Family Pavilion represented a significant shift toward primary care services at the hospitals and clinics. While some departments—such as pediatrics and obstetrics and gynecology—had long maintained a focus on primary care, hospitals and clinics planning until the late 1980s had continued an emphasis on tertiary care. This was, as John Colloton told Duke University's Private Sector Conference in 1987, both "in keeping with our traditional mission of statewide tertiary care" and one of "seven major initiatives" intended to buttress the hospitals and clinics' place "in the increasingly competitive [health care] environment."[74] Colloton might also have noted that the tertiary care emphasis reflected the entrenched preferences of college of medicine clinical faculty.

As Colloton reported to the Duke conference, a planning group working under the authority of the Hospital Advisory Committee in the mid-1980s had studied primary care options, considering in particular whether the hospitals and clinics should develop a health maintenance organization for university faculty and staff and their dependents. By 1987, the university spent some $15 million a year on healthcare for faculty and staff, with about half of that sum going to local providers, and a university-based HMO could conceivably capture much of that market by offering primary care services through the hospitals and clinics while also bolstering the facilities' specialty services through referrals.[75] Based on the analysis and recommendations of the planning group, Colloton and leaders of the compensation committee instead negotiated contracts with existing HMOs with "incentives to maximize the use of UIHC as the preferred center for out-of-area referral services." Likewise, university officials negotiated a contract with Blue Cross and Blue Shield of Iowa, which had included Colloton on its board of directors since 1974, to "create a financial incentive for the Blues and their participating physicians to concentrate all referral care at UIHC."[76] Thus, the choice was to strengthen the hospitals and clinics' relationships with outside primary care providers and to concentrate resources on high-end, specialized referral care, a plan that drew support from the 1987 report of the Governor's Blue Ribbon Commission.

However, 1991 plans for the Pomerantz Family Pavilion marked a significant shift in the direction of primary care for the hospitals and clinics and the college of medicine. Importantly, the turn toward primary care represented a softening of the barriers between physicians in the department of family practice and those in other clinical services, family practice having received at its inception a less than enthusiastic welcome from most other clinical departments. Since the department's establishment in 1970, family practice doctors had been isolated from the hospitals and clinics both physically and in terms of their interrelations with faculty and staff in other departments. While the family practice clinic had moved from Oakdale to remodeled space in Children's Hospital in 1976, the department's physician faculty had only limited admitting privileges to the hospitals and clinics and continued to refer most patients needing inpatient services to Iowa City's Mercy Hospital.[77] This was the case until 1992, when the department reached an agreement lifting many of the existing restrictions on faculty members' participation in inpatient care in the hospitals and clinics.[78] Combining the Family Care Center, the Women's Health Center, the Eye Institute, and geriatric, dental, otolaryngology, and other clinics under one roof, the Pomerantz Family Pavilion was a major step in the integration of primary care services into the overall operations of the University of Iowa Hospitals and Clinics, a step that laid the groundwork for eventual development of a university-based HMO.

In all, the ambitious capital replacement program of the 1970s, 1980s, and early 1990s added more than 2.2 million gross square feet to the hospital complex, more than five times the floor space of the late 1960s hospital complex. The total cost of the capital replacement program, including the projected cost of the Pomerantz Family Pavilion, surpassed

$520 million, almost $323 million of that committed to the four major additions (Figure 6.2). A substantial part of the remainder financed the acquisition of new equipment such as magnetic resonance imaging (MRI) machines, computer-aided tomography (CAT) scanners, and kidney and gall bladder lithotripters.[79] Remarkably, none of the money to pay for the capital program came from state appropriations, and only $13.4 million— less than 5 percent—came from gifts and grants. The rest, some $477 million, came entirely from patient revenues.[80] Nor did the hospitals and clinics incur a large debt burden, borrowing just $60 million in the form of revenue bonds issued between 1973 and 1983. By 1993, the hospitals and clinics owed less than $35 million, with all debt scheduled for repayment by 2003.[81] Among public university teaching hospitals in the midwest, the University of Iowa Hospitals and Clinics was unusual, if not unique, in carrying out significant capital development with no state-appropriated funds.[82] Moreover, most observers agree that the new hospitals and clinics complex stands as testament to the remarkable financial and organizational skills of director John Colloton.

Throughout the period, several factors drove the capital development program. The desire to replace outdated facilities and meet rising standards of hospital care, a concern often cited by university officials when presenting building proposals to the board of regents, was clearly a principal factor. The deficiencies of the hospital's physical plant, discussed at some length in previous chapters, were well documented by both state licensing reports and the Joint Commission on Accreditation of Hospitals from the 1950s on. Hospital officials also from time to time invoked the need to provide appealing facilities to attract patients who now had choices about where to obtain health care services. Likewise, the hospitals and clinics' updated facilities no doubt helped in competing for talented clinical and administrative staff and for physician faculty for the college of medicine as well.

At the same time, the dramatic increase in hospitals and clinics revenues and the excess of revenues over expenses during the 1970s and 1980s constituted an essential factor in the scope and timing of the capital replacement program. That was the case, first, because the program could not have progressed as it did in the absence of self-financing, which in turn owed much to the federal government's continuing commitment to Medicare. Again and again in seeking regents approval for new building projects, university and hospitals and clinics officials buttressed their case with the powerful argument that no state funds would be used for construction. Second, the hospitals and clinics' high margin of revenues over expenses year after year— combined with the forceful leadership of John Colloton—helped to vest its administration with an unprecedented independence of action, boosted also by the strong working relationship between Colloton and presidents Willard

Figure 6.2   The University of Iowa Hospitals and Clinics Phased Capital Replacement Plan Summary, 1970–1999

	Projects Completed or Underway as of 1995									Future Construction	
	Phase I	Phase II	Phase III	Phase IV	Phase V	Phase VI	Phase VII	Phase VIII	Phase IX	Phase X	Phase XI
	Boyd Tower	Carver Pavilion	Colloton Pavilion	Carver Pavilion	Colloton Pavilion	Colloton Pavilion	Pappajohn Pavilion	Pappajohn Pavilion	Pappajohn Pavilion	Pomerantz Family Pavilion	Pomerantz Family Pavilion
		Phases A & B	Phase A	Phase C	Phase B	Phases C & D	Phases A & B	Phases C & D	Phases E & F	Phase A	Phase B
	(1976)	(1978–82)	(1980–82)	(1981–88)	(1983–85)	(1985–92)	(1987–91)	(1989–93)	(1991–99)	(1992–95)	(1996–99)
	186,153 ft²	402,958 ft²	236,778 ft²	63,261 ft²	201,288 ft²	158,960 ft²	211,495 ft²	323,999 ft²		422,769 ft²	

Gifts and Grants — $13,437,619

Total Funding: $521,041,743

Hospitals and Clinics Paying Patient Earnings — $461,705,224

Future Gifts and Paying Patient Revenues — $45,898,900

[Total costs include $194,176,373 for smaller additions (132,250 ft²) and modifications and new equipment.]

Source: University of Iowa Hospitals and Clinics Administrative Offices, September 1995.

Boyd and James Freedman. All of these factors allowed planners to pursue their ambitious building program without pause and, for the most part, without question.

Hand in hand with the hospitals and clinics' aggressive expansion of the 1970s and 1980s, the college of medicine continued to grow under John Eckstein's leadership. Overall, tenure track faculty numbers grew from 476 in 1980 to 636 in 1995, an increase of 33.6 percent (Table 6.2). Significantly, all of this growth occurred in the clinical departments, some of them increasing by more than 50 percent in size; overall, tenured and tenure track faculty in the clinical departments numbered 347 in 1980 and 508 in 1995, a 46.4 percent increase. The number of tenure track faculty in basic science departments and other areas, meanwhile, stayed essentially the same at 129 in 1980 and 128 in 1995. Internal medicine alone accounted for a third of the increase in tenure track faculty, while internal medicine and radiology and radiation research accounted for almost half. The aggregate of tenure track and non–tenure track faculty, meanwhile, rose from 542 in 1980 to 706 in 1995. Also, 5.8 percent of tenured and tenure track faculty were women in 1982; and 11.4 percent were women in 1993. At the same time, 8.6 of all college faculty were women in 1982, and 15 percent were women in 1993.[83]

Gifts, grants, and contract funding in the college of medicine followed much the same pattern as faculty numbers [see Appendix B, Table B.5, "College of Medicine Gift, Grant, and Contract Funding by Department, 1970–1995"]. In 1979–1980, funding from all outside sources totaled about $32.7 million; in 1984–1985, the figure rose to more than $46.5 million; it surpassed $78.3 million in 1989–1990, and reached more than $108.5 million in 1994–1995. From 1980 to 1990, the Department of Internal Medicine attracted just over $116 million in external funding—by a wide margin the largest amount of any department, clinical or basic science. Figures from other clinical departments included more than $75 million in pediatrics, $22 million in psychiatry, and $11 million in neurology. Among departments in the basic sciences and other areas, preventive medicine led the way with a ten-year total of $46.6 million; biochemistry totaled $26.5 million; physiology counted $20.8 million; pharmacology claimed $18.5 million; and microbiology added $15.9 million. The college's expanding roster of interdisciplinary research centers also attracted large sums during the decade; the Cardiovascular Center, for example, totaled $64.4 million in external support.[84] In addition, the college received a $15 million grant in 1992 from the National Center for Human Genome Research (NIH) to establish a genetic research center, one of nine such centers nationwide participating in the Human Genome Project. The rapid growth of research funding in the college of medicine was justly celebrated, but it was also an ongoing source of unease, as faculty felt increasing pressures to fund large

Table 6.2 College of Medicine Tenure-Track Faculty, 1980–1995

	1980	*1985*	*1990*	*1995*
Anatomy*	24	18	18	16
Anesthesiology	24	25	36	37
Biochemistry*	18	16	20	20
Dermatology	7	8	9	10
Family Practice	11	10	9	8
Internal Medicine	77	92	119	131
Microbiology*	18	20	20	23
Neurology	15	16	16	22
Obstetrics-Gynecology	15	17	19	20
Ophthalmology	14	16	19	23
Orthopædics	13	15	17	19
Otolaryngology	13	13	9	16
Pathology	19	31	36	34
Pediatrics	55	58	64	64
Pharmacology*	14	14	17	15
Physical Therapy*	5	3	5	5
Physician Assistant	1	1	1	1
Physiology*	23	16	14	14
Preventive Medicine*	20	21	22	28
Program in Hospital Administration*	5	8	6	5
Psychiatry	25	22	24	33
Radiology-Radiation Research	22	29	39	45
Surgery	30	29	32	39
Urology	8	6	9	8
Totals	**476**	**504**	**580**	**636**

Note: Decimal figures are rounded to the nearest whole number; therefore, totals given here differ slightly from those in the original source.
*Basic science and other departments.
Source: "Filled Positions" binder, University of Iowa College of Medicine.

research projects, and departments became increasingly dependent on soft money for operations, even as the political climate of the late 1980s and early 1990s clouded the future of federal research funding.

Medical Service Plan income also continued its rapid pace of growth through the 1980s and into the 1990s, the expansion in patient service both cause and consequence of the expansion in the hospitals and clinics facilities. From $21.3 million in 1979–1980, Medical Service Plan income grew to $44 million in 1984–1985, to $79.6 million in 1989–1990, and to $94.3 million in 1993–1994—a fourteen-year increase of 344 percent, although the rate of growth slowed considerably toward the end of that period. At the same time, clinical departments came to rely on patient service income to an ever greater extent to finance operations, including educational programs. Service plan income rose from 29 percent of college of medicine expenditures in 1979–1980, to 37 percent in 1984–1985, to 40 percent in 1989–1990 before falling back to 37 percent in 1993–1994.[85] This was perhaps an unhappy reminder of warnings from opponents in the late 1940s and early 1950s that Medical Service Plan earnings would, in the long run, encourage state legislators to reduce appropriations for salaries and other needs.

In the end, the teaching hospital that emerged in the 1980s and 1990s was vastly better organized than its precursor, and offered a wide array of new patient services, many of them—like the cancer and digestive diseases centers—multidisciplinary in nature and drawing staff from several clinical departments. Likewise, the capital replacement program nurtured a rapid expansion in organ transplant services, as new, larger operating suites with expensive and sophisticated equipment allowed the hospitals and clinics to increase its transplant services from two organ systems in 1976 to nine in 1994.[86] In his final report to the board of regents in April 1993, John Colloton reviewed two decades and more of progress in the hospitals and clinics' capital development program, which at the time totaled more than $468 million in self-generated funding with no state capital appropriations. Colloton highlighted the growth of patient service, the number of health science students in training, the number of residents and fellows in specialty training, the hospitals and clinics' educationally related costs and support for faculty clinical research, and the 7,500 current staff.[87] He also compared the hospitals and clinics' 34.8 percent increase in hospital service charges since 1983 with the national average increase of 87.6 percent; showed that the hospitals and clinics had the second-lowest per admission cost ($8,689) among seven midwestern members of the University Hospital Executive Council in 1991; and cited a study showing the hospitals and clinics' $1.5 billion economic impact on the state of Iowa. Without a doubt, the capital development program played a crucial role in transforming the University of Iowa Hospitals and Clinics from a substandard hospital financed mostly by indigent patient service to a premier teaching hospital delivering the most sophisticated of care and financed primarily by earnings from paying patients.

Strains in the Academic Medical Center: A Reprise

By the time the board of regents formally approved plans for the Pomerantz Family Pavilion in December 1991, the last major piece of the capital development program, John Eckstein was retired from the college of medicine deanship, his resignation effective September 1 of that year. Moreover, on November 11, John Colloton had announced his intention to leave the hospitals and clinics directorship in mid-1993 for a newly created position as vice president for statewide health services. Eckstein's and Colloton's resignations, announced several months apart, marked the end of a contest over the distribution of authority and resources within the medical center, a series of episodes that reiterated old and deep-seated frictions between the college of medicine and the hospitals and clinics, frictions either absent or held to manageable levels during the first fifteen years of the Colloton-Eckstein era. Eventually, through a complicated series of events, the board of regents created a health sciences vice presidency, placing the hospitals and clinics director and the deans of dentistry, medicine, nursing, and pharmacy under the new vice president's administrative aegis at the same time that Colloton moved into his new post as vice president for statewide health services, in July 1993.

The most visible milestones along the path to this administrative re-structuring were two reviews of the college of medicine, the first a self-study led by James A. Clifton, the respected professor and former head of internal medicine, and the second a university academic review led by Arthur E. Bonfield, John F. Murray Professor of Law. The latter review, especially, stirred controversy because it sharply criticized the existing asymmetrical reporting relationships of the dean and the hospitals and clinics director, wherein the dean reported to the vice-president for academic affairs while the hospitals director reported directly to the president and the board of regents. Instead, the review committee recommended balancing the administrative positions of the dean and hospitals director by placing the director under the vice-president for academic affairs and giving the dean of medicine a direct relationship with the board of regents—recommendations not, in fact, incorporated in the final restructuring plan.

Several years later, the content and significance of the university review committee's report, and its role—if any—in bringing about the restructuring, were still matters of some disagreement. From a historical perspective, however, the report was important precisely because of the controversy surrounding it, and because it brought to light the gulf in perceptions between the administrations of the college of medicine and those of the hospitals and clinics. Specifically, the report, along with written responses to it by John Eckstein and by John Colloton and his senior administrative staff, provided insights into competing philosophical approaches to the teaching hospital's fundamental nature: Is it an adjunct of the college of medicine—a university facility—serving primarily as a teaching laboratory, or is it a complex service, educational, and research institution—a state facility—accountable, in addition to the university, to the statewide community, to outside accrediting and licensing bodies, and to large payers such as Blue Cross? Colloton and his colleagues, like many if not most of their counterparts across the country, held to that latter, broader view of the teaching hospital, in pronounced contrast to the more limited view that persisted within much of the university community—particularly in the administration of the college of medicine and among the faculty on the academic review committee.

In its October 1989 report, the college of medicine self-study committee headed by James Clifton noted in carefully chosen language that the "complex relationships" between the college of medicine and the hospitals and clinics provided "opportunity for conflict, especially if the administrative bodies of COM [college of medicine] and UIHC do not share the same objectives and do not use mutually agreed upon procedures to reach those objectives." Citing also the unequal status of the college of medicine dean and the hospitals and clinics director in the university hierarchy, the report claimed that the existing administrative structure did not ensure cooperation. Nor, in the committee's view, did the Hospital Advisory Committee provide a structure for joint policymaking between the dean and the hospital director, a situation that "led at times to an uneven pursuit of goals" and "hindered mobilization of the clinical faculty to meet the many current challenges facing COM and UIHC." The self-study report also reviewed troublesome financial issues, including clinic overhead costs assessed to the Medical Service Plan and the level of hospitals and clinics' payments to that plan.[88]

In September 1990, university vice-president for academic affairs Peter Nathan convened a university review committee for the college of medicine as a follow-up to the self-study of the previous year.[89] Nathan's charge to the committee, headed by Arthur Bonfield, included the normal scope of issues to be addressed in collegiate reviews—such as curriculum, organizational and administrative structures, faculty and student affairs, and education, research, and service programs—as required by the university's *Operations Manual*. However, the vice-president also instructed the committee to consider relations between the college of medicine and the hospitals and clinics. "In fact," the charge stated, "that relationship might well be considered a pivotal point for the review because so much flows from it."[90] The unusually wide scope of Nathan's charge to the committee suggested that for the vice-president and for President Hunter Rawlings the consequences of the administrative rift in the academic medical center had become a major concern. The review committee's broad charge, however, was unprecedented in John Colloton's view. Moreover, Colloton later wrote to Nathan that he and his colleagues in the hospitals and clinics administration had not been informed of the committee's full charge.[91]

From September 1990 to April 1991, the review committee met thirty times and held discussions with John Eckstein as well as with members of the Clifton self-study committee, the college of medicine's executive committee, compensation committee, medical education committee, and department heads. Despite the importance assigned to college of medicine–hospitals and clinics relations, however, the review committee appears to have interviewed just one member of the hospitals and clinics administration, director John Colloton. In addition, the committee invited comments from college faculty and students, and, in accordance with university policy, it brought two outside consultants to campus—Thomas Detre, senior vice-president for health sciences at the University of Pittsburgh, and Gerard Burrow, vice-chancellor for health sciences and dean of medicine at the University of California at San Diego—each of whom met with Eckstein, Colloton, and other parties. The review committee distributed its preliminary report on March 29, 1991, and its final report on April 15. It contained some forty recommendations addressing operational and administrative matters of the college of medicine, and three that focused largely on ties between the college of medicine and the hospitals and clinics.

On the issue of college-hospitals relations included in Nathan's charge, the review committee began by praising both the college of medicine and the hospitals and clinics for their major strides in recent decades. The committee noted, for example, that the college of medicine, under John Eckstein's leadership, had "improved dramatically" to become a "highly competitive" institution ranking among the "strongest state medical schools in the country." Likewise, the committee recognized the "talented and hardworking" administrative staff of the hospitals and clinics whose efforts had built "one of the premier university teaching hospitals in the United States." The committee noted also that the primary mission of the college of medicine was education while the primary mission of the hospitals and clinics was patient service, but committee members highlighted the interdependence of the two institutions and maintained that the apparent disparity in missions was in fact a "complementarity" that afforded the basis for a sound partnership.

Having said that, the committee proceeded to a discussion of problems in relations between the administrations of the college and the hospitals and clinics. The committee observed that college of medicine administrators and some faculty regarded the hospitals and clinics administration with both suspicion and admiration, fearing that the hospitals and clinics, thanks both to dynamic and capable leadership and "superior financial resources," threatened to overwhelm the college, "submerging the independent identity and authority of COM." This fear, in the review committee's judgment, had resulted in a "virtual breakdown of communication and cooperation" between the administrations of the two units. The review committee also noted a significant difference between the college of medicine and the hospitals and clinics in their respective approaches to strategic planning. The Hospital Advisory Committee, under John Colloton's leadership, had created a subcommittee on strategic planning in the mid-1980s, a subcommittee that included Colloton, eight clinical department heads, the director of nursing, and executive associate medical dean Paul M. Seebohm. The subcommittee was to monitor shifts in the external health care environment and suggest ways in which the hospitals and clinics could respond to changes in such areas as patient referral trends, alternative healthcare delivery systems, support services for community hospitals and physicians, development of multispecialty clinic services, contractual arrangements with health provider networks, public relations, and indigent patient care.[92] The review committee reported, in contrast, that the college of medicine did "not appear to have an adequate planning process," one that was "systematic," "ongoing," "comprehensive or detailed."

At the same time, the review committee reported dissatisfaction among some college of medicine faculty and administrators with the Hospital Advisory Committee, which Gerhard Hartman had reinstituted in the late 1940s at the behest of executive dean Carlyle Jacobsen. Some advisory committee members, the report said, "believe that this Committee operates in practice only as a rubber stamp for UIHC decisions already taken [i.e., by the hospitals and clinics administration]." The report also alleged that some advisory committee members "apparently do not feel free to dissent publicly from UIHC actions that are presented as a virtual fait accompli because UIHC administration is in a position to control the space and other resources available to their clinical departments." Of course, the report conceded, "the point is not that these perceptions are necessarily accurate in all respects." What was important was that "there is a belief in substantial quarters of COM that they are true."

The report described in some detail the intrinsic ambiguity in the position of clinical department heads, who stood uneasily between the dean and the director, and recommended vesting in the dean the exclusive authority to represent the college of medicine and all of its departments in dealings with the hospitals and clinics in order to "preclude individual units of COM from making any arrangements with UIHC or taking any action in relation to UIHC without approval of the Dean or the Dean's designee." Similarly, the review committee recommended that additional financial resources be made available to the college of medicine to "enable the Dean to compete more effectively with UIHC administration for the allegiance and loyalty of those COM clinical department heads and faculty members who currently perceive that UIHC administration is the only realistic source of additional financial resources for them."

The review committee attributed the observed problems chiefly to institutional factors, particularly to the two institutions' different management structures and styles. The committee characterized the college of medicine as "a loosely run, collegial-oriented, academic bureaucracy," with "a highly decentralized administrative structure," while the hospitals and clinics represented "a multi-service institution with a distinct and separate administrative identity, a highly centralized administrative structure, and all of the typical characteristics of a tightly run, business-like bureaucracy." Like the Clifton committee in 1989, the review committee noted that these structural differences presented "fertile opportunities for conflict."

The review committee report also echoed the earlier Clifton study in assigning considerable importance to the unequal reporting status of the college of medicine dean and the hospitals and clinics director, the former reporting to the vice-president for academic affairs and the latter reporting, since the mid-1970s, directly to the university president. "This arrangement is unwise and has an unhealthy impact on administrative relationships between COM and UIHC," the report said. The committee also reported concerns expressed by "a number of COM faculty members, department heads, and College administrators" about the direct administrative relationship the hospitals director enjoyed with the board of regents by virtue of the regents' role as the hospitals and clinics' governing board, a relationship created in December 1976 at the behest of the Joint Commission on Accreditation of Hospitals and described in the previous chapter. As a result of this direct reporting relationship, the report said, "there is a fear that UIHC is no longer really subject to effective control by UI central administration."

Finally, on the subject of "fiscal interactions," the review committee report cited "discontent and consternation" among some medical faculty about the proportion of clinic overhead costs charged to the Medical Service Plan (MSP) by the hospitals and clinics. "There is considerable difference of opinion as to the justification for the charge, the appropriate amount of the charge, and the allocation of the charge across COM departments," the review committee observed. The committee added, however, that "UIHC has a very different view of its fiscal interactions with COM." Indeed, a hospitals and clinics report cited by the review committee calculated that support for specialty laboratory operations, provision of faculty offices, billing reductions on research-related costs for college investigators, faculty cafeteria subsidies, and reduced rates for hospital and pharmacy services amounted to a $20.3 million annual subsidy of the college by the hospitals and clinics.

The review committee recommended restructuring administrative reporting relationships as the first step toward resolving current problems, a realignment that would have both institutions "report directly to the same UI central administration official." The committee suggested placing the hospitals and clinics director, like the deans of university colleges, under the vice-president for academic affairs. Notwithstanding the primacy of the hospitals and clinics' patient service mission, the committee asserted that the hospitals and clinics existed as a part of the university only to serve the educational needs of the college of medicine and the other health science colleges and programs. The proposed reporting arrangement, in the review committee's view, had "the advantage of stressing the primacy of educational interests in decision making relating to COM/UIHC conflicts" and also ensured "that since the *primary* mission of UI is *educational*, unavoidable and irreconcilable conflicts between the *educational* interests of COM and the *service* interests of UIHC will ordinarily be resolved with a bias towards *educational* interests" [emphases in original]. A disadvantage of this proposal, the report noted, was that of "saddling" the academic affairs vice-president with responsibility for a "huge nonacademic unit only some of whose activities directly involve academic interests."

The review committee also raised the possibility of establishing a new health sciences vice-presidency to which the hospitals and clinics director and the deans of medicine, dentistry, nursing, and pharmacy would report. That alternative would unify responsibility for all health education and service functions in one central administration official, an official who "would be expert in the problems and needs of that particular area and coordinate all UI activities in that area." The review committee did not favor this arrangement, however, because it would divide the academic functions of the health sciences campus from those of the other colleges, "potentially making relationships between health related academic units and other academic units more difficult and complicating university-wide decisions with academic implications"—not an insignificant issue in light of the existing physical and symbolic isolation of the health sciences campus. To address the unequal status of the dean and the director with respect to the board of regents, the review committee recommended automatically appointing the dean of medicine, or the dean's designee, as chief of the hospitals and clinics medical staff with the same access to the board of regents as the hospitals and clinics director.

Finally, to address disagreements over financial arrangements the committee recommended an overall budget for the medical center—although presumably not intending to include the colleges of dentistry, nursing, and pharmacy—to pool the resources of the hospitals and clinics, the college of medicine, and Medical Service Plan and allocate them in such a way as to benefit "the UI medical center as a whole without resorting to accounting squabbles" over who owed what to whom. However, the committee conceded that such an arrangement might be impractical, noting legal obstacles requiring the segregation of the affected funds and budgets and noting also that the system proposed could only be grounded in joint planning and good faith between institutions of equal standing. As an alternative, the committee proposed an independent consultant to determine fair formulas for transfer payments between the college and the hospitals and clinics.

Response to the university review committee's report from the college of medicine and particularly its dean was muted, except with regard to the issue of college-hospital relations. After all, apart from its administrative criticisms in the areas of strategic and contingency planning, Medical Service Plan management, and the high degree of departmental autonomy within the college, the report largely supported the position of the college's administration. Eckstein agreed particularly with the report's strong emphasis on education over service in the mission of the hospitals and clinics and with its view that the hospitals and clinics' prominent role and stature within the university's administrative hierarchy should be curtailed. At the same time, the dean appeared for the most part to agree with the report's recommendations regarding the college's teaching, research, and general operations.

In a nine-page response dated June 10, 1991, Dean John Eckstein, who had already announced his resignation effective August 31, addressed the problem of college of medicine–hospitals and clinics relations head on, charging that the necessary balance among education, patient care, and research was "heavily tilted toward the patient care priorities" of the hospitals and clinics.[93] "In this university, and in others similar to it," the dean argued, "the care of patients is part of education," with patient care "provided by the faculty in a setting in which students are involved." The purpose of the hospitals and clinics, in the dean's view, was to furnish "facilities and services so that teaching and medical care can be provided by the faculty" of the college of medicine. To ensure proper attention to educational concerns and to right the perceived imbalance between the education and service missions, Eckstein endorsed the review committee's proposal to place the hospitals and clinics director, like the dean, under the vice-president for academic affairs. Eckstein also agreed with the review committee's recommendation that the dean should speak for the college of medicine and all of its departments; indeed, he called that recommendation "among the most important" in the report.

For their part, John Colloton and his senior management team rejected the report, its recommendations, and even the review committee's authority to address issues bearing on the hospitals and clinics' management, believing the review itself had been "contrived" to circumscribe the hospital's prestige and autonomy.[94] In sharply worded April 11 reviews of the preliminary draft report and in a detailed June 10 rebuttal to the final report, John Colloton and his associates took the review committee to task on several counts.[95] Colloton's April 11 response to the review committee's preliminary report began with a sharp attack on the committee's charge. Asserting that university policy restricted academic review committees to investigation and recommendations relating to the college under review, Colloton objected that the hospitals and clinics were not an academic unit and not a part of the college of medicine.[96] Moreover, Colloton objected to the review committee's bias toward the academic interests of the college of medicine, a bias that had led to "numerous flaws" in the subsequent report. Overall, Colloton alleged, the review committee had "jumped into a very complex arena" in which the members were clearly ill-informed, leaving them to rely too heavily on hearsay evidence and individual perceptions. While conceding that "perceptions can be a factor, even if wrong," the director argued that "to base far-reaching conclusions and recommendations on perceptions that are not validated or quantified is irresponsible."

In the detailed June 10 rebuttal addressed to Peter Nathan, Colloton and his colleagues challenged the review committee's central claim of deteriorating relations between the college of medicine and the hospitals and clinics. To the contrary, they cited the favorable 1988 accreditation review of the college by the Liaison Committee on Medical Education, for which Dean John Eckstein had given partial credit to the "great university and an outstanding University Hospital," as well as the 1989 college of medicine self-study report's survey of faculty showing only 6 of 173 respondents reporting serious concern about relations between the college and the hospitals and clinics. They also noted recent internal reviews of five clinical departments that "made *no* mention of any stress in relationships with the UIHC." In fact, Colloton believed that claims of deteriorating relations between the hospitals and clinics and the medical faculty were overblown.

In Colloton's view, as explained in his April 11 letter to Nathan, the problem between the hospitals and clinics and the college of medicine was neither institutional nor organizational, but lay instead "in relationships between the UIHC administration and the *Dean of Medicine (DOM)— not the COM*" [emphases in original]. Colloton also suggested that the college of medicine's perceived weakness vis-à-vis the hospitals and clinics was not a function of institutional and administrative structures but of John Eckstein's "lack of . . . interest, experience, and expertise in this segment of the health science center and the fact that he has given priority to other challenging responsibilities in the areas of undergraduate medical education and research." Colloton stated that he had offered "to appoint [Eckstein] to the UIHC Strategic Planning Committee or any other body on which he wished to serve to enhance his involvement in the UIHC," but that, after requesting time to consider the offer, the dean had never responded.

Colloton and his colleagues, in their June 10 letter, stressed their belief that the proposed realignment of reporting relationships within the medical center would not help the college of medicine and, on the other hand, could devastate the hospitals and clinics. In particular, the review committee's suggestion to place the hospitals and clinics director under the vice-president for academic affairs "would simply create potential constraints on the ability of the UIHC to respond to the intense and dynamic demands of the external environment now prevailing in the health sector." Citing disastrous experiences at other university-owned teaching hospitals where "decisions affecting the teaching hospital were often made at university levels with an inadequate understanding of the teaching hospital's needs and external accountabilities," hospitals and clinics administrators raised an issue that had reverberated since Gerhard Hartman's arrival in 1946 in arguing that the hospitals and clinics were not, in fact, "simply another 'academic unit' " of the university. "The unique expertise required to manage a major teaching hospital cannot and should not be duplicated elsewhere in the University," they asserted.

Moreover, Colloton and his colleagues took strong exception to the review committee's recommendation that the dean of medicine have sole authority to represent the college and all of its departments in dealings with the hospitals and clinics. Surely, they argued, the review committee's recommendation to preclude clinical department heads from " 'taking any action in relation to UIHC without approval of the Dean or the Dean's designee,' must be assumed to be hyperbole." To them, it was obvious that "the COM Dean could not, even with a greatly expanded staff, assume these responsibilities in addition to his or her other duties, even if there were a rational basis for such redundancy."

Finally, with regard to the issue of financial transfers between the college of medicine and the hospitals and clinics, Colloton and his senior administrators cited figures showing that the hospitals and clinics had subsidized the Medical Service Plan to the tune of $72.2 million since 1975. In addition, the hospitals and clinics' support for educationally related costs had reached $59.9 million in 1990, while the hospitals and clinics also contributed some $20 million each year in direct operating support to the college, an amount exceeding the $15.4 million that the college received annually from the university's general education fund. Moreover, the hospitals and clinics had invested $218 million in clinical facilities and equipment that helped the medical faculty "multiply Medical Service Plan income from $5 million in 1970 to $78 million in 1990," as well as providing

$24 million worth of office and conference space to clinical faculty and vacating more than 500,000 square feet of space at Oakdale, Children's Hospital, Westlawn, and Psychiatric Hospital, "most of which went to the College of Medicine." Finally, they cited Iowa Code and revenue bond provisions restricting the use of earnings from patient service to uses intended to expand the quantity and quality of such services.

Together, the university review committee report and the responses from dean John Eckstein and from director John Colloton and his administrative colleagues laid bare the ambiguous position of the modern teaching hospital within the university setting. The university review committee report stated plainly that the university owned the hospitals and clinics and that the latter existed to serve the educational needs of the college of medicine, providing the college "with the patient care facilities and nonphysician patient care support staff necessary for clinical teaching of undergraduate medical students," a position in accord with the dean of the college of medicine. While such had clearly been the case prior to World War II, a constellation of postwar developments—including the increasing private patient caseload fueled by both public and private health insurance; the expansion of the hospitals and clinics' role in the education of other health professionals; the extraordinary growth in house staff physicians employed by the hospitals and clinics; and, in general, the teaching hospital's transformation into a complex and dynamic enterprise—had undercut the simple equation of teaching hospitals and medical education, enormously enlarging the hospitals and clinics' service mission and injecting an uncomfortable degree of ambiguity into the meaning of the name teaching hospital.

Certainly, the view enunciated by the review committee and the dean no longer held with John Colloton, his chief aides, and many national teaching hospital authorities. As early as 1978, for example, Robert Derzon, then head of the Health Care Financing Administration, had recognized the increasing potential for conflict latent in the divergent goals of schools of medicine and teaching hospitals and had argued for "recognition that the teaching hospital is first a hospital and, secondly, but not secondarily, a hospital for teaching."[97] Colloton himself later cited a similar remark from John Knowles, president of the Massachusetts General Hospital, maintaining that "teaching hospitals are, by their intrinsic nature, institutions for the care of patients—with education and clinical research being most worthy by-products."[98] From such a perspective, the assumptions underlying the review committee's recommendations did not begin to capture the true function of a modern teaching hospital.

In an uncanny echo of Gerhard Hartman's treatises of nearly half a century earlier, Colloton's senior staff argued in their April 11 letter to Arthur Bonfield that the "UIHC does not 'provide COM' with 'patient care facilities and support staff,' " but rather "brings together the facilities, technology, professional and supporting staff and organizes and manages them in a manner to provide modern, tertiary health care services to patients." Within that complex structure, "the active clinical staff are an essential component of that whole, as are some 7,100 other members of the UIHC staff, including 2,900 other health professionals credentialed in nursing, pharmacy, dentistry and an array of allied health specialties." Medical education, then, was not the hospitals and clinics' *raison d'être*, but was, rather, one function integrated into a larger system of patient care delivery, which also included obligations to the educational programs of the colleges of dentistry, nursing, and pharmacy and other programs in the allied health professions, to state and national licensing agencies, to other healthcare providers, and to the hospitals and clinics' diverse patient population. "Deans of Medicine in the 1990s," Colloton wrote in his April 11 letter to Peter Nathan, "are the chief *academic* officers of academic units and as such are responsible for undergraduate medical education, graduate basic science education, and the complex and extensive research components of academic medical centers, *not for teaching hospitals and clinics*" [emphasis in original].

The points at issue, then, between the college of medicine and the hospitals and clinics administrations cut deeper than representation for the dean on the strategic planning or other hospital committees, deeper even than the formal structure of reporting relationships. At issue were money and the balance of power, both in formal administrative terms and in day-to-day operational terms, between the dean of the college of medicine and the director of the hospitals and clinics. While the dean had maintained his power over appointment, promotion, and salaries of clinical faculty, the overall balance of power had shifted significantly toward the hospitals and clinics director in the 1970s and 1980s, driven chiefly by the force of John Colloton's personality, evolutionary changes in the administrative relationships between the hospitals and clinics and the university president and the board of regents, the unprecedented explosion of hospitals and clinics services, operating revenues, and facilities, and the increasing complexity of the healthcare system. Among the more obvious symptoms of that shifting balance were the director's chairmanship of the Hospital Advisory Committee—ostensibly a forum for mediating among academic, administrative, and clinical interests—and his influence over the clinical chiefs, who were nominally the dean's subordinates but who saw the future of their departments linked increasingly to the hospitals and clinics' soaring resources and prominent stature. Whether that shift in the balance of power was willful or merely the product of circumstances, or some mix of both, was in some sense irrelevant. Whatever the cause, it was certain to incite alarm within the college of medicine administration, and the results would likely be disruptive to the academic medical center as a whole. As Robert Derzon cautioned in his 1978 discussion of relations between schools of medicine and teaching hospitals, "Troubles commence when two entities dissipate their energies protesting process and power rather than promoting results and futures."[99]

At issue, too, but perhaps of lesser importance, were differences in institutional cultures, personalities, and administrative styles. In contrast to the tightly organized administrative structure of the hospitals and clinics, the college of medicine was, by definition and postwar tradition, a collegial enterprise, with limited central authority and direction. As John Eckstein objected in response to the review committee criticisms of his administrative style, the college existed as a "federation of academic departments in which departmental priorities may be emphasized without full consideration of collegiate priorities." While Eckstein was attuned to the less structured academic context dominated by give-and-take among faculty peers and colleagues, John Colloton was, as chief executive of a major business en-terprise, known for his passionate capacity for work, his attention to detail and to strategic planning, and his command of an efficient management structure largely of his own making.

Importantly, the university review committee report bore the impri-matur of a formally constituted academic review panel and, not surprisingly, articulated an academic outlook informed by traditions far older than the college of medicine, the university hospitals and clinics, or the University of Iowa, traditions that conferred a solemn and independent status upon the university and its officers. In arguing that the University of Iowa Hospitals and Clinics were also accountable to agencies—including patients, the board of regents, the state legislature, accrediting and licensing bodies, and third party payers—lying outside the university's purview, John Colloton placed his vision of the academic medical center's covenant with society in partial opposition to some of the most sacred traditions of the parent university. By the same token, the academic nature of the collegiate review process was practically guaranteed to discount the arguments Colloton and his colleagues put forward regarding the changed mission and patient care orientation of the teaching hospital.

It was also the case that John Colloton's standing with the administra-tion of university president Hunter Rawlings was problematic. As a practical matter, university presidents and the board of regents had, for nearly two decades, been content to have the hospitals and clinics director function at a de facto vice-presidential level. That arrangement had evolved under the administration of Willard Boyd, who appears to have shared with John Colloton a genuine mutual admiration. When, on the occasion of the 1978 dedication of the Roy J. Carver Pavilion, Colloton publicly expressed his appreciation for having been "given the tools and the freedom to manage" by the president and for Boyd's stand behind "managerial integrity and accountability,"[100] the director's message was not merely ceremonial excess. In turn, President James Freedman, like Boyd a lawyer by training, inherited that administrative structure and was not inclined to change it. Such was not the case, events suggest, with Hunter Rawlings, who apparently wished to put the hospitals and clinics director on a tighter rein within the university's administrative hierarchy.

Like all such reports, the 1991 university review committee report on the college of medicine passed first to the vice-president for academic affairs, who, the university *Operations Manual* specified, was to make recommendations to the president based on the review findings. Commonly, such reports would also receive consideration by the board of regents, a forum in which John Colloton enjoyed strong support on the basis of his long working relationship with the board and his undisputed acumen as hospitals and clinics director, and where any final decisions on the report's recommendations would be made. But such consideration did not occur. Instead, the review committee report set in motion a convoluted train of issues and interests that left many of the details of subsequent events shrouded in uncertainty. What is clear at this close remove is, first, that John Eckstein had already tendered his resignation by the time of the review report's circulation and, second, that the board of regents was poised to reject the report's recommendations to restructure the hospitals and clinics director's reporting relationships and to pool the medical center's financial resources.[101]

Colloton, however, chose this time to offer an administrative restructuring plan of his own, calling for the creation of a new health science vice-presidency to oversee the hospitals and clinics director, the college of medicine dean, and the dentistry, nursing, and pharmacy deans[102]—an alternative the university review committee had explicitly rejected. Under his plan, Colloton would leave his position as hospitals and clinics director as of July 1, 1993, a change he had actively been considering for some time. At the urging of regents president Marvin Pomerantz, he would then assume a new position as vice-president for statewide health services, an expanded version of his previous role as assistant to the president for statewide health services. Colloton outlined a five-point program that would guide the work of his new office, including representing the University of Iowa in designing a reform plan for Iowa's health system; conceptual planning for the establishment of a health maintenance organization for University of Iowa faculty and staff; fostering the university's role in the twelve-member Academic Medical Center Consortium, which laid the foundation for a major initiative in health services research; developing a specific plan to implement the recommendations of the Governor's Blue Ribbon Commission with regard to financing the hospitals and clinics' education-related costs; and formulating responses to changes in the hospital's statewide referral patterns and to likely reductions by third party payers in reimbursements for teaching hospitals' education- and indigent care-related costs.

The timing of Colloton's proposal—August 14, 1991, some three months after the university review committee report began circulating—suggested that it was related to that report and its recommendations—the more so given Colloton's strong objections to the administrative realignment proposed in the report. Colloton later insisted that was not the case, however, citing his growing involvement with statewide health system reform efforts taking place under the leadership of Robert D. Ray, the former Iowa governor who had become chief executive officer of Blue Cross and Blue Shield of Iowa. Colloton served on Ray's Iowa Leadership Consortium on Health Care, and from this work "had already concluded that the University of Iowa medical center was not currently organized to cope with the dramatic level of change that would come about through the reform movement"; that after nearly twenty years of his leadership, "a new cadre of leaders who could bring continuity was needed in the health center for the era ahead"; and that over the course of his thirty-year career at the University of Iowa he "had acquired a good deal of knowledge and built an array of sound relationships throughout Iowa that could serve the University well in the health reform movement." Thus, according to Colloton, he sought a means to convert his own responsibilities to "working exclusively in the orbit of statewide health reform."[103]

In a series of meetings through the autumn of 1991, regents president Marvin Pomerantz, university president Hunter Rawlings, and John Colloton, with input from acting dean of medicine James Clifton and vice-president for academic affairs Peter Nathan, finalized plans for the proposed reorganization. On November 11, 1991, the twentieth anniversary of his appointment, John Colloton announced his resignation as hospitals and clinics director, effective July 1, 1993. The following day, President Rawlings issued a press release announcing the major points of the administrative reorganization of the health sciences campus, and two weeks later, the board of regents formally approved the plan.[104]

The planned reorganization did not meet with universal approval.[105] Opposition surfaced within a week from the University of Iowa Faculty Senate, when, after a long period of debate, the senate defeated a resolution urging the board of regents to reject the proposed reorganization on the grounds that it was poorly conceived, fiscally irresponsible, and did not reflect faculty input.[106] In the face of such criticism, Colloton, in a mid-December letter to President Rawlings, expressed his concern over the lack of understanding of the reorganization among the medical faculty and other important constituencies; he attributed the problem to the university administration's failure to communicate the underlying rationale for the restructuring, including the creation of the new vice-presidency for statewide health services.[107]

While painful for all concerned, leadership conflict within the academic medical center only raised once again the historical and seemingly inevitable frictions between the administrative hierarchies of colleges of medicine and teaching hospitals. That experience was scarcely unique to the University of Iowa; for example, one 1988 study forecast that current changes in the healthcare system could well mean greater conflict between education and service and between deans and hospital directors in academic medical centers.[108] Indeed, at the University of Iowa, the university review committee report of 1991 did little more than give public voice to observations long discussed in private, while events of the late 1980s and early 1990s served a salutary purpose by bringing to light the extraordinary complexity of the modern university teaching hospital and stimulating debate over its nature and functions in the larger university and in the contemporary healthcare system.

The University Teaching Hospital: Past, Present, and Future

The 1980s and early 1990s brought many challenges to America's university teaching hospitals, and the University of Iowa Hospitals and Clinics was no exception. Prompted by the upward spiral of healthcare costs, public and private insurers instituted limits on hospital reimbursements that diminished the ability of teaching hospitals to shift costs of charity care and medical education onto paying patients—costs that, at the University of Iowa, represented more than one-fifth of total operating expenses. Likewise, large employers, including federal, state, and local governments, increasingly sought to enroll their employees in managed care systems that promised to reduce costs in part by limiting patients' access to tertiary care institutions. At the same time, state policy in Iowa aiming to foster competition in the healthcare sector encouraged more Iowa hospitals to offer tertiary level services. Admittedly, change came more slowly to the state of Iowa than to many other states. Nonetheless, managed care revenues, for example, comprised 20.4 of all patient revenues at the University of Iowa Hospitals and Clinics in the last six months of 1995, an increase of nearly 35 percent from the same period in 1994. Moreover, by the end of 1995, managed care revenues ranked second only to Medicare in the hospitals and clinics' overall revenue structure.

In the face of such challenges, the University of Iowa Hospitals and Clinics' administration responded with a mix of management and strategic planning initiatives, including patient referral agreements with major HMOs, increased statewide outreach programs, and an enlarged focus on primary care in hospitals and clinics operations. In the meantime, the capital replacement program brought about a more organized system of space allocation that consolidated patient services in expanded and modern facilities; eliminated substandard beds; left the old General Hospital largely devoid of inpatient clinical services; and accommodated greatly enlarged numbers of clinical faculty, hospitals staff, and undergraduate and graduate health science students. But the modernization of facilities and initiation of new programs, in the context of major market challenges, also contributed to increasing tensions between the administrations of the hospitals and clinics and the college of medicine—tensions that centered on questions of institutional governance, financial arrangements, and control over strategic planning. In turn, those tensions provided fascinating insight into the ambiguous nature of the modern university teaching hospital.

In his 1988 covenant speech, John Colloton outlined a special relationship between the academic medical center and society at large, one that vested in academic medical centers the responsibility for training the nation's physicians, nurses, and other health professionals, for researching and developing new medical technologies, and for providing care to many of the millions of Americans who could not afford health insurance. In return, Colloton believed, society granted academic medical centers a degree of autonomy in designing and operating their programs and services and granted, too, the financial resources needed to carry out essential aspects of their mission. That covenant vision had deep historical roots, having appeared in varying guises throughout much of this century; more important perhaps, there lay within it abundant potential for conflict both between the academic medical center and the parent university and within the academic medical center itself. While Colloton and other leaders in the field might agree that the academic medical center as a whole had a legitimate claim to a degree of autonomy, the question of just how and by whom that autonomy was to be exercised was quite a different matter, a crucial issue to be settled through public and private negotiation.

At the University of Iowa, where the college of medicine traditionally overshadowed the rest of the health science colleges and, in particular, where deans of medicine long claimed authority over the teaching hospital, two consultants insisted as early as 1914 that the hospital superintendent should wield authority commensurate with his responsibilities. In 1919, another consultant recommended that the superintendent "be responsible to the President of the University and to him alone." Those recommendations did not, of course, bear fruit. However, in the 1930s and early 1940s, superintendent Robert Neff did seize a measure of autonomy for the university hospitals, reporting directly to President Virgil Hancher during an extended interregnum in the college of medicine deanship and continuing to do so after the appointment of a new dean of medicine. Neff's successor, Gerhard Hartman, exemplar of a new and more expansive breed of hospital administrator, sought to consolidate the gains that Neff had claimed, asserting that the "teaching" hospital's first obligation in fact was to patient care and that the hospital drew together the facilities and resources to accomplish a variety of ends, of which medical education was just one. As described in chapter 4, Hartman's efforts were roundly rebuffed by the college of medicine faculty. It was not until the 1970s and 1980s, buoyed chiefly by a rapidly expanding revenue base and by a series of changes in reporting relationships, that the University of Iowa Hospitals and Clinics presented a direct challenge to the college of medicine's long-held primacy within the academic medical center.

   Brilliant, ambitious, and demanding, John Colloton understood the new potential in the director's role and claimed for his hospitals and clinics administration an unprecedented measure of the autonomy posited in the covenant formula. Leveraging the extraordinary flow of patient revenues, Colloton directed a program of capital expansion that was stunning in scale and complexity, one that transformed an outdated indigent teaching hospital of mediocre reputation into a premier specialty care institution. However, the notion of a teaching hospital accountable primarily to agencies outside the university and autonomously formulating its own mission in response to broad social and market forces appeared, to some at least, to challenge both the traditional power of the college of medicine and the authority of the university's central administration. Moreover, Arthur Bonfield, who headed the university review committee of 1991, objected to existing reporting relationships that gave the head of the hospitals and clinics, unlike the dean of medicine, direct access both to the university president and to the board of regents. Bonfield maintained that the need for an equitable mechanism of conflict resolution between the two entities demanded that their respective heads be answerable to the same authority.[109] The administrative reorganization of 1991—proposed by John Colloton, negotiated by key parties, and approved by the board of regents—achieved that goal of parity by establishing a health sciences vice-presidency to whom the health science deans and the director of the hospitals and clinics would report. This administrative structure was increasingly common among academic medical centers. In fact, an Association of Academic Health Centers survey found that as early as 1980, 93 percent of academic health centers had a chief administrative officer, most often a health sciences vice-president; 69 percent of medical deans and 79 percent of teaching hospital directors reported to such administrative officers.[110]

The transition to the new structure, which took nearly three years to complete, involved hiring three new leaders for the health sciences campus. The search for a health sciences vice-president concluded in September 1993 when Henri Manasse assumed the post, leaving the University of Illinois–Chicago Circle Health Center where he had served since 1981 as dean of pharmacy, and most recently as interim vice-chancellor for health services. Meanwhile, when John Colloton stepped down as hospitals and clinics director at the end of June 1993, the board of regents appointed an interim director, hospitals and clinics associate director John Staley, and the college of medicine continued, as it had since 1991, under the interim deanship of first James Clifton and then Richard G. Lynch, professor and head of pathology. Finally, in August 1994, R. Edward Howell assumed the post of director and chief executive officer of the hospitals and clinics, and Robert P. Kelch became dean of the college of medicine. Howell came to Iowa from the Medical College of Georgia Hospitals and Clinics, where he had served as executive director; before that he had been associate director of the University of Minnesota Hospitals and Clinics. Kelch left the University of Michigan to assume the deanship of the University of Iowa College of Medicine; at Michigan, he had headed the pediatrics department and served as both physician-in-chief of the C. S. Mott Children's Hospital and as chief of clinical affairs of the University of Michigan Hospitals.

Perhaps the most striking aspect of the new leaders at Iowa was the lengths to which they went to demonstrate cooperation and goodwill between the college of medicine and the hospitals and clinics administrations. Indeed, according to Henri Manasse, the selections of Howell and Kelch hinged importantly on their commitment to a more collaborative administrative style embracing the hospitals and clinics and all of the health science colleges, especially the college of medicine.[111] The two employed a new rhetoric of openness and joint decision making that began shortly after their arrival in a series of communications with faculty and staff of the medical center. In December 1994 Kelch wrote that he and Howell had "spent many hours together working to help chart our future" and that both realized the importance of cooperative effort between the college of medicine and the hospitals and clinics "to deliver quality patient care and services, teach and train and conduct top quality research."[112] Continuing this theme, Kelch and Howell wrote to faculty and staff in September 1995 that "indeed, we were convinced that contentious or competitive behavior among components of our medical center would be counter-productive."[113]

In addition to distributing occasional written reports on the progress of their joint planning efforts, Kelch and Howell held a series of forums for all college of medicine and hospitals and clinics personnel to provide opportunities "for broad input into the management process."[114]

Howell and Kelch also forged a five-year "College of Medicine/UIHC Management and Financial Agreement" to guide relations between their two units. The centerpiece of this agreement was what they called the "Clinical Enterprise," of which more will be said further on. Other critical elements included a one-time transfer of $3 million from the hospitals and clinics to the college of medicine dean's enrichment fund in fiscal 1995 to support recruitment of department heads, the long transition to new leadership having built a backlog of six vacant departmental chairs, with a seventh soon to follow; graduate medical education payments from the hospital to the college totaling $4.2 million in 1995, most of which would go to departments with the remainder slated for curriculum and program development; and an exchange of service agreement whereby the college would pay the hospital for collection of patient accounts, clinical overhead, and other services. Significantly, Howell and Kelch agreed as well that any hospital revenues over and above a 3 percent operating margin, up to $10 million, would be shared by the college and hospital on a 60:40 basis.[115]

The above-mentioned clinical enterprise aimed to provide a "joint staff and joint decision-making model" to manage all clinical activities of the hospitals and clinics and college of medicine. Internally, the enterprise focused on enhancing existing clinical programs and considering new ones; capital development and space management; and efforts to cut costs within both the college of medicine and the hospitals and clinics. Hospitals and clinics officials at first set a goal of reducing the teaching hospital's budget by $15 million a year for four years, but when that target could not be met they aimed instead to save from $50 million to $65 million over five years. Officials expected these cost-cutting efforts to remove more than 300 beds from service over the long term—thereby reducing the hospitals and clinics' bed complement to about 500—as well as to cut the size of the hospitals and clinics workforce. Not surprisingly, the prospect of layoffs contributed to rising concern among hospital staff, particularly nurses and service workers, and officials set up a hotline to counteract rumors and dispense what information they could to worried employees.[116] Howell and Kelch also secured board of regents approval to revise the Medical Service Plan, partitioning faculty salaries between clinical and academic components and allowing faculty members' income from medical practice to fluctuate. For the first time in at least three decades, then, clinical faculty members' salaries would bear a direct relation to what Howell and Kelch called the "individual and/or collective performance of the practice plans," performance that would be "subject to the economic realities of the health care marketplace."[117]

Externally, the clinical enterprise launched a major initiative to organize new managed care and community health services under the rubric of the University of Iowa Health System, a nonprofit holding company funded jointly and equally by the college of medicine and the hospitals and clinics. University of Iowa Health System's first subsidiary was a regional physician-hospital organization (PHO) called University of Iowa Affiliated Health Providers, L.C., which in turn joined with Mercy Health Services' Iowa division and Blue Cross–Blue Shield of Iowa and South Dakota to form yet another company, Integrated Health Care Delivery, Inc. Integrated Health Care Delivery's purpose was to develop a managed care insurance product called Unity Choice for large employers and other consumers in Iowa, and Unity Choice later absorbed one of the two managed care packages the University of Iowa offered its employees. University of Iowa Affiliated Health Providers also continued to develop its own referral network, contracting with 170 physicians and four regional hospitals by early 1996.[118]

Meanwhile, the clinical enterprise soon spawned a for-profit company, University of Iowa Community Medical Services, to allow for joint ventures with physicians, physician groups, and communities. University of Iowa Community Medical Services' first spin-off was a home healthcare company called University of Iowa Community Homecare, which, Howell and Kelch wrote, "will allow us to deliver the full range of home health care services including complicated chemotherapy and infusion therapies."[119] Moreover, the board of regents authorized $19 million to purchase physician practices, a sum Kelch termed "modest" compared with plans at other academic health centers.[120]

The purpose of all of these initiatives was to assure an adequate flow of patients for teaching, which, according to Howell, required as many as 3 million "covered lives," and to provide enough sites for training primary care physicians, which became a top priority for medical education at Iowa. And indeed, the University of Iowa's efforts to position its academic health center to compete in the market closely paralleled those of other universities, which also were emphasizing primary care training in community-based programs; consolidating and marketing their faculty clinical practices; and affiliating with other providers, acquiring existing medical practices, and establishing health maintenance organizations.[121] Even the closer ties and cooperation between the college of medicine and the hospitals and clinics at Iowa, as well as establishment of the health sciences vice-presidency, matched a discernible nationwide trend among academic health centers anxious to improve management in order to trim costs and maximize patient revenues.[122] Still, how well such strategies of innovation in programs and administration will work, at the University of Iowa Hospitals and Clinics and at other academic health centers, remains to be seen. Conflicts between the two units are sure to continue, as are difficulties in ensuring a "rational" approach to strategic planning.

It seems reasonable to believe as well that the century-long story of the University of Iowa Hospitals and Clinics describes the economic trajectory of the teaching hospital in America. For throughout its history the teaching hospital has struggled to lay claim to a place in a healthcare system shaped—notwithstanding the myth of the kindly family doctor of a long ago golden age—by economic forces. Within that context, as this case study has shown, the teaching hospital's missions of charity care and medical education, as well as its commitment to providing an environment for clinical research, have been valued more often in rhetoric than in action, subject to continual reassessment in light of shifting economic circumstances and cultural values. Indeed, the vulnerability of the teaching hospital's mission and its position in a market-oriented culture have remained remarkably constant over time; what has changed over the course of the twentieth century is the degree to which—and the means by which—government agencies and, more recently, concentrations of economic power within the market itself have sought to impose their own vision of order on the healthcare system, often with little thought for the fate of teaching hospitals.

Floating as they have at the margins of the market economy, teaching hospitals since their inception have been critically dependent on charitable contributions and subsidies, by whatever name and from whatever sources. In the case of the University of Iowa Hospitals and Clinics, those contributions came first from local and state governments and chiefly in the form of funding for capital improvements and for subsidized indigent care. But it became clear early on at the University of Iowa that local and state resources, provided grudgingly and in limited quantities, were not sufficient to underwrite the full cost of a modern teaching hospital; it was only a massive infusion of capital from the Rockefeller philanthropies in the 1920s that made that possible—and then only for a brief historical moment. As state and philanthropic funding shrank during the Depression and World War II, the foundations of the University of Iowa's teaching hospital, unstable in the best of circumstances, grew increasingly shaky. But the growth of private hospitalization plans (as well as the quasi-private Blue Cross plans) after the war strengthened the teaching hospital in the 1950s, turning its balance sheet from red to black; and upon this new footing the federal government's Medicare and Medicaid programs, two pillars of the Great Society, helped raise the teaching hospital from medical school adjunct to major service institution and economic powerhouse.

Not just at the University of Iowa but across the United States, the unbridled application of market rationality to healthcare in the 1980s and

1990s introduced an unprecedented level of uncertainty into the future of the academic medical center and the university teaching hospital. Despite notes of optimism from some observers,[123] the survival of those institutions in recognizable form seemed far from assured. In the most extreme scenario, the competition between teaching hospitals and other providers for patients presaged a potentially ruinous head-to-head competition among academic medical centers for increasingly scarce resources allocated to "orphan" functions, such as education and research, with little or no short-term market value. Such competition would in turn lead to a significant attrition in the number of academic medical centers and perhaps to the emergence of a two- or three-tiered system in which a handful of centers continued to conduct the full range of operations, from basic science research to graduate medical education, while others functioned at lower levels, perhaps maintaining only limited educational functions and restricted research programs. Already in November 1995, a Pew Health Professions Commission recommended a 20 to 25 percent reduction in the number of medical schools, with similar reductions in pharmacy and nursing programs.[124] It is perhaps not too farfetched to suppose that, in an extension of Arnold Relman's metaphor of the "medical-industrial complex," teaching hospitals and even entire academic medical centers could become targets of market takeovers and buyouts, returning American medical education to the proprietary basis of the nineteenth century.

But if the survival of the academic medical center depends on a wide-ranging reassessment of its makeup and mission, with the emphasis in both education and patient care turning toward primary care—and especially managed care—then a good many questions remain unanswered. Is it feasible to redesign the teaching hospital in the image of a market-oriented health-care system, effecting the fundamental changes in organizational culture throughout the academic medical center necessary to make it a viable market competitor? If such a redesign is possible, who will pay for the societal goods, especially graduate medical education and indigent care, that leaders acknowledge must remain a part of the academic medical center's mission but that carry no immediate and obvious economic value to the third parties who pay the bills?[125] Perhaps most important, it remains to be seen whether or not the academic medical center can adopt market-oriented behaviors selectively and in measured doses without being consumed by the dynamic of the market—calling to mind the old saw about the woman who was only a little bit pregnant.

A working compromise with prevailing market forces, one that would maintain the distinctive identity of the academic medical center and the university teaching hospital, would not only represent a delicate balancing act; it would also mark a significant departure from many of the major postwar trends that have shaped the University of Iowa Hospitals and

Clinics and the University of Iowa College of Medicine. Contrary to the seemingly inexorable postwar trend toward constant expansion of services and programs and the ever closer embrace of "big medicine," with its overtones of high technology and high cost, the revamped medical center and teaching hospital proposed at the University of Iowa will be shaped, to an unprecedented degree if all goes according to plan, by market demand across a wide range of issues, from decisions on appropriate levels of technology to the size and mix of clinical services and the nature and scope of educational and research programs.

Within the state of Iowa at large and certainly at the University of Iowa, the will to sustain the academic health center enterprise despite the difficulties and challenges, is a powerful one—a will that has triumphed over logic more than once. If the institution seems now poised at the brink of an unfathomable future, so, too, must it have seemed on several other occasions—for example, in 1910 after Abraham Flexner's devastating critique, again in 1927 after the forced resignation of Dean Lee Wallace Dean and the loss of several key faculty and administrators, or in 1945 after a decade and a half of struggle and neglect caused by depression and war. Leaping from crisis to crisis and molded by the dynamics of both cooperation and conflict, the University of Iowa's academic health center has insinuated itself deeply into the local economy, as well as the academic culture, over the course of a century. Given such an incalculable investment of human effort and belief, sheer will, and pride, few if any of the academic medical center's proponents expect the teaching hospital to abandon its multiple missions, whatever trials the era of free market healthcare may bring.

Notes

1. Colloton's address was reprinted in *Academic Medicine* 64 (February 1989), pp. 55–60. Colloton, incidentally, was the second non-physician to serve as AAMC chairman; his term spanned 1987–1988.

2. An early warning came from Irving J. Lewis and Cecil G. Sheps, *The Sick Citadel: The American Academic Medical Center and the Public Interest* (Cambridge, MA: Oelgeschlager, Gunn & Hain, 1983).

3. See, as examples, Task Force on Academic Health Centers, *Prescription for Change* (New York: The Commonwealth Fund, 1985); Association of American Medical Colleges, *Financing Graduate Medical Education* (Washington, DC: AAMC, 1986); Josiah Macy, Jr., Foundation, *Financing of Medical Education in an Era of Healthcare Reform* (New York: Josiah Macy, Jr., Foundation, 1995).

4. Arthur Andersen & Co., *The Future of Healthcare: Changes and Choices* (Chicago: Arthur Andersen & Co., 1987).

5. *AAMC Data Book: Statistical Information Related to Medical Education* (Chicago: Association of American Medical Colleges, 1992), Table L1; Health Insurance Association of America, *Sourcebook of Health Insurance Data*, 1963–1990 editions.

6. A useful explanation of DRGs is contained in the Commonwealth Fund's *Prescription For Change*; see Section III, pp. 6–7. See also the Iowa Hospital Association's *Iowa Hospitals: A Profile of Service to the People*, 1992 edition, p. 37.

7. Hospital Advisory Committee Minutes, June 15, 1983, File 26.8, J. O. Freedman Papers, University of Iowa Archives.

8. Hospital Advisory Committee Minutes, February 14, 1984, File 26.8, J. O. Freedman Papers, University of Iowa Archives.

9. Council on Graduate Medical Education, *Second Report of the Council: The Financial Status of Teaching Hospitals and the Underrepresentation of Minorities in Medicine* (Washington, DC: Department of Health and Human Services, Government Printing Office, 1990).

10. Michael E. Whitcomb and William O. Cleverly, "Financial Performance of Academic Medical Center Hospitals," *Academic Medicine* 68 (October 1993): 729–731.

11. Board of Regents, meeting as University of Iowa Hospitals and Clinics trustees, December 19, 1990, University of Iowa Business Office.

12. See also, for example, Nathan J. Stark, "Academic Health Centers: An Uncertain Future," in *Hospitals* (August 20, 1986); the author was a former undersecretary of Health and Human Services.

13. Iowa Hospital Association, *Iowa Hospitals: A Profile of Service to the People*, 1987 edition, p. 27.

14. Annual Statistical Reports, University of Iowa Hospitals and Clinics, Office of Financial Management and Control.

15. Blue Cross of Iowa, under orders from the state insurance commissioner, implemented a prospective payment system beginning in 1983 and planned to implement DRGs in 1988. See the Iowa Hospital Association's *Iowa Hospitals: A Profile of Service to the People*, 1987 edition, p. 33.

16. Iowa Hospital Association, *Iowa Hospitals: The 1992 Guide to Utilization, Personnel and Financial Operations, 1988/1989/1990*, pp. 10–12.

17. Ibid., pp. 13–14. Health maintenance organizations are an interesting case in point. As the number of Iowans enrolled in HMOs expanded from 181,633 in 1986 to 307,914 in 1990, the discounts to these HMOs (combined with preferred provider organizations and self-funded employer plans) increased from 2.1 percent to 15.6 percent. See also the Iowa Hospital Association's *Iowa Hospitals: A Profile of Service to the People* 1991 edition, p. 40.

18. Hospital Advisory Committee Minutes, September 5, 1984, File 26.8, J. O. Freedman Papers, University of Iowa Archives.

19. Task Force on Graduate Medical Education, *Graduate Medical Education: Proposals for the Eighties* (Washington, DC: Association of American Medical Colleges, 1980).

20. Board of Regents Minutes, December 19, 1990, University of Iowa Business Office.

21. Arnold M. Epstein, "US Teaching Hospitals in the Evolving Health Care System," *Journal of the American Medical Association* 273 (April 19, 1995): 1203–1207.

22. Graduate Medical Education National Advisory Committee, *Summary Report of the Graduate Medical Education National Advisory Committee* (Washington, DC: Department of Health and Human Services, Government Printing Office, 1980).

23. Office of Technology Assessment, *Forecast of Physician Supply and Requirements* (Washington, DC: Government Printing Office, 1980).

24. See *Graduate Medical Education: Proposals for the Eighties.*

25. John K. Iglehart, "Federal Support of Graduate Medical Education," *The New England Journal of Medicine* 312 (April 11, 1985): 1000–1004.

26. Iowa Hospital Association, *Iowa Hospitals: A Profile of Service to the People*, dated January 1992, pp. 13–14.

27. Ibid., p. 15. Also see 1987 edition, p. 18.

28. John Colloton and John Strauss, "The Changing Nature of the Academic Medical Center: The University of Iowa Experience," delivered at the Duke University Private Sector Conference, March 9–10, 1987, provided by the authors.

29. Iowa Hospital Association, *Iowa Hospitals: A Profile of Service to the People*, 1991 edition, p. 34.

30. Iowa Hospital Association, *Iowa Hospitals: A Profile of Service to the People*, 1988–1992; section consistently titled "Operating Margins." Data cover the years 1986–1990. It bears noting that when nonpatient revenues are considered, far fewer hospitals report negative operating margins; even so, more than a quarter of all rural Iowa hospitals lost money in 1990, compared with just one of the state's 25 urban hospitals.

31. Iowa Hospital Association, *Iowa Hospitals: A Profile of Service to the People*, 1992 edition, p. 41.

32. Remarks by John W. Colloton and John S. Strauss on "The Changing Nature of the Academic Medical Center: The University of Iowa Experience." Colloton, incidentally, served as a member of the Duke University Hospital Advisory Board from 1985 to 1991.

33. Such an arrangement was one reason Robert Neff did not want University Hospitals to provide hospitalization to a group faculty insurance plan proposed in 1941; the plan would have paid only $4.50 a day for private rooms for which the hospital could otherwise charge $6. See Virgil M. Hancher memo dated February 20, 1941, File 57, 1940–41, V. M. Hancher Papers, University of Iowa Archives.

34. Hardin to Merritt Ludwig, February 2, 1968, File 65, 1967–68, Folder 65, H. R. Bowen Papers, University of Iowa Archives.

35. Governor's Commission on Health Care Costs, "Final Report," undated (c. 1982), pp. 9–10.

36. Hospital Advisory Committee Minutes, August 18, 1982, File 26.1, J. O. Freedman Papers, University of Iowa Archives.

37. Iowa Hospital Association, *Iowa Hospitals: A Profile of Service to the People*, 1987–92 editions.

38. John W. Colloton and John S. Strauss, "The Changing Nature of the Academic Medical Center: The University of Iowa Experience."

39. Board of Regents Minutes, September 16, 1987, University of Iowa Archives.

40. Information provided by each hospital; the University of Iowa Hospitals and Clinics' kidney transplant program began in 1970.

41. Hospital Advisory Committee Minutes, July 18, 1984, University of Iowa Hospitals and Clinics Administrative Offices.

42. A synopsis of the legislative history of indigent care decentralization appears in Hospital Advisory Committee Minutes, October 2, 1985, University of Iowa Hospitals and Clinics Administrative Offices.

43. Josephine Gittler, "Hospital Cost Containment in Iowa: A Guide for State Public Policymakers," *Iowa Law Review* 69 (July 1984): 1263–1349.

44. Hospital Advisory Committee Minutes, March 2, 1983, University of Iowa Hospitals and Clinics Administrative Offices.

45. Hospital Advisory Committee Minutes, October 2, 1985, University of Iowa Hospitals and Clinics Administrative Offices; University of Iowa Hospitals and Clinics Annual Statistical Reports, University of Iowa Hospitals and Clinics Office of Financial Management and Control.

46. John Colloton elaborated the political dimensions of the indigent care debate in Hospital Advisory Committee Minutes, October 2, 1985, University of Iowa Hospitals and Clinics Administrative Offices.

47. Hospital Advisory Committee Minutes, March 5, 1986, University of Iowa Hospitals and Clinics Administrative Offices.

48. See *House Files and Resolutions* (Des Moines: State of Iowa, 1986).

49. Hospital Advisory Committee Minutes, March 5, 1986, University of Iowa Hospitals and Clinics Administrative Offices.

50. *Iowa Acts, 1986*, chapter 1246, p. 712.

51. *Iowa Acts, 1987*, chapter 233, pp. 571–574.

52. Board of Regents Minutes, July 12, 1984, University of Iowa Archives.

53. *Report of the Governor's Blue Ribbon Commission on Future Financing of Educationally Related Costs of the University of Iowa Hospitals and Clinics*, Section II, "Introduction and Background," p. 4.

54. A standard chart showing the cost of each phase of the capital replacement program appears in successive UIHC reports to the Board of Regents and other governing bodies and officials. See, for example, "Statewide Service and Educational Roles and Capital Replacement Plan With Associated Financing," c. September 1987, Section 5, "Capital Financing Plan," University of Iowa Hospitals and Clinics Administrative Offices. The $120 million figure for total capital replacement costs is taken from Board of Regents Minutes, September 23, 1982, University of Iowa Archives.

55. Board of Regents Minutes, March 31, 1983, and September 14, 1983, University of Iowa Business Office.

56. University of Iowa Hospitals and Clinics, "Statewide Service and Educational Roles and Capital Replacement Plan With Associated Financing," Section 4, "Capital Replacement Plan," p. 12, University of Iowa Hospitals and Clinics Administrative Offices.

57. Ibid., pp. 4–5, 12. The certificate-of-need application for this project, cited earlier, calculated that it would bring UIHC up to just 1,390 gross square feet per bed. Note also that a total of 83 additional beds were scattered throughout services excluded from the bed count cited here.

58. Board of Regents Minutes, September 23, 1982, and March 31, 1983, University of Iowa Business Office.

59. Ibid.

60. University of Iowa Hospitals and Clinics, "Statewide Service and Educational Roles . . . ," Section 4, "Capital Replacement Plan," p. 4; and Section 5, "Capital Financing Plan," Exhibit I, University of Iowa Hospitals and Clinics Administrative Offices. Later versions of the chart contained in Exhibit I show a lower cost and somewhat reduced gross square footage total for Phase C, owing, possibly, to some elements being shifted to Phase D.

61. University of Iowa Hospitals and Clinics, "Orientation to the UIHC For Christopher Atchison and Laverne Wintermeyer, Iowa Department of Public Health," dated June 3, 1991, Section 1, "UIHC Profile Exhibits," Exhibit XIV. Also see University of Iowa Hospitals and Clinics and Hansen Lind Meyer, "The University of Iowa Hospitals and Clinics," c. 1994, pp. 7, 10, and 14, University of Iowa Hospitals and Clinics Administrative Offices.

62. Psychiatric Pavilion was first proposed to the Board of Regents in September 1987, at which time the board gave approval for planning to proceed. See Regents Minutes, September 16, 1987, University of Iowa Business Office.

63. Psychiatry department head George Winokur noted concern about the armory when he presented the concept for the new pavilion to the regents in September 1987. See also Board of Regents Minutes for January 20, 1988, University of Iowa Business Office, regarding plans and financing for the Field House remodeling project.

64. University of Iowa Hospitals and Clinics and Hansen Lind Meyer, "The University of Iowa Hospitals and Clinics," p. 14, University of Iowa Hospitals and Clinics Administrative Offices.

65. Ibid., p. 10.

66. This concern is only retrospectively recorded in regents minutes; see Board of Regents, September 20, 1989, University of Iowa Business Office.

67. See Board of Regents Minutes, September 20, 1989, University of Iowa Business Office. Also, "Pappajohns' Gift to UIHC a 'Payback' to Iowa," *Pacemaker* (official University of Iowa Hospitals and Clinics publication) 16 (September 1989): 2–5. Also, Dean Borg, "Gift Tops Off Hospitals Replacement Plans," *Spectator Special* (official University of Iowa publication) (Fall 1989): 1–2.

68. Board of Regents Minutes, June 21, July 25, and September 20, 1989, University of Iowa Business Office. Also, University of Iowa Hospitals and Clinics and Hansen Lind Meyer, "The University of Iowa Hospitals and Clinics," p. 10, University of Iowa Hospitals and Clinics Administrative Offices.

69. Board of Regents Minutes, July 1 and September 25, 1991, University of Iowa Business Office.

70. Board of Regents Minutes, September 20, 1989, and April 21, 1993, University of Iowa Business Office. See also University of Iowa Hospitals and Clinics, "Statewide Service and Educational Roles . . ." Section 4, "Capital Development Plan," p. 13, University of Iowa Hospitals and Clinics Administrative Offices.

71. "Pappajohns' Gift to UIHC a 'Payback' to Iowa," *Pacemaker* 16, no. 9 (September 1989): 2–5. Also see Dean Borg, "Gift Tops Off Hospitals Replacement Plans," *Spectator Special* (Fall 1989): 1–2. These official publications leave no impression to chance; it is unlikely that these articles, as they appeared word for word, would have bypassed approval by hospitals and clinics director John Colloton.

72. Board of Regents Minutes, September 20, 1989, University of Iowa Business Office.

73. Board of Regents Minutes, October 16 and December 18, 1991, University of Iowa Business; see also May 20, 1992. Also, University of Iowa Hospitals and Clinics quarterly report to Board of Regents, September 1994, Exhibit XIV, University of Iowa Business Office.

74. John Colloton and John Strauss, "The Changing Nature of the Academic Medical Center: The University of Iowa Experience."

75. Ibid.

76. Ibid.

77. The story of the family practice department's often less-than-happy relations with the University of Iowa Hospitals and Clinics—or more precisely, with the departments of internal medicine and pediatrics—is contained in college of medicine reviews of the department dated 1978 and 1986. In the former, see pp. 2–4, 6, 14, and 20; in the latter, see pp. 6, 15–16, 20–21, 26–27, 45–46, and 77. Departmental reviews are held by the Office of the Dean of Medicine.

78. Personal conversation with Charles Driscoll, head of family practice from 1985 to 1994, and Ruben Widmer, professor emeritus, on May 21, 1993.

79. University of Iowa Hospitals and Clinics quarterly report to Board of Regents, September 1994, Exhibit XIV, University of Iowa Hospitals and Clinics Administrative Offices.

80. Presentation to the Board of Regents by John Colloton, April 21, 1993; see Board of Regents Minutes for that date, University of Iowa Business Office.

81. Ibid.

82. University of Iowa Hospitals and Clinics quarterly report to the Board of Regents, September 1994, table labeled "Sources of Capital Development Funds for Midwest State University–Owned Teaching Hospitals," comparing the Ohio State University, the University of Michigan, the University of Wisconsin, the University of Illinois, Indiana University, and the University of Minnesota.

83. College of Medicine Faculty Gender Report 1982–1993, University of Iowa College of Medicine.

84. Gift, Grant, and Contract reports, University of Iowa College of Medicine; additional figures supplied by the Division of Sponsored Programs, University of Iowa. Note that totals include awards for all purposes, including training, fellowships, and community service projects as well as basic and applied research.

85. Annual reports AE 3506, University of Iowa College of Medicine.

86. Doctors performed 177 kidney and cornea transplant procedures at the hospitals and clinics in 1976; in 1994, they performed 732 procedures involving corneas, kidneys, the pancreas, bone, bone marrow, liver, heart, skin, and lungs: University of Iowa Hospitals and Clinics quarterly report to Board of Regents, September 1994, University of Iowa Hospitals and Clinics Administrative Offices.

87. University of Iowa Hospitals and Clinics quarterly report to Board of Regents, April 21, 1993, Section 1, "Past Two Decades in Review and a Perspective of the Future," pp. 13–14, University of Iowa Hospitals and Clinics Administrative Offices.

88. "College of Medicine Self-Study Committee Report," October 1989, pp. 205, 262. Copy provided by the Office of the Vice President for Statewide Health Services.

89. In addition to chairman Arthur Bonfield, the committee—referred to often as the Bonfield Committee—consisted of associate dean of the college of business administration Willis R. Greer, Jr., liberal arts professor Edward Lawler, and professor of engineering Virendra C. Patel.

90. "Final Report of the University Review Committee for the College of Medicine," provided by the Office of the Vice President for Statewide Health Services.

91. J. W. Colloton to P. E. Nathan, April 11, 1991, provided by the Office of the Vice President for Statewide Health Services.

92. See history of the strategic planning program in University of Iowa Hospitals and Clinics Quarterly Report to the Board of Regents, July 18, 1991, Section 2, "UIHC Strategic Planning Program," pp. 21–30.

93. J. W. Eckstein, "Response to the Final Report of the University Review Committee for the College of Medicine," Office of the Dean of the College of Medicine.

94. J. W. Colloton, personal communication with the authors, January 25, 1996.

95. J. W. Colloton to P. E. Nathan, April 11, 1991; H. J. Black, E. A. Borg, W. W. Hesson, S. A. Mathis, A. B. O'Deen, W. D. Petasnick, J. H. Staley, and K. H. Yerington to A. A. Bonfield, April 11, 1991; and Colloton, et al., to P. E. Nathan, June 10, 1991, Office of the Vice President for Statewide Health Services.

96. Indeed, Colloton later complained that the review committee's expanded scope was communicated neither to him nor to the board of regents during the course of its review; moreover, Colloton charged, the review committee spoke with no members of the hospitals and clinics' administrative staff other than himself. These observations were contained in a personal communication with the authors, January 25, 1996.

97. Robert A. Derzon, "The Marriage of Medical Schools and Teaching Hospitals," *Journal of Medical Education* 53 (January 1978): 20.

98. J. W. Colloton to Health System Reform Seminar Group, October 14, 1993, Office of the Vice President for Statewide Health Services.

99. Derzon, "The Marriage of Medical Schools and Teaching Hospitals," pp. 20–21.

100. John Colloton, "Remarks at the Dedication Banquet of the Roy J. Carver Pavilion, October 6, 1978," Office of the Vice President for Statewide Health Services.

101. Interviews with Marvin Pomerantz, who was board of regents president when the review committee report was issued, and with John Colloton.

102. John Colloton, "Re: Plan for Transitional Reorganization of the U. of I. Health Science Center Commencing in Late 1991," August 14, 1991, Office of the Vice President for Statewide Health Services.

103. John Colloton, personal communication with the authors, January 25, 1996.

104. Board of Regents Minutes, November 24, 1991, University of Iowa Business Office.

105. The first newspaper account of the review committee report appears to have surfaced only in late August; see Lyle Muller, "Problems Cited Between U of I Hospitals, Faculty," *The Cedar Rapids Gazette,* August 27, 1991; also, "2 U of I Chiefs Clash Over Cooperation," *The Cedar Rapids Gazette,* September 29, 1991.

106. Charles Bullard, "U of I Reorganization Criticized," *The Des Moines Register,* November 20, 1991.

107. J. W. Colloton to H. R. Rawlings, December 12, 1991, Office of the Vice President for Statewide Health Services.

108. Roy J. Amara, J. Ian Morrison, and Gregory Schmid, "Impact on Academic Medical Centers." In *Looking Ahead at American Health Care* (Washington, DC: Healthcare Information Center, 1988), pp. 103–118.

109. Arthur Bonfield, personal interview with the authors, February 15, 1996.

110. See Organization and Governance Project of the Association of Academic Health Centers, *The Organization and Governance of Academic Health Centers* (Washington, DC: AAHC, 1980), Vol. 2, pp. 35–38.

111. Scott Hauser, "Healing the Rift: Partners Tackle Health Care Goals," *Iowa City Press-Citizen* (September 14, 1994): 1A, 3A.

112. Robert P. Kelch, "New Agreements Highlight College–UIHC Cooperation," *The University of Iowa College of Medicine News* (December 1994–January 1995): 1, 4.

113. R. Edward Howell and Robert P. Kelch to Faculty and Staff, September 7, 1995.

114. Howell and Kelch to Faculty and Staff, February 9, 1996.

115. Robert P. Kelch, "New Agreements Highlight College–UIHC Cooperation."

116. "Summary of Questions and Responses, Kelch & Howell Open Forum"; also see John Kirsch, "Hot Line Responds to UI Hospital Rumors," *Iowa City Press-Citizen* (March 1, 1996): 1A.

117. Howell and Kelch to Faculty and Staff, September 7, 1995.

118. Howell and Kelch to Faculty and Staff, February 9, 1996.

119. Ibid.

120. "Summary of Questions and Responses, Kelch & Howell Open Forum."

121. Eric B. Munson, "Issues Regarding Graduate Medical Education and Teaching Hospitals," Presentation to Subcommittee on Health, House Committee on Ways and Means, March 23, 1995. Munson was executive director of the University of North Carolina Hospitals.

122. Fred C. Munson and Thomas D'Aunno, "Structural Change in Academic Health Centers," *Hospital and Health Services Administration* 34 (Fall 1989): 413–425. The two authors also collaborated to produce the 1987 study, "The University Hospital in the Academic Health Center: Finding the Right Relationship," sponsored and published jointly by the Association of Academic Health Centers and the Association of American Medical Colleges.

123. See, for example, Jordan J. Cohen, "Finding the Silver Lining Without the Golden Eggs," *Academic Medicine* 70 (February 1995): 98–103.

124. Executive Summary of the Third Report of the Pew Health Professions Commission, "Critical Challenges: Revitalizing the Health Professions for the Twenty-first Century," November 16, 1995.

125. See Jordan J. Cohen, "The Emerging Market for Health Services and Implications for Academic Medicine," AAMC Policy Statement presented to the Physician Payment Review Commission, November 21, 1994. Cohen proposed one all-payer fund to spread the costs of graduate medical education more equitably, and another to support "the unique costs of teaching hospitals."

Appendix A: Chronological Tables

Table A.1 Presidents of the University of Iowa, 1855–1995

Amos Dean	1855–1859	Thomas H. Macbride	1914–1916
Silas Totten	1859–1862	Walter A. Jessup	1916–1934
Oliver Spencer	1862–1867	Eugene A. Gilmore	1934–1940
Nathan Leonard	1867–1868	Chester A. Phillips (Int.)	1940
James Black	1868–1870	Virgil M. Hancher	1940–1964
Nathan Leonard (Int.)	1870–1871	Howard R. Bowen	1964–1969
George Thacher	1871–1877	Willard L. Boyd	1969–1981
Christian Slagle (Int.)	1877–1878	D. C. Spriestersbach (Int.)	1981–1982
Josiah Pickard	1878–1887	James O. Freedman	1982–1987
Charles A. Schaeffer	1887–1898	Richard D. Remington (Int.)	1987–1988
Amos Currier (Int.)	1898–1899	Hunter R. Rawlings III	1988–1995
George E. MacLean	1899–1911	Peter E. Nathan (Int.)	1995
John G. Bowman	1911–1914	Mary Sue Coleman	1995–

Source: University of Iowa Catalogs.

Table A.2 Superintendents and Directors of University Hospitals, 1898–1995

Jennie Cottle	1898–1900	William T. Graham	1920–1921
Florence Brown	1900–1901	Alan J. Lomas	1921–1923
Susan Parish	1901–1902	Bert Caldwell	1923–1925
Antonia Epeneter	1902–1903	Jesse L. McElroy	1925–1927
Mary Nesbitt	1904–1913	Robert E. Neff	1927–1945
Anna Goodale	1913–1914	Gerhard Hartman	1946–1971
Josephine Creelman	1914–1915	John W. Colloton	1971–1993
William T. Graham	1915–1919	John H. Staley (Int.)	1993–1994
Herbert O. Collins	1919–1920	R. Edward Howell	1994–

Note: Beginning in 1898 the medical faculty designated one of its members as the hospital's medical director, a largely superfluous position that was eliminated in 1921; see chapter 2. Also, in 1969 the title *hospital superintendent* was changed to *hospital director*; see chapter 5.
Source: University of Iowa Catalogs.

Table A.3   Deans of College of Medicine, 1870–1995

Washington F. Peck	1870–1891	Mayo H. Soley	1948–1949
John C. Shrader	1891–1896	Interim Committee†	1949–1953
William D. Middleton	1896–1902	Norman B. Nelson	1953–1962
James R. Guthrie	1902–1914	Robert C. Hardin	1962–1969
Lee W. Dean	1914–1927	William O. Reike (Int.)	1969–1970
John T. McClintock (Int.)	1927–1928	John W. Eckstein	1970–1990
Henry S. Houghton	1928–1932	James A. Clifton (Int.)	1990–1993
Interim Committee*	1932–1935	Richard G. Lynch (Int.)	1993–1994
Ewen M. MacEwen	1935–1947	Robert P. Kelch	1994–
Carlyle Jacobsen (Int.)	1947–1948		

*Interim Committee was composed of John T. McClintock, Everett D. Plass, and Howard L. Beye; see chapter 3.

†Interim Committee was chaired first by Robert Tidrick and later by Willis Fowler; see chapter 4.

Source: University of Iowa Catalogs.

Table A.4   Heads of Department of Anesthesia, 1963–1995

William K. Hamilton	1963–1967	Wendell C. Stevens	1978–1982
Jack Moyers	1967–1977	Peter J. R. Jebson (Int.)	1982–1983
Samir D. Gergis (Int.)	1977–1978	John H. Tinker	1983–

Note: Prior to its establishment as an independent department, the anesthesia service existed as a division of the department of surgery. The service was headed by Lewis Harding from 1914 to 1927; by Dorothy Dimond from 1927 to 1937; and by Stuart Cullen from 1937 to 1958.

Source: University of Iowa College of Medicine.

Table A.5   Heads of Department of Dermatology, 1899–1995

John B. Kessler	1899–1934
Ruben Nomland	1936–1960
Robert G. Carney	1961–1976
Richard M. Caplan (Int.)	1976–1977
John S. Strauss	1977–

Source: University of Iowa College of Medicine.

Table A.6   Heads of Department of Family Practice, 1971–1995

Robert E. Rakel	1971–1985
Charles E. Driscoll	1985–1994
Gerald J. Jogerst (Int.)	1994–1995
Evan W. Kligman	1995–

Source: University of Iowa College of Medicine.

Table A.7   Heads of Department of Internal Medicine, 1870–1995

William S. Robertson	1870–1887	Fred M. Smith	1924–1946
William D. Middleton	1887–1891	William M. Fowler (Int.)	1946–1948
Lawrence W. Littig	1891–1904	William B. Bean	1948–1970
Walter L. Bierring	1904–1910	James A. Clifton	1970–1976
Campbell P. Howard	1910–1924	Francois M. Abboud	1976–

Note: Prior to 1947, the department was named the department of theory and practice of medicine.
Source: University of Iowa College of Medicine.

Table A.8   Heads of Department of Neurology, 1919–1995

Clarence E. Van Epps	1919–1945
Adolph L. Sahs	1945–1974
Maurice W. Van Allen	1974–1985
Robert L. Rodnitzky (Int.)	1985–1986
Antonio J. G. Damasio	1986–

Source: University of Iowa College of Medicine.

Table A.9   Heads of Department of Obstetrics and Gynecology, 1870–1995

John C. Shrader	1870–1898	John H. Randall	1950–1959
James R. Guthrie	1898–1916	William C. Keettel	1959–1977
William R. Whiteis	1916–1920	Roy M. Pitkin	1977–1987
Frederick H. Falls	1921–1926	Frank J. Zlatnik (Int.)	1987–1988
Everett D. Plass	1926–1950	Jennifer R. Niebyl	1988–

Source: University of Iowa College of Medicine.

Table A.10 Heads of Department of Ophthalmology, 1871–1995

Edward H. Hazen	1871–1875	Alson E. Braley	1950–1967
C. M. Hobby	1875–1879	Frederick C. Blodi	1967–1984
James W. Dalbey	1889–1903	Charles D. Phelps	1984–1985
Lee W. Dean	1903–1925	Hansjoerg E. Kolder (Int.)	1985–1986
Cecil S. O'Brien	1925–1949	Thomas A. Weingeist	1986–
Glenn L. Walker (Int.)	1949–1950		

Note: Prior to its establishment as an independent department in 1925, ophthalmology fell under the rubric of the eye, ear, nose, and throat service, which also encompassed head and neck surgery. See also Table A.12.
Source: University of Iowa College of Medicine.

Table A.11 Heads of Department of Orthopædic Surgery, 1925–1995

Arthur Steindler	1925–1948
Robert W. Newman (Int.)	1949–1950
Carroll B. Larson	1950–1973
Reginald R. Cooper	1973–

Note: Prior to its establishment as an independent department in 1925, the orthopaedic service existed as a division of the department of surgery. Arthur Steindler headed the service from 1913 to 1925.
Source: University of Iowa College of Medicine.

Table A.12 Heads of Department of Otolaryngology—Head and Neck Surgery, 1925–1995

Lee W. Dean	1925–1927
Dean M. Lierle	1927–1964
Brian F. McCabe	1964–1994
Bruce J. Gantz	1994–

Note: Prior to its establishment as an independent department in 1925, head and neck surgery fell under the rubric of the eye, ear, nose, and throat service, which also encompassed ophthalmology. For otolaryngology department heads prior to 1925, see Table A.10.
Source: University of Iowa College of Medicine.

Table A.13 Heads of Department of Pathology, 1891–1995

J. M. Parker, Jr.	1891–1893	George H. Hansmann (Int.)	1925–1930
Walter L. Bierring	1893–1903	Harry P. Smith	1930–1945
Henry Albert	1903–1922	Emory D. Warner	1945–1970
Edgar M. Medlar (Int.)	1921–1923	George D. Penick	1970–1981
Frederick W. Mulsow (Int.)	1923–1925	Richard G. Lynch	1981–

Note: The department of pathology encompassed the field of bacteriology until 1933, when the latter was attached to the department of hygiene and preventive medicine. See Table A.21.
Source: University of Iowa College of Medicine.

Table A.14   Heads of Department of Pediatrics, 1915–1995

Albert H. Byfield	1915–1924	Wallace W. McCrory	1958–1961
Philip C. Jeans	1924–1952	Donal Dunphy	1961–1973
Charles D. May	1952–1957	Fred G. Smith	1973–1986
John C. MacQueen (Int.)	1957–1958	Frank H. Morriss	1986–

Source: University of Iowa College of Medicine.

Table A.15   Heads of Department of Psychiatry, 1915–1995

Samuel T. Orton	1919–1927	Paul E. Huston	1955–1971
Thomas P. Brennan (Int.)	1927–1929	George Winokur	1971–1990
Andrew H. Woods	1929–1941	Robert G. Robinson	1990–
Wilbur R. Miller	1941–1955		

Note: Prior to establishment of the department of psychiatry in 1919, the college of medicine engaged a lecturer on mental and nervous diseases. Max Witte served as de facto psychiatrist for University Hospital from 1906 to 1919.
Source: University of Iowa College of Medicine.

Table A.16   Heads of Department of Radiology, 1915–1995

Bundy Allen	1915–1926	James H. Christie	1968–1978
Thomas F. Baxter	1926–1928	Rolf L. Shapiro (Int.)	1978–1979
Otis W. Britt	1929	Edmund A. Franken	1979–1994
H. Dabney Kerr	1930–1955	Wilbur L. Smith (Int.)	1994–
Eugene F. Van Epps	1955–1968		

Note: Prior to 1935 the department was named the department of roentgenology.
Source: University of Iowa College of Medicine.

Table A.17   Heads of Department of Surgery, 1870–1995

Washington F. Peck	1870–1891	Robert T. Tidrick	1951–1969
William D. Middleton	1891–1902	Sidney E. Ziffren (Int.)	1969–1970
William Jepson	1902–1912	Robert E. Condon	1971–1972
Charles J. Rowan	1913–1927	Sidney E. Ziffren	1971–1981
Howard L. Beye	1927–1936	Edward E. Mason (Int.)	1981–1982
Frank R. Peterson	1936–1947	Robert J. Corry	1982–1992
Robert T. Tidrick (Int.)	1947–1948	Robert T. Soper (Int.)	1992–1995
Nathan A. Womack	1948–1951	Carol Scott-Conner	1995–

Source: University of Iowa College of Medicine.

Table A.18   Heads of Department of Urology, 1925–1995

Nathaniel G. Alcock	1925–1949
Rubin H. Flocks	1949–1974
David A. Culp	1974–1984
Richard D. Williams	1984–

Note: Prior to its establishment as an independent department in 1925, urology existed as a division of the department of surgery; Nathaniel Alcock headed the division from 1915 to 1925. The department was named the department of genito-urinary surgery from 1925 to 1939.
Source: University of Iowa College of Medicine.

Table A.19   Heads of Department of Anatomy, 1870–1995

James H. Boucher	1870	Walter R. Ingram	1940–1966
Elmer F. Clapp	1871–1888	William O. Rieke	1966–1971
Lawrence W. Littig	1889–1891	Interim Committee*	1971–1973
Woods Hutchison	1891–1896	Terence H. Williams	1973–1983
John W. Harriman	1897–1904	Rex Montgomery (Int.)	1983–1985
Henry J. Prentiss	1904–1931	Joe D. Coulter	1985–1992
Ewen M. MacEwen	1931–1940	John P. Long (Int.)	1992–

*Interim Committee was composed of Nicholas Halmi, David Moffatt, and Jonathan Parsons.
Source: University of Iowa College of Medicine.

Table A.20   Heads of Department of Biochemistry, 1924–1995

Victor C. Myers	1924–1927	Edward C. Heath	1976–1984
Henry A. Mattill	1927–1952	Charles A. Swenson (Int.)	1984–1987
Henry B. Bull	1952–1963	Alan G. Goodridge	1987–
Carl S. Vestling	1963–1976		

Source: University of Iowa College of Medicine.

Table A.21   Heads of Department of Microbiology, 1938–1995

William M. Hale	1938–1949	Irving P. Crawford	1977–1989
John R. Porter	1949–1977	Allen J. Markovetz (Int.)	1989–1993
Allen J. Markovetz (Int.)	1977	Michael A. Apicella	1993–

Note: Prior to its establishment as an independent department in 1937, microbiology fell under the rubric first of pathology and, in 1933, of hygiene and preventive medicine. The department was named the department of bacteriology from 1937 to 1962.
Source: University of Iowa College of Medicine.

Table A.22   Heads of Department of Pharmacology, 1870–1995

Philo J. Farnsworth	1870–1892	John P. Long	1970–1983
Charles S. Chase	1892–1920	Gerald F. Gebhart	1983–1984
Oscar H. Plant	1920–1939	P. Michael Conn	1984–1995
Erwin G. Gross	1939–1960	Arthur A. Spector (Int.)	1995–
Lauren A. Woods	1960–1970		

Source: University of Iowa College of Medicine.

Table A.23   Heads of Department of Physiology and Biophysics, 1870–1995

William D. Middleton	1870–1887	Harry M. Hines	1944–1961
Richard W. Hill	1887–1889	C. Adrian Hogben	1961–1973
James R. Guthrie	1889–1898	Friedrich P.J. Diecke (Int.)	1973–1975
Lee W. Dean	1898–1901	Michael I. Phillips (Int.)	1975–1976
John T. McClintock	1901–1944	Robert E. Fellows	1976–

Note: Prior to 1966 the department was named the department of physiology.
Source: University of Iowa College of Medicine.

Table A.24   Heads of Department of Preventive Medicine and Environmental Health, 1921–1995

Don M. Griswold	1921–1927	Keith R. Long (Int.)	1971–1972
Albert V. Hardy	1927–1930	Edwin P. Isacson	1972–1985
Milford E. Barnes	1930–1952	Robert B. Wallace	1985–1994
Franklin H. Top	1952–1971	Leon F. Burmeister (Int.)	1994–

Note: Prior to its establishment as an independent department in 1921, preventive medicine existed as a lectureship in sanitary science and public hygiene. The department was named the department of hygiene and preventive medicine until 1964.
Source: University of Iowa College of Medicine.

Appendix B: Statistical Data

Table B.1   Admissions, Patient-Days, and Average Length of Stay by Payment Category, 1930–1995*

Fiscal Year	Admissions				Patient Days				Average Length of Stay			
	Private†	State	Other‡	Total	Private†	State	Other‡	Total	Private†	State	Other‡	Total
1929–30	1,400	8,590	2,810	12,800	14,779	200,513	19,116	234,408	10.56	23.34	6.80	18.31
1934–35	1,514	14,957	1,761	18,232	14,784	249,494	20,212	284,490	9.76	16.08	11.48	15.60
1939–40	2,307	15,063	2,316	19,686	22,931	233,723	28,418	275,072	9.94	15.52	12.27	13.97
1944–45	3,236	10,262	3,255	16,753	33,855	164,855	40,084	238,794	10.46	16.06	12.31	14.25
1949–50	3,963	11,392	3,970	19,325	30,537	192,476	45,992	269,005	7.70	16.89	11.58	13.92
1954–55	4,962	12,139	3,925	21,026	41,435	196,939	42,124	280,498	8.35	16.22	10.73	13.34
1959–60	6,023	13,642	5,212	24,877	49,682	189,408	40,137	279,227	8.25	13.88	7.71	11.23
1964–65	7,082	18,675	6,869	32,626	60,532	206,210	58,405	325,147	8.55	11.04	8.11	9.97
1969–70	8,537	17,368	7,773	33,678	84,490	167,008	69,448	320,946	9.90	9.62	8.94	9.53
1974–75	17,855	11,404	6,642	35,901	165,170	99,185	51,061	315,416	9.25	8.70	7.69	8.79
1979–80	25,440	11,535	3,229	40,204	208,093	89,184	15,532	313,009	8.18	7.73	4.81	7.79
1984–85	25,059	13,024	178	38,261	186,737	82,093	390	269,220	7.45	6.30	2.19	7.04
1989–90	28,560	5,925	40	34,525	222,899	36,944	42	259,885	7.80	6.24	1.05	7.53
1994–95	32,256	4,747	70	37,073	207,956	26,358	215	234,529	6.45	5.55	3.07	6.33

*All categories include newborn children and subacute as well as acute patients.

†This category includes self-pay patients as well as those with commercial insurance and Blue Cross coverage; beginning in 1969–70, it also includes Medicare and Medicaid patients.

‡Includes clinical pay, county pay, county clinical pay, research, staff, and Medical Assistance for the Aged patients.

Source: 1929–30: Superintendent's Reports; 1934–35 to 1994–95: *Annual Statistical Reports*, University of Iowa Hospitals and Clinics.

Table B.2 Admissions, Patient-Days, Average Length of Stay, and Clinic Visits by Primary Payer, 1990 and 1995

Payer	Admissions		Patient-Days		Length of Stay		Clinic Visits	
	1989–90	*1994–95*	*1989–90*	*1994–95*	*1989–90*	*1994–95*	*1989–90*	*1994–95*
Blue Cross/Blue Shield	4,772	5,210	32,248	30,642	6.76	5.88	118,405	136,254
Commercial Insurance	6,296	6,771	50,219	46,155	7.98	6.82	90,344	104,454
Medicare	8,286	10,357	77,222	72,909	9.32	7.04	94,911	112,048
Medicaid	6,078	7,191	46,987	45,412	7.73	6.32	40,711	48,322
State Indigent	5,925	4,747	36,944	26,358	6.24	5.55	37,801	38,168
County Pay	40	70	42	215	1.05	3.07	2,187	1,812
Self-Pay	1,779	1,460	9,985	6,565	5.61	4.50	36,411	27,046
Other	1,349	1,267	6,238	6,273	4.62	4.95	30,866	34,474
Total	**34,525**	**37,073**	**259,885**	**234,529**	**7.53**	**6.33**	**451,636**	**502,578**

Note: Inpatient statistics include subacute as well as acute admissions.
Source: *Annual Statistical Reports*, University of Iowa Hospitals and Clinics Office of Financial Management and Control.

Table B.3 State Indigent Care Appropriation as a Proportion of Total Patient Care Revenues, 1930–1995

Fiscal Year	State		Paying Patient		Total Expenditures (Dollars)
	Appropriation (Dollars)	Percent of total	Income (Dollars)	Percent of total	
1929–30	991,194	80.0	247,543	20.0	1,238,737
1934–35	900,000	78.3	249,849	21.7	1,149,849
1939–40	1,000,310	74.2	347,683	25.8	1,347,993
1944–45	1,100,000	65.9	568,130	34.1	1,668,130
1949–50	2,581,007	70.6	1,074,899	29.4	3,655,906
1954–55	3,782,087	67.5	1,821,718	32.5	5,603,805
1959–60	5,256,263	60.8	3,384,880	39.2	8,641,143
1964–65	6,994,020	54.6	5,807,662	45.4	12,801,682
1969–70	8,635,265	40.1	12,888,335	59.9	21,523,600
1974–75	11,904,000	30.6	26,944,755	69.4	38,848,755
1979–80	20,115,663	24.0	63,706,427	76.0	83,822,090
1984–85	26,015,531	18.0	118,877,493	82.0	144,893,024
1989–90	27,893,767	11.5	213,684,363	88.5	241,578,130
1994–95	28,722,559	7.9	335,109,923	92.1	363,832,482

Note: Figures do not include expenses of or appropriations for Psychiatric Hospital or University Hospital School.
Source: "Proportionality of Support of Total Operating Expense—Appropriation versus Paying Patient Income, 1927–28 to Date," dated January 28, 1995; University of Iowa Hospitals and Clinics Office of Financial Management and Control.

Table B.4 University Hospitals Operating Expenditures, 1975–1995*

Department/Expense Category	1974–75 Amount (Dollars)	1974–75 Percent of Total	1984–85 Amount (Dollars)	1984–85 Percent of Total	1994–95 Amount (Dollars)	1994–95 Percent of Total
Professional Services and Education						
Graduate Medical Education	3,081,804	7.59	7,819,374	5.44	13,111,129	3.69
Nursing Service	12,944,154	31.87	47,028,102	32.73	99,584,981	28.02
Clinic Support Services	1,445,987	3.56	3,131,506	2.18	23,297,863	6.55
Material Services	(Not reported separately)		10,712,852	7.46	18,351,966	5.16
Pharmacy Services and Education	3,953,715	9.73	11,269,616	7.84	36,697,666	10.32
Laboratory Services and Education	3,477,238	8.56	8,846,481	6.16	17,508,811	4.93
Radiology Services and Education	1,400,978	3.45	6,126,022	4.26	11,576,789	3.26
College of Medicine Support Services	(Not reported separately)				20,985,503	5.90
Other Diagnostic and Therapeutic Services†	411,537	1.02	11,749,377	8.18	13,029,203	3.67
Special Services	1,302,763	3.21	3,944,968	2.75	7,335,251	2.06
Subtotal Professional Services	28,018,176	68.99	110,628,298	77.00	261,479,162	73.56
Dietary Services and Education	3,024,370	7.45	4,990,076	3.47	12,141,266	3.42
Admissions, Business Office and Other	3,752,513	9.24	9,195,944	6.40	27,623,641	7.77
Housekeeping, Security, Architectural Services	2,472,551	6.09	7,582,394	5.28	14,053,390	3.96
Plant Operations and Maintenance	2,483,604	6.12	8,676,903	6.04	18,853,303	5.31
State Patient Transportation	431,817	1.06	855,584	0.59	970,839	0.27
Administration	427,760	1.05	1,496,379	1.04	2,639,919	0.74
Bad Debt Expense	—‡	—	—‡	—	14,335,768	4.03
Staff Benefits §	(Not reported separately)		252,380	0.17	3,353,546	0.94
Subtotal	**12,592,615**	**31.01**	**33,049,660**	**23.00**	**93,971,672**	**26.44**
Total Operating Expenses**	**40,610,791**	**100.00**	**143,677,958**	**100.00**	**355,450,884**	**100.00**

*Includes University Hospitals and Psychiatric Hospital; does not include University Hospital School.
†In 1974–75, this category includes $226,641 for anesthesia services; in 1984–85, it includes $335,471 in professional services deductions.
‡Bad debt expenses were reported as deductions from gross patient revenues in these years.
§ In 1984–85 this category includes sick leave benefits, a comparable worth adjustment, and a workers compensation fund credit; in 1994–95 it includes sick leave benefits, early retirement benefits, and self-funded health benefits.
**Figures do not include certain equipment and repair, replacement, and alteration expenses that appear in University of Iowa Hospitals and Clinics' state-approved operating budgets.
Source: *Annual Statistical Reports*, University of Iowa Hospitals and Clinics Office of Financial Management and Control.

Table B.5   College of Medicine Gift, Grant, and Contract Funding by Department, 1970–1995

Department	Funding in Dollars for Fiscal Year					
	1970	*1975*	*1980*	*1985*	*1990*	*1995*
Anatomy	249,590	239,381	845,371	935,288	1,750,451	1,588,961
Anesthesia	5,090	1,098	500	178,262	995,070	1,493,085
Biochemistry	557,759	944,251	2,059,541	2,508,088	3,887,471	3,417,697
Cancer Center				83,306	69,356	
Cardiovascular Center			2,204,629	6,623,883	9,304,131	669,178
Clinical Research Center			45,078	1,558,686		2,222,626
Dermatology	6,200		290,076	655,505	1,506,563	1,181,628
Family Practice		1,800	640,078	390,164	143,093	123,974
Hospital & Health Admin.	11,647		311,810	271,615	76,282	100,076
Hospital School	35,485	74,195	158,931	504,877	264,055	2,164,040
Internal Medicine	1,575,381	3,888,394	7,683,571	10,300,248	16,028,099	27,568,373
Medical College Admin.	2,004,990	4,056,560	3,182,941	1,082,090	2,343,497	4,267,686
Microbiology	115,258	379,960	1,188,389	1,570,010	2,530,798	3,569,955
Neurology	522,769	725,573	115,732	1,025,465	2,100,741	3,428,584
Obstetrics & Gynecology	98,046	447,222	558,435	299,246	734,333	1,081,135
Ophthalmology	677,409	475,099	158,493	694,294	1,439,170	1,387,268
Orthopaedic Surgery	176,249	377,760	872,789	1,009,081	426,335	520,735
Otolaryngology	519,921	760,399	441,729	761,018	1,819,514	1,179,583
Pathology	28,394	39,044	158,667	997,350	1,979,549	3,385,737
Pediatrics	450,141	1,167,312	3,880,937	5,727,567	12,260,166	18,862,470
Pharmacology	1,341,798	1,429,073	1,889,330	1,382,149	1,673,267	3,323,076
Physical Therapy		200,717	114,155	163,895	206,020	309,146
Physician Asst. Prog.			150		104,163	109,062
Physiology	428,803	752,042	1,134,050	2,173,519	2,789,594	3,798,819
Preventive Medicine	976,993	420,467	2,306,466	3,098,441	8,005,114	11,505,028
Psychiatry	277,104	647,075	1,612,866	1,530,014	4,623,222	6,072,864
Radiation Research Lab.		132,441	252,853	255,500	186,190	
Radiology	112,157	6,000	219,062	86,887	290,067	1,627,622
Surgery	49,154	22,560	107,267	385,654	561,798	1,086,068
Univ. Hygienic Lab.					75,491	743,348
Urology	25,724	77,275	291,722	257,765	116,220	502,678
College of Medicine Total	11,135,727	17,545,078	32,729,018	46,524,272	78,374,230	108,549,495

Source: Gift, grant, and contract reports, approved and funded, University of Iowa College of Medicine.

Table B.6   College of Medicine Faculty by Gender, 1985 and 1990

1985

Tenure and Tenure-Track Positions	Male	Female	Total	Percent Male	Percent Female	Average Salary Male	Average Salary Female
Professor	217.75	6.00	223.75	97.30	2.70	94,510.36	73,498.33
Associate Professor	120.00	11.10	131.10	91.50	8.50	76,524.34	61,337.03
Assistant Professor	125.50	17.35	142.85	87.90	12.10	64,918.46	59,735.50
Instructor	3.00		3.00	100.00		51,666.67	
Total	466.25	34.45	500.70	93.10	6.90	*(Not reported)*	*(Not reported)*
Non-Tenure-Track Positions							
Lecturer	3.00	0.50	3.50	85.70	14.30	33,397.00	33,500.00
Associate	40.00	16.05	56.05	71.40	28.60	57,751.73	46,651.65
Total	43.00	16.55	59.55	72.20	27.80	*(Not reported)*	*(Not reported)*
Grand Total	**509.25**	**51.00**	**560.25**	**90.90**	**9.10**	*(Not reported)*	*(Not reported)*

1990

Tenure and Tenure-Track Positions	Male	Female	Total	Percent Male	Percent Female	Average Salary Male	Average Salary Female
Professor	244.15	9.00	253.15	96.40	3.60	131,832.27	124,670.67
Associate Professor	127.75	16.63	144.38	88.50	11.50	109,286.04	87,004.39
Assistant Professor	152.12	30.00	182.12	83.50	16.50	91,776.38	73,995.13
Total	524.02	55.63	579.65	90.40	9.60	*(Not reported)*	*(Not reported)*
Non-Tenure-Track Positions							
Lecturer	2.00	2.50	4.50	44.40	55.60	35,122.50	44,179.60
Associate	57.75	26.85	84.60	68.30	31.70	77,182.16	66,657.09
Total	59.75	29.35	89.10	67.10	32.90	*(Not reported)*	*(Not reported)*
Grand Total	**583.77**	**84.98**	**668.75**	**87.30**	**12.70**	*(Not reported)*	*(Not reported)*

Source: College of Medicine Faculty Gender Report 1982–1993, dated July 21, 1994; College of Medicine Administration.

Appendix C: Maps and Organization Charts

Figure C.1 University of Iowa Organization, 1995, Adapted and Simplified

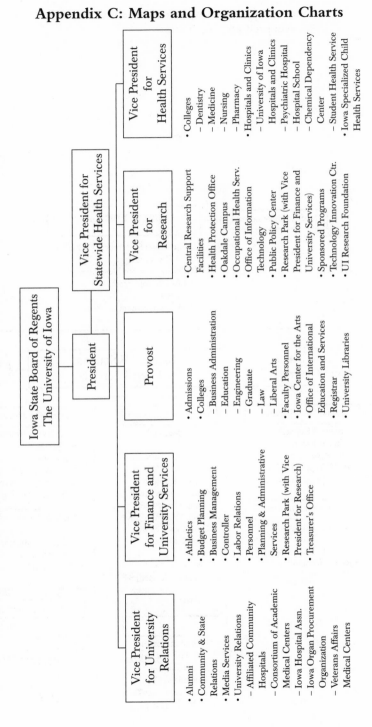

Figure C.2 University of Iowa Hospitals and Clinics Organization, 1995, Adapted and Simplified

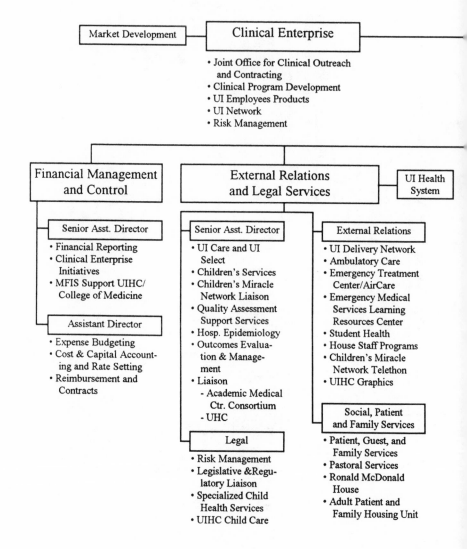

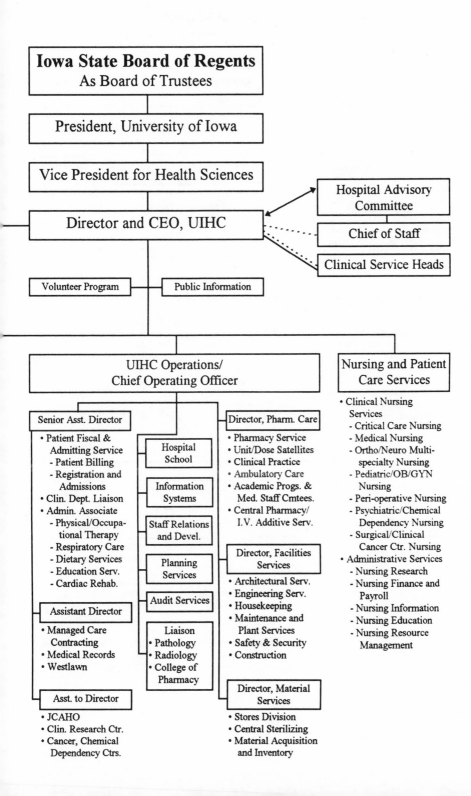

Iowa State Board of Regents
As Board of Trustees

President, University of Iowa

Vice President for Health Sciences

Director and CEO, UIHC

Hospital Advisory Committee

Chief of Staff

Clinical Service Heads

Volunteer Program — Public Information

UIHC Operations/ Chief Operating Officer

Nursing and Patient Care Services

Senior Asst. Director

• Patient Fiscal & Admitting Service
  - Patient Billing
  - Registration and Admissions
• Clin. Dept. Liaison
• Admin. Associate
  - Physical/Occupational Therapy
  - Respiratory Care
  - Dietary Services
  - Education Serv.
  - Cardiac Rehab.

Hospital School

Information Systems

Staff Relations and Devel.

Planning Services

Audit Services

Director, Pharm. Care

• Pharmacy Service
• Unit/Dose Satellites
• Clinical Practice
• Ambulatory Care
• Academic Progs. & Med. Staff Cmtees.
• Central Pharmacy/ I.V. Additive Serv.

Director, Facilities Services

• Architectural Serv.
• Engineering Serv.
• Housekeeping
• Maintenance and Plant Services
• Safety & Security
• Construction

• Clinical Nursing Services
  - Critical Care Nursing
  - Medical Nursing
  - Ortho/Neuro Multi-specialty Nursing
  - Pediatric/OB/GYN Nursing
  - Peri-operative Nursing
  - Psychiatric/Chemical Dependency Nursing
  - Surgical/Clinical Cancer Ctr. Nursing
• Administrative Services
  - Nursing Research
  - Nursing Finance and Payroll
  - Nursing Information
  - Nursing Education
  - Nursing Resource Management

Assistant Director

• Managed Care Contracting
• Medical Records
• Westlawn

Liaison
• Pathology
• Radiology
• College of Pharmacy

Asst. to Director

• JCAHO
• Clin. Research Ctr.
• Cancer, Chemical Dependency Ctrs.

Director, Material Services

• Stores Division
• Central Sterilizing
• Material Acquisition and Inventory

Figure C.3   University of Iowa College of Medicine Organization, 1995

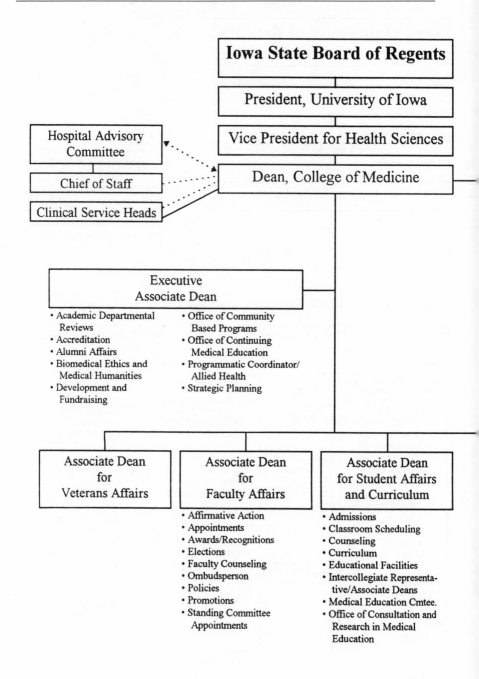

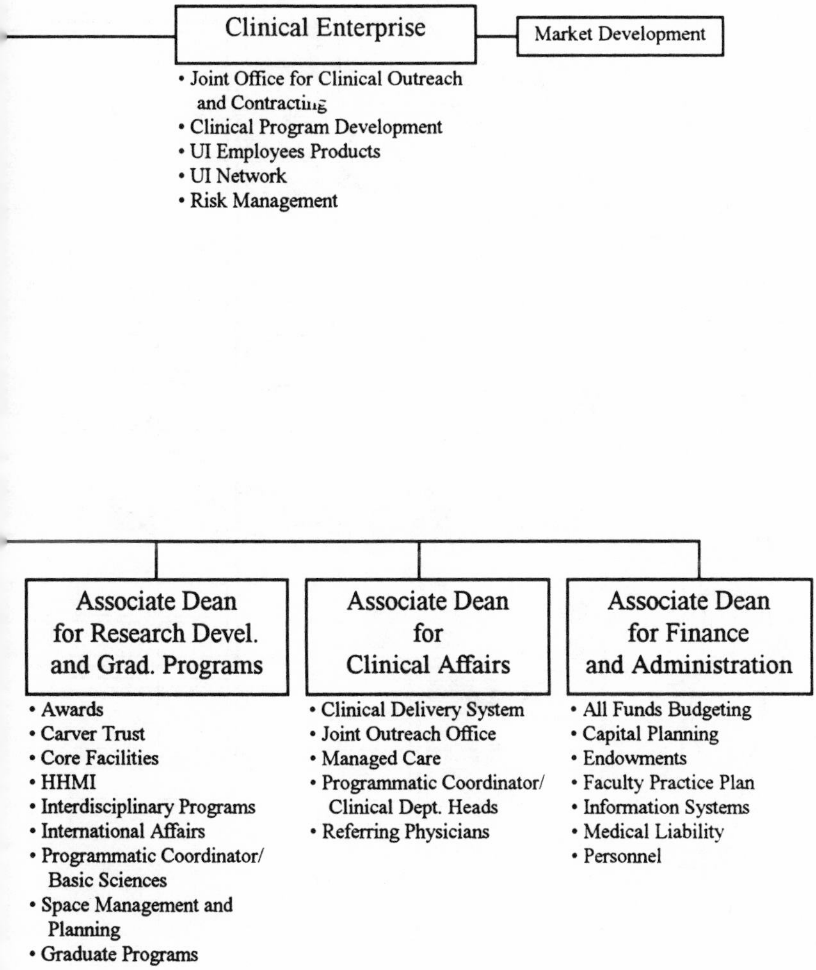

Clinical Enterprise

Market Development

- Joint Office for Clinical Outreach and Contracting
- Clinical Program Development
- UI Employees Products
- UI Network
- Risk Management

Associate Dean for Research Devel. and Grad. Programs

- Awards
- Carver Trust
- Core Facilities
- HHMI
- Interdisciplinary Programs
- International Affairs
- Programmatic Coordinator/ Basic Sciences
- Space Management and Planning
- Graduate Programs

Associate Dean for Clinical Affairs

- Clinical Delivery System
- Joint Outreach Office
- Managed Care
- Programmatic Coordinator/ Clinical Dept. Heads
- Referring Physicians

Associate Dean for Finance and Administration

- All Funds Budgeting
- Capital Planning
- Endowments
- Faculty Practice Plan
- Information Systems
- Medical Liability
- Personnel

This map shows University Hospital as item 24, located between Iowa Avenue and Jefferson Street at Linn Street. Other points of interest include the Medical Laboratory (item 21) at Dubuque and Jefferson streets; the Anatomy Building (item 20) immediately southwest of the Medical Laboratory; the Isolation Hospital (item 30) at Jefferson and Gilbert streets; the nursing school dormitory (item 26) at Iowa Avenue and Gilbert Street; the Homeopathic Hospital (item 23) at Jefferson and Dubuque streets; the Dental Building (item 13) on Jefferson Street at Capitol Street; and the Chemistry Building (item 22), which housed the College of Pharmacy, at Iowa Avenue and Dubuque Street. South Hall and the original medical building, which burned in 1901, had been located immediately south of Old Capitol (item 9). *Courtesy University of Iowa Archives.*

Figure C.4 University of Iowa Campus, 1915

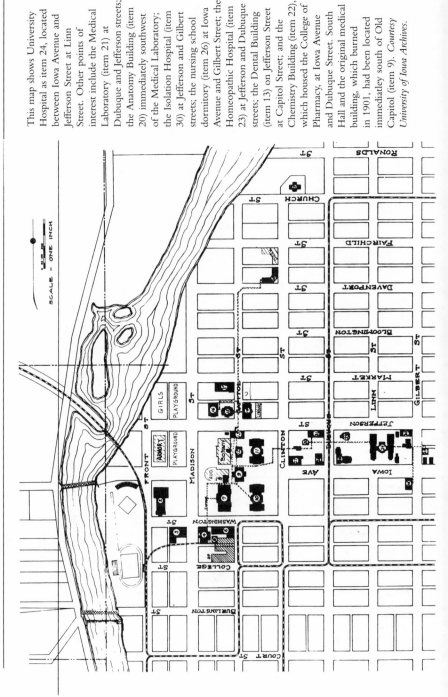

Figure C.5 University of Iowa Campus, 1946

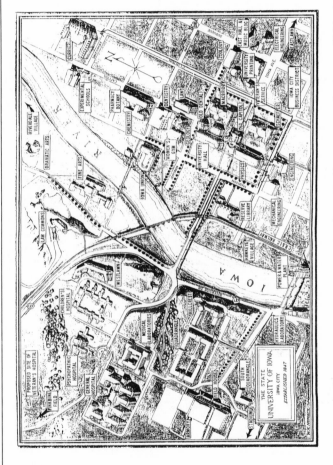

By this time development of the west campus was well under way. The first medical buildings to occupy the site were Children's Hospital and Westlawn, the nursing school building, followed by Psychopathic Hospital. The new Medical Laboratories building and General Hospital, funded half by the state of Iowa and half by the Rockefeller philanthropies, opened in 1926 and 1928, respectively. Meanwhile, the old University and Isolation hospitals, renamed East Hall and the Music Building, respectively, were given over to classrooms and offices for psychology, music, and other departments; and the old Medical Laboratory and Anatomy buildings were converted to use by the Zoology Department. The colleges of dentistry and pharmacy remained on the east side of the Iowa River. *Courtesy University of Iowa Archives.*

Figure C.6 University of Iowa West Campus, about 1972

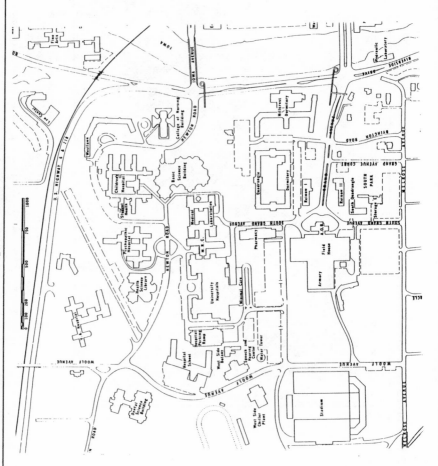

A flurry of construction in the 1960s and early 1970s consolidated the development of a health sciences campus and greatly expanded facilities for teaching, research, and clinical service. The colleges of dentistry and pharmacy moved to the west campus, the College of Nursing occupied a new building overlooking the Iowa River, and the College of Medicine built the monolithic Basic Science Building, later named for University of Iowa President Howard R. Bowen. Other new facilities included the Speech and Hearing Center, the University Hospital School, and the Health Science Library, later named for Dean Robert C. Hardin. Meanwhile, modest additions to General Hospital, notably the South Wing (labeled Minimal Care) and adjacent Medical Research Facility, increased the space available for patient service and clinical research. *Courtesy University of Iowa Archives.*

Figure C.7   University of Iowa West Campus, 1996

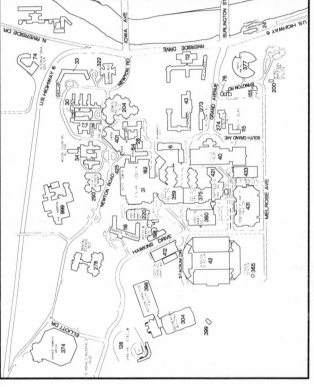

Beginning in 1973, construction never stopped at the University of Iowa Hospitals and Clinics. By 1996 this expansion had cost more than $500 million and roughly quintupled the floor space of the 1960s-era hospital. The result—in addition to Boyd Tower, which framed the north side of the hospital and enclosed the lower portion of the Gothic tower—was a series of pavilions extending southward to Iowa City's Melrose Avenue. The College of Medicine added a research building named for Dean John W. Eckstein (labeled EMRB), and the College of Pharmacy also built a six-story addition. In 1996, the state Board of Regents approved a seven-year plan to construct a $70 million medical research building on the site then occupied by the Steindler Building (formerly Children's Hospital), as well as relocate Newton Road to the north of the Hardin Library and Medical Education Building (formerly Psychopathic Hospital) to create a pedestrian mall through the heart of the health sciences campus. *Courtesy University of Iowa Planning and Administrative Services.*

Appendix D: Full Text of Legislation and Other Documents

ABRAHAM FLEXNER'S REPORT ON
APRIL 1909 VISIT
TO IOWA CITY

[Received June 11, 1909]

STATE UNIVERSITY OF IOWA MEDICAL DEPARTMENT

The medical department of the State University of Iowa must be considered in two sections. The equipment and instruction in the scientific branches occupying the first two years are generally good and at some points excellent. The work in anatomy is admirable. A better equipped department, more enthusiastically conducted, is hardly to be found anywhere in the country. There is unmistakable evidence of excellent teaching and intelligent scientific activity. To some extent, the same may be said of physiology, pathology, bacteriology, and other fundamental branches, though these departments have been less generously treated in the way of skilled assistants. The men in charge of them are, however, zealous and energetic; their ideals are high, and the equipment in the shape of apparatus and books, modern and sufficient.

The clinical situation is of a different order, altogether. In the first place, it lacks the close correlation which the scientific departments have achieved. The executive officer of the department lives at Dubuque and comes to Iowa City two days weekly. The professor of surgery resides at Sioux City. It is clear that under these conditions the clinical side cannot develop as a unit, nor can there grow up between the scientific men and the partly non-resident clinicians the close interrelations characteristic of a medical department that functions as a whole.

Facts confirm this criticism. The clinical instruction is given in the university hospital, in which less than 90 beds are available for teaching purposes. With the question as to how far the actual needs of clinical teaching can be met by this number of beds, I shall deal later. The point now is that the conduct of the hospital, as a teaching adjunct, reflects just the disorganization above hinted at. The hospital is, in its teaching aspects, headless. President MacLean witnessed my unavailing efforts to find anyone—nurse or physician—who could describe the system on which the bedside teaching was conducted. There are, for example, no hospital records worthy the name [sic]. No hospital report has been compiled. It is impossible to say what ground the clinical teaching has actually covered, just as it is impossible succinctly to describe what takes place in the way of clinical discipline.

444

Now, as the technique of clinical teaching is in these days quite definite, the conclusion is irresistible that vagueness indicates unorganized and more or less antiquated methods of teaching. One of the clinical men admitted frankly that "boys don't follow medical cases as closely as they might."

The inference fairly to be made from the preceding facts is sustained by the dispensary. The only records there are notes in a book. I was told that at the close of the year a card index would be compiled; but just where complete data for this index were to come from or why it should be made at the close of the year or what its character or use was to be, I could not learn. The eye and ear clinic is large; the medical clinic small. There are no clinics in surgery, gynecology, or g–u.

Now there are two points of view from which to survey the preceding situation:

1. Taking the clinical opportunities as they stand, they are not used for all they are worth; nor can they be so used, until a resident dean, a resident clinical faculty, and a hospital superintendent familiar with the technique of modern medical teaching are secured. It is necessary at once to adopt a more adequate form of taking case histories and keeping case records; the students must be trained to be parts of the hospital in its primary function of curing disease, and the records of every case should at every stage indicate what the student has seen and done and how it has been checked up or controlled by interne, staff officer, and professor, so that the complete record may regularly form the basis of conference and discussion. It is obvious that this involves increased expense at the start, though the point I have thus far emphasized is mere *organization* of what already exists.

2. It is doubtful, however, whether, even if the foregoing policy be pursued, the school will become clinically adequate. There are 100 students in the third and fourth years. They have access to less than 90 beds. This is much too little for general medicine and surgery, and yet it includes everything that the clinical teachers of all departments can use. Some branches, e.g. infectious diseases, are altogether omitted. Post-mortem work is far too limited. In obstetrics there were last year 45 cases available; this year, "not so many." Yet a senior class of 50 students—the present enrollment—ought to have at least 250 obstetrical cases. It is thus absolutely indisputable that more clinical material, and of greater variety, must be obtained.

To this increase, the local situation is not readily favorable. On the other hand, it may be at once conceded that indefinite increase of clinical material is not essential, and may prove embarrassing. Granted a barely adequate supply, the thoroughness with which it is used to train a small student body in painstaking methods of studying and handling their cases may more than outweigh a few deficiencies.

To sum up:

Iowa fails to provide clinical training of high technical quality; it fails to furnish an adequate supply of material. These defects can perhaps both be remedied by the formation of a really eminent faculty which, reinforced by liberal state support, will probably draw to Iowa City all the clinical material that is needed; and by the same token, such a faculty would promptly reconstruct the clinical teaching. There is thus presented a fairly sharp alternative; the clinical teaching can be improved without any greater expenditure than is involved in securing a permanent resident dean, a permanent resident surgeon, and a hospital head. But these steps will not of themselves cure the more fundamental difficulty. That calls for an enlarged hospital, an increased and expensive faculty. Is it worth while to take the first step unless in the near future Iowa will be ready to take the second? And considering its splendid opportunities for expansion in other directions, on which no natural handicap is imposed, is it wise educational statesmanship to endeavor, against the grave obstacles inhering in the situation, to develop a department which will at every stage consume an ever increasing proportion of the resources of the university? A proper provision for medical education in centres of population like Chicago and Minneapolis is proving a heavy load to carry. Far heavier, of course, will be a satisfactory provision in a small inland residential community; and in view of the fact that a decided reduction in the number of medical schools is called for, it is worth considering whether the general interest, educational and social, will not best be served by a differentiation which will in future limit medical teaching to institutions in large centres, plus perhaps one or two like Ann Arbor, already so highly developed that just now it costs less to go on than to stop. These considerations ought to be carefully weighed by institutions that, now comparatively undeveloped on the clinical side, must contemplate in the near future a large expenditure on that score, if they persist.

Three institutions whose experience is of suggestive value to Iowa at this crisis may be cited:

Ann Arbor, already alluded to, where a really admirable department has been developed at great expense, and during a time when the general level of clinical instruction was low. Now, however, that this level has risen, Ann Arbor feels keenly the competition of institutions more favorably situated, so that, despite its great start, the question of the future of its clinical department gives rise to serious concern. There is little doubt that if the clinical department were at this moment relatively undeveloped, the institution would hesitate to embark on its development now.

Madison, where, despite local opportunities greatly superior to those of Iowa City, the university has contentedly limited itself to two years' work.

Missouri, where, in a situation analogous to Iowa City, the regents confronted with the choice between greatly augmenting the expenditure on clinical medicine or abandoning it altogether, have just chosen the latter alternative and voted to discontinue the clinical department.

In deciding a similar question, Iowa must, in addition to considerations already stated, reflect that its present clinical department—100 students strong—is on a high school basis and has grown up in competition with the hitherto weak clinical schools of the west. A year or more hence, two years of college work are to be required to entrance to the department of medicine. This change will greatly reduce numbers. Simultaneously, a much more critical attitude in respect to clinical opportunities is growing; and students better trained in fundamental branches will be in position to distinguish between real and half-way clinical opportunities. So far, there has perhaps been little to choose between. But in the near future, certainly Minneapolis and probably Chicago will furnish clinical instruction that will crowd schools of inadequate clinical resources very hard. It would seem inevitable that to hold its own in such a competition will prove an increasingly disproportionate burden on the income of any institution laboring, on account of location, under grave disadvantages.

[signed] Abraham Flexner

FLEXNER'S FOLLOW-UP REPORT
ON OCTOBER 1909 VISIT
TO IOWA CITY

[Dated November 8, 1909, and addressed to James Trewin, president of the Iowa State Board of Education.]

Dear Mr. Trewin:

Since my visit to Iowa City last spring, there has been a certain degree of activity in the medical department; but while a genuine desire to improve conditions is evident, the steps taken do not, in my opinion, indicate a clear grasp of the methods by which alone the necessary improvements can be brough[t] about.

The connection with the Sisters' hospital is valuable, but chiefly as a supplement to what the University hospital provides; it cannot be relied on even in part as a substitute. While it is an important adjunct, its significance can be easily overestimated. The Tuberculosis Sanitarium is an excellent addition to your clinical resources, and will probably prove of increasing value. A valuable Hospital index has been started.

These are the main improvements that have been initiated. I want to give them full weight, for they are not to be lightly dismissed. On the other hand, the handling of the cases in the hospital is still on the whole educationally weak. The records are scattered, uneven, incomplete; some of the date [sic] being in one place, some in another, some nowhere. There is nothing approaching uniformity or thoroughness of system. A University hospital such as yours is under complete control of the medical faculty. The teachers can do anything they please. When therefore important steps are neglected or omitted, the conclusion is irresistible that something is radically wrong. To some extent these defects are attributable to non-residence of important teachers; but I incline to believe that in part they must be explained on the ground that the clinical teachers are not themselves in all respects modern men.

I am the more inclined to take this view because the plans for the new wing do not appear to me calculated to remedy your present deficiencies. I am of course not a hospital expert, so that I speak subjec[t] to correction; but the large amphitheatre and the location of the autopsy room on the main floor seem to me doubtful features; the failure to include a clinical laboratory adequate to the needs of the students is surely a grave omission. I strongly advise you to to postpone the erection of this addition until its details have been further passed on. Temporary quarters for additional beds can, if need be, be perhaps procured meanwhile in a residence close by.

The first need of the department is a leader. It is easy to point out defects; to cure them you must install some one who is conversant with the subject, has actual authority over his faculty and can with your board work out a comprehensive plan that will step by step strengthen and complete the school. As the hospital is weakest on the medical side, (there are at this date only nine medical cases in the wards), as the medical discipline is educationally central, I suggest as the first and most important step, the appointment of a resident Dean, who will also be chief clinician. It will be difficult to find the man you want; he will require to be well paid. When found, he will want resident teachers in branches now taught by non-residents; and he will want to infuse new blood even into subordinate positions, for the department suffers seriously from inbreeding. A strong faculty thus organized as a unit will quickly increase the teaching value of your present plant; they will also attract medical cases to your wards. I venture to repeat what I have before said: It is difficult to develop a medical department in a small residential town. But it is not impossible. If you will but procure the right leader and stand behind him, you can achieve a result for which the people of Iowa will be grateful to you; and you will set an example that will be potent for good throughout the country.

May I add that your attitude and that of your associates on the Board leads me to believe that you are thoroughly alive to the needs of the situation and thoroughly equal to them?

I am, with best wishes, Very sincerely yours, Abraham Flexner.

THE PERKINS AND HASKELL-KLAUS BILLS FOR MEDICAL AND SURGICAL TREATMENT OF INDIGENT PERSONS

[From the 1919 *Code of Iowa*, Title X; references to previous *Code* and legislative index deleted.]

CHAPTER 9.
MEDICAL AND SURGICAL TREATMENT
FOR INDIGENT CHILDREN.

Section 2375. Medical and surgical treatment for indigent children.

Any district or superior court of the state, or any judge thereof sitting or acting as a juvenile court, as provided by law, may on his own motion, or on complaint filed by any probation officer, school teacher or officer, superintendent of the poor, or physician authorized to practice his profession in the state of Iowa, alleging that the child named therein is under sixteen years of age and is afflicted with some deformity or suffering from some malady that can probably be remedied, and that the parents or other persons legally chargeable with the support of such child are unable to provide means for the surgical and medical treatment and hospital care of such child, shall appoint some physician who shall personally examine said child with respect to its malady or deformation. Such physician shall make a written report to the court or judge, giving such history of the case as will be likely to aid the medical or surgical treatment of said deformity or malady and describing the same, all in detail, and stating whether or not in his opinion the same can probably be remedied. Such report shall be made within such time as may be fixed by the court, and upon blanks to be furnished as hereinafter provided. The court or judge may also appoint some suitable person to investigate and report on the other matters charged in said complaint.

Sec. 2376. Hearing—duty of county attorney—order committing child to hospital—consent of parent.

Upon the filing of such report or reports, the court or judge shall fix a day for the hearing upon the complaint and shall cause the parent or parents, guardian or other person having the legal custody of said child to be served with a notice of the hearing, and shall also notify the county attorney, who shall appear and conduct the proceedings, and upon the hearing of such complaint evidence may be introduced. And if the court or judge finds that the said child is suffering from a deformity or malady which can probably be remedied by medical or surgical treatment and hospital care, and that the parent or parents, guardian or other person legally chargeable with his support is unable to pay the expenses thereof, the court or judge, with the consent of the parent or parents, guardian or other person having the legal custody of such child, shall enter an order directing that the said child shall be taken or sent to the hospital of the medical college of the state university of Iowa for free medical and surgical treatment and hospital care.

Sec. 2377. Hospital treatment at state university.

It shall be the duty of the person in charge of the hospital of the college of medicine of the state university, or other person designated by the authorities in control of said medical college, upon such child being received into the hospital, to provide for such child, if available, a cot or bed, or room in the hospital, and such person shall also designate the clinic of the college of medicine at the state university hospital to which the patient shall be assigned for treatment of the deformity or malady in each particular case.

The hospital shall not be required to receive any child into the hospital unless the physician or surgeon in charge of the department of said medical college in which such surgical or medical treatment is to be furnished shall be of the opinion that there is a reasonable probability that the child will be benefited by the proposed medical or surgical treatment.

If the physician or surgeon of the clinic to which such child has been assigned for treatment declines to treat such child, he shall make a report, in duplicate, of his examination of such child and state therein his reason or reasons for declining such treatment; and one of said duplicates shall be preserved in the records of said hospital and the other transmitted to the clerk of the court of said county where said order committing said child to the hospital was entered.

When any patient has been admitted to the clinic for treatment the physician or surgeon in charge thereof shall proceed with all proper diligence to perform such operation and bestow such treatment upon such patient as in his judgment shall be proper, and such patient shall receive proper hospital care while therein.

Sec. 2378. Treatment gratuitous.

No compensation shall be charged by or allowed to the physician or surgeon or nurse who shall treat such patient other than the compensation received from the university.

Sec. 2379. Record of treatment—expense—filing statement.

The superintendent of the university hospital, or other person designated by the authorities in control of the university college of medicine shall keep a correct account of the medicine, treatment, nursing and maintenance furnished to said patient, and shall set forth therein the actual, reasonable and necessary cost thereof, and shall make and file with the secretary of the state board of audit an itemized, sworn statement, as far as possible, of the expense so incurred at said hospital other than the free medical and surgical treatment and nursing, as hereinbefore provided, and the said statement shall be made in conformity with rules prescribed by the said board.

Sec. 2380. Expenses—how paid.

The secretary of the state board of audit shall present the said statement to the said board which, upon being satisfied that the same is correct and reasonable, shall approve the same, and shall direct that warrants be drawn by the auditor of state upon the treasurer of state for the amount of such bills as are allowed from time to time and the said warrants shall be forwarded as drawn by the auditor of state to the treasurer of the state university of Iowa, and the same shall be by him placed to the credit of the university funds which are set aside for the support of the university hospital, and the treasurer of state shall pay said warrants from the general funds of the state not otherwise appropriated.

Sec. 2381. Attendant for child—compensation—compensation of physician.

The court or judge may, in his discretion, appoint some person to accompany such child from the place where he may be, to the hospital of the medical college of the state university at Iowa City, Iowa, or to accompany such child from the said hospital to such place as may be designated by the court, the parent or parents, guardians or person having legal custody of said child, consenting.

Any person appointed by the court or judge to accompany said child to or from the hospital, or to make an investigation and report on any of the questions involved in the complaint other than the physician making the examination, shall receive the sum of three dollars per day for the time actually spent in making such investigations (except in cases where the person appointed by the court is a parent or relative or where the officer appointed therefor receives a fixed salary or compensation, in which cases there shall be no compensation) and his actual necessary expenses incurred in making such investigation or trip. The physician appointed by the court to make the examination and report shall receive the sum of five dollars for each and every examination and report so made, and his actual necessary expenses incurred in making such investigation, in conformity to the requirements of this chapter. The person making claim to such compensation shall present to the court or judge an itemized sworn statement thereof, and when such claim for compensation has been approved by the court or judge the same shall be filed in the office of the county auditor, and shall be allowed by the board of supervisors and paid out of the funds of the county collected for the relief of the poor.

Sec. 2382. Returning child—expense—how paid.

The university hospital may in the discretion of the superintendent or other person designated by the authorities in control thereof, pay the actual, reasonable necessary expenses of returning the said patient to his home, and pay the attendant not to exceed three dollars per day for the time thus necessarily employed, unless said attendant be a parent or other relative or be an officer or employee receiving other compensation, and his actual, reasonable and necessary expenses incurred in accompanying such patient to his home, and such per diem and expenses shall be itemized and verified, and presented to and allowed by the state board of audit, in connection with the bills for hospital maintenance, as hereinbefore provided.

Sec. 2383. Faculty to prepare blanks—printing— distribution—report to accompany patient.

The medical faculty of the university hospital shall prepare a blank or blanks containing such questions and requiring such information as may in its judgment be necessary and proper to be obtained by the physician who examines the patient under order of court; and such blanks shall be printed by the state and a supply thereof shall be sent to the clerk of each superior and district court of the state of Iowa; and the physician making such examination shall make his report to the court in duplicate on said blanks, answering the questions contained therein, and setting forth the information required thereby, and one of said duplicate reports shall be sent to the university hospital with the patient, together with a certified copy of the order of court. The executive council of the state of Iowa shall determine the number of such blanks to be printed and distributed to the clerks of the superior and district courts of the state of Iowa, and the state board of audit shall audit, allow and pay the bills therefor, as other bills are allowed and paid for public printing.

Sec. 2384. Patients in state institutions—authority to send to state university hospital—authority to pay expense.

The board of control of the state institutions of Iowa may, in its discretion, send any inmate of said institutions, or any person committed or applying for admission thereto, to the hospital of the medical college of the state university of Iowa for treatment and care as provided in this chapter, without securing an order of court as provided in other cases, and the said patient so sent to the hospital of the medical college of the state university shall be accompanied by a report and history of the case made by the physician in charge of the institution to which said patient has been committed, or to which application has been made for his admission, containing a history of the case and information as required by said blanks, and the hospital expenses of such patient shall be paid as in other cases. State board of education for any such patient from the college for the blind and the board of control for any such patient from any institution under its control may pay the expenses of transporting such patient to and from the hospital out of any funds appropriated for the use of the institution from which such patient is sent, and may, when necessary, send an attendant with such patient, and pay his traveling expenses in like manner.

Sec. 2385. Treatment authorized—experimentation forbidden.

No child, under the terms of this chapter, shall be treated for any ailment except such as is described by the order of the court, unless permission for such treatment is granted by the parents or guardians, and no child shall be used for the purpose of experimentation.

CHAPTER 10
MEDICAL AND SURGICAL
TREATMENT OF INDIGENT PERSONS
OVER SIXTEEN

Section 2386. Medical and surgical treatment for indigent persons over sixteen—report to and order of court— examination by physician and report.

Whenever it shall appear to any physician, county supervisor, township trustee, public health nurse, overseer of the poor, policeman, priest or minister that there is any legal resident of his or her county over sixteen years of age, afflicted with any malady or deformity which can probably be remedied by proper care and medical or surgical treatment, if said person, or the parent, parents or guardian, or other person having legal custody of said person, as the case may be, is unable financially to provide proper care and medical or surgical treatment, it shall be the duty of such physician, county supervisor, township trustee, public health nurse, overseer of the poor, policeman, priest or minister to report the same to the judge of the district or superior court having jurisdiction in the county in which said person resides.

Upon the filing of such report with the judge of the district or superior court as aforesaid, he shall appoint some physician who shall personally examine said person with respect to the malady or deformity. Such physician shall make a written report to said judge, giving such history of the case as will be likely to aid the medical or surgical treatment of such deformity or malady, and describing the same, all in detail, and state whether or not, in his opinion, the same can probably be remedied. Such report shall be made within such time as may be fixed by the court and upon blanks to be furnished as hereinafter provided. It shall also be the duty of said judge to have a thorough investigation made by the county attorney of his county regarding the financial condition of the said person, or of the parent or parents, guardian or other person having legal custody of said person, as the case may be.

Sec. 2387. Action of court on report of physician—time of hearing— order of court committing to state university hospital.

Upon the filing of such report or reports, said judge of the district or superior court, as aforesaid, shall fix a date for the hearing upon the complaint and shall cause the person, or the parent or parents, guardian or other person having legal custody of said person, as the case may be, to be served with a notice of the hearing and he shall also notify the county attorney who shall appear and conduct the proceedings and, upon such complaint, evidence may be introduced. If the judge finds that the said person is suffering from a deformity or malady which can probably be remedied by medical or surgical treatment or hospital care, and that the person, or the parent or parents, guardian or other person having legal custody of said person, as the case may be, is unable to pay the expenses thereof, said judge may, with the consent of the said person, or parent or parents, guardian or other person having legal custody of said person, as the case may be, enter an order directing that the said person shall be taken to the hospital of the college of medicine of the state university of Iowa at Iowa City for proper hospital care and medical or surgical treatment; the expense of such hospital care and treatment to be met in the manner hereinafter provided; provided that no such person shall be received into said hospital of the college of medicine of the state university of Iowa for care and treatment, unless, in the judgment of the admitting physician, there shall be a reasonable probability of such person's being benefited by such hospital care and medical or surgical treatment.

Sec. 2388. Duty of admitting officer at hospital.

It shall be the duty of the admitting officer of the said hospital of the college of medicine of the state university of Iowa, upon receiving any such person, to provide a proper bed in said hospital and to assign or designate the clinic of the said hospital to which such person shall be assigned for treatment; and the physician or surgeon in charge of said person shall proceed with proper care to perform such operation and bestow such treatment upon said person as, in his judgment, shall be proper and necessary.

A proper and competent nurse shall also be assigned to look after and care for said person during such hospital care and medical or surgical treatment, as aforesaid.

Sec. 2389. No compensation.

No compensation shall be charged or received by the admitting officer of the medical faculty, or by the physician or surgeon or nurse who shall treat and care for such person, other than the salaries received by them provided by the Iowa state board of education.

Sec. 2390. Record and report of expenses.

The superintendent of the hospital of the college of medicine of the state university of Iowa shall keep a correct account of all medicine, nursing, food and necessaries furnished to said persons and shall make and file with the state board of audit of the state of Iowa an itemized, sworn statement of all expenses incurred at said hospital in the treatment, nursing and care of said persons.

Sec. 2391. State board of audit to pass upon expenses.

The state board of audit, upon being satisfied that the same is correct and reasonable, shall approve the same and shall direct that warrants be drawn by the auditor of state upon the treasurer of state for the amount of said bills as they are allowed from time to time; and the said warrants, as drawn by the auditor of state on the treasurer of state, shall be forwarded to the treasurer of the state university of Iowa, and the same shall be by him placed to the credit of the university funds which are set aside for the support of the state university hospital; and the treasurer of state shall pay the said warrants from the general funds of the state not otherwise appropriated.

Sec. 2392. Court may appoint person to accompany patient—expenses.

The court or judge may, in his discretion, appoint some person to accompany said patient from the place where he may be to the hospital of the college of medicine of the state university at Iowa City, Iowa, or to accompany said patient from the said hospital to such place as may be designated by the court; the said patient or the parent or parents, guardian or other person having legal custody of said patient, as the case may be, consenting.

The physician appointed by the judge of the district or superior court as aforesaid to make such examination and report shall receive therefor the sum of five dollars, together with the expenses incurred by him in making such examination; and the said charges for services and expenses, and all expenses incurred in conveying such person to and from the said hospital of the college of medicine of the state university of Iowa, shall, when approved by the judge ordering such services, be filed with the superintendent of the state university hospital and charged on the regular bill for maintenance; provided that if the party conveying said patient to or from said hospital is a salaried officer of a township, a county, a city, or a state institution, or a member of the patient's immediate family, said officer or relative shall receive no per diem, but only his actual traveling expenses. If another person is appointed to conduct said patient to and from said hospital, he shall receive compensation, in addition to his traveling expenses, in the sum of three dollars a day.

Sec. 2393. Expenses of returning patient to his home—how paid.

The superintendent of the hospital of the college of medicine of the state university of Iowa or other person designated by the authorities in control thereof may pay the actual, reasonable and necessary expenses of returning the said patient to his home, and pay the attendant not to exceed three dollars a day for the time thus necessarily employed; provided that if such attendant is a salaried officer of a township, a county, a city or a state institution, or a member of the patient's immediate family, he shall receive the actual, reasonable and necessary expenses incurred in accompanying said patient to his home.

Such per diem and expenses shall be itemized and verified and presented to and allowed by the state board of audit in connection with the bills for hospital maintenance as hereinbefore provided.

Sec. 2394. Preparation of blanks for examining physician—payment therefor—report of physician and order of court certified to hospital authorities.

The medical faculty of the hospital of the college of medicine of the state university of Iowa shall prepare blanks containing such questions and requiring such information as may be necessary and proper to be obtained by the physician who examines the patient under order of court; and such blanks shall be printed by the state and a supply thereof shall be sent to the clerk of each district and superior court of the state of Iowa; and the physician making such examination shall make his report to the court in duplicate on said blanks, answering the questions contained therein and setting forth the information required thereby, and one of said duplicate reports shall be sent to the hospital of the college of medicine of the state university of Iowa with the patient, together with a certified copy of the order of the court. The state board of audit shall audit, allow and pay the cost of the bills as other bills are allowed and paid for public printing.

Index